Contents

S0-AXZ-991

HEAD OFFICE
Belleek Road, Ballyshannon, Co. Donegal.
Tel: 072-22222 / 51377 Fax: 072-22224 / 51207
(MONDAY-FRIDAY 9AM-5PM)
http://www.commerce.ie/towns_and_country

Chief Executive
Mrs. Mary T. McGee, Belleek Road, Ballyshannon,
Co. Donegal.
Tel: 072-51377. Fax: 072-51207.

Chairman
Mrs. Vera Feeney, Ardmor Country House, Greenhill,
Spiddal, Co. Galway.
Tel: 091-553145. Fax: 091-553596.

Vice-Chairman
Mrs. Noreen McBride, 3 Rossmore Grove,
off Wellington Lane, Templeogue, Dublin 6W.
Tel: 01-490 2939, Fax: 01-492 9416.

Secretary
Mrs. Fiona Byrne, Glen na Smole, Ashtown Lane,
Marlton Road, Wicklow, Co. Wicklow.
Tel: 0404-67945. Fax: 0404-68155.

Treasurer
Mrs. Tess Haughey, "Rathnashee", Teesan,
Donegal Road N15, Sligo, Co. Sligo.
Tel: 071-43376. Fax: 071-42283.

Public Relations Officer
Mrs. Ann Foley, Riversdale House, Lower William Street,
New Ross, Co. Wexford.
Tel: 051-22515. Fax: 051-422800.

Turasoireacht Culturtha na Gaeltachta
Tugann an Ghaeltacht seans do thurasoiri laethanta saoire a chaitheam, gceantair airithe ina labhraitear an Ghaeilge mar ghaith theanga. Tá teaghlaigh loista againn leis an siombal 🍀 san leabhar agus beidh siad sud lan tsasta an teanga a usaid. Bain usaid as do chuid Ghaeilge!

Ar ndoigh is feidir cultur speisialta a bhalaiseadh sna teaghlaigh seo freisin.

Public Holidays for 1998

New Years Day	Thursday,	January 1st
St. Patrick's Day	Sunday,	March 17th
Good Friday	Friday,	April 10th
Easter Sunday	Sunday,	April 12th
Easter Monday,	Monday,	April 13th
May Day Holiday	Monday,	May 4th
June Holiday	Monday,	June 1st
August Holiday	Monday,	August 3rd
October Holiday	Monday,	October 26th
Christmas Day	Friday,	December 25th
St. Stephen's Day	Saturday,	December 26th
(St. Stephen's Day Holiday)	Monday	December 28th
New Years Day 1999	Friday,	January 1st

Tourist Regions of Ireland

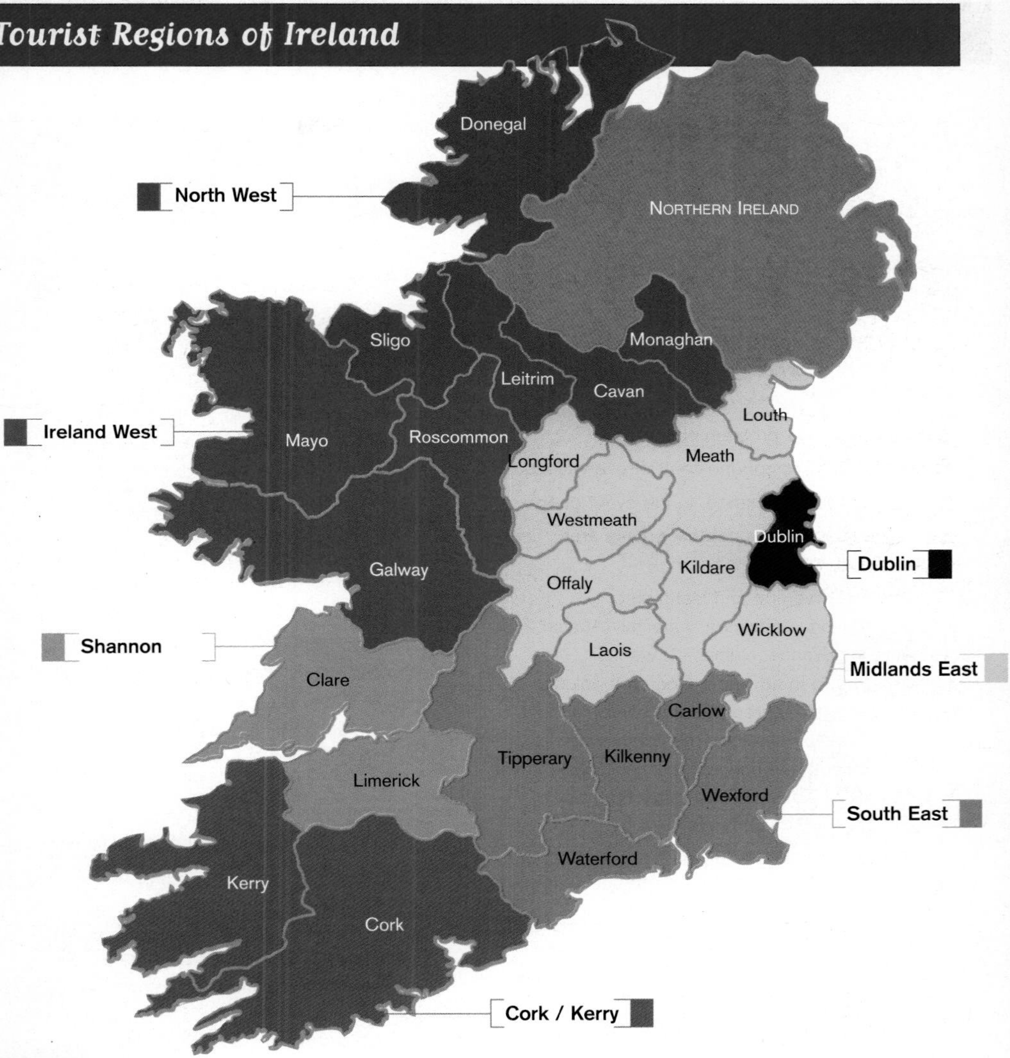

Donegal

North West

NORTHERN IRELAND

Sligo

Monaghan

Leitrim

Cavan

Louth

Ireland West

Mayo

Roscommon

Meath

Longford

Westmeath

Dublin

Dublin

Galway

Offaly

Kildare

Shannon

Laois

Wicklow

Clare

Midlands East

Carlow

Tipperary

Kilkenny

Limerick

Wexford

South East

Kerry

Waterford

Cork

Cork / Kerry

Approved Accommodation Signs
This sign will be displayed at most premises which are approved by Quality Approved Bed & Breakfast Association Ltd., to Irish Tourist Board Standards.

Panneaux d'homologation des établissements
Ces panneaux sont affichés dans la plupart des établissements homologués par Quality Approved Bed & Breakfast Association Ltd., selon les normes de l'Office du tourisme irlandais.

Plakette fúr Geprúfte Unterkunft
Diese Plaketten werden an den meisten Häusern angezeigt, die von der Quality Approved Bed & Breakfast Association Ltd. auf die Einhaltung der Normen der irischen Fremdenverkehrsbehörde überprüft und zugelassen wurden.

Borden voor goedgekeurde accommodatie
Deze borden vindt u bij de meeste huizen die zijn goedgekeurd door de Quality Approved Bed & Breakfast Association Ltd voor de normen van de Ierse Toeristenbond.

Simbolo di sistemazione approvata
Questi simboli saranno esposti nella maggior parte delle case approvate dalla Quality Approved Bed & Breakfast Association Ltd (associazione dei Bed & Breakfast approvati per qualità), rispondenti agli standard dell'Ente del Turismo Irlandese.

Símbolo de alojamiento aprobado
Estos símbolos se muestran en los establecimientos que han sido aprobados por la Quality Approved Bed and Breakfast Association Ltd, bajos los estandars de la Oficina de Turismo Irlandesa.

Skyltar för Godkänd logi
Dessa skyltar finns vid de flesta gästhus som har godkänts av Quality Approved Bed & Breakfast Association Ltd. (Föreningen för kvalitetsgodkända gästhus AB), enligt irländska turisföreningens normer.

The guide is divided into seven geographical regions which are subdivided into counties (see page 3 for map of regions and counties). The regions are: **South East**, **Cork/Kerry**, **Shannon**, **Ireland West**, **North West**, **Midlands East**, **Dublin**.

Reservations

Reservations can be made by contacting the home directly or through a tourist information office. You should confirm your booking in writing and enclose the required deposit. Should you have a problem obtaining accommodation, telephone central reservations (072-22222) for assistance. In the event of an emergency contact the nearest county area representative.

Always reserve first and last nights accommodation in advance. June/July/August – 48 hours in advance. Dublin – 2 weeks, preferably more in advance. Confirm booking within 7 days with agreed deposit. Rooms may be guaranteed by credit card – check when booking. Check rate and cancellation policy when booking. Late arrivals – after 6pm by special agreement with home.

Onward reservations will be made for the cost of the phone call. To avoid disappointment, please avail of this facility.

Rates

Rates quoted include the minimum to maximum charges in respect of overnight accommodation per person sharing including Irish breakfast. The prices are inclusive of VAT.

Travel Agents Vouchers

Please present your voucher on arrival. Vouchers are only valid in homes displaying Ⓥ. Standard vouchers cover B&B in room without private facilities. To upgrade to en suite rooms the charge is £2.00 per person. Maximum £5.00 per room for three or more persons sharing.

En suite vouchers covers a room with full private facilities. No extra charge is payable.

Cancellation policy

Please telephone immediately in the event of a cancellation. The following charges may apply:
- **14 days notice:** no charge
- **7 days notice:** 50% of B&B for first night.
- **24 hours notice:** 75% of B&B for first night.
- **Failure to show:** Full cost for first night.

Check In/Out

Please advise of early arrival.
- Rooms available between 2pm and 6pm.
- Check out should be no later than 11am.
- Reservations should be taken up by 6pm. If late arrival, please confirm on day of arrival with host/hostess.

Reduction for Children

Applies where children share parents room or three or more children share one room. Full rate applies when one or two children occupy separate rooms. Please check that the home is suitable for children when booking. Cots 🛏 are available in some homes – there may be a nominal charge.

Evening Meals

Book in advance preferably before 12 noon on the day. Light meals ☒ available on request.

Pets

With the exception of Guide Dogs, in the interest of hygiene pets are not allowed indoors.

Disabled Persons/Wheelchair Users

The National Rehabilitation Board (NRB) have approved homes suitable for disabled people with a helper and these are listed by the symbol ♿.

Electrical Current

The standard electrical supply is 230 volts (50 cycles). To use small appliances, you may need a plug adapter to fit our 3-pin flat or 2-pin round wall sockets. If required, small travel transformers and adapters should be purchased before departure.

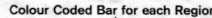
Colour Coded Bar for each Region

Family Name
NAME OF TOWN AND
COUNTRY HOME
Address
TEL: FAX: EMAIL:

Description of Town and Country Home

Facility Symbols

Area

OPEN:
NO. ROOMS:
ENSUITE:

(V)

BUS NO:

Nearest Town distance in km

B&B PPS:	MIN £/ MAX £	SNGL OCC. DBLE/TPL:	MIN £/ MAX £	SNGL RM:	MIN £/ MAX £
PART BRD:	MIN £/ MAX £	% RED. CHILDREN:	%	DINNER:	£

B+B PPS: Bed & Breakfast per person sharing
PART BRD: Bed & Breakfast, Evening meal.
SNGL OCC. DBLE/TPL: Single Occupancy of
Double/Triple Room

% RED. CHILDREN: % Reduction for Children
sharing parents room or where three or more
children share one room
SNGL RM: Single Room

Symbols

cc	Credit Cards accepted		☕	Tea/Coffee facilities in bedrooms
♀	Wine Licence		🛏	Cot available
♱	Babysitter, normally to 12 midnight		🐾	Pets allowed
©	Direct dial telephone in bedrooms		♣	Irish spoken
(P)	Private off-street parking		♪	Fishing available in the vicinity
♿	Access for disabled with helper		⚑	Golf available in the vicinity
⊗	No smoking house		🐴	Horse riding available in the vicinity
R✗	No smoking bedrooms		S	Single Room
📺	TV in bedrooms		(V)	Travel Agency Vouchers Accepted.
✗	Light meals available		(V̸)	Travel Agency Vouchers Not Accepted

Compliments and Comments

Complaints should always be brought to the
attention of the proprietor before departure.
Failing satisfaction and in the case of alleged
overcharging, your receipt should be sent with
your complaint to: **Customer Care, Quality
Approved Bed & Breakfast, Bachelors Walk,
Ballyshannon, Co. Donegal.**

To maintain the high standards which the
Association is renowned for, all comments on
the general level of service and the standards
you have experienced are welcome. All
constructive criticisms will be taken seriously to
ensure continued service improvement.

Errors and Omissions

Every care has been taken to ensure accuracy
in this publication in compliance with the
Consumer Protection Laws of Ireland. The
Town & Country Homes Association Ltd.
cannot accept responsibility for errors or
omissions in material supplied by members for
inclusion in this publication, or for any loss or
disappointment caused by dependence on
information contained herein. Where such are
brought to our attention, future editions will be
amended accordingly. There may be changes
after going to press where properties are sold,
and the home changes ownership.

Der Führer ist in sieben geographische Regionen gegliedert, die wiederum in die einzelnen Grafschaften aufgeteilt sind (Karte der Regionen und Grafschaften s. S. 3). Die Regionen sind: **Südost, Cork/Kerry, Shannon, Westirland, Nordwest, östliche Midlands, Dublin**

Reservierungen

Sie können Ihre Unterkunft buchen, indem Sie die Pension direkt oder über ein Fremdenverkehrsbüro kontaktieren. Bitte bestätigen Sie Ihre Buchung schriftlich und fügen Sie die erforderliche Anzahlung bei. Sollten Sie Probleme haben, eine Unterkunft zu bekommen, rufen Sie bitte den zentralen Buchungsdienst an (072-22222). In Notfällen wenden Sie sich bitte an den naheliegendsten Gebietsvertreter.

Bitte reservieren Sie immer die erste und die letzte Übernachtung im voraus. Juni/Juli/August - 48 Stunden im voraus, für Dublin mindestens 2 Wochen im voraus.

Bestätigen Sie die Buchung innerhalb von 7 Tagen mit der vereinbarten Anzahlung. Die Buchung kann mit Kreditkarte garantiert werden. Bitte fragen Sie danach, wenn Sie die Buchung vornehmen und fragen Sie auch nach dem Preis und dem Verfahren im Fall einer Stornierung.

Späte Ankunft - nach 18.00 nach Vereinbarung mit dem Unterkunftsbesitzer.

Vorausbuchungen für die weitere Reise werden gerne gegen Erstattung der Telefonkosten vorgenommen. Bitte nutzen Sie diese Möglichkeit, um Enttäuschungen zu vermeiden.

Preise

Die Preise beziehen sich auf die Minimum- bis Maximumrate für eine Übernachtung pro Person in einem Zweibettzimmer einschließlich irisches Frühstück. Sie enthalten die gesetzliche Mehrwertsteuer.

Reisebürogutscheine

Bitte legen Sie Ihre Unterkunftsgutscheine bei Ihrer Ankunft vor. Die Gutscheine gelten nur in Häusern, die mit dem Symbol Ⓥ gekennzeichnet sind. Die Standardgutscheine beziehen sich auf Übernachtung und Frühstück in einem Zimmer ohne eigenes Bad. Die Gebühr für Zimmer mit Bad/Waschgelegenheit beträgt £2.00 pro Person oder maximal £5.00 pro Zimmer, das von drei oder mehr Personen geteilt wird.

"En-suite" Gutscheine beziehen sich auf ein Zimmer mit eigenem Bad. Eine zusätzliche Gebühr fällt nicht an.

Verfahren im Fall einer Stornierung

Bitte benachrichtigen Sie die Pension so bald wie möglich telefonisch, wenn Sie Ihren Aufenthalt absagen müssen. Folgende Gebühren werden berechnet:
- **14 Tage vor dem vereinbarten Ankunftstermin:** keine Gebühr
- **7 Tage vor dem vereinbarten Ankunftstermin:** 50% der Übernachtungs- u. Frühstückkosten für die erste Nacht
- **24 Stunden vor dem vereinbarten Ankunftstermin:** 75% der Übernachtungs- u. Frühstückskosten für die erste Nacht
- **bei Nichterscheinen:** Gesamtpreis für die erste Nacht

Ankunft/Abreise:

Bitte teilen Sie mit, wenn Sie sehr früh ankommen.
- Zimmer verfügbar zwischen 14.00 und 18.00 Uhr
- Die Abreise sollte nicht später als 11.00 Uhr erfolgen
- Ankunft nach Möglichkeit vor 18.00 Uhr. Bitte informieren Sie Ihren Gastgeber, wenn Sie verspätet (nach 18.00 Uhr) eintreffen werden.

Kinderermäßigung

Ermäßigung wird gewährt, wenn Kinder das Zimmer der Eltern teilen oder wenn drei oder mehr Kinder ein Zimmer teilen. Ein oder zwei Kinder in einem separaten Zimmer zahlen den vollen Preis. Bitte fragen Sie bei der Reservierung, ob das Haus für Kinder geeignet ist.

In einigen Häusern stehen Kinderbetten 🛏 zur Verfügung, für die U. eine kleine Gebühr erhoben wird.

Abendmahlzeiten

Können im voraus gebucht werden, nach Möglichkeit vor 12 Uhr mittags. Imbisse ✖ werden auf Anfrage serviert.

Haustiere

Mit Ausnahme von Blindenhunden sind Haustiere auch hygienischen Gründen nicht im Haus erlaubt.

Behinderte Personen/Rollstuhlfahrer

Das National Rehabilitation Board (NRB) hat Häuser auf ihre Eignung für behinderte Personen und deren Helfer überprüft. Diese sind mit dem Symbol ♿ gekennzeichnet.

Stromspannung

Die Standardstromspannung beträgt 230V Wechselstrom (50 Zyklen). Für den Gebrauch von kleinen Elektrogeräten ist ein Adapter erforderlich, der in die in Irland üblichen Steckdosen paßt. Bitte beschaffen Sie sich kleine Reisetransformatoren und Adapter vor Beginn Ihrer Reise.

Nächste Stadt/Ortschaft Entfernung in km

Familienname
NAME DES TOWN AND
COUNTRY HAUSES
Anschrift

TEL:　　　　　　　　　　FAX:　　　　　　　EMAIL:

Beschreibung des Town and Country Hauses

Region	
GEÖFFNET:	
ANZ. DER: ZIMMER:	
MIT BAD/DUSCHE:	(V)

Symbole der Einrichtungen　　　　　LINIENBUSNR.:

| B&B PPS: | MIN £/ MAX £ | SNGL OCC. DBLE/TPL: | MIN £/ MAX £ | SNGL RM: | MIN £/ MAX £ |
| PART BRD: | MIN £/ MAX £ | % RED. CHILDREN: | % | DINNER: | £ |

B+B PPS: Übern./Frühst. pro Person im
2-Bett-Zimmer
PART BRD: Übern./Frühst., Abendessen
SNGL OCC. DBLE/TPL: Einzelbelegung eines
Mehrbettzimmers

% RED. CHILDREN: %Nachlaß f. Kinder, im
Zimmer d. Eltern, od. drei oder mehr Kinder in
einem Zimmer
SNGL RM: Einzelzimmer

Symbole:

cc	Kreditkarten werden akzeptiert	☕	Tee /Kaffeezubereitungsmöglichkeit im Zimmer
♀	Weinlizenz		
♯	Babysitter, normalerweise bis 24.00 Uhr	🛏	Kinderbett erhältlich
©	Telefon mit Direktwahl im Zimmer	🏠	Haustiere willkommen
℗	Privatparkplatz	☘	Gälisch wird gesprochen
♿	Für behinderte Personen und Helfer geeignet	🐟	Angelmöglichkeiten in der Nähe
⊗	Nichtraucherhaus	⚑	Golfplatz in der Nähe
⚱	Nichtraucherschlafzimmer	🐎	Pferdereiten in der Nähe
🖵	Fernsehgerät im Zimmer	S	Einzelzimmer
✗	Imbißmöglichkeit	V	Reisebürogutscheine werden akzeptiert
		Ⓦ	Reisebürogutscheine werden nicht akzeptiert

Komplimente und Kommentare

Beschwerden sollten vor der Abreise zunächst an
den Eigentümer des Hauses gerichtet werden.
Sollte dies bei Verdacht auf eine überhöhte
Berechnung zu keiner Einigung führen, senden Sie
Ihre Rechnung bitte an **"Customer Care", Quality
Approved Bed & Breakfast, Bachelors Walk,
Ballyshannon, Co. Donegal.**

Um den hohen Standard aufrecht zu erhalten,
für den unser Verband bekannt ist, sind uns Ihre
Anmerkungen über den Service allgemein und über
das Niveau, das Sie in den Häusern vorgefunden
haben, sehr willkommen. Ihre konstruktive Kritik
wird ernstgenommen und hilft uns, unsere
Leistungen laufend zu verbessern.

Fehler und Auslassungen

Die Information in dieser Broschüre wurde mit der
größten Sorgfalt unter Berücksichtigung der
irischen Verbraucherschutzgesetze
zusammengestellt. Town & Country Homes
Association übernimmt jedoch keine Gewähr für
Fehler oder Ungenauigkeiten, die in der uns zur
Verfügung gestellten Information enthalten sind
oder für Schäden und Enttäuschungen, die durch
ein Verlassen auf diese Information entstehen.
Fehler, die Town & Country Homes Association zur
Kenntnis gebracht werden, werden in der nächsten
Ausgabe berücksichtigt. Änderungen können
eintreten, wenn ein Haus nach Drucklegung dieses
Führers verkauft wird und der Eigentümer
wechselt.

Ce guide est divisé en sept régions géographiques, qui sont subdivisées en comtés (voir la carte des régions et comtés page 3). Les régions sont les suivantes: **South East (Sud-Est), Cork/Kerry, Shannon, Ireland West (Irlande Ouest), North West (Nord-Ouest), Midlands East (Centre-Est), Dublin.**

Réservations

Les réservations peuvent se faire directement auprès de l'établissement ou par l'intermédiaire d'un bureau d'information touristique. Les réservations doivent être confirmées par écrit, accompagnées des arrhes requis. Si vous avez des difficultés à trouver un hébergement, vous pouvez appeler le bureau central de réservation (072-22222) qui vous aidera. En cas d'urgence, contacter le représentant local le plus proche.

Il est recommandé de toujours réserver d'avance l'hébergement de la première et de la dernière nuit, 48 heures à l'avance en juin/juillet/août, 2 semaines ou plus si possible à Dublin. Confirmer la réservation sous sept jours avec les arrhes convenus. Une carte de crédit peut être demandée pour garantir la chambre – se renseigner lors de la réservation. Vérifier les tarifs et les pénalités éventuelles d'annulation lors de la réservation. Arrivées tardives – après 18.00 heures avec l'accord de l'établissement.

Les réservations pour les étapes suivantes seront faites pour vous moyennant le prix de la communication téléphonique. Afin d'éviter toute déception, nous vous recommandons d'utiliser ce service.

Tarif

Les tarifs indiqués incluent le prix minimum à maximum pour l'hébergement d'une personne pour une nuit en chambre double, petit déjeuner irlandais inclus. Les prix comprennent la TVA.

Bons d'agents de voyage

Ceux-ci sont à présenter dès l'arrivée. Les bons ne sont acceptés que par les établissements affichant le symbole ⓥ. Les bons standard assurent l'hébergement et le petit déjeuner en chambre sans salle de bain. Supplément pour salle de bain privée: £2.00 par personne, maximum £5.00 par chambre de trois personnes ou plus.

Les bons "en suite" concernent les chambres avec salle de bain, sans aucun supplément.

Annulations

En cas d'annulation, prévenir immédiatement l'établissement par téléphone. Les pénalités d'annulation suivantes pourront être demandées:

- **Préavis de 14 jours:** aucune pénalité
- **Préavis de 7 jours:** 50 % du tarif B&B pour la première nuit.
- **Préavis de 24 heures:** 75 % du tarif B&B pour la première nuit.
- **Absence:** Tarif B&B pour la première nuit.

Arrivées/départs

Prévenir de toute arrivée en avance.
- Chambres mises à disposition entre 14.00 h et 18.00 h.
- Les chambres sont à libérer avant 11.00 heures.
- Les réservations sont à honorer avant 18.00 heures. En cas d'arrivée tardive, prévenir votre hôte/hôtesse le jour de votre arrivée.

Réductions pour les enfants

Celle-ci est consentie lorsque les enfants partagent la chambre des parents ou lorsqu'une chambre est occupée par trois enfants ou plus. Le tarif normal s'applique lorsqu'un ou deux enfants occupent des chambres séparées. Veuillez vérifier lors de la réservation que l'établissement convient aux enfants. Certains établissements peuvent mettre des lits d'enfant 🛏 à votre disposition. Un léger supplément pourra vous être demandé.

Repas du soir

À réserver à l'avance, de préférence avant midi le même jour. Collations ✗ servies sur demande dans certains établissements.

Animaux domestiques

À l'exception des chiens d'aveugle et pour des raisons d'hygiène, les animaux domestiques ne sont pas admis à l'intérieur des établissements.

Personnes handicapées et utilisateurs de chaises roulantes

Le National Rehabilitation Board (NRB) a approuvé un certain nombre d'établissements convenant aux personnes handicapées accompagnées. Ceux-ci sont repérés par le symbole ♿.

Courant électrique

L'alimentation électrique standard est le 230 volts (CA). Lors de l'utilisation de petits appareils, vous pourrez avoir besoin d'un adaptateur pour nos prises plates à trois trous ou rondes à deux trous. Vous devrez éventuellement vous munir d'un transformateur de voyage ou d'un adaptateur avant votre départ.

Distance jusqu'à la ville la plus proche en km

Nom de famille
NOM DE L'ÉTABLISSEMENT
TOWN AND COUNTRY
Adresse
TÉL: FÉLÉC: EMAIL:

Description de l'établissement Town and Country Home

Symboles équipements   BUS N° :

Région
OUVERTURE:
NBRE CHAMBRES:
AVEC SALLE DE B.:

Ⓥ

B&B PPS:	MIN £/ MAX £	SNGL OCC. DBLE/TPL:	MIN £/ MAX £	SNGL RM: MIN £/ MAX £
PART BRD:	MIN £/ MAX £	% RED. CHILDREN: %		DÎNER: £

B+B PPS: chambre et petit déj. par personne partageant une chambre
PART BRD: Chambre, petit déj. et dîner
SNGL OCC. DBLE/TPL: une seule personne dans une chambre pour 2 ou 3 personnes

% RED. CHILDREN: % de réduction pour les enfants partageant la chambre des parents ou lorsque trois enfants ou plus partagent une chambre
SNGL RM: Chambre pour une personne

Symboles

CC	Cartes de crédit acceptées		☕	Possibilité de faire thé/café dans les chambres
♈	Licence vin		🍼	Lits d'enfant disponibles
🕇🕇	Baby-sitter, en principe jusqu'à minuit		🐕	Animaux domestiques autorisés
📞	Téléphone direct dans les chambres		☘	On parle irlandais
Ⓟ	Parking privé		🐟	Pêche dans les environs
♿	Accès pour personnes handicapées accompagnées		⚑	Golf dans les environs
🚫	Interdiction de fumer dans l'établissement		🐎	Équitation dans les environs
R✗	Interdiction de fumer dans les chambres		S	Chambre unique
🖵	Télévision dans les chambres		Ⓥ	Bons d'agents de voyage acceptés.
✖	Collations servies		ⓥ̶	Bons d'agents de voyage non acceptés

Compliments et commentaires

Les sujets de mécontentement doivent toujours être portés à l'attention du propriétaire avant le départ. Si vous ne pouvez obtenir satisfaction en cas de tarif jugé excessif, vous enverrez votre reçu accompagné de votre réclamation à l'adresse suivante : **Customer Care, Quality Approved Bed & Breakfast, Bachelors Walk, Ballyshannon, Co. Donegal.**

Pour maintenir l'excellence qui fait notre réputation, vos commentaires sur le niveau général du service et la qualité des prestations sont les bienvenus. Toute critique constructive sera examinée attentivement afin d'assurer l'amélioration constante du service.

Erreurs et omissions

Nous avons fait tout notre possible pour veiller à l'exactitude de cette publication conformément aux lois irlandaises de protection du consommateur. La Town & Country Homes Association Ltd. n'accepte aucune responsabilité pour les erreurs ou omissions dans les documents fournis par ses membres pour inclusion dans cette publication, ni pour toute perte ou déception par rapport aux attentes suscitées par l'information contenue dans ladite publication. Si de telles erreurs ou omissions sont portées à notre attention, les éditions suivantes seront modifiées en conséquence. Des changements peuvent intervenir après mise sous presse lorsque les propriétés sont vendues et que les établissements changent de propriétaire.

Cómo utilizar esta guía

La guía está dividida en siete regiones geográficas que se encuentran subdivididas en condados (véase la página 3 para el mapa de regiones y condados). Las regiones son: **Sureste, Cork/Kerry, Shannon, Oeste de Irlanda, Noroeste, Región central este, Dublín.**

Reservas

Las reservas se pueden hacer contactando directamente con la casa o a través de una oficina de información turística. Deberá confirmar su reserva por escrito y adjuntando el depósito necesario. En caso de que tuviera algún problema al encontrar alojamiento, telefonée a la central de reservas (072-22222) para que le ayuden. En caso de emergencia, contacte con el representante del área del condado más cercano.

Reserve siempre la primera y la última noche de alojamiento por adelantado, junio/julio/agosto- con 48 horas de antelación. Dublín -2 semanas, preferentemente más, de antelación. Confirme la reserva antes de 7 días con el depósito acordado. Las habitaciones se pueden garantizar mediante tarjeta de crédito -compruébelo al hacer la reserva. Llegadas tardías -después de las 6pm por acuerdo especial con la casa.

Las reservas posteriores se realizarán por lo que cuesta una llamada telefónica. Para evitar decepciones, le rogamos se aproveche de este servicio.

Tarifas

Las tarifas indicadas incluyen los precios mínimos a máximos con respecto a alojamiento nocturno de una persona compartiendo incluido desayuno irlandés. Los precios incluyen el IVA.

Vales de agencias de viaje

Le rogamos presente los vales a su llegada. Los vales sólo serán validos en aquellas casas que muestren el símbolo (V). Los vales estándar cubren habitación en B&B sin servicio privado. Para elevarse a la categoría de habitaciones con baño privado (en suite) el recargo será de £2.00 por persona. Un máximo de £5 por habitación para 3 o más personas compartiendo.

Los vales en suite cubren la estancia en una habitación con instalaciones privadas completas. No se ha de pagar ningún recargo adicional.

Política de cancelaciones

Le rogamos llame por teléfono inmediatamente en caso de cancelación. Se podrán aplicar las siguientes tarifas:

- **con 14 días de aviso:** no recargo
- **con 7 días de aviso:** 50% de B&B la primera noche
- **con 24 horas de aviso:** 75% de B&B la primera noche
- **Sin aparecer:** coste completo la primera noche

Horas de entrada/salida

Le rogamos comunique llegadas tempranas.
- Las habitaciones están disponibles de 2pm a 6pm
- La hora de salida no deberá realizarse más tarde de las 11am.
- Las reservas se deberán realizar antes de las 6pm. En caso de que vaya a llegar tarde, le rogamos confirme el mismo día de llegada con el/la anfitrión/a.

Descuento para niños

Se aplica cuando los niños comparten la habitación de los padres o cuando tres o más niños comparten una habitación. Se aplica la tarifa completa cuando uno o dos niños ocupan habitaciones separadas. Le rogamos compruebe que la casa es adecuada para niños cuando realice la reserva. En algunas casas se encuentran disponibles cunas ➤ -puede haber un recargo nominal.

Cenas

Reserve con antelación preferiblemente antes de las 12 del medio día de ese mismo día. Comidas ligeras ☒ disponibles a petición suya.

Animales domésticos

Con la excepción de perros-guías, por cuestiones de higiene, no se permite la entrada de animales domésticos en las casas.

Personas con minusvalías/usuarios de sillas de ruedas

El Consejo de Rehabilitación Nacional (National Rehabilitation Board "NRB") ha dado su aprobación a casas adecuadas para personas con minusvalías y sus ayudantes y éstas se encuentran en la lista bajo el símbolo ♿.

Corriente eléctrica

El abastecimiento eléctrico normal es de 230 voltios CA (50 ciclos). Para usar pequeños aparatos, puede que necesite un adaptador para nuestros enchufes de 3 clavijas planas o de 2 clavijas redondas. En caso necesario, se deberán comprar pequeños transformadores y adaptadores de viaje antes de la salida.

Apellido
NOMBRE DE LA CIUDAD Y
DE LA CASA
Dirección
TEL: FAX: EMAIL:

Descripción de la ciudad y de la Casa

Area

ABIERTO:
Nº DE HABITACIONES:
EN SUITE:

Distancia en kilómetros **a la ciudad
más cercana**

Símbolos de Instalaciones   AUTOBÚS Nº:

| B&B PPS: | MIN £/ MAX £ | SNGL OCC. DBLE/TPL: | MIN £/ MAX £ | SNGL RM: | MIN £/ MAX £ |
| PART BRD: | MIN £/ MAX £ | % RED. CHILDREN: | % | CENA: | £ |

B+B PPS: Bed & Breakfast por persona
compartiendo
PART BRD: Bed & Breakfast, media pensión -
cena-.
SNGL OCC. DBLE/TPL: Ocupación sencilla de
una habitación doble o triple

% RED. CHILDREN: % de descuento por niños
que comparten la habitación de los padres o
cuando tres o más niños compartan una
habitación
SNGL RM: Habitación sencilla

Símbolos

| cc | Se aceptan tarjetas de crédito |

⚕ Licencia para vinos

👶 Canguro, normalmente hasta las
12 de la noche

📞 Teléfono directo en las habitaciones

Ⓟ Aparcamiento privado fuera de la vía pública

♿ Acceso a minusválidos con ayudante

🚭 Prohibido fumar en la casa

R🚭 Prohibido fumar en las habitaciones

📺 TV en las habitaciones

✗ Comidas ligeras disponibles

☕ Servicios para té/café en las habitaciones

🛏 Cuna disponible

🐕 Animales domésticos permitidos

☘ Se habla irlandés

🎣 Posibilidad de pescar en las proximidades

⚑ Posibilidad de practicar golf en las
proximidades

🐴 Posibilidad de practicar equitación en las
proximidades

S Habitación sencilla

Ⓥ Se aceptan vales de agencias de viaje

Ⓥ No se aceptan vales de agencias de viaje

Quejas y comentarios

Las reclamaciones se deberán hacer primero ante
los propietarios de las casas antes de la salida. Si
ésta no es atendida satisfactoriamente en el caso
de que presuntamente le hubieran cobrado de
más, deberá enviar el recibo junto con su queja a:
**Customer Care, Quality Approved Bed &
Breakfast Association Ltd., Bacherlor's Walk,
Ballyshannon, Co Donegal.**

Para mantener los altos estandars por los que
se conoce a la Asociación, todos los comentarios
sobre el nivel general de servicio y estandars que
ha recibido serán bienvenidos y todas las críticas
constructivas se tomarán seriamente en cuenta
para asegurar la continua mejora de los servicios.

Errores y Omisiones

Se ha cuidado todo lo posible la exactitud de esta
publicación conforme a las Leyes de Protección al
Cliente de Irlanda. La Asociación de Casas de
Ciudad y Campo Ltd. no puede aceptar
responsabilidad por errores u omisiones de
material facilitado para su inclusión en esta
publicación o por cualquier pérdida o decepción
causadas por dependencia de información incluida
en ésta. Cuando se nos haga saber, se
enmendarán futuras ediciones en consecuencia.
Puede que ocurran ciertos cambios después de
llevar este folleto a imprimir, como que se vendan
propiedades o que las casas cambien de
propietarios.

La guida è divisa in sette regioni geografiche che sono a loro volta suddivise in contee (vedi pagina 3 per mappa della regioni e contee). Le regioni sono: **Sud Ovest, Cork/Kerry, Shannon, Ovest, Nord Ovest, Centro Est, Dublino.**

Prenotazioni

Le prenotazioni possono essere effettuate contattando direttamente la casa o tramite un ufficio informazioni turistiche. La prenotazione va confermata per iscritto e allegando il deposito richiesto. Nel caso di problemi nel trovare una sistemazione, telefonare alle prenotazioni centrali (072-22222) per richiedere assistenza. Nel caso di un'emergenza contattare il più vicino rappresentante di contea.

Prenotate sempre la sistemazione per la prima e l'ultima notte in anticipo. Giugno/luglio/agosto - 48 ore in anticipo. Dublino - 2 settimane di anticipo, preferibilmente di più. Confermare la prenotazione entro 7 giorni con il deposito pattuito. Le camere possono essere garantite tramite Carta di Credito - controllate quando prenotate e controllate al momento della prenotazione anche la penale e la prassi in caso di annullamento. Arrivi a tarda ora: dopo le ore 18.00 solo previo accordo speciale con i proprietari della casa.

Prenotazioni successive verranno fatte al costo della telefonata. Per evitare delusioni avvaletevi di questo servizio.

Tariffe

Le tariffe quotate includono dal minimo al massimo prezzo per una sistemazione per persona in condivisione inclusa prima colazione irlandese. I prezzi sono comprensivi di IVA.

Voucher delle agenzie di viaggio

Presentate il voucher al momento dell'arrivo. I voucher sono validi solo nelle case indicate con il simbolo ⓥ. Normalmente i voucher includono pernottamento e prima colazione in camera senza servizi privati. Per le camere con servizi privati (en-suite) il supplemento è di IR£ 2.00 a persona. Massimo IR£ 5.00 a camera per tre o più persone in condivisione.

I voucher "ensuite" includono una camera con servizi privati completi. Non è previsto nessun altro supplemento.

Prassi di Annullamento

Telefonate immediatamente in caso di annullamento. Si potrebbero applicare le seguenti penali:
- **14 giorni di preavviso:** nessuna penale
- **7 giorni di preavviso:** 50% della tariffa B&B per la prima notte
- **24 ore di preavviso:** 75% della tariffa B&B per la prima notte
- **Mancato arrivo:** Tariffa intera per la prima notte

Arrivo/Partenza

Avvisate se prevedete di arrivare in anticipo.
- Le camere sono disponibili fra le ore 14.00 e le ore 18.00
- Partenza: non oltre le 11.00
- Le camere vanno occupate entro le ore 18.00. In caso di arrivo in ritardo: chiedete conferma il giorno dell'arrivo ai proprietari della casa

Riduzioni per Bambini

Si applicano se i bambini condividono la camera dei genitori o se tre o più bambini condividono la stessa camera. La tariffa intera si applica se uno o due bambini occupano una camera separata. Controllate al momento della prenotazione che la casa sia adatta ad ospitare bambini. In alcune case sono disponibili lettini: potrebbe esserci un addebito simbolico 🛏.

Pasti Serali

Prenotate in anticipo preferibilmente non più tardi di mezzogiorno del giorno stesso. Spuntini disponibili su richiesta.

Animali Domestici

Ad eccezione dei cani guida per ciechi, per motivi igienici, gli animali non sono ammessi nei locali.

Disabili/Invalidi

Il National Rehabilitation Board (NRB: ente nazionale riabilitazione) ha approvato case attrezzate per l'accoglienza dei disabili con accompagnatore, indicate con il simbolo ♿.

Corrente Elettrica

L'erogazione standard di energia elettrica è di 230 volt (50 cicli). Per l'uso di piccoli apparecchi potrebbe essere necessario un adattatore per prese a 3 punte piatte o 2 punte rotonde. Se necessario, piccoli trasformatori e adattatori da viaggio dovrebbero essere acquistati prima della partenza.

Nome della Famiglia
NOME DELLA CASA DI CITTÀ E
CAMPAGNA
Indirizzo
Tel: Fax: Email:
Descrizione della Casa di Città e Campagna

Area

Aperto:
No. Camere:
Con bagno in camera:

(V)

Simboli Servizi   Autobus No:

Città più vicina distanza in km

| B&B pps: | Min £/ Max £ | Sngl Occ. Dble/Tpl: | Min £/ Max £ | Sngl Rm: | Min £/ Max £ |
| Part Brd: | Min £/ Max £ | % Red. Children: | % | Cena: | £ |

B+B pps: Pernottamento e Prima colazione per persona in condivisione
Part Brd: Pernottamento e Prima colazione, Pasto serale.
Sngl Occ. Dble/Tpl: Singolo Occupante Camera Doppia/Tripla

% Red. Children: % Riduzione per Bambini in condivisione con i genitori o se tre o più bambini dividono una camera
Sngl Rm: Camera Singola

Simboli

cc	Si accettano carte di credito	☕	Possibilità di preparare té/caffé in camera
Licenza vendita vini	🐖	Lettino disponibile
[††]	Babysitter, generalmente fino a mezzanotte	🐕	Sono ammessi animali domestici
(C)	Telefono diretto nelle camere	☘	Si parla irlandese
(P)	Posto macchina privato	🐟	Possibilità di pesca nelle vicinanze
Accesso disabili con accompagnatore	⚑	Possibilità di golf nelle vicinanze
(X)	Casa non fumatori	🐎	Possibilità di equitazione nelle vicinanze
Camere non fumatori	[S]	Camera singola
TV nelle camere	(V)	Si accettano voucher di agenzie di viaggio
[X]	Spuntini disponibili	(V̸)	Non si accettano voucher di agenzie di viaggio

---

Complimenti e Commenti

Eventuali reclami vanno sempre portati all'attenzione del proprietario della casa prima della partenza. In caso di mancata soddisfazione nel caso di presunto eccesso di prezzo, inoltrare la ricevuta con il reclamo a: **Customer Care, Quality Approved Bed & Breakfast, Bachelors Walk, Ballyshannon, Co. Donegal.**

Al fine di mantenere gli alti standard per i quali l'Associazione è rinomata, saranno apprezzati tutti i commenti sul livello generale del servizio e gli standard che avete incontrato. Tutte le critiche costruttive verranno prese in attenta considerazione per assicurare un continuo miglioramento del servizio.

Errori e Omissioni

È stata posta ogni cura per assicurare accuratezza in questa pubblicazione in conformità alle leggi irlandesi a tutela dei consumatori. La Town & Country Homes Association Ltd. non si assume alcuna responsabilità per eventuali errori o omissioni nel materiale fornito dai membri per questa pubblicazione, o per qualsiasi perdita o delusione risultanti dall'uso delle informazioni qui contenute. Nel caso questi siano portati alla nostra attenzione, le future edizioni verranno emendate di conseguenza. Potrebbero esserci cambiamenti dopo l'andata in stampa nel caso in cui le proprietà siano vendute e la casa cambi di proprietario.

De gids is verdeeld in zeven geografische streken die weer in graafschappen worden onderverdeeld (zie pagina 3 voor een kaart van de streken en graafschappen). De streken zijn: het Zuidoosten, **Cork/Kerry, Shannon, West Ierland, het Noordwesten, Centraal Ierland, Dublin.**

Reserveringen

Reserveringen kunnen worden gemaakt door het landhuis zelf of via een toeristenbureau te benaderen. U dient uw reservering schriftelijk te bevestigen en de aanbetaling bij te sluiten.

Mocht u een probleem hebben bij het verkrijgen van accommodatie, kunt u de centrale reserveringen (072-22222) opbellen voor assistentie. In noodgevallen kunt u contact opnemen met de dichtstbijzijnde vertegenwoordiger voor het betreffende graafschap.

Reserveer voor de eerste en laatste nacht altijd accommodatie vooraf. Juni/juli/augustus - 48 uur vooraf. Dublin - 2 weken vooraf reserveren, bij voorkeur eerder. Bevestig de reservering binnen 7 dagen met de overeengekomen aanbetaling

Kamers kunnen met een credit card worden gegarandeerd - controleer bij het reserveren. Controleer het tarief en de annuleringsregels bij het reserveren. Late aankomst na 18.00 uur dient speciaal met het huis afgesproken te worden. Voor de prijs van een telefoontje kunt u ter plaatse een reservering laten maken naar het volgende huis voor de volgende nacht. Gebruik deze service om teleurstelling te voorkomen.

Prijzen

De aangehaalde prijzen zijn de minimum en maximum kosten voor een overnachting per persoon op een gedeelde kamer, inclusief Iers ontbijt. De prijzen zijn exclusief BTW.

Cheques van reisbureaus

Overhandig uw cheque bij aankomst. Cheques zijn alleen geldig in huizen met het Ⓥ symbool. Standaard cheques zijn geldig voor Bed & Breakfast in een kamer zonder privé-faciliteiten. Voor opwaardering tot een kamer met badkamer wordt een toeslag van £2,00 per persoon in rekening gebracht. Maximum £5,00 per kamer voor 3 of meer personen op één kamer.

Cheques voor kamers met badkamer zijn voor kamers met volledige privé-faciliteiten. Geen extra kosten worden in rekening gebracht.

Annuleringen

In geval van een annulering dient u onmiddellijk op te bellen. De volgende kosten worden in rekening gebracht:
- **Kennisgeving van 14 dagen:** geen kosten
- **Kennisgeving van 7 dagen:** 50% van B&B voor de eerste nacht
- **Kennisgeving van 24 uur:** 75% van B&B voor de eerste nacht
- **Geen verschijning:** volle kosten van de eerste nacht.

Aankomst / Vertrek

Een vroege aankomst graag vooraf meedelen
- Kamers worden tussen 14.00 en 18.00 uur beschikbaar gesteld
- Vertrek - niet later dan 11.00 uur
- Gereserveerde kamers dienen om 18.00 uur te zijn ingenomen Bij late aankomst - bevestig op de dag van aankomst bij de gastheer/-vrouw.

Kinderkorting

Een kinderkorting is van toepassing indien kinderen de kamer met hun ouders delen of indien 3 of meer kinderen de kamer delen. Het volle tarief is van toepassing wanneer 1 of 2 kinderen aparte kamers innemen. Controleer bij de reservering dat het huis geschikt is voor kinderen. Wiegen 🍼 zijn in sommige huizen beschikbaar - soms tegen een nominaal tarief

Avondmaaltijden

Deze dienen vooraf te worden gereserveerd, liefst voor 12.00 uur op de betreffende dag. Lichte maaltijden ✖ zijn op verzoek beschikbaar.

Huisdieren

In het belang van de hygiëne worden huisdieren niet binnenshuis toegelaten, met uitzondering van blindengeleidehonden

Gehandicapten/rolstoelgebruikers

De nationale revalidatieraad (NRB) heeft huizen goedgekeurd die geschikt zijn voor gehandicapten met helper en deze zijn op de lijst herkenbaar aan het symbool ♿ .

Elektriciteit

De standaard elektriciteitstoevoer is 230V (50 Hz). Om kleine apparaten te gebruiken, is een adapter vereist voor onze stopcontacten met drie platte pennen of twee ronde pennen. Zo nodig dienen kleine reistransformatoren en -adapters vóór vertrek te worden aangeschaft.

Familienaam		Streek		
FNAAM VAN STAD EN LANDHUIS		OPEN:		
Adres		AANTAL KAMERS:		
		MET BADKAMER:		(V)
TEL:	FAX:		EMAIL:	
Beschrijving van Town & Country Home				
Faciliteiten		BUSNUMMER:		

Afstand naar dichtstbijzijnde stad in kilometers

B&B PPS:	MIN £/ MAX £	SNGL OCC. DBLE/TPL:	MIN £/ MAX £	SNGL RM: MIN £/ MAX £
PART BRD:	MIN £/ MAX £	% RED. CHILDREN:	%	MAALTIJD: £

B+B PPS: Bed & Breakfast per persoon in dezelfde kamer
PART BRD: Bed & Breakfast, avondmaaltijd
SNGL OCC. DBLE/TPL: Bezetting van twee-of driepersoonskamer door één persoon

% RED. CHILDREN: Percentage korting voor kinderen die de kamer van de ouders delen of waar drie of meer kinderen een kamer delen.
SNGL RM: Eenpersoonskamer

Symbolen

cc	Credit cards worden geaccepteerd	⊔̣	Thee- en koffiefaciliteiten op de kamer
☿	Wijnvergunning	⇔	Wieg beschikbaar
⊞	Babysitter, gewoonlijk tot middernacht	🐕	Huisdieren toegestaan
☎	Telefoon op de kamer	☘	Iers gesproken
℗	Privé parkeerplaats	🐟	Vissen in de omtrek
♿	Toegang voor gehandicapten met helper	▶	Golf in de omtrek
⊗	Roken verboden in het huis	🐎	Paardrijden in de omtrek
ᴿ⚡	Roken verboden op de kamer	S	Eenpersoonskamer
⬚	TV op de kamer	V	Cheques van reisbureaus worden geaccepteerd
✗	Lichte maaltijden zijn beschikbaar	⍉	Cheques van reisbureaus worden niet geaccepteerd

Complimenten en opmerkingen

Klachten dienen in de eerste instantie vóór vertrek te worden besproken met de eigenaar van de accommodatie. Wanneer de klacht niet naar uw tevredenheid wordt afgehandeld, dient u contact op te nemen met: **Customer Care, Quality Approved Bed & Breakfast, Bachelors Walk, Ballyshannon, Co. Donegal.**

Om de hoge standaarden waar de Association bekend om staat, te handhaven, worden alle opmerkingen over het algemene niveau van service en de standaarden die u heeft ervaren zeer gewaardeerd. Alle nuttige kritiek wordt serieus genomen om de verbetering van onze service te kunnen voortzetten.

Fouten en omissies

Wij trachten nauwkeurigheid van deze publikatie te verzekeren en te voldoen aan de Ierse Wet Consumentenbescherming. De Town & Country Homes Association Ltd. aanvaart geen verantwoordelijkheid voor fouten of omissies in materiaal dat is geleverd door leden voor opname in deze publikatie of voor verlies of teleurstelling door afhankelijkheid van informatie in deze publikatie. Waar dit tot onze aandacht wordt gebracht, worden toekomstige uitgaven gewijzigd. Er kunnen zich wijzigingen voordoen na de druk van deze publikatie waar huizen zijn verkocht en het eigenaarschap van het huis wordt veranderd.

Denna guidebok har indelats i sju geografiska regioner, dessa regioner har sedan indelats i landskap (se sid. 3 för kartor för regionerna och landskapen). Regionerna är: **Sydöst, Cork/Kerry, Shannon, västra Irland, Nordväst, östra inlandet och Dublin.**

Bokning

Bokning kan göras genom att kontakta huset direkt eller genom en turistinformationsbyrå. Bekräfta bokningen skriftligt och bifoga den handpenning som begärts. Skulle du ha problem med att få tag i logi ringer du det centrala bokningskontoret (072-22222) för att få hjälp. I nödfall tar du kontakt med den närmsta områdesrepresentanten.

Boka alltid logi för första och sista natten i förväg. Juni/juli/augusti - 2 dygn i förväg. Dublin - 2 veckor eller helst mer, i förväg. Bekräfta bokningen inom 7 dagar med den begärda handpenningen. Logi kan garanteras med kreditkort, kontrollera detta när du bokar. Kontrollera också pris och avbeställningsregler när du bokar. Sen ankomst - efter kl. 18.00 enligt särskild överenskommelse med huset.

Förhandsbokning för kommande nätter kan göras, det enda du behöver betala för är telefonsamtalet. För att undvika besvikelse rekommenderar vi att du utnyttjar denna möjlighet.

Pris

Angivna priser täcker de lägsta och högsta avgifterna som gäller för logi per person som delar rum, detta inkluderar irländsk frukost. Priserna inkluderar MOMS.

Resebyråkuponger

Var vänlig att visa kupongerna vid ankomsten. Kuponger gäller endast på de gästhus som uppvisar Ⓥ symbolen. Standardkuponger täcker Bed and Breakfast med rum utan privat badrum. Önskas privat badrum tillkommer en extra kostnad på 2 pund per person. Den högsta avgiften är 5 pund per rum för 3 eller fler personer som delar ett rum. Det finns kuponger som täcker kostnaden för rum med privat badrum. Inga andra kostnader tillkommer.

Avbeställningsregler

Var vänlig ring omedelbart om avbeställning måste göras.
Följande avgifter gäller:
- **14 dagars varsel:** Ingen avgift
- **7 dagars varsel:** 50% av B & B för första natten
- **Ett dygns varsel:** 75% av B & B för första natten
- **Utebliven ankomst:** Full kostnad för första natten

In-/Utcheckning

Var vänlig meddela om tidig ankomst.
- Rummen kan intagas mellan kl. 14.00 och 18.00.
- Utcheckning måste göras innan kl. 11.00.
- Bokade rum måste intagas före kl. 18.00. Bekräfta sen ankomst med värden/värdinnan på ankomstdagen.

Rabatt för barn

Gäller där barn delar rum med föräldrar, eller om 3 eller fler barn delar ett rum. Fullt pris när 1 eller 2 barn bor i separat rum. Kontrollera att huset är lämpligt för barn när ni bokar. Barnsängar 🛒 finns på vissa ställen och kan lånas för en liten avgift.

Kvällsmåltider

Beställs i förväg, helst före kl. 12.00 dagen ifråga. Lätta måltider ✖ serveras efter önskemål.

Sällskapsdjur

Förutom guidehundar för blinda tillåts inga djur inne i husen av hygieniska skäl.

Rörelsehindrad person/rullstolsbunden person

Det irländska rehabiliteringsförbundet (NRB) har godkänt gästhus som är lämpliga för personer med handikapp och som har ressällskap, dessa gästhus är markerade med symbolen ♿

Elektrisk ström

Standarden är 230 volt växelström (50 perioder). Det är möjligt att en adapter med 3 platta kontaktstift eller 2 runda väggstift måste användas för mindre elektriska apparater. Om en liten restransformator behövs bör denna inköpas innan avresan.

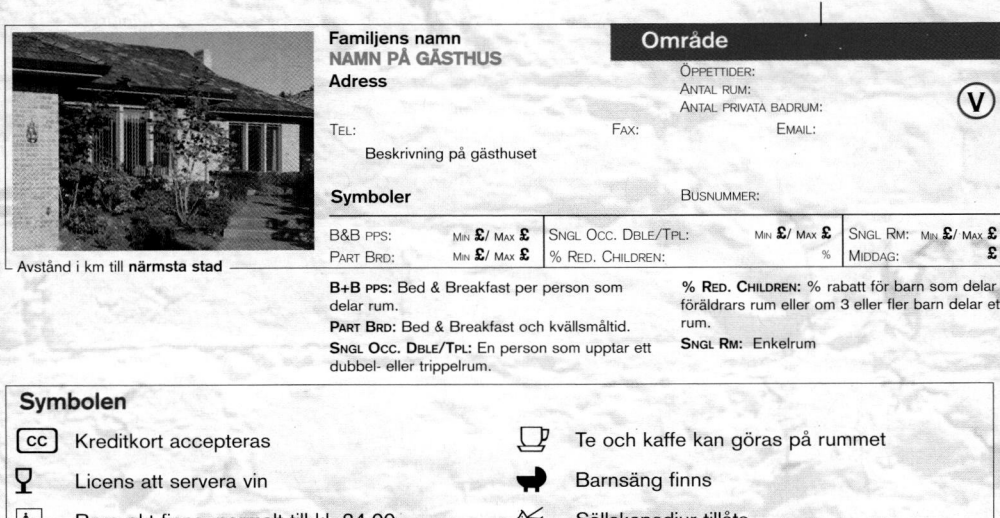

Familjens namn
NAMN PÅ GÄSTHUS
Adress

TEL: FAX: EMAIL:
Beskrivning på gästhuset

Symboler

Område	
ÖPPETTIDER:	
ANTAL RUM:	
ANTAL PRIVATA BADRUM:	

(V)

BUSNUMMER:

Avstånd i km till **närmsta stad**

B&B PPS:	MIN £/ MAX £	SNGL OCC. DBLE/TPL:	MIN £/ MAX £	SNGL RM:	MIN £/ MAX £
PART BRD:	MIN £/ MAX £	% RED. CHILDREN:	%	MIDDAG:	£

B+B PPS: Bed & Breakfast per person som delar rum.
PART BRD: Bed & Breakfast och kvällsmåltid.
SNGL OCC. DBLE/TPL: En person som upptar ett dubbel- eller trippelrum.

% RED. CHILDREN: % rabatt för barn som delar föräldrars rum eller om 3 eller fler barn delar ett rum.
SNGL RM: Enkelrum

Symbolen

cc	Kreditkort accepteras		Te och kaffe kan göras på rummet
	Licens att servera vin		Barnsäng finns
	Barnvakt finns, normalt till kl. 24.00		Sällskapsdjur tillåts
	Telefon med direktanslutning i rum		Irländsktalande
P	Privat bilparkering på gård		Fiske finns i närheten
	Åtkomst för handikappad person och medhjälpare		Golf finns i närheten
			Hästridning finns i närheten
	Rökfritt hus	S	Enkelrum
	Rökfritt rum	(V)	Resebyråkuponger accepteras
	TV finns i rummet		Resebyråkuponger accepteras inte
	Lätta måltider serveras		

Komplimanger och klagomål

Eventuella klagomål ska lämnas till gästhusets ägare innan ni åker därifrån. Om inget resultat erhålls om det skulle gälla eventuellt överpris, skickar du kvittot med ditt klagomål till **Customer Care, Quality Approved Bed & Breakfast Co. Ltd., Bachelor's Walk, Ballyshannon, Co. Donegal.**

För att kunna behålla den höga standarden som föreningen är känd för, tar vi gärna emot alla kommentarer om den allmänna servicen och standarden så som du har upplevt den. Vi tar all konstruktiv kritik på allvar så att vi kan fortsätta förbättra servicen.

Fel eller utelämnanden

Vi har gjort vårt bästa för att alla fakta i den här broschyren skall stämma, detta enligt den irländska konsumentskyddslagen. Föreningen för Town & Country Homes Ltd. kan dock inte hållas ansvarig för fel eller utelämnanden i material som inkommer från medlemmar för publicering i denna utgåva, eller för förlust eller besvikelse som orsakats till följd av informationen, men om fel har uppkommit och detta meddelas till föreningen kommer framtida utgåvor följaktligen att korrigeras. Ändringar kan förekomma efter utgåvan gått i tryck i fall där hus har sålts eller bytt ägare.

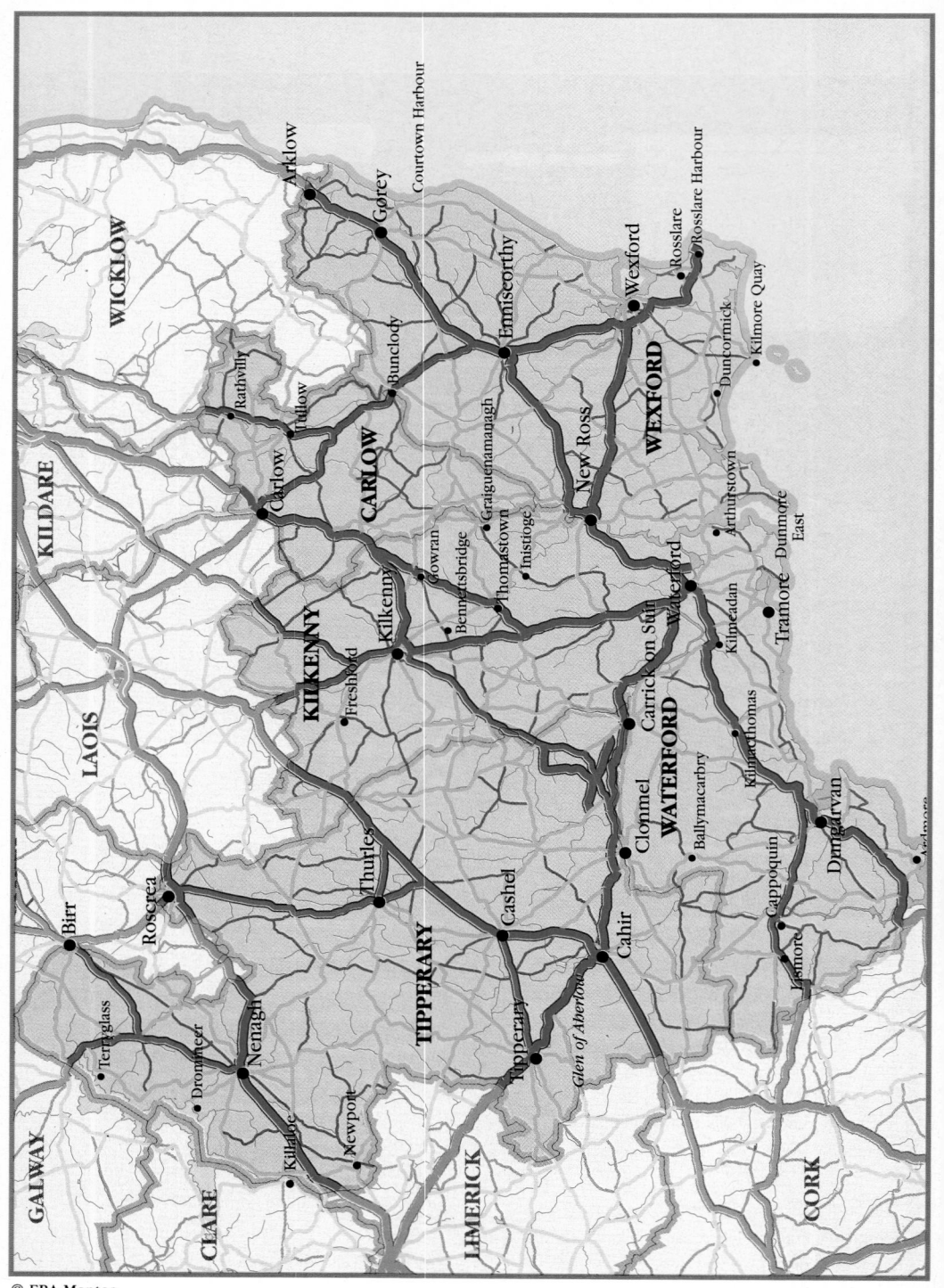

© ERA-Maptec

The South East comprises the counties of Carlow, Kilkenny, Tipperary, Waterford and Wexford. They are linked by the five great river systems of the Slaney, Barrow, Nore, Suir and Blackwater, once the arteries of exploration, invasion and trade, now meandering peacefully through one of the great farming regions of Ireland.

The South East is particularly rich in heritage and history with castles, fortresses, great houses and abbeys dotted generously throughout the scenic river-valley landscape. Its pleasant, rolling pastures and sun-washed coast offer great opportunities for activity holidays with abundant golf, angling, horse-riding, walking and cycling.

Area Representatives

KILKENNY
Mrs. Marie Brennan, White Oaks, Tennypark, Callan Road, Kilkenny, Co. Kilkenny. Tel: 056-63295.

Mrs. Theresa Nolan, The Laurels, College Road, Kilkenny, Co. Kilkenny. Tel: 056-61501. Fax: 056-61501 (manual).

TIPPERARY
Mr. Pat Duane, Maryville, Bank Place, Cashel, Co. Tipperary. Tel: 062-61098.

Mrs. Kathleen Healy, Rathnaleen House, Golf Club Road (Old Birr Road), Nenagh, Co. Tipperary. Tel: 067-32508.

WATERFORD
Mrs. Margo Slater, Rosebank House, Coast Road, Dungarvan, Co. Waterford. Tel: 058-41561.

Mrs. Margaret Power, Talginn, Ballynaneashagh, Cork Road, Waterford, Co. Waterford. Tel: 051-373798. Fax: 051-370086.

WEXFORD
Mrs. Ann Sunderland, Hillside House, Tubberduff, Gorey, Co. Wexford. Tel: 055-21726/22036. Fax: 055-22567.

CARLOW
Mrs. Treresa O'Donovan, Cloonlara, Kilkenny Road, Carlow, Co. Carlow. Tel: 0503 41863.

Tourist Information Offices

Waterford
41, The Quay
Tel: (051) 875788

Carlow
Tel: (O503) 31554

Clonmel
Tel: (052) 22960

Dungarvan
Tel: (058) 41741

Gorey
Tel: (055) 21248

Kilkenny
Tel: (056) 51500

Rosslare Terminal
Tel: (053) 33232

Wexford
Tel: (053) 23111

Carlow 1km

Gerard McCormack & Thomas Donagher
TOM & GERRY'S B & B
6 Oaklawns, Dublin Road, Carlow
TEL: **0503 40557/ 087 2342678**   FAX: **0503 40557**

Carlow		
OPEN:	**1st January-31st December**	
NO. ROOMS:	4	
ENSUITE:	4	(V)

Tour South East from Celtic centre Ireland. Quiet area, bedrooms offer, tea facilities, hairdryers, trouser press. Free taxi / restaurants reservations.

B&B PPS:	**£17/£21**	SNGL OCC. DBLE/TPL:	**£23.50/£26.50**	SNGL RM:	**£20/£23**
PART BRD:	**£200**	% RED. CHILDREN:	**30%**	DINNER:	**£12**

Carlow 3km

Mrs Therese O'Donovan
CLOONLARA
Kilkenny Road, Carlow, Co Carlow
TEL: **0503 41863**   FAX: -

Carlow		
OPEN:	**1st March-31st October**	
NO. ROOMS:	3	
ENSUITE:	3	(V)

Modern residence situated on N9 (Kilkenny Rd) Landscaped gardens with River Barrow at rear. Fishing, Golf and Dolmen Hotel nearby.

B&B PPS:	**£17/£18**	SNGL OCC. DBLE/TPL:	**£23.50/£24.50**	SNGL RM:	-
PART BRD:	-	% RED. CHILDREN:	**20%**	DINNER:	-

Mrs Geraldine O'Loughlin
ROSS NA MULLEN
Portlaoise Road, Carlow, Co Carlow
TEL: **0503 42064**   FAX: **0503 30718**

Carlow		
OPEN:	**1st March-31st October**	
NO. ROOMS:	4	
ENSUITE:	4	(V)

Ross na Mullen a superb residence in scenic landscaped gardens. Quiet peaceful setting. Convenient Swimming pool, Golf club. Carlow 1 km.

B&B PPS:	**£17**	SNGL OCC. DBLE/TPL:	**£23.50**	SNGL RM:	-
PART BRD:	-	% RED. CHILDREN:	**50%**	DINNER:	-

Carlow 1km

Carmel & James O'Toole
BORLUM HOUSE
Kilkenny Road, Carlow, Co Carlow
TEL: **0503 41747**   FAX: -

Carlow Town		
OPEN:	**1st February-30th November**	
NO. ROOMS:	4	
ENSUITE:	4	(V)

Delightful early 18C residence in secluded gardens, where guests can enjoy Georgian charm and the comforts expected by decerning visitors.

B&B PPS:	**£17/£18**	SNGL OCC. DBLE/TPL:	**£23.50/£25**	SNGL RM:	**£20/£23**
PART BRD:	-	% RED. CHILDREN:	**25%**	DINNER:	-

In Carlow

Carlow 2km

Mrs Mary Ruane
MEELTRANE HOUSE
Link Road, Brownshill, Carlow, Co Carlow
TEL: **0503 42473**   FAX: -

Carlow		
OPEN:	**1st March-31st October**	
NO. ROOMS:	3	
ENSUITE:	2	(V)

Modern, spacious country home in peaceful setting. Adjacent Golf, Dolmen, Fishing. Proximity to town & all routes. Warm Irish welcome.

B&B PPS:	**£15/£20**	SNGL OCC. DBLE/TPL:	**£21.50/£23.50**	SNGL RM:	-
PART BRD:	-	% RED. CHILDREN:	-	DINNER:	-

In Rathvilly

Mr & Mrs E Tononi
THE WATERMILL
Rathvilly, Co Carlow

Rathvilly

OPEN:	April-October
No. ROOMS:	5
ENSUITE:	3

TEL: **0503 61392**   FAX: -

Ⓥ

16th Century Watermill on river Slaney, N 81 midway Dublin/Rosslare. Free fishing. Continental cuisine, Home grown vegetables. Italian, French spoken.

B&B PPS:	**£16/£20**	SNGL OCC. DBLE/TPL:	**£22.50/£26.50**	SNGL RM:	-
PART BRD:	**£210**	% RED. CHILDREN:	-	DINNER:	**£12**

Tullow 1km

Anne & Edward Byrne
LABURNUM LODGE
Bunclody Road N81, Tullow, Co Carlow

Tullow

OPEN:	All Year except Christmas
No. ROOMS:	4
ENSUITE:	4

TEL: **0503 51718**   FAX: -

Ⓥ

Elegant Georgian house in Slaney Valley. Downstairs accommodation overlooking Golf Course. Mid-way Dublin/Rosslare. Relaxing leisurely ambience awaits you.

B&B PPS:	**£17**	SNGL OCC. DBLE/TPL:	**£23.50**	SNGL RM:	-
PART BRD:	-	% RED. CHILDREN:	**25%**	DINNER:	-

— In Bennettsbridge

Mrs Sheila Cole
NORELY THEYR
**Barronsland, Bennettsbridge,
Co Kilkenny**

Bennettsbridge

TEL: **056 27496**   FAX: -

OPEN: **1st January-31st December**
NO. ROOMS: **4**
ENSUITE: **1**

 (V)

Luxurious, spacious bungalow, Rosslare/Kilkenny Road. Quiet, restful, friendly accommodation. Tea/coffee room facilites. Restaurant. Visa/Access Brochure available.

| B&B PPS: | **£15/£17** | SNGL OCC. DBLE/TPL: | **£21.50/£23.50** | SNGL RM: | - |
| PART BRD: | **£180** | % RED. CHILDREN: | **25%** | DINNER: | **£12** |

— Kilkenny 6km

Margaret Cullen
THE LOFT
Bennettsbridge, Co Kilkenny

Bennetts Bridge

TEL: **056 27147**   FAX: -

OPEN: **All Year**
NO. ROOMS: **4**
ENSUITE: **2**

(V)

Family run, large rooms, Tea/Coffee. Walking distance Pubs, Restaurants, Mosse J Jackson Pottery's. Close: Golf, Fishing, Pet Farm. Touring Base.

| B&B PPS: | **£15/£17** | SNGL OCC. DBLE/TPL: | **£22.50/£23.50** | SNGL RM: | **£18/£20** |
| PART BRD: | **£180** | % RED. CHILDREN: | **30%** | DINNER: | **£12** |

— In Freshford

Mrs Priscilla Flanagan
POMADORA HOUSE
**Clinstown Road, Freshford,
Co Kilkenny**

Freshford

TEL: **056 32256**   FAX: -

OPEN: **All Year**
NO. ROOMS: **3**
ENSUITE: **3**

(V)

Home on Hunter Stud on R693 to Cashel. Gardens, Fishing, Horseriding, Hunting in Winter. Stabling for Horses, Dog Kennels, meals.

| B&B PPS: | **£18** | SNGL OCC. DBLE/TPL: | **£24.50** | SNGL RM: | - |
| PART BRD: | **£180** | % RED. CHILDREN: | **50%** | DINNER: | **£12** |

— Freshford 3km

Mrs Bridget Nolan
CASTLE VIEW
**Balleen, Freshford,
Co Kilkenny**

Freshford

TEL: **056 32181**   FAX: -

OPEN: **All Year**
NO. ROOMS: **3**
ENSUITE: **2**

(V)

Bungalow, peaceful location, panoramic view of country side. Orthopaedic beds. Convenient to Kilkenny City, Dunmore Caves, Rock of Cashel.

| B&B PPS: | **£15/£17** | SNGL OCC. DBLE/TPL: | **£21.50** | SNGL RM: | - |
| PART BRD: | - | % RED. CHILDREN: | **50%** | DINNER: | - |

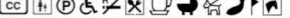
— Kilkenny 10km

Mrs Ann Kenny
WHITETHORNS
**Flagmount, Clifden, Gowran,
Co Kilkenny**

Gowran

TEL: **056 26102**   FAX: -

OPEN: **1st March-31st October**
NO. ROOMS: **3**
ENSUITE: **1**

(V)

Quiet friendly atmosphere. On 2 acres with magnificent views. 300m off N10 and Paddys Pub. Ideal for touring Waterford, Cashel, Dublin.

| B&B PPS: | **£15/£19** | SNGL OCC. DBLE/TPL: | **£21.50/£25.50** | SNGL RM: | **£12** |
| PART BRD: | **£180** | % RED. CHILDREN: | **33.3%** | DINNER: | - |

Graiguenamanagh

Terence & Kathleen Kennedy
MULVARRA HOUSE,
**St Mullins, Graiguenamanagh,
Co Kilkenny**

Graiguenamanagh

OPEN:	March-October
NO. ROOMS:	3
ENSUITE:	3

TEL: **051 424936**   FAX: -

(V)

Mulvarra House is a dormer bungalow which is set in a beautiful Valley overlooking the River Barrow with balcony to enjoy.

B&B PPS:	**£18/£20**	SNGL OCC. DBLE/TPL:	**£24.50/£26.50**	SNGL RM:	-
PART BRD:	-	% RED. CHILDREN:	**20%**	DINNER:	-

Graiguenamanagh 5km

Mrs Helen Lewis
BARLEYCROFT
**Ballyvarra, Graiguenamanagh,
Co Kilkenny**

Graiguenamanagh

OPEN:	All Year except Christmas
NO. ROOMS:	3
ENSUITE:	3

TEL: **051 423668**   FAX: **051 423668**

(V)

RAC acclaimed country home. Panoramic mountain views, German and French spoken. Ideal for Touring, Golfing, Walking , Fishing. Rosslare 40 miles.

B&B PPS:	**£17.50**	SNGL OCC. DBLE/TPL:	**£24**	SNGL RM:	-
PART BRD:	**£200**	% RED. CHILDREN:	-	DINNER:	**£15**

Inistioge 1km

Mrs Maura Naddy
ASHVILLE
**Kilmacshane, Inistioge,
Co Kilkenny**

Inistioge

OPEN:	1st March-31st October
NO. ROOMS:	4
ENSUITE:	3

TEL: **056 58460**   FAX: -

(V)

Situated on Kilkenny/Rosslare Road, in the beautiful Nore Valley. Ideal touring base, Jerpoint, Duishe Abbey, Lounge room. Children welcome.

B&B PPS:	**£15/£17**	SNGL OCC. DBLE/TPL:	**£23.50**	SNGL RM:	-
PART BRD:	-	% RED. CHILDREN:	**50%**	DINNER:	-

In Inistioge

Leslie & Lucy Rothwell
NORE VALLEY VILLA
**Inistioge, Kilkenny,
Co Kilkenny**

Inistioge

OPEN:	1st March-31st October
NO. ROOMS:	4
ENSUITE:	2

TEL: **056 58418**   FAX: **056 58418**

(V)

Peaceful setting overlooking River Nore. Ideal location for touring South East Fishing, Golfing Hill Walking. Local pub "craic". Cadogan guide.

B&B PPS:	**£15/£17**	SNGL OCC. DBLE/TPL:	**£21.50/£23.50**	SNGL RM:	-
PART BRD:	**£180**	% RED. CHILDREN:	**20%**	DINNER:	**£12**

Kilkenny City 4km

Pat & Monica Banahan
CHURCH VIEW
**Cuffesgrange, Callan Road, Kilkenny,
Co Kilkenny**

Kilkenny

OPEN:	All Year
NO. ROOMS:	4
ENSUITE:	3

TEL: **056 29170**   FAX: -

(V)

Comfortable luxury home. Callan - Clonmel - Cork Road (N76). Only 4 mins drive from the Medieval City. A warm welcome awaits you.

B&B PPS:	**£17**	SNGL OCC. DBLE/TPL:	**£25**	SNGL RM:	-
PART BRD:	-	% RED. CHILDREN:	**20%**	DINNER:	-

Mrs Breda Beirne
ANNA VILLA
4 College Road, Kilkenny,
Co Kilkenny

Kilkenny

OPEN:	**1st March-30th November**
NO. ROOMS:	**4**
ENSUITE:	**4**

TEL: **056 62680**   FAX: **056 62680**

"Anna Villa" town house in residential area. Family run B & B. 5 mins walk to City Centre.

In Kilkenny City

B&B PPS:	**£17/£18.50**	SNGL OCC. DBLE/TPL:	**£23.50/£25.00**	SNGL RM:	**£22/£23.50**
PART BRD:	-	% RED. CHILDREN:	**20%**	DINNER:	-

Mrs Maria Brennan
WHITE OAKS
Tennypark, Callan Road, Kilkenny,
Co Kilkenny

Kilkenny

OPEN:	**1st February-30th November**
NO. ROOMS:	**4**
ENSUITE:	**3**

TEL: **056 63295**   FAX: -

Modern bungalow on N76 with guest lounge, conservatory, breakfast menu, spacious gardens, car park, tea/coffee facilities and friendly welcome.

Kilkenny 3 km

B&B PPS:	**£15/£18**	SNGL OCC. DBLE/TPL:	**£22/£25**	SNGL RM:	-
PART BRD:	-	% RED. CHILDREN:	**25%**	DINNER:	-

Mrs Nuala Brennan
MELROSE HOUSE
Circular Road, Kilkenny,
Co Kilkenny

Kilkenny

OPEN:	**1st March-31st October**
NO. ROOMS:	**3**
ENSUITE:	**2**

TEL: **056 65289**   FAX: -

Spacious Georgian family home. Opposite Hotel Kilkenny (off N76). 8 mins walk to City Centre. Quiet location. Hairdryers, Clockradio, TV bedrooms

In Kilkenny City

B&B PPS:	**£15/£18**	SNGL OCC. DBLE/TPL:	**£21.50/£24.50**	SNGL RM:	-
PART BRD:	-	% RED. CHILDREN:	**25%**	DINNER:	-

Mrs Rita Byrne
MAJELLA
Waterford Road, Kilkenny,
Co Kilkenny

Kilkenny

OPEN:	**All Year except Christmas**
NO. ROOMS:	**4**
ENSUITE:	**4**

TEL: **056 21129**   FAX: -

Modern detached bungalow on main Kilkenny/Waterford Road. Convenient to city and all amenities. Reduction low season. Visa/Acess accepted.

Kilkenny 1km

B&B PPS:	**£17/£17.50**	SNGL OCC. DBLE/TPL:	**£23.50/£24**	SNGL RM:	-
PART BRD:	-	% RED. CHILDREN:	**50%**	DINNER:	-

John & Sandra Cahill
LAUNARD HOUSE
Maiden Hill, Kells Road, Kilkenny,
Co Kilkenny

Kilkenny

OPEN:	**All Year except Christmas**
NO. ROOMS:	**5**
ENSUITE:	**5**

TEL: **056 51889/087 509867**   FAX: **056 71017**   EMAIL: **launard@iol.ie**

Luxurious purpose built home, overlooking Ring Road. All bedrooms televisions, hairdryers. Best Guides "Irish Experts" recommended. "A Touch of Class".

Kilkenny 1km

B&B PPS:	**£17/£19**	SNGL OCC. DBLE/TPL:	-	SNGL RM:	-
PART BRD:	-	% RED. CHILDREN:	-	DINNER:	-

Kilkenny 1km

Mary Cahill
BREAGAGH VIEW
**1 Maiden Hill, Kells Road, Kilkenny,
Co Kilkenny**
TEL: 056 61353　　　　　　FAX: -

Kilkenny

OPEN:	All Year except Christmas
NO. ROOMS:	4
ENSUITE:	3

(V)

Purpose built house overlooking Ring Rd and Countryside yet very close to Town and adjacent to Hotel Kilkenny.

| B&B PPS: | **£16.50/£17.50** | SNGL OCC. DBLE/TPL: | **£25** | SNGL RM: | - |
| PART BRD: | - | % RED. CHILDREN: | - | DINNER: | - |

Kilkenny 2km

Mrs Marie Callan
LICHFIELD
**Kilfera, Bennettsbridge Rd, Kilkenny,
Co Kilkenny**
TEL: 056 65232　　　　　FAX: 056 70614

Kilkenny

OPEN:	1st Feburary-30th November
NO. ROOMS:	3
ENSUITE:	2

(V)

Georgian Country Home on 1 acre. Quiet location (R700). Breakfast menu, TV Room. Ideal Touring Base. Main New Ross/Rosslare Road.

| B&B PPS: | **£15/£17** | SNGL OCC. DBLE/TPL: | **£21.50/£24** | SNGL RM: | - |
| PART BRD: | - | % RED. CHILDREN: | **25%** | DINNER: | - |

Kilkenny 4km

Mrs Joan Cody
OAKLAWN B & B
**8 Oakwood, Kilfera, Bennettsbridge
Road, Kilkenny, Co Kilkenny**
TEL: 056 61208　　　　　FAX: -

Kilkenny

OPEN:	1st March-31st October
NO. ROOMS:	3
ENSUITE:	2

(V)

Modern detached bungalow on the R700 main New Ross/Rosslare Road. Quiet area. Tastefully decorated. Set in mature lawns.

| B&B PPS: | **£15/£17** | SNGL OCC. DBLE/TPL: | **£21.50/23.50** | SNGL RM: | **£15** |
| PART BRD: | - | % RED. CHILDREN: | **50%** | DINNER: | **£12** |

In Kilkenny

Mrs Mary Cody
OLINDA
**Castle Road, Kilkenny,
Co Kilkenny**
TEL: 056 62964　　　　　FAX: -

Kilkenny

OPEN:	March-November
NO. ROOMS:	3
ENSUITE:	2

(V)

Dormer Bungalow, main Kilkenny, Rosslare Road R700. Convenient to Hotels, Castle, City, Golf. Bedrooms inc. Hairdryers, Alarm Clocks, Quiet area.

| B&B PPS: | **£15/£17** | SNGL OCC. DBLE/TPL: | **£23.50** | SNGL RM: | - |
| PART BRD: | - | % RED. CHILDREN: | **25%** | DINNER: | - |

In Kilkenny

Mrs Vicky Comerford
PARK VILLA
**Opposite Newpark Hotel, Castlecommer
Road, Kilkenny, Co Kilkenny**
TEL: 056 61337/088 610343　　　FAX: -

Kilkenny

OPEN:	All Year except Christmas
NO. ROOMS:	5
ENSUITE:	5

(V)

Modern family run home. N78. Television all rooms. Prize gardens. Kettle always boiling. Adjacent to Hotel, Swimming, Pubs, Theatres, Restaurants.

| B&B PPS: | **£17** | SNGL OCC. DBLE/TPL: | **£23.50** | SNGL RM: | - |
| PART BRD: | - | % RED. CHILDREN: | **20%** | DINNER: | - |

Mrs Kitty Dowling
GLEN VIEW
Castlecomer Rd.
Kilkenny, Co Kilkenny
TEL: 056 62065   FAX: -

Kilkenny	
OPEN:	All Year except Christmas
NO. ROOMS:	3
ENSUITE:	1

Cead Mile Failte. Warm friendly welcome assured. Complimentary tea. Medieval city, Theatre 15 mins walk. Adj Golf & Newpark Hotel on N77.

Ⓟ♿✄🚶▸🏠

— Kilkenny 1km —

B&B PPS:	£16/£17	SNGL OCC. DBLE/TPL:	-	SNGL RM:	-
PART BRD:	-	% RED. CHILDREN:	-	DINNER:	-

Mrs Margaret Drennan
HILLGROVE
Warrington, Bennettsbridge Road,
Kilkenny, Co Kilkenny
TEL: 056 51453/22890   FAX: -

Kilkenny	
OPEN:	1st February-30th November
NO. ROOMS:	5
ENSUITE:	4

Ⓥ

National Breakfast Award-Winning Country Home, furnished with antiques, on R700. Orthopaedic beds, Electric Blankets. Recommended Frommer, Dillard/Causin, Denver Post.

Ⓟ⊗🚶▸🏠

— Kilkenny 2km —

B&B PPS:	£16/£18	SNGL OCC. DBLE/TPL:	£22.50/£24.50	SNGL RM:	-
PART BRD:	-	% RED. CHILDREN:	50%	DINNER:	-

Mrs Helen Dunning
DUNBOY
Parkview Drive, off Freshford Road,
Kilkenny, Co Kilkenny
TEL: 056 61460   FAX: -

Kilkenny	
OPEN:	March-October
NO. ROOMS:	3
ENSUITE:	2

Ⓥ

Guide de Routard recommended situated end of quiet cul-de-sac. Take Freshford Road (R693). Turn left at second roundabout, then right into Cul-de-sac.

CC Ⓟ🚶▸🏠

— Kilkenny 1km —

B&B PPS:	£15/£18	SNGL OCC. DBLE/TPL:	-	SNGL RM:	-
PART BRD:	-	% RED. CHILDREN:	25%	DINNER:	-

Mrs Ella Dunphy
AUBURN LODGE
Warrington, Bennettsbridge Road,
Kilkenny, Co Kilkenny
TEL: 056 65119   FAX: 056 70008

Kilkenny	
OPEN:	1st January-20th December
NO. ROOMS:	4
ENSUITE:	2

Ⓥ

Country home with private tennis court (R700). Beside Riding School. Orthopaedic beds, electric blankets, breakfast menu, TV lounge, tea facilities.

— Kilkenny 2km —

B&B PPS:	£15/£17	SNGL OCC. DBLE/TPL:	£21.50/£23.50	SNGL RM:	£15.15
PART BRD:	-	% RED. CHILDREN:	10%	DINNER:	-

Mrs Bernadette Egan
KNOCKAVON HOUSE,
Dublin/Carlow Road, Kilkenny,
Co Kilkenny
TEL: 056 64294   FAX: -

Kilkenny	
OPEN:	All Year except Christmas
NO. ROOMS:	5
ENSUITE:	5

Ⓥ

Luxurious town house accommodation. Beside city centre. 3 Minutes to bus and train station, pubs, restaurants, theatre and golf club.

— In Kilkenny City —

B&B PPS:	£17	SNGL OCC. DBLE/TPL:	£23.50	SNGL RM:	-
PART BRD:	-	% RED. CHILDREN:	25%	DINNER:	-

In Kilkenny

Mrs Oonagh Egan Twomey
CARRAIG RUA
Carlow/Dublin Rd, Kilkenny City, Co Kilkenny
TEL: **056 22929**   FAX: -

Kilkenny

OPEN:	**All Year except Christmas**
NO. ROOMS:	6
ENSUITE:	3

(V)

Two storey house on main Dublin Road, 2 mins walk to Bus/Rail services. Close to City Centre, Hotels, Golf clubs.

B&B PPS:	**£15/£17**	SNGL OCC. DBLE/TPL:	**£21.50/£23.50**	SNGL RM:	-
PART BRD:	-	% RED. CHILDREN:	**20%**	DINNER:	-

Kilkenny 2km

Agnes & Frank Fennelly
SAN JOSE
Baun, Castlecomer Road, Kilkenny, Co Kilkenny
TEL: **056 21198**   FAX: -

Kilkenny

OPEN:	**1st February-30th November**
NO. ROOMS:	3
ENSUITE:	2

(V)

Elegant villa style residence, antique furnished . 2 km north of Newpark Hotel N77. Mature gardens, Breakfast menu. Hairdryers,Tea, Electric blankets.

B&B PPS:	**£16/£18**	SNGL OCC. DBLE/TPL:	**£20/£25**	SNGL RM:	-
PART BRD:	-	% RED. CHILDREN:	**20%**	DINNER:	-

Kilkenny 1km

Mrs Marie Finnegan
ARDEE HOUSE
Springmount, Waterford Road, Kilkenny, Co Kilkenny
TEL: **056 62699**   FAX: **056 62699**

Kilkenny

OPEN:	**All Year except Christmas**
NO. ROOMS:	4
ENSUITE:	3

(V)

Suburban Georgian style home on N10. Enjoy Golf, Angling, Shooting, Horse-Riding locally. TV Lounge. All rooms Tea facilities and Hairdryers.

B&B PPS:	**£15/£17**	SNGL OCC. DBLE/TPL:	**£21.50/£23.50**	SNGL RM:	**£21.50/£23.50**
PART BRD:	-	% RED. CHILDREN:	-	DINNER:	

Kilkenny 1km

Mrs Joan Flanagan
BURWOOD
Waterford Road, Kilkenny, Co Kilkenny
TEL: **056 62266**   FAX: -

Kilkenny

OPEN:	**April-September**
NO. ROOMS:	3
ENSUITE:	3

(V)

Modern bungalow on Kilkenny/Waterford Road. Enclosed car-park. "300 Best B & B's" Recommended. Convenient to City Centre.

B&B PPS:	**£17/£17.50**	SNGL OCC. DBLE/TPL:	**£25**	SNGL RM:	-
PART BRD:	-	% RED. CHILDREN:	**50%**	DINNER:	-

Kilkenny 1km

Pauline Flannery
ASHLEIGH
Waterford Rd, Kilkenny, Co Kilkenny
TEL: **056 22809**   FAX: -

Kilkenny

OPEN:	**All Year except Christmas**
NO. ROOMS:	3
ENSUITE:	2

(V)

Bungalow main Waterford Rd (N10). Convenient Hotels, City.Breakfast menu. Tea/Coffee available. Reduction low season. Frommer Guide, Berkeley Europe recommended.

B&B PPS:	**£15/£17**	SNGL OCC. DBLE/TPL:	**£22/£25**	SNGL RM:	**£22**
PART BRD:	-	% RED. CHILDREN:	**50%**	DINNER:	-

Kilkenny 1km

Mrs Paula Gaule
ST IVES
Shellumsrath, Callan Road, Kilkenny, Co Kilkenny

Kilkenny

OPEN:	2nd January-30th November
NO. ROOMS:	3
ENSUITE:	3

TEL: **056 22144**   FAX: -

Ⓥ

Spacious dormer bungalow, off main Clonmel/Cork Road (N76). Quiet area offering restful accommodation. Tastefully decorated. Private parking. Breakfast choice.

B&B PPS:	£17	SNGL OCC. DBLE/TPL:	£23.50	SNGL RM:	-
PART BRD:	-	% RED. CHILDREN:	-	DINNER:	-

— Kilkenny 2km —

Mrs Una Hayes
SONORA
Drakelands, Kilkenny, Co Kilkenny

Kilkenny

OPEN:	1st April-30th September
NO. ROOMS:	3
ENSUITE:	3

TEL: **056 22877 / 21734**   FAX: **056 22877**   EMAIL: **jimhayes@ iol.ie**

Ⓥ

Modern house. Spacious antique furnished rooms, ensuite, TV. Beautiful mature gardens with conservatory, waterfall & pools. German spoken. Extensive Breakfast Menu.

B&B PPS:	£20	SNGL OCC. DBLE/TPL:	£30	SNGL RM:	-
PART BRD:	-	% RED. CHILDREN:	25%	DINNER:	-

— Kilkenny 1.5km —

Mrs Breda Hennessy
SILVER SPRINGS
Waterford Road, Kilkenny, Co Kilkenny

Kilkenny

OPEN:	All Year except Christmas
NO. ROOMS:	4
ENSUITE:	3

TEL: **056 62513**   FAX: -

Ⓥ

Beautiful dormer bungalow on main Kilkenny/Waterford Rd. (N10) Convenient to Hotels, Castle, City, Golf. Breakfast menu, tea/coffee making facilities.

B&B PPS:	£16/£17	SNGL OCC. DBLE/TPL:	£22.50/£24	SNGL RM:	-
PART BRD:	-	% RED. CHILDREN:	33.3%	DINNER:	-

— Kilkenny City 1km —

Mrs Gillian Hennessy
CILL PHAOIN
Greenshill (Off Castlecomer Road), Kilkenny, Co Kilkenny

Kilkenny

OPEN:	1st January-12th December
NO. ROOMS:	4
ENSUITE:	4

TEL: **056 22857**   FAX: -

Ⓥ

Luxury accommodation overlooking River Nore. Convenient to Bus, Rail, Golf, Fishing. Private guest kitchen. AA listed.QQQ. Breakfast menu.

B&B PPS:	£17/£18	SNGL OCC. DBLE/TPL:	-	SNGL RM:	-
PART BRD:	-	% RED. CHILDREN:	35%	DINNER:	-

— In Kilkenny —

Mrs Teresa Holden
AUBURNDALE
Springmount, Waterford Rd, Kilkenny, Co Kilkenny

Kilkenny

OPEN:	All Year except Christmas
NO. ROOMS:	4
ENSUITE:	4

TEL: **056 62716**   FAX: **056 71238**

Ⓥ

Town house adjacent Springhill Hotel, Hotel Kilkenny. Ideal Touring Base, Reading Lounge, Bedrooms TV, Hairdryers, Tea/Coffee faciltiies. Mount Juillet 6Km.

B&B PPS:	£17	SNGL OCC. DBLE/TPL:	-	SNGL RM:	-
PART BRD:	-	% RED. CHILDREN:	-	DINNER:	-

— Kilkenny 1km —

Kilkenny 1km

Liam & Brigid Holohan
ALCANTRA
Maidenhill, Kells Road, Kilkenny, Co Kilkenny

Kilkenny

TEL: 056 61058   FAX: -

OPEN:	All Year except Christmas
NO. ROOMS:	3
ENSUITE:	3

From City Centre, ten minutes walk via Patrick St, right at Rover Garage. Alcantra 400m. Comfortable spacious home. AA listed

B&B PPS:	£17	SNGL OCC. DBLE/TPL:	£23.50	SNGL RM:	-
PART BRD:	£190	% RED. CHILDREN:	50%	DINNER:	£14

Kilkenny 1km

Mrs Mary Langton-Hennessy
VIEWMOUNT HOUSE
Castlecomer Road, Kilkenny City, Co Kilkenny

Kilkenny

TEL: 056 62447   FAX: 056 64828

OPEN:	All Year except Christmas
NO. ROOMS:	4
ENSUITE:	4

Luxurious home situated between Newpark Hotel and Kilkenny Golf Club on N77. Breakfast menu. Tea/Coffee making facilities. Le Routard recommended.

B&B PPS:	£16/£17	SNGL OCC. DBLE/TPL:	-	SNGL RM:	-
PART BRD:	-	% RED. CHILDREN:	-	DINNER:	-

Kilkenny 1km

Mrs Mary Lawlor
RODINI
Waterford Road, (R910 off N10), Kilkenny, Co Kilkenny

Kilkenny

TEL: 056 21822/70836   FAX: -

OPEN:	All Year except Christmas
NO. ROOMS:	5
ENSUITE:	5

Comfortable home in quiet area. Convenient Hotels, Castle, City Centre. Family rooms. Electric blankets. Breakfast menu. Reduction low season.

B&B PPS:	£17	SNGL OCC. DBLE/TPL:	£23.50/£25	SNGL RM:	£21/£25
PART BRD:	-	% RED. CHILDREN:	50%	DINNER:	-

In Kilkenny City

Bill & Helen McEvoy
BREFFNI
Waterford Road, Kilkenny, Co Kilkenny

Kilkenny

TEL: 056 63344   FAX: -

OPEN:	All Year except Christmas
NO. ROOMS:	3
ENSUITE:	3

Detached Dormer Bunglow. Easy access to Hotels, Castle, Golf Clubs, Fishing, Shops. Tea/Coffee available. Reduction Low Season. Kilkenny 1 Km.

B&B PPS:	£17	SNGL OCC. DBLE/TPL:	£23.50/£25	SNGL RM:	-
PART BRD:	-	% RED. CHILDREN:	50%	DINNER:	-

In Kilkenny City

Ms Katherine Molloy
MENA HOUSE
(Opposite Newpark Hotel), Castlecomer Road (N78), Kilkenny, Co Kilkenny

Kilkenny

TEL: 056 65362   FAX: -

OPEN:	All Year except Christmas
NO. ROOMS:	9
ENSUITE:	7

Antique furnished home. N78. Breakfast choice. Homemade preserves. Tea making facilities. Television en-suite bedrooms. Adjacent Newpark Hotel, Golf, Swimming, Horse-Riding.

B&B PPS:	£15/£17	SNGL OCC. DBLE/TPL:	£21.50/£23.50	SNGL RM:	£18
PART BRD:	-	% RED. CHILDREN:	50%	DINNER:	-

— Kilkenny 1km

Anne Moore D. Sc.I.
BEAUPRE
Waterford Road, Kilkenny, Co Kilkenny

Kilkenny

TEL: **056 21417**   FAX: -

OPEN:	All Year except Christmas
NO. ROOMS:	4
ENSUITE:	2

Ⓥ

Convenient Springhill & Hotel Kilkenny. Breakfast menu, electric blankets, family room, tea/coffee . Visa/access, reduction low-season. Berkeley Europe recommended.

B&B PPS:	£15/£17.50	SNGL OCC. DBLE/TPL:	-	SNGL RM:	£20/£21
PART BRD:	-	% RED. CHILDREN:	50%	DINNER:	-

— Kilkenny 1km

Margaret & Bill Morgan
SHILLOGHER HOUSE
Callan Road (N76), Kilkenny, Co Kilkenny

Kilkenny City

TEL: **056 63249/64865**   FAX: **056 64865**

OPEN:	All Year
NO. ROOMS:	5
ENSUITE:	5

Ⓥ

Luxurious home, all bedrooms television, phones, electric blankets. Breakfast menu. Garden/tea room. Susan Causin recommended. RAC selected, AA QQQQ.

B&B PPS:	£17/£18.50	SNGL OCC. DBLE/TPL:	-	SNGL RM:	-
PART BRD:	-	% RED. CHILDREN:	20%	DINNER:	-

— In Kilkenny City

Jack & Teresa Nolan
THE LAURELS
College Road, (Opposite Hotel Kilkenny Entrance), Kilkenny City, Co Kilkenny

Kilkenny City

TEL: **056 61501**   FAX: **056 61501(Man)**

OPEN:	All Year except Christmas
NO. ROOMS:	4
ENSUITE:	4

Ⓥ

Luxurious warm Family Home, City Centre, Quiet location (off N76). Televisions, Orthopaedic beds, Hairdryers, Breakfast Menu, Numerous Recommendations. Local Heritage Tour Guide.

B&B PPS:	£17/£18	SNGL OCC. DBLE/TPL:	-	SNGL RM:	-
PART BRD:	-	% RED. CHILDREN:	20%	DINNER:	-

— In Kilkenny City 1km

Mrs Nora O'Connor
SUNDOWN
Freshford Rd, Kilkenny, Co Kilkenny

Kilkenny

TEL: **056 21816**   FAX: -

OPEN:	1st February-20th December
NO. ROOMS:	4
ENSUITE:	3

Ⓥ

Comfortable residence convenient to Bus, Rail, City Centre. Large family room. Rooms include radio, hairdryers. Breakfast menu, private parking.

B&B PPS:	£16/£18	SNGL OCC. DBLE/TPL:	£23.50/£24.50	SNGL RM:	-
PART BRD:	-	% RED. CHILDREN:	25%	DINNER:	-

— Kilkenny 3km

Margaret O'Keeffe
TWELVE OAKS
Dunmore, Co Kilkenny

Kilkenny

TEL: **056 67123**   FAX: **056 64182**   EMAIL: **oaksok@iol.ie**

OPEN:	1st February-30th November
NO. ROOMS:	4
ENSUITE:	4

Ⓥ

A warm welcome awaits you at our luxurious family home. All rooms TV/radio etc 3- minutes city. 3 miles from Newpark Hotel.

B&B PPS:	£17/£19	SNGL OCC. DBLE/TPL:	£23.50/£25	SNGL RM:	-
PART BRD:	-	% RED. CHILDREN:	50%	DINNER:	-

Kilkenny 1km

Mrs Teresa O'Neill
HILLCREST COLLEGE GARDENS
Callan Rd, Kilkenny, Co. Kilkenny

Kilkenny

OPEN:	1st March-20th December
No. ROOMS:	4
ENSUITE:	2

(V)

TEL: **056 65560**   FAX: -

Comfortable quiet home. Off Callan/Cork Rd. (N76) Hotel Kilkenny 300m. Orthopaedic Beds, Electric Blankets, Hairdryers. Walking distance of City.

B&B PPS:	£15/£17	SNGL OCC. DBLE/TPL:	£21.50/£23.50	SNGL RM:	£21.50
PART BRD:	-	% RED. CHILDREN:	25%	DINNER:	-

In Kilkenny

Josephine O'Reilly
CARRIGLEA
Archers Avenue, Castle Road, Kilkenny, Co Kilkenny

Kilkenny City

OPEN:	1st February-30th November
No. ROOMS:	3
ENSUITE:	2

(V)

TEL: **056 61629**   FAX: -

Comfortable family run home adjacent Castle Park. Warm friendly atmosphere, situated quiet residential area, short walking distance Castle, City Centre.

B&B PPS:	£15/£17	SNGL OCC. DBLE/TPL:	£21.50/£23.50	SNGL RM:	-
PART BRD:	-	% RED. CHILDREN:	50%	DINNER:	-

Kilkenny 1.5km

Mrs Ann Peters
DERDIMUS B & B
Callan Road (N76), Kilkenny, Co Kilkenny

Kilkenny

OPEN:	All Year except Christmas
No. ROOMS:	3
ENSUITE:	2

(V)

TEL: **056 65782** .   FAX: -

First class accommodation. Friendly luxurious (award winning) home, peacful location. Garden/Patio. Cork/Clonmel (N76). Convenient to Hotel Kilkenny. Breakfast menu.

B&B PPS:		SNGL OCC. DBLE/TPL:	-	SNGL RM:	-
PART BRD:	£15/£17	% RED. CHILDREN:		DINNER:	-

Majella & Michael Prendergast
ASHGROVE
Dunglen Court, Castlecomer Road, Kilkenny, Co Kilkenny

Kilkenny

OPEN:	All Year
No. ROOMS:	4
ENSUITE:	2

(V)

TEL: **056 63359**   FAX: **056 63359**

Warm welcome, Tea/Coffee arrival. Good nights sleep, information places to visit/do. Close to Golf, Cave, Fishing, Walking, Equestrian etc.

B&B PPS:	£15/£17	SNGL OCC. DBLE/TPL:	£21.50/£23.50	SNGL RM:	£15/£17
PART BRD:	-	% RED. CHILDREN:	50%	DINNER:	-

In Kilkenny City

Mrs V Rothwell
DUNROMIN
Dublin Rd, Kilkenny, Co Kilkenny

Kilkenny

OPEN:	All Year except Christmas
No. ROOMS:	3
ENSUITE:	3

(V)

TEL: **056 61387**   FAX: **056 70736**

Warm welcome to our 19th Century, family home. Walking distance Medieval City Centre. Golf, Horse Riding nearby. Kettle always boiling.

B&B PPS:	£17	SNGL OCC. DBLE/TPL:	£25	SNGL RM:	-
PART BRD:	-	% RED. CHILDREN:	25%	DINNER:	-

Kilkenny City 1km

Mrs Ann Ryan
PARK GATE
1 St James Park, Greenfields, Freshford Road, Kilkenny, Co Kilkenny

TEL: **056 63106**   FAX: -

Kilkenny	
OPEN:	**All Year except Christmas**
NO. ROOMS:	3
ENSUITE:	1

Ⓥ

Quiet home R693. Walking distance city. Opposite Greyhound Racing. TV, tea facilities, orthopaedic beds, breakfast menu. Seasonal reductions. Credit Cards.

B&B PPS:	**£15/£20**	SNGL OCC. DBLE/TPL:	**£21.50/£26.50**	SNGL RM:	**£18/£20**
PART BRD:	-	% RED. CHILDREN:	25%	DINNER:	-

Kilkenny City 1km

Kathleen Ryan
THE MEADOWS
6 Greenfields Road, Bishops Meadows, Kilkenny, Co Kilkenny

TEL: **056 21649**   FAX: -

Kilkenny	
OPEN:	**All Year except Christmas**
NO. ROOMS:	3
ENSUITE:	2

Ⓥ

Warm comfortable home in quiet Cul-de-Sac off Freshford Rd. walking distance City Centre. Orthopaedic beds, Electric blankets, Hairdryers.

B&B PPS:	**£17/£18.50**	SNGL OCC. DBLE/TPL:	**£23.50/£25**	SNGL RM:	**£19/£22**
PART BRD:	-	% RED. CHILDREN:	25%	DINNER:	-

Kilkenny City 1km

Mrs Helen Sheehan
CNOC MHUIRE
Castle Road, Kilkenny, Co Kilkenny

TEL: **056 62161**   FAX: **056 62161**

Kilkenny	
OPEN:	**All Year except Christmas**
NO. ROOMS:	4
ENSUITE:	4

Ⓥ

Comfortable, well heated home off New Ross/Rosslare Road (R700). Orthopaedic beds, electric blankets, quiet area. Walking distance of City.

B&B PPS:	**£17/£18**	SNGL OCC. DBLE/TPL:	**£23.50**	SNGL RM:	-
PART BRD:	-	% RED. CHILDREN:	33.3%	DINNER:	-

In Kilkenny City

Jim & Joan Spratt
CHAPLINS
Castlecomber Road, Kilkenny, Co Kilkenny

TEL: **056 52236**   FAX: -

Kilkenny	
OPEN:	**All Year except Christmas**
NO. ROOMS:	4
ENSUITE:	4

Ⓥ

Chaplins is a spacious Town House with warm hospitality rooms equipped with multi-channel TV, Hair-dryers, Tea/Coffee trays.

B&B PPS:	**£17/£18**	SNGL OCC. DBLE/TPL:	**£23.50/£24.50**	SNGL RM:	-
PART BRD:	-	% RED. CHILDREN:	25%	DINNER:	-

Kilkenny 2km

Mrs Mary Trant
BROOKFIELD
Castlecomer Road, Kilkenny, Co Kilkenny

TEL: **056 65629**   FAX: -

Kilkenny	
OPEN:	**All Year except Christmas**
NO. ROOMS:	4
ENSUITE:	2

Ⓥ

Modern bungalow on N77. Frommer Guide recommended. Wheelchair access. Quiet location convenient to Newpark Hotel, Golf-Club, Dunmore Caves.

B&B PPS:	**£15/£18.50**	SNGL OCC. DBLE/TPL:	**£21.50/£25**	SNGL RM:	-
PART BRD:	-	% RED. CHILDREN:	50%	DINNER:	-

In Kilkenny City

Mary & Eamonn Wogan
TIR NA NOG
Greenhill, (off Castlecomer Rd),
Kilkenny, Co Kilkenny
TEL: **056 65250/62345**

Kilkenny

OPEN:	**All Year**
NO. ROOMS:	**4**
ENSUITE:	**4**

FAX: **056 63491**   EMAIL: **emw@iol.ie**

Luxurious ensuite roooms, incl. Tv/Radio, Trouserpress/Iron, Hairdryer, Breakfast menu. Convenient to Bus/Rail Station and City Centre.

B&B PPS:	**£17/£18**	SNGL OCC. DBLE/TPL:	**£24.50**	SNGL RM:	-
PART BRD:	-	% RED. CHILDREN:	-	DINNER:	-

Thomastown

Mrs Helen Blanchfield
ABBEY HOUSE "AA QQQQ"
Jerpoint Abbey, Thomastown,
Co Kilkenny
TEL: **056 24166**

Thomastown

OPEN:	**All Year except Christmas**
NO. ROOMS:	**7**
ENSUITE:	**7**

FAX: **056 24192**

Period house directly opposite Jerpoint Abbey. 1 mile from Mount Juliet Golf. Half way between Kilkenny & Waterford, 1 hour from Rosslare.

B&B PPS:	**£17.50/£22**	SNGL OCC. DBLE/TPL:	**£25/£35**	SNGL RM:	**£25/£30**
PART BRD:	**£200**	% RED. CHILDREN:	**50%**	DINNER:	**£16.50**

Thomastown 3km

Mrs Julie Doyle
CARRICKMOURNE HOUSE
New Ross Road, Thomastown,
Co Kilkenny
TEL: **056 24124**

Thomastown

OPEN:	**All Year except Christmas**
NO. ROOMS:	**5**
ENSUITE:	**5**

FAX: **056 24124**

House on elevated site, surrounded by scenic views in peaceful country setting. Convenient; Jerpoint Abbey, Mount Juliet Golf, Fishing, Restaurants.

B&B PPS:	**£17/£18.50**	SNGL OCC. DBLE/TPL:	**£23/£28**	SNGL RM:	-
PART BRD:	-	% RED. CHILDREN:	-	DINNER:	-

Thomastown

Mr & Mrs B Hennessy
TOWER HOUSE
Low Street, Thomastown,
Co Kilkenny
TEL: **056 24500**

Thomastown

OPEN:	**All Year**
NO. ROOMS:	**4**
ENSUITE:	**4**

FAX: **056 24500**

12th Century Tower house with new accommodation block in courtyard. Mount Juliet Country Club 1 mile.

B&B PPS:	**£17.50/£20**	SNGL OCC. DBLE/TPL:	**£25/£30**	SNGL RM:	-
PART BRD:	-	% RED. CHILDREN:	**50%**	DINNER:	-

SYMBOLS

LOOK OUT FOR THESE SYMBOLS WHICH SHOULD BE DISPLAYED BY ALL MEMBERS OF TOWN & COUNTRY HOMES.

Joe & Lynda Buckley
LADY'S ABBEY
Ardfinnan, Clonmel,
Co Tipperary

Cahir

Open:	**All Year**
No. Rooms:	3
Ensuite:	3

(V)

Tel: **052 66209** Fax: **052 66209**

Secluded country home on 12 acres of mature gardens/lawns in the picturesque village of Ardfinnan. Ideal for touring Southeast.

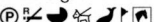

B&B PPS:	**£20**	Sngl Occ. Dble/Tpl:	**£26.50**	Sngl Rm:	-
Part Brd:	**£240**	% Red. Children:	**25%**	Dinner:	**£16**

Cahir 8 km

Butler Family
CARRIGEEN CASTLE
Cork Road, Cahir,
Co Tipperary

Cahir

Open:	**All Year except Christmas**
No. Rooms:	7
Ensuite:	3

(V)

Tel: **052 41370** Fax: -

Manor of Cahir, Historic (prison) home 1600, Frommer Ireland cover picture. Warm comfortable, spacious, overlooking town, Walled garden. Near Bus, Train.

B&B PPS:	**£16/£18**	Sngl Occ. Dble/Tpl:	**£25**	Sngl Rm:	-
Part Brd:	-	% Red. Children:	-	Dinner:	-

Cahir 1km

Mrs Anne Devereaux
SPRINGHILL
Cashel Road N8, Cahir,
Co Tipperary

Cahir

Open:	**1st April-31st October**
No. Rooms:	4
Ensuite:	3

(V)

Tel: **052 41754** Fax: -

Spacious country home overlooking farmlands on the outskirts of Cahir on N8. Tea/coffee making facilities. Ideal Touring Centre.

B&B PPS:	**£15/£17**	Sngl Occ. Dble/Tpl:	**£21.50/£23.50**	Sngl Rm:	-
Part Brd:	-	% Red. Children:	**25%**	Dinner:	-

Cahir 3.5km

Mrs Jo Doyle
KILLAUN
Clonmel Road, Cahir,
Co Tipperary

Cahir

Open:	**All Year except Christmas**
No. Rooms:	3
Ensuite:	2

(V)

Tel: **052 41780** Fax: -

Bungalow, Spacious gardens, 5mins walk from town, Bus and Train Station. Golf, Fishing and Horseriding closeby. On N24

B&B PPS:	**£15/£17**	Sngl Occ. Dble/Tpl:	**£21.50/£23.50**	Sngl Rm:	-
Part Brd:	-	% Red. Children:	**25%**	Dinner:	-

In Cahir

Mrs Marian Duffy
THE HOMESTEAD
Mitchelstown Road, Cahir,
Co Tipperary

Cahir

Open:	**All Year except Christmas**
No. Rooms:	4
Ensuite:	4

(V)

Tel: **052 42043** Fax: -

Spacious modern bungalow near Town Centre, TV bedrooms; Large private car park; Families welcome; Ideal Touring Base;Tea/Coffee on arrival

B&B PPS:	**£17**	Sngl Occ. Dble/Tpl:	**£23.50**	Sngl Rm:	-
Part Brd:	-	% Red. Children:	**25%**	Dinner:	-

In Cahir

Cahir 1km

Mrs Mary English
BROOKFIELD HOUSE
Cashel Road, Cahir,
Co Tipperary

Cahir

TEL: **052 41936**　　FAX: -

OPEN:	1st April-30th September
NO. ROOMS:	3
ENSUITE:	2

(V)

Large comfortable residence, homely atmosphere. Tea/coffee making facilities. Spacious car park. Landscaped gardens. Conservatory for guests use.

| B&B PPS: | £15/£17 | SNGL OCC. DBLE/TPL: | £21.50/£23.50 | SNGL RM: | - |
| PART BRD: | - | % RED. CHILDREN: | 25% | DINNER: | - |

Cahir 1km

Mrs Breda Fitzgerald
ASHLING
Cashel Road, Cahir,
Co Tipperary

Cahir

TEL: **052 41601**　　FAX: -

OPEN:	All Year
NO. ROOMS:	4
ENSUITE:	3

(V)

Ground level family home, smoke free. Antique furnishing. Prize winning gardens, electric blankets, Tea/Coffee making facilities. Country Inns recommended.

| B&B PPS: | £16/£17.50 | SNGL OCC. DBLE/TPL: | £25 | SNGL RM: | - |
| PART BRD: | - | % RED. CHILDREN: | 20% | DINNER: | - |

Cahir 2km

Margaret Neville
HOLLYMOUNT HOUSE
Upper Cahir Abbey, Cahir,
Co Tipperary

Cahir

TEL: **052 42888/088 2769641**　　FAX: -

OPEN:	All Year
NO. ROOMS:	4
ENSUITE:	2

(V)

Country home in peaceful woodlands via Mountain Road. Breathtaking views Comeragh and Knockmealdown Mountains. Walkers paradise. Private car park.

| B&B PPS: | £15/£17 | SNGL OCC. DBLE/TPL: | £21.50/£23.50 | SNGL RM: | - |
| PART BRD: | - | % RED. CHILDREN: | 20% | DINNER: | - |

In Cahir

Mrs Hannah-Mai O'Connor
SILVER ACRE
Clonmel Road, Cahir,
Co Tipperary

Cahir

TEL: **052 41737**　　FAX: -

OPEN:	All Year except Christmas
NO. ROOMS:	3
ENSUITE:	2

(V)

Modern bungalow, Tourism award winner, in quiet cul-de-sac. Private parking. Bus, Train, Fishing, Golf, Scenic Walks, Tea and Coffee facilities

| B&B PPS: | £15/£17 | SNGL OCC. DBLE/TPL: | £21.50/£23.50 | SNGL RM: | - |
| PART BRD: | - | % RED. CHILDREN: | 33.3% | DINNER: | - |

Carrick-on-Suir 11km

Mrs Ann Coady
THE GRAND INN
Nine-Mile-House, Carrick-On-Suir,
Co Tipperary

Carrick-On-Suir

TEL: **051 647035**　　FAX: -

OPEN:	All Year
NO. ROOMS:	5
ENSUITE:	3

(V)

Former 17th century Bianconi Inn in scenic Valley of Slievenamon. Spacious gardens. Antique furnishing. AA listed. On Clonmel/Kilkenny Road N76.

| B&B PPS: | £15/£17 | SNGL OCC. DBLE/TPL: | £21.50/£22 | SNGL RM: | £20 |
| PART BRD: | £180 | % RED. CHILDREN: | 50% | DINNER: | £12 |

Michael & Margaret Courtney
COPPERFIELD HOUSE
Cashel,
Co Tipperary
TEL: **062 61075**   FAX: -

Cashel

OPEN:	**All Year except Christmas**
NO. ROOMS:	6
ENSUITE:	5

Comfortable home situated within walking distance of Town. Secure car park. Large garden with scenic view of the Rock.

cc Ⓟ ⓇⓍⒷ♨♣🐾🏠

In Cashel Town

B&B PPS:	**£16/£18**	SNGL OCC. DBLE/TPL:	**£23/£28**	SNGL RM:	-
PART BRD:	-	% RED. CHILDREN:	**50%**	DINNER:	-

Mrs Eileen Creed
TIR-NA-NOG
Dualla, Cashel,
Co Tipperary
TEL: **062 61350**   FAX: **062 62411**

Cashel

Ⓥ

OPEN:	**All Year except Christmas**
NO. ROOMS:	6
ENSUITE:	5

Warm friendly luxurious country home. Peaceful surroundings. Home baking. Peat fires. Orthopaedic beds. R691 Cashel/Kilkenny road. Dinner/breakfast menu.

cc ♿ Ⓟ ⊗ ⓇⒷⓍ♨🐾🏠

Cashel 5km

B&B PPS:	**£15/£25**	SNGL OCC. DBLE/TPL:	**£24/£31.50**	SNGL RM:	-
PART BRD:	-	% RED. CHILDREN:	**25%**	DINNER:	**£12.50**

Mary & Pat Duane
MARYVILLE
Bank Place, Cashel,
Co Tipperary
TEL: 062 61098   FAX: -

Cashel

Ⓥ

OPEN:	**All Year except Christmas**
NO. ROOMS:	8
ENSUITE:	4

Panoramic view "Rock Cashel", 13th Century Abbey adjoining gardens. Photographers/artists delight. Dillard/Birnbaum recommended. Beverages, Private parking, credit cards.

cc ♿ Ⓟ ⓇⒷ🐾🏠

Cashel

B&B PPS:	**£16/£20**	SNGL OCC. DBLE/TPL:	**£23/£28**	SNGL RM:	-
PART BRD:	-	% RED. CHILDREN:	-	DINNER:	-

Mrs Mary Hickey
GORT-NA-CLOC
Ardmayle, Cashel,
Co Tipperary
TEL: **0504 42362/088 602630**   FAX: -

Cashel

Ⓥ

OPEN:	**All Year except Christmas**
NO. ROOMS:	3
ENSUITE:	2

Home, peaceful countryside L185 Goolds Cross road. Cashel 7 km. Fishing, Golf locally. River Suir .5 km. Private car parking. Credit cards.

cc ♿ Ⓟ ⒷⓍ♨🐾🏠Ⓢ

Cashel 7km

B&B PPS:	**£15/£17**	SNGL OCC. DBLE/TPL:	**£23.50**	SNGL RM:	**£19**
PART BRD:	-	% RED. CHILDREN:	**50%**	DINNER:	-

Mr Rem Joy
GEORGESLAND B&B,
Dualla/Kilkenny Road, Cashel,
Co Tipperary
TEL: **062 62788**   FAX: **062 62788**

Cashel

Ⓥ

OPEN:	**1st March-31st October**
NO. ROOMS:	6
ENSUITE:	3

Modern Country Home, situated on R691 Dualla/Kilkenny road. Set in peaceful landscaped gardens, surrounded by Scenic Countryside. Secure parking.

Ⓟ ⊗ Ⓡ🐾🏠

Cashel 1km

B&B PPS:	**£16/£18**	SNGL OCC. DBLE/TPL:	**£22.50/£25**	SNGL RM:	-
PART BRD:	-	% RED. CHILDREN:	**20%**	DINNER:	-

Cashel 1km

Mrs Mary A Kennedy
THORNBROOK HOUSE
Dualla Road, Cashel,
Co Tipperary
Tel: **062 62388**   Fax: **062 61480**

Cashel	
Open:	March-November
No. Rooms:	5
Ensuite:	3

Ranch type family home. Antique Furnishing, Extensive lawns, Peaceful surroundings, Frommer and Birnbaum's recommended. Hairdryers, Tea/coffee all bedrooms. Credit cards.

B&B PPS:	**£15.50/£19**	Sngl Occ. Dble/Tpl:	**£22.50/£26**	Sngl Rm:	-
Part Brd:	-	% Red. Children:	**20%**	Dinner:	-

Cashel 1km

Mrs Evelyn Moloney
ROS-GUILL HOUSE
Kilkenny/Dualla Road, Cashel,
Co Tipperary
Tel: **062 61507/62699**   Fax: **062 61507**

Cashel	
Open:	1st May-20th October
No. Rooms:	5
Ensuite:	3

Elegant country home, overlooking Rock of Cashel. Superbly appointed. Breakfast Award Winner. Hairdryers, Tea/coffee in bedrooms. Recommended Internationally. Credit Cards.

B&B PPS:	**£15.50/£19**	Sngl Occ. Dble/Tpl:	**£22.50/£26**	Sngl Rm:	-
Part Brd:	-	% Red. Children:	**20%**	Dinner:	-

In Cashel

Mrs Sarah Murphy
INDAVILLE
Cashel,
Co Tipperary
Tel: **062 61933**   Fax: **062 61329**

Cashel	
Open:	16th March-31st October
No. Rooms:	4
Ensuite:	4

Historic Georgian home, 50 metres from town centre. On left after N8 turn south to Cork after Main Street. Secure parking.

B&B PPS:	**£17.50**	Sngl Occ. Dble/Tpl:	**£26**	Sngl Rm:	-
Part Brd:	-	% Red. Children:	**25%**	Dinner:	-

Cashel

Mrs Breda O'Grady
ROCKVIEW HOUSE
Bohermore, Cashel,
Co Tipperary
Tel: **062 62187**   Fax: -

Cashel	
Open:	17th March-31st October
No. Rooms:	3
Ensuite:	3

Modern bungalow situated in Town of Cashel, with view of Rock from bedrooms. Friendly hospitality.

B&B PPS:	**£18**	Sngl Occ. Dble/Tpl:	**£25**	Sngl Rm:	-
Part Brd:	-	% Red. Children:	-	Dinner:	-

In Cashel

Ellen Ryan & Carmel Lawrence
ABBEY HOUSE
1 Dominic Street, Cashel,
Co Tipperary
Tel: **062 61104**   Fax: **062 61104**

Cashel	
Open:	1st February-30th November
No. Rooms:	5
Ensuite:	3

Town House, opposite Dominic's Abbey. 150 metres Rock of Cashel. Television/tea/coffee all bedrooms. Parking. Town Centre 50 metres.

B&B PPS:	**£16/£18**	Sngl Occ. Dble/Tpl:	**£22.50/£26**	Sngl Rm:	**£18**
Part Brd:	-	% Red. Children:	**25%**	Dinner:	-

Michael & Laura Ryan
ASHMORE HOUSE
**John Street, Cashel,
Co Tipperary**
TEL: **062 61286**   FAX: **062 62789**

Cashel		
OPEN:	All Year except Christmas
NO. ROOMS:	5
ENSUITE:	1

Georgian Family Home in heart of Cashel, Warm Welcome, Spacious Gardens, Private Parking, Residents Lounge, Touring Base, all amenities nearby.

[cc] [t] [P] [symbols] [S]

B&B PPS:	£15/£20	SNGL OCC. DBLE/TPL:	£21.50/£26.50	SNGL RM:	£17
PART BRD:	-	% RED. CHILDREN:	50%	DINNER:	£15

— In Cashel

Mrs Mary Stapleton
PALM GROVE HOUSE
**Dualla/Kilkenny Road, Cashel,
Co Tipperary**
TEL: **062 61739**   FAX: -

Cashel		
OPEN:	1st May-26th October
NO. ROOMS:	5
ENSUITE:	3

Highly recommended family home, situated on R691 Dualla/Kilkenny Road. Landscaped garden and scenic surroundings. Secure parking at rear.

[t] [P] [symbols]

B&B PPS:	£15/£17	SNGL OCC. DBLE/TPL:	£21.50/£23.50	SNGL RM:	-
PART BRD:	-	% RED. CHILDREN:	20%	DINNER:	-

— Cashel 1km

Mrs Sheila Cox
EDERMINE HOUSE
**Rathronan, Fethard Rd, Clonmel,
Co Tipperary**
TEL: **052 23048**   FAX: **052 23048**

Clonmel		
OPEN:	1st January-10th December
NO. ROOMS:	4
ENSUITE:	2

Spacious dormer bungalow overlooking farm beside modern Equestrian Centre. Secure private parking. Golf, Fishing nearby.

[P] [symbols]

B&B PPS:	£15/£17	SNGL OCC. DBLE/TPL:	£21.50/£23.50	SNGL RM:	-
PART BRD:	-	% RED. CHILDREN:	25%	DINNER:	-

— Clonmel 2km

Olive Creighton
RAVENSDALE
**Marlfield, Clonmel,
Co Tipperary**
TEL: **052 21089**   FAX: -

Clonmel		
OPEN:	All Year except Christmas
NO. ROOMS:	3
ENSUITE:	3

Delightful modern home in a beautiful setting. Cascading stream in rear garden. Situated in old world Village of Marlfield.

[cc] [t] [P] [symbols] [S]

B&B PPS:	£16/£18	SNGL OCC. DBLE/TPL:	£21.50/£24.50	SNGL RM:	£17
PART BRD:	-	% RED. CHILDREN:	50%	DINNER:	£12

— Clonmel 2km

Mrs Lily Deely
BEENTEE
**Ballingarrane, Cahir/Limerick Road,
Clonmel, Co Tipperary**
TEL: **052 21313**   FAX: -

Clonmel		
OPEN:	All Year
NO. ROOMS:	4
ENSUITE:	3

Comfortable family bungalow, quiet cul-de-sac main Limerick/Cork/Waterford/ Rosslare Rd N24. Private parking, Scenic countryside. Visa-Master Card accepted.

[cc] [t] [P] [symbols] [S]

B&B PPS:	£15/£18	SNGL OCC. DBLE/TPL:	£21.50/£24.50	SNGL RM:	£18
PART BRD:	-	% RED. CHILDREN:	33%	DINNER:	-

— Clonmel 1km

Denis & Kay Fahey
FARRENWICK COUNTRY HSE
**Poulmucka, Curranstown, Clonmel,
Co Tipperary**
TEL: **052 35130**   FAX: **052 35377**   EMAIL: **kayden@clubi.ie**

Clonmel

OPEN:	All Year except Christmas
NO. ROOMS:	4
ENSUITE:	3

(V)

AA QQQ accommodation on R687, 3km, NW off N24 and 6.5km, SE off N8. Family Rooms, Credit Cards. Tour Guide.

B&B PPS:	£15/£17	SNGL OCC. DBLE/TPL:	£21.50	SNGL RM:	-
PART BRD:	£180	% RED. CHILDREN:	-	DINNER:	-

— Clonmel 9km —

Mrs Nuala Healy
OAK HILL LODGE
**Kilcash, Clonmel,
Co Tipperary**
TEL: **052 33503**   FAX: **052 33503**   EMAIL: **healy@tinet.ie.**

Clonmel

OPEN:	All Year
NO. ROOMS:	3
ENSUITE:	3

(V)

Country Lodge 20 acres. Under Slievenamon & Kilcash Castle 0n N76. Kilkenny 29 kms,Clonmel 10 kms. Gardens,Woodlands. Tea & Scones on arrival.

B&B PPS:	£17	SNGL OCC. DBLE/TPL:	£23.50	SNGL RM:	-
PART BRD:	-	% RED. CHILDREN:	33%	DINNER:	-

— Ballypatrick 2km —

Mrs Rita Morrissey
HILLCOURT
**Marlfield, Clonmel,
Co Tipperary**
TEL: **052 21029/29711**   FAX: -

Clonmel

OPEN:	All Year
NO. ROOMS:	5
ENSUITE:	5

(V)

Bungalow in peaceful surroundings 300 meters off main Cork/Limerick Rd (N24). Golf, Fishing within 2 miles. TV.

B&B PPS:	£16/£18	SNGL OCC. DBLE/TPL:	£22.50	SNGL RM:	£21.50
PART BRD:	-	% RED. CHILDREN:	50%	DINNER:	-

— Clonmel 1.5 km —

Mrs Margaret Whelan
AMBERVILLE
**Glenconnor Rd, (off Western Rd),
Clonmel, Co Tipperary**
TEL: **052 21470**   FAX: -

Clonmel

OPEN:	All Year except Christmas
NO. ROOMS:	5
ENSUITE:	3

(V)

Spacious bungalow (300m off Western Road, near hospitals). RAC listed. Adjacent Golf,Fishing, Hillwalking, Dog/Horse Racing. Guests TV lounge.

B&B PPS:	£15/£17	SNGL OCC. DBLE/TPL:	£21.50/£23.50	SNGL RM:	£15
PART BRD:	-	% RED. CHILDREN:	33%	DINNER:	-

— In Clonmel —

Mrs Ann Flannery
OTWAY LODGE
**Dromineer, Nenagh,
Co Tipperary**
TEL: **067 24133/24273**   FAX: -

Dromineer Village

OPEN:	All Year except Christmas
NO. ROOMS:	6
ENSUITE:	4

(V)

Residence situated in Dromineer Harbour, Central for touring midlands. Fishing; All Water Sports; Table Tennis room. Horse riding, Hunting arranged.

B&B PPS:	£17.50	SNGL OCC. DBLE/TPL:	£24	SNGL RM:	-
PART BRD:	-	% RED. CHILDREN:	33.3%	DINNER:	-

— Nenagh 8km —

---Tipperary 13km

Chris & Imelda Stanley
BALLINACOURTY HOUSE
Glen of Aherlow,
Co. Tipperary
TEL: **062 56230**   FAX: **062 56230**

Glen of Aherlow

OPEN:	February-November
NO. ROOMS:	5
ENSUITE:	4

(V)

Beautifully restores 18th century dwelling in courtyard setting. Restaurant with resident chef. Tennis and minigolf. Family run home.

B&B PPS:	£15/£17	SNGL OCC. DBLE/TPL:	£21.50/£23.50	SNGL RM:	-
PART BRD:	£190	% RED. CHILDREN:	20%	DINNER:	£14

---Nenagh 1km

Teresa Delaney
TYONE HOUSE
Tyone, Nenagh,
Co Tipperary
TEL: **067 32053**   FAX: -

Nenagh

OPEN:	All Year except Christmas
NO. ROOMS:	4
ENSUITE:	4

(V)

Georgian house built 1771. Walking distance from town. Golf, Fishing, Tennis nearby. TV lounge, Tea & Coffee facilities.

B&B PPS:	£17	SNGL OCC. DBLE/TPL:	£23.50	SNGL RM:	£21
PART BRD:	-	% RED. CHILDREN:	-	DINNER:	-

---In Nenagh

Brian & Mary Devine
WILLIAMSFERRY HOUSE
Fintan Lalor Street, Nenagh,
Co Tipperary
TEL: **067 31118**   FAX: -

Nenagh

OPEN:	All Year
NO. ROOMS:	6
ENSUITE:	6

(V)

Elegant Townhouse (1830). TV, Hairdryer, Tea/Coffee facilities in rooms. Central Town. Ideal base for Golf, Fishing and Touring. Tipperary Lakeside area.

B&B PPS:	£17/£18	SNGL OCC. DBLE/TPL:	£22.50/£24.50	SNGL RM:	£19/£21
PART BRD:	£195	% RED. CHILDREN:	33%	DINNER:	£14

Mrs Kathleen Healy
Nenagh 2km

Mrs Kathleen Healy
RATHNALEEN HOUSE
Golf Club Road, Old Birr Road,
Nenagh, Co Tipperary
TEL: **067 32508**   FAX: -

Nenagh

OPEN:	All Year except Christmas
NO. ROOMS:	5
ENSUITE:	2

(V)

Neo-Georgian house, antique furniture in all rooms. Quiet location. Spacious grounds, Golf, Fishing, Horse Riding Arena nearby. Good touring base.

B&B PPS:	£16/£18	SNGL OCC. DBLE/TPL:	£22.50/£23.50	SNGL RM:	£21/£23
PART BRD:	£185	% RED. CHILDREN:	20%	DINNER:	£14

---Nenagh 6km

Mrs Joan Kennedy
THE COUNTRY HOUSE
Thurles Road, Kilkeary, Nenagh,
Co Tipperary
TEL: **067 31193**   FAX: -

Nenagh

OPEN:	All Year
NO. ROOMS:	4
ENSUITE:	3

(V)

Luxurious residence recommended Frommer Guide. Breakfast menu. Rooms Tea/coffee facilities, Orthopaedic beds. Fishing, Golf, Dromineer Lake nearby. Airport 60km.

B&B PPS:	£15/£17	SNGL OCC. DBLE/TPL:	£21.50/£23.50	SNGL RM:	-
PART BRD:	-	% RED. CHILDREN:	33%	DINNER:	-

Dromineer 1.5km

Nenagh

Mrs Mary Lynch
SHANNONVALE HOUSE
**Dromineer, Nenagh,
Co Tipperary**
TEL: **067 24102**   FAX: -

OPEN:	All Year except Christmas
NO. ROOMS:	3
ENSUITE:	2

Modern two storey house, close to Lough Derg. Quiet location in an idyllic setting. All the comforts of home.

B&B PPS:	£17	SNGL OCC. DBLE/TPL:	£23.50	SNGL RM:	£21.50/£
PART BRD:	-	% RED. CHILDREN:	50%	DINNER:	23.50£13

Nenagh 1km

Nenagh

Mrs Gay McAuliffe
AVONDALE
**Tyone, Nenagh,
Co Tipperary**
TEL: **067 31084**   FAX: -

OPEN:	All Year
NO. ROOMS:	4
ENSUITE:	2

Comfortable, detached residence, quiet location. Tea/coffee facilities. Two guest bathrooms, Orthopaedic beds.

B&B PPS:	£15/£17	SNGL OCC. DBLE/TPL:	£21.50/£23.50	SNGL RM:	-
PART BRD:	-	% RED. CHILDREN:	20%	DINNER:	-

Terryglass 5km

Nenagh/Terryglass

Mary McGeeney
BROCKA
**Ballinderry, Nenagh,
Co Tipperary**
TEL: **067 22164**   FAX: -

OPEN:	All Year
NO. ROOMS:	3
ENSUITE:	3

Timber and brick house with spectacular views of Lough Derg. Ideal location for walking, cycling, touring and all water activities.

B&B PPS:	£17	SNGL OCC. DBLE/TPL:	£23.50	SNGL RM:	-
PART BRD:	£180	% RED. CHILDREN:	50%	DINNER:	£12

Nenagh

Nenagh/Lough Derg

Margaret & PJ Mounsey
ASHLEY PARK HOUSE
**Ashley Park, Nenagh,
Co Tipperary**
TEL: **067 31474/38223**   FAX: **067 38223**

OPEN:	All Year
NO. ROOMS:	5
ENSUITE:	2

17th Century house stands on the shores of Lough Orna. Centrally located, ideal for those who love tranquility, fishing, golfing.

B&B PPS:	£20	SNGL OCC. DBLE/TPL:	£20	SNGL RM:	£20
PART BRD:	-	% RED. CHILDREN:	30%	DINNER:	£15

Newport 2km

Newport

Mrs Grainne Carey
BIRCHWOOD HOUSE
**Shower, Newport,
Co Tipperary**
TEL: **061 378033**   FAX: **061 378033**

OPEN:	All Year except Christmas
NO. ROOMS:	5
ENSUITE:	4

Spacious country residence set in mature grounds. Excellent accommodation. Offers in-house Gymnasium, Snooker, Tennis. Angling, Golf, Horseriding nearby.

B&B PPS:	£16/£18	SNGL OCC. DBLE/TPL:	£22.50/£24.50	SNGL RM:	£20/£22
PART BRD:	£196	% RED. CHILDREN:	33%	DINNER:	£13.50

In Roscrea

Mrs Mae Fallon
CREGGANBELL
**Birr Road, Roscrea,
Co Tipperary**
TEL: **0505 21421**   FAX: -

Roscrea	
OPEN:	**All Year except Christmas**
NO. ROOMS:	4
ENSUITE:	3

(V)

Spacious bungalow, Quiet location, Electric blankets, Golf, Fishing, Forest and Mountain Walks. Ideal for touring midlands. 3 mins off N7.

B&B PPS:	**£15/£17**	SNGL OCC. DBLE/TPL: **£21.50/£23.50**	SNGL RM:	-
PART BRD:	-	% RED. CHILDREN: **20%**	DINNER:	-

Roscrea 3km

Miss Helen Powell
DERRYVALE HOUSE
**Dublin Road, Roscrea,
Co Tipperary**
TEL: **0505 21429**   FAX: -

Roscrea	
OPEN:	**1st April-31st October**
NO. ROOMS:	4
ENSUITE:	-

(V)

Georgian home in secluded grounds. On N7. Opposite Golf Course. Ideal for touring Ely O'Carroll Country. Riding, Walking, Fishing nearby.

B&B PPS:	**£16/£20**	SNGL OCC. DBLE/TPL: **£22.50/£26.50**	SNGL RM:	-
PART BRD:	-	% RED. CHILDREN: **25%**	DINNER:	-

In Terryglass

Sheila & Oliver Darcy
LAKE LAND LODGE
**Terryglass, Nenagh,
Co Tipperary**
TEL: **067 22069**   FAX: -

Terryglass	
OPEN:	**All Year except Christmas**
NO. ROOMS:	3
ENSUITE:	2

(V)

Luxurious accomodation , beautiful scenic area. "A home away from home" Close to Lake amenities, Fishing, Water sports, Golf, Traditional Music.

B&B PPS:	**£17**	SNGL OCC. DBLE/TPL:	**£23.50**	SNGL RM:	-
PART BRD:	-	% RED. CHILDREN:	**33%**	DINNER:	-

In Thurles

Mrs. Ellen Cavanagh
CUILIN HOUSE
**Templemore Road N62
Thurles, Co Tipperary**
TEL: **0504 23237**   FAX: -

Thurles	
OPEN:	**20th February-30th November**
NO. ROOMS:	3
ENSUITE:	3

(V)

Elegant accommodation with large spacious rooms. Antique furrniture. Genealogy tracing assistance TV lounge with tea - coffee facilities. Home made produce.

B&B PPS:	**£17/£20**	SNGL OCC. DBLE/TPL:	**£23.50**	SNGL RM:	-
PART BRD:	-	% RED. CHILDREN:	**25%**	DINNER:	-

Thurles 6km

Anna Stakelum
BOHERNA LODGE
**Clohane, Tipperary Road, Holycross,
Thurles, Co Tipperary**
TEL: **0504 43121**   FAX: -

Thurles	
OPEN:	**All Year except Christmas**
NO. ROOMS:	4
ENSUITE:	3

(V)

Spacious bungalow, quiet location, homely atmosphere, convenient Holycross Abbey, Rock of Cashel, Golf, Fishing, Horseriding, country walks nearby, touring base.

B&B PPS:	**£15/£17**	SNGL OCC. DBLE/TPL: **£21.50/£23.50**	SNGL RM:	-
PART BRD:	-	% RED. CHILDREN: **50%**	DINNER:	-

Tipperary 1.5km

Norah Coleman
ROSE LAWN
Bohercrowe, Emly Road, Tipperary, Co Tipperary
TEL: **062 52225**   FAX: -

 Tipperary

OPEN:	April-October
NO. ROOMS:	4
ENSUITE:	3
-	

(V)

Spacious bungalow, panoramic view of Galtee Mountains. Extensive gardens, visitors lounge, breakfast menu. Rooms on ground floor. R515 to Killarney.

| B&B PPS: | £15/£17 | SNGL OCC. DBLE/TPL: | £21.50/£23.50 | SNGL RM: | - |
| PART BRD: | - | % RED. CHILDREN: | 25% | DINNER: | - |

Tipperary 1.5km

Mrs Noreen Collins
PURT HOUSE
Bohercrowe, Emly Road, Tipperary Town, Co Tipperary
TEL: **062 51938**   FAX: -

Tipperary

OPEN:	1st April-31st October
NO. ROOMS:	6
ENSUITE:	5

(V)

Warm welcome R515 to Killarney, Tea/ Coffee, TV, Hairdryers in bedrooms. (hot scones) Credit cards, laundry facilities, Irish Night arranged.

| B&B PPS: | £18 | SNGL OCC. DBLE/TPL: | £24.50 | SNGL RM: | £20 |
| PART BRD: | - | % RED. CHILDREN: | 33% | DINNER: | £13 |

Tipperary Town 3km

Douglas & Angela Edinborough
BALLYKISTEEN LODGE
Monard, Co Tipperary
TEL: **062 33403**   FAX: -

Tipperary

OPEN:	All Year
NO. ROOMS:	4
ENSUITE:	4

(V)

Luxurious residence. Adjacent Ballykisteen Golf Country club, Tipperary racecourse. 10 minutes Tipperary. Breakfast menu, TV, Tea/Coffee facilities. Guest TV lounge.

| B&B PPS: | £17/£20 | SNGL OCC. DBLE/TPL: | £23.50/£24.50 | SNGL RM: | £18/£22 |
| PART BRD: | - | % RED. CHILDREN: | 50% | DINNER: | - |

In Tipperary Town

Brenda McKenna
ARRA VIEW
Bohercrowe, Emly Road, Tipperary, Co Tipperary
TEL: **062 51879**   FAX: -

Tipperary

OPEN:	All Year
NO. ROOMS:	3
ENSUITE:	2

(V)

Warm welcome, Breakfast/Dinner menu. 0.5 KM Tipperary Town, R515 to Killarney. All rooms: TV, Hairdryer, Tea/Coffee facilities. Private parking.

| B&B PPS: | £18 | SNGL OCC. DBLE/TPL: | £24.50 | SNGL RM: | - |
| PART BRD: | £180 | % RED. CHILDREN: | 33% | DINNER: | £12 |

Tipperary 1.5km

Mrs Margaret Merrigan
TEACH GOBNATHAN
Glen of Aherlow, Golf Links Road, Brookville, Tipperary, Co Tipperary
TEL: **062 51645**   FAX: -

 **Tipperary**

OPEN:	1st Feburary-31st October
NO. ROOMS:	4
ENSUITE:	3

(V)

Beside Golf Course, Scenic route. Turn down at traffic lights (Bridge Street), right at roundabout, two bends after Golf Course.

| B&B PPS: | £15/£17 | SNGL OCC. DBLE/TPL: | £21.50/£23.50 | SNGL RM: | - |
| PART BRD: | £180 | % RED. CHILDREN: | 25% | DINNER: | £12 |

Mrs Mary O'Neill
VILLA MARIA
Limerick Road, Tipperary Town, Co Tipperary

TEL: 062 51557   FAX: -

Tipperary	
OPEN:	May - September
NO. ROOMS:	3
ENSUITE:	2

(V)

Modern bungalow on N24 Waterford/ Limerick Road. Ballykisteen Golf, Tipperary Racecourse, Limerick Junction Station all 1.5KM. Swimming Pool, Sports Complex, 2KM.

B&B PPS:	£15.50/£17.50	SNGL OCC. DBLE/TPL:	£22/£24	SNGL RM:	-
PART BRD:	-	% RED. CHILDREN:	25%	DINNER:	-

└ Tipperary 2km

Mrs Nuala O'Sullivan
WOODLAWN
Galbally Road, Tipperary Town, Co Tipperary

TEL: 062 51272   FAX: -

Tipperary	
OPEN:	1st April-30th November
NO. ROOMS:	3
ENSUITE:	3

(V)

Modern spacious and comfortable home in peaceful surroundings on Galbally/Cork road.(R662) Large landscaped gardens and ample parking.

B&B PPS:	£17	SNGL OCC. DBLE/TPL:	£23.50	SNGL RM:	-
PART BRD:	-	% RED. CHILDREN:	25%	DINNER:	-

└ Tipperary 3 km

Mrs Mary Quinn
CLONMORE HOUSE
Cork/Galbally Rd, Tipperary Town, Co Tipperary

TEL: 062 51637   FAX: -

Tipperary	
OPEN:	March-October
NO. ROOMS:	4
ENSUITE:	4

(V)

Bungalow 5mins walk town, scenic surroundings, overlooking Galtee Mountains, Frommer, Birnbaun, Best B&B Guides recommended. Ground floor bedrooms, Electric blankets.

B&B PPS:	£17	SNGL OCC. DBLE/TPL:	£23.50	SNGL RM:	-
PART BRD:	-	% RED. CHILDREN:	20%	DINNER:	-

└ In Tipperary

Mrs Teresa Russell
BANSHA CASTLE
Bansha, Co Tipperary

TEL: 062 54187   FAX: 062 54294

Tipperary	
OPEN:	All Year
NO. ROOMS:	6
ENSUITE:	3

Historic country house. Private gardens, Mature trees. Snooker room. Superb cooking. Walking/cycling. Pre booking recommended. 10 mins south Tipperary N24.

B&B PPS:	£18/£21	SNGL OCC. DBLE/TPL:	£24.50/£27.50	SNGL RM:	-
PART BRD:	£220	% RED. CHILDREN:	50%	DINNER:	£15

└ Tipperary 8km

TELEPHONE

- Operator assisted calls within Ireland   Dial 10
- International telephone operator   Dial 114
- Directory Enquiries   Dial 1190

FOR TROUBLE-FREE TELEPHONE CALLS FROM PUBLIC PAY PHONES IT IS ADVISABLE TO PURCHASE A TELEPHONE CALLCARD AVAILABLE IN POST OFFICES AND WHEREVER YOU SEE A CALLCARD SIGN.
TO DIAL IRELAND FROM ABROAD: Country Access Code + 353 + Area Code (omit first zero) + Local Number

In Ardmore

Mrs Mary Byron Casey
BYRON LODGE
Ardmore,
Co Waterford

Ardmore

OPEN:	1st April-31st October
NO. ROOMS:	6
ENSUITE:	3

TEL: **024 94157**   FAX: -

(V)

Georgian house, 150 years - On superb location overlooking Beach and Countryside in prize winning Fishing Village. Private parking, Monastic Settlement.

B&B PPS:	£15/£17	SNGL OCC. DBLE/TPL:	£21.50/£23.50	SNGL RM:	£21
PART BRD:		% RED. CHILDREN:	20%	DINNER:	£12

Clonmel 14km

Richard & Nora Harte
CNOC-NA-RI
Nire Valley, Ballymacarby (Via Clonmel),
Co Waterford

Ballymacarbry - Nire Valley

OPEN:	All Year except Christmas
NO. ROOMS:	3
ENSUITE:	3

TEL: **052 36239**   FAX: -

(V)

Luxurious friendly home set in Comeragh Mountains. Walking, Golfing, Touring, Relaxing. Hairdryers, TVs, Electric Blankets rooms. Drying area, Breakfast menu.

B&B PPS:	£18	SNGL OCC. DBLE/TPL:	£25	SNGL RM:	-
PART BRD:	£220	% RED. CHILDREN:	50%	DINNER:	£15

Clonmel 15km

Martin & Una Moore
BENNETTS CHURCH
Old School House, Ballymacarbry (R672),
Nire Valley (via Clonmel), Co Waterford

Ballymacarbry - Nire Valley

OPEN:	1st January-19th December
NO. ROOMS:	3
ENSUITE:	2

TEL: **052 36217/088 571203**   FAX: -   EMAIL: **richiem@tinet.ie**

(V)

Converted old school house. Antique Furniture. Lawns with rippling stream. Excellent food. Perfect for Activity/ Leisure, Walking, Horseriding, Fishing, Cycling (R672).

B&B PPS:	£15.50/£18	SNGL OCC. DBLE/TPL:	£22/£24.50	SNGL RM:	-
PART BRD:	-	% RED. CHILDREN:	50%	DINNER:	£15

Cappoquin 5km

Mrs Catherine Mary Scanlan
COOLHILLA
Ballyhane, Cappoquin,
Co Waterford

Cappoquin

OPEN:	All Year except Christmas
NO. ROOMS:	3
ENSUITE:	3

TEL: **058 54054**   FAX: **058 54054**

(V)

'Ambassador of Tourism' winner. Gardens, Home Cooking, Tea on arrival. TV Lounge. Vee Drive, Mount Melleray Abbey nearby. N72. Visa.

B&B PPS:	£17.50	SNGL OCC. DBLE/TPL:	£24	SNGL RM:	-
PART BRD:	£180	% RED. CHILDREN:	10%	DINNER:	£14.50

RESERVATIONS

- Confirm phone bookings in writing without delay with agreed deposit.
- To avoid misunderstandings later, check rate on booking and clarify any additional changes which may apply to your booking.
- Give details of any special requirements.
- State clearly day, date of arrival and departure date.

Maura Fahey
CURTISWOOD
Windgap, Dungarvan,
Co Waterford
TEL: **058 44688 / 088 617753**   FAX: -

Dungarvan

OPEN:	**All Year**
NO. ROOMS:	3
ENSUITE:	3

(V)

Modern bungalow on Youghal/Cork Rd. (N25), overlooking Comeragh and Knockmealdown Mountains. Award winning Seanachie Bar/Restaurant within Walking distance.

B&B PPS:	**£17/£19**	SNGL OCC. DBLE/TPL:	**£23.50/£25.50**	SNGL RM:	-
PART BRD:	-	% RED. CHILDREN:	-	DINNER:	-

Dungarvan 8km

Mrs Nora Fahey
SEAVIEW
Windgap Pulla, Dungarvan West,
Youghal Road, Co Waterford
TEL: **058 41583/087 2398563**   FAX: -

Dungarvan

OPEN:	**All Year except Christmas**
NO. ROOMS:	5
ENSUITE:	3

(V)

West of Dungarvan on N25. Overlooking Dungarvan Bay and Mountains. Seanachie Restaurant 300 metres. Irish Music, Local Tours available.

B&B PPS:	**£15.50/£17.50**	SNGL OCC. DBLE/TPL:	**£22/£24**	SNGL RM:	-
PART BRD:	-	% RED. CHILDREN:	**50%**	DINNER:	**£12**

Dungarvan 5km

Sheila Lane
BALLINAMORE HOUSE
Ballyduff, Dungarvan,
Co Waterford
TEL: **058 42146**   FAX: -

Dungarvan

OPEN:	**All Year except Christmas**
NO. ROOMS:	3
ENSUITE:	3

(V)

Superior accomodation and homely atmosphere in idyllic setting. Minutes from Town, Golf, Fishing, Horseriding and Walking areas etc.

B&B PPS:	**£17**	SNGL OCC. DBLE/TPL:	**£23.50**	SNGL RM:	-
PART BRD:	-	% RED. CHILDREN:	-	DINNER:	-

Dungarvan 4km

Bridget Maher
HELVICK VIEW
Ring, Dungarvan,
Co Waterford
TEL: **058 46297**   FAX: -

Dungarvan

OPEN:	**22nd April-30th September**
NO. ROOMS:	4
ENSUITE:	2

(V)

Seaside bungalow 5-miles east Dungarvan off N25. Rooms overlooking Dungarvan Bay and Helvick Harbour. Prize winning Rose Garden for visitors.

B&B PPS:	**£15/£17**	SNGL OCC. DBLE/TPL:	-	SNGL RM:	-
PART BRD:	-	% RED. CHILDREN:	-	DINNER:	-

Dungarvan 8km

Helen O'Connell
HILLCREST
Tarr's Bridge, Dungarvan,
Co Waterford
TEL: **058 42262**   FAX: -

Dungarvan

OPEN:	**April-October**
NO. ROOMS:	3
ENSUITE:	2

(V)

Bungalow in Waterford/Cork Rd. (N25). Adjacent 18 hole Golf Course. Rosslare 1.5 hours. Electric blankets. Teamaking facilities in bedrooms.

B&B PPS:	**£15/£17**	SNGL OCC. DBLE/TPL:	**£21.50/£23.50**	SNGL RM:	-
PART BRD:	-	% RED. CHILDREN:	**50%**	DINNER:	-

Dungarvan 3km

In Dungarvan

Mrs Kathleen Phelan
ABBEY HOUSE
Friars Walk, Abbeyside, Dungarvan, Co Waterford

Dungarvan

TEL: **058 41669**   FAX: -

OPEN:	All Year except Christmas
NO. ROOMS:	3
ENSUITE:	2

(V)

Luxury bungalow by the Sea. Stroll to Town or Beach. 3 X 18 Hole Golf Courses close by. Warm welcome assured.

B&B PPS:	**£15/£18**	SNGL OCC. DBLE/TPL:	**£21.50/£24.50**	SNGL RM:	-
PART BRD:	-	% RED. CHILDREN:	-	DINNER:	

In Dungarvan

Mrs R Prendergast
THE OLD RECTORY
Waterford Rd, Dungarvan, Co Waterford

Dungarvan

TEL: **058 41394**   FAX: -

OPEN:	1st February-20th December
NO. ROOMS:	4
ENSUITE:	2

(V)

Ideally located outskirts of town on N25. Adjacent championship Golf Course, TV in Bedrooms, Sun Room, Tea/Coffee Making Facilities.

B&B PPS:	**£15/£18**	SNGL OCC. DBLE/TPL:	**£21.50/£24.50**	SNGL RM:	-
PART BRD:	-	% RED. CHILDREN:	**50%**	DINNER:	-

Dungarvan 3km

Mrs Margo Sleator
ROSEBANK HOUSE
Coast Road, Dungarvan, Co Waterford

Dungarvan

TEL: **058 41561**   FAX: -

OPEN:	1st January-23rd December
NO. ROOMS:	4
ENSUITE:	3

(V)

2km off N25. Refreshments on arrival. Frommer recommended. Mountain views, firm beds, electric blankets, breakfast menu, secure parking, Golf 1.50km.

B&B PPS:	**£15.50/£17.50**	SNGL OCC. DBLE/TPL:	**£22/£24**	SNGL RM:	-
PART BRD:	-	% RED. CHILDREN:	-	DINNER:	-

Dunmore East 1km

Mrs Breda Battles
ASHGROVE
Dunmore East, Co Waterford

Dunmore East

TEL: **051 383195**   FAX: -

OPEN:	March-October
NO. ROOMS:	4
ENSUITE:	3

(V)

Country home situated in peaceful scenic surroundings. Sign-posted in village at junction across from "The Church". Frommer/Le Routard recommended.

B&B PPS:	**£15/£17**	SNGL OCC. DBLE/TPL:	**£21.50/£23.50**	SNGL RM:	**£20/£21**
PART BRD:	**£196**	% RED. CHILDREN:	**25%**	DINNER:	**£13.50**

In Dunmore East

Winnie & Tony Brooke
SPRINGFIELD
Dunmore East, Co Waterford

Dunmore East

TEL: **051 383448**   FAX: -

OPEN:	1st March-30th November
NO. ROOMS:	6
ENSUITE:	6

(V)

Luxurious home in beautiful peaceful surroundings yet 200 metres from Beach, Restaurants etc. Tea/Coffee facilities in Conservatory. Breakfast menu.

B&B PPS:	**£17/£18**	SNGL OCC. DBLE/TPL:	**£23.50/£26**	SNGL RM:	-
PART BRD:	-	% RED. CHILDREN:	**25%**	DINNER:	-

Kathleen & Jim Burke
CARRAIG LIATH
**Harbour Road, Dunmore East,
Co Waterford**

Tel: 051 383273/087 2394763   Fax: -

Dunmore East

Open:	1st April-31st October
No. Rooms:	3
Ensuite:	3

Large residence in Village centre. Overlooking Harbour, Sailing Club. Walking distance Beaches, Tennis, Swimming Pool, Restaurants. Golf 4 mins drive.

B&B PPS:	**£17/£20**	Sngl Occ. Dble/Tpl:	-	Sngl Rm:	-
Part Brd:	-	% Red. Children:	25%	Dinner:	-

In Dunmore East

Elizabeth Hayes
COPPER BEECH
**Dock Road, Dunmore East,
Co Waterford**

Tel: **051 383187**   Fax: -

Dunmore East

Open:	1st March-31st October
No. Rooms:	4
Ensuite:	4

Panoramic view Dunmore Harbour. Beside Beaches, Tennis, Sailing, Golf. Excellent Restaurants. Private parking. Tea/coffee facilities. Breakfast menu. Waterford 12km.

B&B PPS:	**£17/£18**	Sngl Occ. Dble/Tpl:	**£23.50/£24.50**	Sngl Rm:	-
Part Brd:	-	% Red. Children:	25%	Dinner:	-

Waterford 12km

Mrs Kathleen Martin
CREADEN VIEW
**Dunmore East,
Co Waterford**

Tel: **051 383339**   Fax: **051 383339**

Dunmore East

Open:	March-November
No. Rooms:	5
Ensuite:	5

Charming home in centre of Village. Beautiful views of Sea & Cliffs. Golf Club 2 km. TV in bedrooms . Frommer recommended.

B&B PPS:	**£17/£18**	Sngl Occ. Dble/Tpl:	**£23.50/£25**	Sngl Rm:	-
Part Brd:	-	% Red. Children:	25%	Dinner:	-

In Dunmore East

The Sutton Family
GLOR NA MARA
**Kilmacleague, Dunmore East,
Co Waterford**

Tel: **051 383361**   Fax: -

Dunmore East

Open:	1st March-30th September
No. Rooms:	3
Ensuite:	3

Modern family home. Tranquil rural setting. Located centrally between Dunmore East, Tramore & Waterford City. Airport 2 km. Adjacent to Beaches.

B&B PPS:	**£17**	Sngl Occ. Dble/Tpl:	**£23.50**	Sngl Rm:	-
Part Brd:	-	% Red. Children:	50%	Dinner:	-

Dunmore East 5km

Pauline Humphreys
COUMSHINGAUN LODGE
**Kilclooney, Kilmacthomas,
Co Waterford**

Tel: **051 646238**   Fax: -

Kilmacthomas/Comeragh Mtns

Open:	15th March-October
No. Rooms:	5
Ensuite:	5

Magnificent mountain setting near Lough Coumshingaun on scenic Comeragh Drive (R676). Excellent cuisine, relaxed atmosphere, open fire, traditional musicians. Smoking restrictions.

B&B PPS:	**£18**	Sngl Occ. Dble/Tpl:	**£24.50**	Sngl Rm:	-
Part Brd:	£220	% Red. Children:	20%	Dinner:	£15

Kilmacthomas 12km

Mrs Ann Fitzgerald
DAWN B & B
Kildarmody,
Kilmeaden, Co Waterford

Kilmeaden

OPEN:	31st March-31st October
No. ROOMS:	3
ENSUITE:	3

 (V)

TEL: **051 384465**   FAX: -

Modern 5 bedroomed bungalow in partly wooded area. 1/2 km. off N25. Private carpark. Pubs, Restaurants, Waterford Crystal nearby. Visa accepted.

B&B PPS:	£17	SNGL OCC. DBLE/TPL:	£23.50	SNGL RM:	-
PART BRD:	-	% RED. CHILDREN:	-	DINNER:	-

— Waterford City 12km —

Mrs June Power
BEECHCROFT
Deerpark Road, Lismore,
Co Waterford

Lismore

OPEN:	All Year except Christmas
No. ROOMS:	3
ENSUITE:	2

(V)

TEL: **058 54273**   FAX: -

Warm welcome awaits you in our home. All rooms TV & Tea /Coffee making facilities. Frommer, AA QQQ recommended. Mature Gardens.

B&B PPS:	£17	SNGL OCC. DBLE/TPL:	£23.50	SNGL RM:	-
PART BRD:	-	% RED. CHILDREN:	25%	DINNER:	-

— Lismore 1km —

Mrs Rosaleen Breen
SEACREST
Pickardstown, Tramore,
Co Waterford

Tramore

OPEN:	May-September
No. ROOMS:	3
ENSUITE:	2

(V)

TEL: **051 381888**   FAX: -

Peaceful secluded country home adjacent to R675 from Waterford. Algemeen Dagblad Best B&B's. Breakfast choice. Parking. Hairdryers. Triple/Family rooms.

B&B PPS:	£17	SNGL OCC. DBLE/TPL:	£25	SNGL RM:	£19
PART BRD:	-	% RED. CHILDREN:	50%	DINNER:	-

— In Tramore —

Irene & Sean Brennan
EASTON
Lower Branch Road, Tramore,
Co Waterford

Tramore

OPEN:	1st April-31st October
No. ROOMS:	4
ENSUITE:	3

(V)

TEL: **051 381750**   FAX: **051 381750**

Georgian house with spacious rooms, overlooking boating lake, Splashworld and Tramore Bay. Tea/coffee making facilities in TV lounge.

B&B PPS:	£15/£17	SNGL OCC. DBLE/TPL:	£21.50/£23.50	SNGL RM:	-
PART BRD:	-	% RED. CHILDREN:	50%	DINNER:	-

— In Tramore —

Mrs Maria Byrne
KILLERIG HOUSE
Lower Branch Rd., Tramore,
Co Waterford

Tramore

OPEN:	All Year
No. ROOMS:	4
ENSUITE:	4

(V)

TEL: **051 381075**   FAX: -

200 year old Georgian town house on sea front. Beside Majestic Hotel opposite Splashworld. With panoramic view overlooking Tramore Bay.

B&B PPS:	£17/£18	SNGL OCC. DBLE/TPL:	£24/£26	SNGL RM:	-
PART BRD:	-	% RED. CHILDREN:	25%	DINNER:	-

Mrs Margaret Collins
WOODBROOK
**Drumcannon, Tramore,
Co Waterford**

Tel: **051 386455**   Fax: -

Tramore	
Open:	15th March-31st October
No. Rooms:	4
Ensuite:	2

(V)

Spacious comfortable house, secure parking. Guide De Routard recommended. Tea/coffee facilities, breakfast menu.

B&B pps:	£15/£17	Sngl Occ. Dble/Tpl:	£21.50/£23.50	Sngl Rm:	-
Part Brd:	-	% Red. Children:	50%	Dinner:	-

Tramore 1km

Cyril & Frances Darcy
SEAVIEW LODGE
**Sea View Park, Tramore,
Co Waterford**

Tel: **051 381122**   Fax: **051 381122**

Tramore	
Open:	March-October
No. Rooms:	5
Ensuite:	4

(V)

Spectacular seaview, Parking. Frommer/Le Routard, AA QQQQ acclaimed. TV, Hairdryer, Tea/coffee in bedrooms. Extensive menu. In Tramore off R675.

B&B pps:	£17.50/£18.50	Sngl Occ. Dble/Tpl:	£24/£25	Sngl Rm:	-
Part Brd:	-	% Red. Children:	20%	Dinner:	-

In Tramore

Mrs Lillian Delaney
WESTCLIFFE
**5 Newtown, Tramore,
Co Waterford**

Tel: **051 381365**   Fax: -

Tramore	
Open:	All Year except Christmas
No. Rooms:	3
Ensuite:	3

(V)

New modern two storey house overlooking Tramore Bay, 2 mins from 18 hole Golf Course.

B&B pps:	£17.50/£20	Sngl Occ. Dble/Tpl:	£24/£26.50	Sngl Rm:	-
Part Brd:	-	% Red. Children:	50%	Dinner:	-

In Tramore

Frank & Majella Heraughty
GLENART HOUSE
**Tivoli Rd, Tramore,
Co Waterford**

Tel: **051 381236**   Fax: -

Tramore	
Open:	1st March-30th November
No. Rooms:	4
Ensuite:	4

(V)

Elegant restored 1920's detached residence.Convenient Racecourse, Splashworld, Beach & Golf. Friendly atmosphere. Breakfast menu. Tea/coffee facilities. Ideal touring base.

B&B pps:	£18/£20	Sngl Occ. Dble/Tpl:	£24.50/£26.50	Sngl Rm:	-
Part Brd:	-	% Red. Children:	50%	Dinner:	-

In Tramore

Mrs Bernie Keating
ROXBORO HOUSE
**Church Road Grove, Tramore,
Co Waterford**

Tel: **051 381035**   Fax: -

Tramore	
Open:	1st June-30th September
No. Rooms:	3
Ensuite:	3

(V)

Bungalow in quiet cul-de-sac, friendly & comfortable. Close to all amenities. Private garden & parking. Golf & Tennis nearby. Breakfast menu.

B&B pps:	£17.50/£18	Sngl Occ. Dble/Tpl:	£24/£24.50	Sngl Rm:	-
Part Brd:	-	% Red. Children:	33.3%	Dinner:	-

In Tramore

Tramore 1km

Anne Lawlor
FERN HILL
Newtown, Tramore,
Co Waterford

TEL: **051 390829**   FAX: -

Tramore

OPEN:	1st March-30th October
NO. ROOMS:	4
ENSUITE:	3

(V)

Luxurious purpose built house situated opposite Tramore Golf Club & 1 km from Beach. Views of Tramore Bay.

| B&B PPS: | **£17.50/£19** | SNGL OCC. DBLE/TPL: | **£24/£25.50** | SNGL RM: | **£19** |
| PART BRD: | - | % RED. CHILDREN: | **50%** | DINNER: | - |

Tramore 1km

Mrs Anne McCarthy
SEAMIST
Newtown, Tramore,
Co Waterford

TEL: **051 381533**   FAX: **051 381533**   EMAIL: **annflor@iol.ie**

Tramore

OPEN:	1st April-31st October
NO. ROOMS:	3
ENSUITE:	3

(V)

Friendly spacious home private grounds. Westside Tramore off R675, 300 metres Golf Club. Renowned home cooking. Secure parking. Selected Brittany Ferries.

| B&B PPS: | **£17** | SNGL OCC. DBLE/TPL: | **£23.50** | SNGL RM: | - |
| PART BRD: | - | % RED. CHILDREN: | **50%** | DINNER: | - |

In Tramore

Mrs Olive McCarthy
OBAN
1 Eastlands, Pond Road, Tramore,
Co Waterford

TEL: **051 381537**   FAX: -

Tramore

OPEN:	10th January-12th December
NO. ROOMS:	4
ENSUITE:	3

(V)

"Breakfast over the Bay" in central, quiet, comfortable home. Walking distance Sea, Pubs, Restaurants. Breakfast menu. Tea/making facilities. Visa/Access.

| B&B PPS: | **£15/£17** | SNGL OCC. DBLE/TPL: | **£21.50/£23.50** | SNGL RM: | - |
| PART BRD: | - | % RED. CHILDREN: | **50%** | DINNER: | - |

In Tramore

Mrs Rita McGivney
RUSHMERE HSE
Branch Rd, Tramore,
Co Waterford

TEL: **051 381041**   FAX: -

Tramore

OPEN:	All Year except Christmas
NO. ROOMS:	6
ENSUITE:	3

(V)

Georgian House with character, with panoramic view of Tramore Bay. Frommer Guide, AA and Elsie Dillard recommended. Tea/Coffee making facilities.

| B&B PPS: | **£15/£17** | SNGL OCC. DBLE/TPL: | **£21.50/£23.50** | SNGL RM: | - |
| PART BRD: | - | % RED. CHILDREN: | - | DINNER: | - |

In Tramore

Mrs Rosaleen McGrath
ARD MOR HOUSE
Doneraile Drive, Tramore,
Co Waterford

TEL: **051 381716**   FAX: -

Tramore

OPEN:	1st April-30th September
NO. ROOMS:	3
ENSUITE:	3

(V)

Family home in quiet area overlooking Tramore Bay. Walking distance to all amenities, Restaurants etc. Tea/coffee available. Breakfast menu.

| B&B PPS: | **£17/£18** | SNGL OCC. DBLE/TPL: | **£23.50/£24.50** | SNGL RM: | - |
| PART BRD: | - | % RED. CHILDREN: | **33.3%** | DINNER: | - |

In Tramore

Oliver & Deirdre McSherry
THE ANNER
33 Newtown Hill, Tramore,
Co Waterford

Tramore

OPEN:	All Year except Christmas
NO. ROOMS:	3
ENSUITE:	3

Ⓥ

TEL: 051 381628   FAX: -

Luxury welcoming family home overlooking Bay. Hearty Breakfast. Quiet secluded residential Cul-de-sac. (2nd right turn in development opposite golf club.)

B&B PPS:	**£17**	SNGL OCC. DBLE/TPL:	**£23.50**	SNGL RM:	-
PART BRD:	-	% RED. CHILDREN:	**50%**	DINNER:	-

In Tramore

Mrs Marie Murphy
GLENORNEY
Newtown, Tramore,
Co Waterford

Tramore

OPEN:	1st March-30th November
NO. ROOMS:	6
ENSUITE:	5

Ⓥ

TEL: 051 381056   FAX: **051 381103**   EMAIL: **gleoney@iol.ie**

Award winning home. Panoramic view Tramore Bay. Secure parking. AA QQQQ selected. R.A.C. highly acclaimed. 2 family ensuites. Breakfast menu.

B&B PPS:	**£16.50/£20**	SNGL OCC. DBLE/TPL:	**£23/£26.50**	SNGL RM:	**£23/£25**
PART BRD:	-	% RED. CHILDREN:	**20%**	DINNER:	-

In Tramore

Mrs Anne O'Connor
ARDVIEW HOUSE
Lower Branch Road, Tramore,
Co Waterford

Tramore

OPEN:	All Year
NO. ROOMS:	6
ENSUITE:	5

Ⓥ

TEL: **051 381687**   FAX: -

Georgian house - panoramic view of bay. Satellite TV all rooms. Tea/Coffee. Breakfast menu. Credit cards, Central location. Warm Welcome.

B&B PPS:	**£15/£18**	SNGL OCC. DBLE/TPL:	**£21.50/£24.50**	SNGL RM:	-
PART BRD:	-	% RED. CHILDREN:	**50%**	DINNER:	-

Tramore 2 km

Ann & John O'Meara
KNOCKVILLE
Moonvoy, Tramore,
Co Waterford

Tramore

OPEN:	March-November
NO. ROOMS:	5
ENSUITE:	3

Ⓥ

TEL: **051 381084**   FAX: -

Country home on private grounds in rural area. Owner chef. Breakfast and dinner menu. Tea/coffee making facilities. Credit Cards welcome.

B&B PPS:	**£15/£17**	SNGL OCC. DBLE/TPL:	**£21.50/£23.50**	SNGL RM:	-
PART BRD:	**£180**	% RED. CHILDREN:	**50%**	DINNER:	**£12**

In Tramore

Pat & Hilary O'Sullivan
CLIFF HOUSE
Cliff Road, Tramore,
Co Waterford

Tramore

OPEN:	15th March-30th November
NO. ROOMS:	6
ENSUITE:	5

Ⓥ

TEL: 051 381497   FAX: **051 381497**

Panoramic view Tramore Bay. Landscaped gardens. Parking. Le Routard/Dillard/Causin/R.A.C. highly acclaimed. Family suite. Breakfast menu. Tea/coffee facilities.

B&B PPS:	**£16.50/£18.50**	SNGL OCC. DBLE/TPL:	**£23/£25**	SNGL RM:	-
PART BRD:	-	% RED. CHILDREN:	**20%**	DINNER:	-

In Tramore

Mrs Teresa O'Sullivan
TIVOLI HOUSE

Tramore

Waterford Road, Tramore, Co Waterford

OPEN:	All Year except Christmas
NO. ROOMS:	3
ENSUITE:	3

TEL: **051 390208**   FAX: **051 390208**

(V)

Spacious modern house overlooking Tramore Bay. Car park. Breakfast menu. Tea/Coffee making facilities. Golf 4 km. Credit Cards accepted.

B&B PPS:	£17/£18	SNGL OCC. DBLE/TPL:	£23.50/£25	SNGL RM:	-
PART BRD:	-	% RED. CHILDREN:	50%	DINNER:	-

In Tramore

Neil & Maria Skedd
CLONEEN
Tramore

Love Lane, Tramore, Co Waterford

OPEN:	1st March-31st October
NO. ROOMS:	3
ENSUITE:	3

TEL: **051 381264**   FAX: -

(V)

Modern detached bungalow set in landscaped gardens. Quiet location. Private parking. Beaches, Golf and Splashworld nearby. Visa/Access.

B&B PPS:	£17	SNGL OCC. DBLE/TPL:	£23.50	SNGL RM:	-
PART BRD:	£180	% RED. CHILDREN:	50%	DINNER:	£12

In Tramore

Mrs Jo St John
VENEZIA HOUSE
Tramore

Church Road Grove, Tramore, Co Waterford

OPEN:	May-October
NO. ROOMS:	3
ENSUITE:	3

TEL: **051 381412**   FAX: -

(V)

Spacious bungalow quiet cul de sac, landscaped gardens, secure parking. 3 mins beach & amenities. Lonely Planet, Let's Go, Dillard/Causin Guides acclaimed. Breakfast menu.

B&B PPS:	£16/£18	SNGL OCC. DBLE/TPL:	-	SNGL RM:	-
PART BRD:	-	% RED. CHILDREN:	-	DINNER:	-

Tramore 1km

Mary Walsh
GLENCORA
Tramore

Newtown, Coast Road, Tramore, Co Waterford

OPEN:	1st May-30th September
NO. ROOMS:	3
ENSUITE:	3

TEL: **051 386813**   FAX: -

(V)

Spacious, modern bungalow overlooking Tramore Golf Course. Friendly and Comfortable. Breakfast menu. Tea/coffee facilities. Secure parking. All amenities close by .

B&B PPS:	£17/£18	SNGL OCC. DBLE/TPL:	£23.50/£27	SNGL RM:	-
PART BRD:	-	% RED. CHILDREN:	25%	DINNER:	-

Waterford 5km

Susan Bailey-Daunt
SAMUELS HERITAGE
Waterford

Ballymaclode, Halfway House, Dunmore Rd, Co Waterford

OPEN:	All Year
NO. ROOMS:	3
ENSUITE:	3

TEL: **051 875094**   FAX: -

(V)

Panoramic views, quiet and peaceful country surroundings, close proximity to Beaches, Golf, Angling, Walking, Horseriding and wide choice of Restaurants.

B&B PPS:	£17	SNGL OCC. DBLE/TPL:	£23.50	SNGL RM:	-
PART BRD:	-	% RED. CHILDREN:	-	DINNER:	-

Waterford

Teresa Begadon
RONCALLI
**Ballynaneashagh, Cork Road,
Waterford, Co Waterford**
TEL: **051 375632**   FAX: **051 872833**

Waterford

OPEN:	1st March-30th November
NO. ROOMS:	6
ENSUITE:	6

(V)

Modern house. Spacious bedrooms. Large car park. Tea/coffee making facilities in bedrooms. Non smoking throughout. Waterford Crystal Factory 1km.

| B&B PPS: | **£17** | SNGL OCC. DBLE/TPL: | **£23.50** | SNGL RM: | **£23.50** |
| PART BRD: | - | % RED. CHILDREN: | **10%** | DINNER: | - |

Waterford 9km

Mrs Eithne Brennan
HILLVIEW LODGE
**Kilmeaden,
Co Waterford**
TEL: **051 384230**   FAX: -

Waterford

OPEN:	1st March-31st October
NO. ROOMS:	5
ENSUITE:	1

(V)

Two storey house with large mature garden on N25. Horse Riding and Golf, Driving Range nearby. Convenient to Waterford Crystal.

| B&B PPS: | **£15/£17** | SNGL OCC. DBLE/TPL: | **£21.50/£23.50** | SNGL RM: | **£20** |
| PART BRD: | - | % RED. CHILDREN: | **20%** | DINNER: | - |

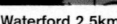 Waterford 2.5km

Miriam Corcoran
CLADDAGH
**Lr Newrath, Ferrybank, Waterford,
Co Waterford**
TEL: **051 854797**   FAX: -

Waterford

OPEN:	All Year except Christmas
NO. ROOMS:	4
ENSUITE:	4

(V)

Large modern house in quiet suburb area, 500 metres from WFD Golf 18 hole Club. Accommodation ground floor.

| B&B PPS: | **£17/£17.50** | SNGL OCC. DBLE/TPL: | **£25** | SNGL RM: | **£20** |
| PART BRD: | - | % RED. CHILDREN: | **50%** | DINNER: | - |

Patrick & Noreen Dullaghan
LOUGHDAN
**Newrath, Dublin Rd, Waterford,
Co Waterford**
TEL: **051 876021**   FAX: -

Waterford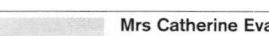

OPEN:	All Year except Christmas
NO. ROOMS:	6
ENSUITE:	5

(V)

Modern house Dublin/Limerick Rd. N9/N24. Convenient Golf, Bus/Train Station. Tea/coffee facilities, TV, hairdryers in bedrooms. Breakfast menu.

| B&B PPS: | **£15.50/£17.50** | SNGL OCC. DBLE/TPL: | **£23/£25** | SNGL RM: | - |
| PART BRD: | - | % RED. CHILDREN: | **20%** | DINNER: | - |

Waterford 1km

Waterford City 3km

Mrs Catherine Evans
ROSEWOOD
**Slieverue (Via Waterford),
Co Waterford**
TEL: **051 832233/77905**   FAX: -

Waterford

OPEN:	All Year except Christmas
NO. ROOMS:	3
ENSUITE:	3

(V)

Modern house in Slieverue Village, 3 Km from Waterford on N25 close to Waterford Golf Club, 5 miles from Crystal Factory.

| B&B PPS: | **£17.50** | SNGL OCC. DBLE/TPL: | **£24** | SNGL RM: | - |
| PART BRD: | - | % RED. CHILDREN: | **25%** | DINNER: | - |

Margaret C Fitzmaurice
BLENHEIM HOUSE
**Blenheim Heights, Waterford,
Co Waterford**

Waterford

OPEN:	All Year except Christmas
NO. ROOMS:	6
ENSUITE:	6

TEL: **051 874115**   FAX: -

Georgian residence C1763. Furnished throughout with Antiques & object d'art. Surrounded by lawns and private Deer Park. Golf Courses nearby.

| B&B PPS: | **£18** | SNGL OCC. DBLE/TPL: | **£21.50** | SNGL RM:**£20/£21.50** |
| PART BRD: | - | % RED. CHILDREN: | **20%** | DINNER: | - |

Waterford 3.5km

Phil Harrington
BROOKDALE HOUSE
**Carrigrue, Ballinaneeshagh,
Waterford, Co Waterford**

Waterford

OPEN:	1st May-30th September
NO. ROOMS:	3
ENSUITE:	3

TEL: **051 375618**   FAX: -

Modern home, quiet location, landscaped surroundings 400m off Cork/Waterford Rd (N25). Spacious Car Park, Tea/Coffee rooms. 3 km City.

| B&B PPS: | **£17/£18.50** | SNGL OCC. DBLE/TPL: | **£23.50/£25** | SNGL RM: | - |
| PART BRD: | - | % RED. CHILDREN: | **50%** | DINNER: | - |

Waterford 3km

Marie & Noel Harty
SUNCROFT
**Ballinakina, Dunmore Rd, Waterford,
Co Waterford**

Waterford

OPEN:	1st March-31st October
NO. ROOMS:	3
ENSUITE:	2

TEL: **051 382366**   FAX: -   EMAIL: **hartyn@iol.ie**

Midway between Waterford & Dunmore East. TV, Hairdryers in bedrooms, Breakfast menu, Golf, Horseriding, Restaurants, Beaches nearby. Visa/Mastercard accepted.

| B&B PPS: | **£15.50/£17.50** | SNGL OCC. DBLE/TPL: | **£22/£24** | SNGL RM: | - |
| PART BRD: | - | % RED. CHILDREN: | - | DINNER: | - |

Waterford 7km

Mrs Margaret Hayes
ARRIVISTE
**Holycross, Hillcrest Grove, Butlerstown,
Co Waterford**

Waterford

OPEN:	All Year except Christmas
NO. ROOMS:	5
ENSUITE:	5

TEL: **051 354080**   FAX: **051 354080**

Country house. Central heated. TV rooms. Private car park. Lounge. Tea/Coffee facilities in room. Large relaxing conservatory.

| B&B PPS: | **£17/£18** | SNGL OCC. DBLE/TPL: | **£23.50/£24.50** | SNGL RM: | **£21** |
| PART BRD: | - | % RED. CHILDREN: | **20%** | DINNER: | **£12** |

Waterford 3.5km

Mrs Alice O'Sullivan-Jackman
THE PINES
**Knockboy, Dunmore Road, Waterford,
Co Waterford**

Waterford

OPEN:	All Year
NO. ROOMS:	5
ENSUITE:	4

TEL: **051 874452**   FAX: **051 841566**   EMAIL: **bjackman@tinet.ie**

Picturesque rural bungalow, near Regional hospital and Airport. Breakfast menu. Smoke free bedrooms. Fishing, Golf, Walking, Beaches, Excellent Seafood Restaurants locally.

| B&B PPS: | **£15/£17** | SNGL OCC. DBLE/TPL: | **£21.50/£23.50** | SNGL RM: | - |
| PART BRD: | - | % RED. CHILDREN: | - | DINNER: | - |

Waterford City 3km

In Waterford City

George Kavanagh
SION HILL HOUSE
Ferrybank, Waterford,
Co Waterford

Waterford

OPEN:	**All Year except Christmas**
No. ROOMS:	4
ENSUITE:	4

(V)

TEL: **051 851558**   FAX: **051 851678**

Period house circa 1800 on 4 acres of mature gardens overlooking City Centre and River. Next to Jurys Hotel on N25.

B&B PPS:	**£21/£26**	SNGL OCC. DBLE/TPL:	**£27.50/£35**	SNGL RM:	-
PART BRD:	-	% RED. CHILDREN:	**20%**	DINNER:	-

Waterford City 2km

Mrs Eileen Landy
VILLA EILDON
Belmont Road, Rosslare Road,
Ferrybank, Waterford, Co Waterford

Waterford

OPEN:	**May-October**
No. ROOMS:	4
ENSUITE:	3

(V)

TEL: **051 832174**   FAX: -

Modern dormer bungalow. Waterford/Rosslare Road (N25). Private parking. AA listed. Non Smoking House. Convenient to Crystal, City, Golf. Waterford 2 km.

B&B PPS:	**£16/£18**	SNGL OCC. DBLE/TPL:	**£26/£28**	SNGL RM:	-
PART BRD:	-	% RED. CHILDREN:	-	DINNER:	-

Waterford 4km

Phyllis McGovern
ASHLEIGH
Holy Cross, Cork Road, Waterford,
Co Waterford

Waterford

OPEN:	**All Year except Christmas**
No. ROOMS:	6
ENSUITE:	5

(V)

TEL: **051 375171**   FAX: -

Spacious family home large mature gardens on N25. Close to Waterford Crystal. TV, Tea/coffee facilities in bedrooms, Breakfast menu.

B&B PPS:	**£15/£18**	SNGL OCC. DBLE/TPL:	**£23.50**	SNGL RM:	**£20/£21**
PART BRD:	-	% RED. CHILDREN:	**25%**	DINNER:	-

Kilmeaden 1.5km

Mr & Mrs John & Ann Morrissey
WOODSIDE HOUSE
Whitfield, Cork Rd, Waterford,
Co Waterford

Waterford

OPEN:	**3rd January-20th December**
No. ROOMS:	4
ENSUITE:	4

(V)

TEL: **051 384381**   FAX: -

Spacious country house 5 mins drive Waterford Crystal, Main Cork Road (N25). Scenic area, Mature gardens, Ideal touring, golfing. Highly recommended.

B&B PPS:	**£17/£18**	SNGL OCC. DBLE/TPL:	-	SNGL RM:	**£18/£22**
PART BRD:	-	% RED. CHILDREN:	**33%**	DINNER:	**£12**

Dunmore East 8km

Mrs Anne-Marie Newport
ARDILAUN
Woodstown,
Co Waterford

Waterford

OPEN:	**All Year except Christmas**
No. ROOMS:	3
ENSUITE:	-

(V)

TEL: **051 382231**   FAX: -

Luxurious house in woodland area, 2km from Beach, 10km from Waterford City, 9km from Waterford Crystal. Excellent restaurants nearby.

B&B PPS:	**£15**	SNGL OCC. DBLE/TPL:	**£21.50/£23.50**	SNGL RM:	-
PART BRD:	-	% RED. CHILDREN:	**25%**	DINNER:	-

Waterford 2km

Mrs Marian O'Keeffe
ST ANTHONYS
Ballinaneesagh
Cork Road, Waterford, Co Waterford

Waterford

TEL: 051 375887   FAX: **051 353063**

OPEN:	8th January-20th December
NO. ROOMS:	6
ENSUITE:	6

Bungalow with landscaped gardens near Waterford Glass factory. Tours arranged. Breakfast menu. Colour TV, Tea/Coffee facilities in bedrooms.

| B&B PPS: | **£17** | SNGL OCC. DBLE/TPL: | **£23.50** | SNGL RM: | - |
| PART BRD: | - | % RED. CHILDREN: | **20%** | DINNER: | - |

Waterford City 1km

Mrs Phyllis O'Reilly
ANNVILL HOUSE
1 The Orchard, Kingsmeadow,
Waterford, Co Waterford

Waterford

TEL: **051 373617**   FAX: -

OPEN:	2nd January-20th December
NO. ROOMS:	5
ENSUITE:	4

Situated on N25 opposite Crystal Factory and sports centre. Frommer recommended. Tea/ Coffee facilities. Breakfast menu. City bus. Hairdryers.

| B&B PPS: | **£15/£17** | SNGL OCC. DBLE/TPL: | **£23.50** | SNGL RM: | - |
| PART BRD: | - | % RED. CHILDREN: | - | DINNER: | - |

Waterford City 1.5km

Paul & Breda Power
DUNROVEN B&B,
Ballinaneesagh, Cork Rd (N25),
Waterford City, Co Waterford

Waterford

TEL: **051 374743**   FAX: -   -

OPEN:	1st January-22nd December
NO. ROOMS:	6
ENSUITE:	6

Modern house. Cork/Waterford N25. 2 mins crystal factory, Cable TV, Coffee/tea facilities bedrooms, breakfast choice. City IMP bus service.

| B&B PPS: | **£17** | SNGL OCC. DBLE/TPL: | - | SNGL RM: | **£23.50** |
| PART BRD: | - | % RED. CHILDREN: | **10%** | DINNER: | - |

Waterford 2km

Mrs Margaret Power
TALGINN
Ballynaneashagh, Cork Road,
Waterford, Co Waterford

Waterford

TEL: **051 373798**   FAX: **051 370086**

OPEN:	May-August
NO. ROOMS:	4
ENSUITE:	4

Dormer Bungalow, landscaped gardens on N25. Frommer guide recommended. Near Crystal Factory, Golf. Breakfast menu. Tea/coffee facilities in bedrooms.

| B&B PPS: | **£17** | SNGL OCC. DBLE/TPL: | **£23.50** | SNGL RM: | - |
| PART BRD: | - | % RED. CHILDREN: | **25%** | DINNER: | - |

Waterford 9 km

Mrs Rena Power
GLENCREE
The Sweep, Kilmeaden,
Co Waterford

Waterford

TEL: **051 384240**   FAX: -

OPEN:	1st March-31st October
NO. ROOMS:	5
ENSUITE:	3

Country home off Cork/Waterford Rd. (N25). Frommer recommended. Crystal Factory, Horse Riding nearby. Ideal for Coastal, Mountain, Heritage Drives.

| B&B PPS: | **£15/£17** | SNGL OCC. DBLE/TPL: | **£21.50/£23.50** | SNGL RM: | - |
| PART BRD: | - | % RED. CHILDREN: | **20%** | DINNER: | - |

Waterford 8km

Mrs Marie Prendergast
TORY VIEW
Mullinavat,
Co Waterford
TEL: **051 885513**   FAX: -

Waterford	
OPEN:	March-October
NO. ROOMS:	5
ENSUITE:	4

(V)

Spacious family home with landscaped grounds. Situated on N9 - 8km north Waterford on Kilkenny/Dublin Rd. Tea/Coffee in rooms.

B&B PPS:	**£15/£17**	SNGL. OCC. DBLE/TPL:	**£21.50/£23.50**	SNGL RM:	-
PART BRD:	**£180**	% RED. CHILDREN:	**50%**	DINNER:	**£12**

Waterford 3km

Mrs Mary Spillane
AISLING
Passage East Road, off Dunmore Road,
Waterford, Co Waterford
TEL: **051 877076**   FAX: -

Waterford	
OPEN:	1st March-31st October
NO. ROOMS:	3
ENSUITE:	2

(V)

Spacious family home situated off (R684). Convenient to Passage East, Car ferry, Hospital, Airport, Golf, Beaches. Excellent Seafood Restaurants, Pubs.

B&B PPS:	**£15/£17**	SNGL. OCC. DBLE/TPL:	**£23.50**	SNGL RM:	-
PART BRD:	-	% RED. CHILDREN:	**25%**	DINNER:	-

Waterford 3km

Mrs Maureen Wall
SUNCREST
Slieverue, Ferrybank Via Waterford,
Co Waterford
TEL: **051 832732**   FAX: -

Waterford	
OPEN:	1st March-30th November
NO. ROOMS:	5
ENSUITE:	5

(V)

Quiet location. 300 metres off N25 Waterford/Rosslare Rd, in Slieverue Village. Waterford 3km. Convenient Golf and Crystal.

B&B PPS:	**£17.50**	SNGL. OCC. DBLE/TPL:	**£24**	SNGL RM:	-
PART BRD:	-	% RED. CHILDREN:	**20%**	DINNER:	-

BOOKINGS

We recommend your first and last night is pre-booked. Your hosts will make a booking for you at your next selected home for the cost of the phone call. When travelling in high season (June, July, August), it is essential to pre-book your accommodation – preferably the evening before, or the following morning to avoid disappointment.

SOME HOMES ARE CLOSED DURING THE WINTER.
WHEN TRAVELLING OFF-SEASON IT IS ADVISABLE TO CALL
AHEAD AND GIVE A TIME OF ARRIVAL TO ENSURE YOUR HOSTS
ARE AT HOME TO GREET YOU.

Waterford City 3km

Mrs Patricia Wall
SAN-MARTINO
Ballinaneeshagh, Cork Rd, Waterford, Co Waterford
TEL: **051 374949**   FAX: -

	Waterford	
OPEN:	February-November	
NO. ROOMS:	5	
ENSUITE:	5	

Modern bungalow on main Waterford/Cork Road (N25). 3 mins from Waterford Crystal & Regional Sports Centre. Tea/coffee facilities.

B&B PPS:	£17	SNGL OCC. DBLE/TPL:	£23.50	SNGL RM:	-
PART BRD:	-	% RED. CHILDREN:	20%	DINNER:	-

Waterford 9km

Siobhan Walsh
KINARD
Adamstown
Kilmeaden, Co Waterford
TEL: **051 384505**   FAX: -

	Waterford	
OPEN:	1st May-30th September	
NO. ROOMS:	3	
ENSUITE:	2	(V)

Modern country home, set back from N25. Crystal Factory, Beaches, Mountains, Restaurants nearby. Orthopaedic Beds, Electric Blankets. Ideal for touring.

B&B PPS:	£15/£17	SNGL OCC. DBLE/TPL:	£21.50/£23.50	SNGL RM:	-
PART BRD:	-	% RED. CHILDREN:	20%	DINNER:	-

Waterford 6km

Mrs Stella White
BALLYCANAVAN LODGE
Faithlegg, Half Way House, Waterford, Co Waterford
TEL: **051 873928**   FAX: -

	Waterford	
OPEN:	17th March-31st October	
NO. ROOMS:	3	
ENSUITE:	1	(V)

Country house set in mature gardens.Adjacent to Golf Courses. Passage East car ferry 4 KM. Ideal location for activity holiday.

B&B PPS:	£15/£17.50	SNGL OCC. DBLE/TPL:	£21.50/£24	SNGL RM:	-
PART BRD:	£195	% RED. CHILDREN:	25%	DINNER:	£13

Waterford 7km

Mrs Ann Crosbie
GLENDINE HOUSE
Arthurstown
New Ross, Co Wexford

Arthurstown

OPEN:	1st March-1st November
NO. ROOMS:	4
ENSUITE:	4

TEL: 051 389258   FAX: 051 389258

Captivating period house built 1830, offers a taste of real Irish hospitality in estuary village. Wexford 25 km. New Ross 15km.

B&B PPS:	£17/£18.50	SNGL OCC. DBLE/TPL:	£23.50/£25	SNGL RM:£23.50/£25
PART BRD:	-	% RED. CHILDREN:	25%	DINNER: -

Enniscorthy

Ms Phil Kinsella
MEADOW SIDE B&B
Ryland St, Bunclody,
Co Wexford

Bunclody

OPEN:	January-December
NO. ROOMS:	4
ENSUITE:	3

TEL: 054 76226/77459   FAX: -

Elegant stone Georgian Town House ideally situated. Tea/Coffee on arrival, TV Lounge, spacious rooms ensuite. Private Car Park.

B&B PPS:	£15/£18	SNGL OCC. DBLE/TPL:	£24.50	SNGL RM:	-
PART BRD:	-	% RED. CHILDREN:	-	DINNER:	-

In Gorey Town

Mrs Noelle Conroy
MACAMORE HOUSE
Ounavarra Road, Courtown Harbour,
Co Wexford

Courtown Harbour

OPEN:	All Year except Christmas
NO. ROOMS:	3
ENSUITE:	3

TEL: 055 25353   FAX: 055 25353

Georgian style country home overlooking woodlands. Peaceful surrounding's only 10 mins walk Courtown Sandy Beaches, Restaurants, Golf. Ideal base for touring.

B&B PPS:	£17/£18	SNGL OCC. DBLE/TPL:	£23.50/£24.50	SNGL RM:	-
PART BRD:	-	% RED. CHILDREN:	25%	DINNER:	£14

Wexford 22.4km

Mary Parle,
ARAS - MUILLINN
Ambrosetown, Duncormick,
Co Wexford

Duncormick

OPEN:	All Year
NO. ROOMS:	3
ENSUITE:	2

TEL: 051 563145   FAX: 051 563245

New refurbished modern house. Comfortable surroundings and homely atmosphere. 20 mins from Ferry Port. Early Breakfast and meals on request.

B&B PPS:	£15/£17	SNGL OCC. DBLE/TPL:	£21.50	SNGL RM:	-
PART BRD:	£210	% RED. CHILDREN:	-	DINNER:	£14

Enniscorthy 4km

Mrs A Delany
ST JUDES
Munfin, Tomnalossitt, Enniscorthy,
Co Wexford

Enniscorthy

OPEN:	All Year
NO. ROOMS:	5
ENSUITE:	4

TEL: 054 33011   FAX: -

Home located 2km off N30 on Bree Rd. Scenic countryside. 15 minutes Heritage Park. 35km Rosslare Ferryport. Early breakfast. Electric blankets.

B&B PPS:	£15/£17	SNGL OCC. DBLE/TPL:	£21.50/£23.50	SNGL RM:	£23.50
PART BRD:	-	% RED. CHILDREN:	25%	DINNER:	£12

Mrs Attracta J. Doyle
OAKVILLE LODGE
**Ballycarney, Enniscorthy,
Co Wexford**
TEL: 054 88626   FAX: -

Enniscorthy

OPEN:	May-31st October
NO. ROOMS:	5
ENSUITE:	2

Situated on Rosslare/Carlow Rd. N80. Ideal location for 1798 Commemorations, Game Fishing, Golfing, Pub/Restaurants nearby.

| B&B PPS: | **£15/£20** | SNGL OCC. DBLE/TPL: | - | SNGL RM: **£21.50/£23.50** |
| PART BRD: | - | % RED. CHILDREN: | **33%** | DINNER: | - |

— Enniscorthy 9km —

Helen Kenny
MOYHILL
**Bellefield, Enniscorthy,
Co Wexford**
TEL: 054 34739   FAX: -

Enniscorthy

OPEN:	All Year except Christmas
NO. ROOMS:	3
ENSUITE:	2

Situated 50m off the Enniscorthy to Kiltealy/Kilkenny Rd (R702). Bungalow with easy access, quiet location. Ideal base in South East.

| B&B PPS: | **£17/£18** | SNGL OCC. DBLE/TPL: | **£23.50/£24.50** | SNGL RM: **£16/£20** |
| PART BRD: | - | % RED. CHILDREN: | **50%** | DINNER: | - |

— Enniscorthy 1km —

Pat & Siobhan McGee
VINEGAR HILL COUNTRY HOUSE
**Clonhaston, Enniscorthy,
Co Wexford**
TEL: 054 35127   FAX: -

Enniscorthy

OPEN:	All Year
NO. ROOMS:	3
ENSUITE:	3

Situated on Blackwater Road, 2km ex Enniscorthy. Own par 3 Golf Course (free to Guests). Tea/coffee making facilities.

| B&B PPS: | **£17/£19** | SNGL OCC. DBLE/TPL: | **£23.50/£30** | SNGL RM: | - |
| PART BRD: | - | % RED. CHILDREN: | **50%** | DINNER: | - |

— Enniscorthy 2km —

Colm and Ann McGibney
LEMONGROVE HOUSE
**Blackstoops, Enniscorthy,
Co Wexford**
TEL: 054 36115   FAX: -

Enniscorthy

OPEN:	1st January-20th December
NO. ROOMS:	5
ENSUITE:	5

Spacious home 1 km north of Enniscorthy at roundabout on Dublin/Rosslare Road (N11). Rooms en-suite with TV. AA listed. Guide du Routard.

| B&B PPS: | **£17/£25** | SNGL OCC. DBLE/TPL: | **£21/£55** | SNGL RM: | - |
| PART BRD: | - | % RED. CHILDREN: | **25%** | DINNER: | - |

— Enniscorthy 1km —

Mrs Noreen Byrne
PERRYMOUNT
**Inch, Gorey,
Co Wexford**
TEL: 0402 37418   FAX: -

Gorey

OPEN:	1st January-20th December
NO. ROOMS:	3
ENSUITE:	3

Modern dormer bungalow situated 50 metres off Dublin/Rosslare Road (N11) at Inch. TV, Tea/coffee facilities in rooms. Pub, Restaurant 50 metres.

| B&B PPS: | **£17** | SNGL OCC. DBLE/TPL: | **£23.50** | SNGL RM: | - |
| PART BRD: | **£190** | % RED. CHILDREN: | **50%** | DINNER: | **£12** |

— Gorey 8km —

Mrs Martina Redmond
CARRAIG VIEW
Ballycale
Gorey, Co Wexford

Gorey

OPEN:	1st January-20th December
No. ROOMS:	3
ENSUITE:	2

Ⓥ

TEL: **055 21323**   FAX: **055 21323**

Select accommodation, rooms ensuite with TV, Hairdryer, Tea/Coffee facilities. Situated R741, off N11 at Clough. Ideal base for touring.

B&B PPS:	**£15/£19**	SNGL OCC. DBLE/TPL: **£21.50/£25.50**	SNGL RM:	-
PART BRD:	-	% RED. CHILDREN: **30%**	DINNER:	-

Gorey 2km

Mrs Ann Sunderland
HILLSIDE HOUSE
Tubberduff, Gorey,
Co Wexford

Gorey

OPEN:	All Year except Christmas
No. ROOMS:	6
ENSUITE:	6

Ⓥ

TEL: **055 21726/22036**   FAX: **055 22567**

3km off Dublin/Rosslare Rd. (N11) North Gorey. Rural setting, views Tara Hill, Beaches nearby. Open fire. AA selected QQQQ Award.

B&B PPS:	**£17/£18.50**	SNGL OCC. DBLE/TPL: **£23.50/£25**	SNGL RM:	**£20/£23**
PART BRD:	**£190**	% RED. CHILDREN: **50%**	DINNER:	**£14**

Gorey 5km

Mrs Marion Whelan,
TOMAR
Coolgreany,
Gorey, Co Wexford

Gorey

OPEN:	All Year except Christmas
No. ROOMS:	3
ENSUITE:	2

Ⓥ

TEL: **0402 37440**   FAX: -

Excellent Accommodation 2 km off N11. Wicklow/Wexford border. Walking distance pubs. Tea/Coffee on arrival. 1 hour Dublin - Rosslare. Golf, Walking, Cycling.

B&B PPS:	**£15/£17**	SNGL OCC. DBLE/TPL: **£21.50/£23.50**	SNGL RM:	-
PART BRD:	**£180**	% RED. CHILDREN: **50%**	DINNER:	**£12**

Arklow 6km

Sean & Mary Cousins
GROVESIDE
Ballyharty, Kilmore,
Co Wexford

Kilmore Quay

OPEN:	15th April-30th September
No. ROOMS:	3
ENSUITE:	2

Ⓥ

TEL: **053 35305/088 2785558**   FAX: **053 35305**

Situated Tillage Farm. Guest Lounge, Peaceful, Gardens, Tea, Coffee arrival. Ideal Fishing, Golf, Horseriding, Rosslare 20 mins. Kilmore Quay 5 km.

B&B PPS:	**£15/£17**	SNGL OCC. DBLE/TPL: **£21.50/£23.50**	SNGL RM:	-
PART BRD:	-	% RED. CHILDREN: **33%**	DINNER:	-

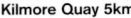
Kilmore Quay 5km

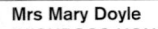

Mrs Mary Doyle
INISHROSS HOUSE
96 Mary Street, New Ross,
Co Wexford

New Ross

OPEN:	All Year except Christmas
No. ROOMS:	6
ENSUITE:	-

Ⓥ

TEL: **051 421335**   FAX: -

Spacious Town House, all amenities. Private car park 200m off N25 at Town Bridge. Early breakfast.

B&B PPS:	**£15**	SNGL OCC. DBLE/TPL: **£21.50**	SNGL RM:	-
PART BRD:	-	% RED. CHILDREN: **20%**	DINNER:	-

In New Ross

New Ross 2km

Mrs Noreen Fallon S.R.N, S.C.M.
KILLARNEY HOUSE
The Maudlins, New Ross,
Co Wexford

New Ross

Tel: 051 421062   Fax: -

OPEN:	May-September
No. Rooms:	3
Ensuite:	2

(V)

Frommer recommended. Bedrooms ground floor. Peaceful setting. Breakfast Menu. Electric Blankets. Reduction for more than 1 night. Rosslare ferries 45 mins.

B&B PPS:	£15/£17	SNGL OCC. DBLE/TPL:	£21.50/£23.50	SNGL RM:	-
PART BRD:	-	% RED. CHILDREN:	50%	DINNER:	-

In New Ross

Mrs Ann Foley
RIVERSDALE HOUSE
Lr William Street, New Ross,
Co Wexford

New Ross

Tel: 051 422515   Fax: 051 422800

OPEN:	1st March-1st November
No. Rooms:	4
Ensuite:	4

(V)

Spacious ensuite bedrooms (one triple) with Television, Tea/coffee facilities. Gardens. Private parking. Guest Sun Conservatory. Frommer Dillard/ Causin recommended.

B&B PPS:	£17	SNGL OCC. DBLE/TPL:	£25	SNGL RM:	-
PART BRD:	-	% RED. CHILDREN:	20%	DINNER:	-

New Ross 1km

Mrs Philomena Gallagher
ROSVILLE HOUSE
Knockmullen, New Ross,
Co Wexford

New Ross

Tel: 051 421798   Fax: -

OPEN:	March-November
No. Rooms:	5
Ensuite:	4

(V)

Modern home in peaceful surroundings. Guaranteed hospitatilty and comfort. Overlooking river Barrow. Rosslare Ferries 40mins. Early breakfast. Private Car Park.

B&B PPS:	£15/£17	SNGL OCC. DBLE/TPL:	£21.50/£23.50	SNGL RM:	-
PART BRD:	-	% RED. CHILDREN:	20%	DINNER:	-

New Ross 10km

Mrs Susan Halpin
WOODLANDS HOUSE
Carrigbyrne, Newbawn,
Co Wexford

New Ross

Tel: 051 428287   Fax: 051 428287

OPEN:	1st March-30th November
No. Rooms:	4
Ensuite:	3

(V)

On N25 - Rosslare/New Ross Road near Cedar Lodge Hotel. Rosslare 30 minutes - Bedrooms Ensuite with TV, Tea/coffee, Early Breakfast, Access, Visa.

B&B PPS:	£17	SNGL OCC. DBLE/TPL:	£23.50	SNGL RM:	£18
PART BRD:	-	% RED. CHILDREN:	20%	DINNER:	-

New Ross 4km

Mrs Eileen Kent
HILL VIEW
Ballyreddy, New Ross,
Co Wexford

New Ross

Tel: 051 427457   Fax: -

OPEN:	May-15th September
No. Rooms:	3
Ensuite:	2

(V)

Dormer home near New Ross and 50 kms from Rosslare Ferries. Early breakfast if required. Ideal base for touring South East.

B&B PPS:	£15/£17	SNGL OCC. DBLE/TPL:	£21.50/£23.50	SNGL RM:	-
PART BRD:	£180	% RED. CHILDREN:	50%	DINNER:	£13

In New Ross

New Ross

Mrs Sadie Michels
VENROODE
**(off Wiliam St) Lr South Knock,
New Ross, Co Wexford**

TEL: **051 421446**   FAX: -

OPEN:	All Year except Christmas
NO. ROOMS:	3
ENSUITE:	2

 V

"Venroode" is set in peaceful mature gardens overlooking River Barrow. Ideal base for touring. Early breakfast. Dutch and German spoken.

| B&B PPS: | £15/£17 | SNGL OCC. DBLE/TPL: £21.50/£23.50 | SNGL RM: | - |
| PART BRD: | - | % RED. CHILDREN: | 30% | DINNER: | - |

Rosslare 1km

Rosslare

Mrs Lynda Doyle
BALLYBRO LODGE
**Rosslare,
Co Wexford**

TEL: **053 32333**   FAX: -

OPEN:	All Year except Christmas
NO. ROOMS:	5
ENSUITE:	5

V

Modern home, Landscaped Gardens, Guest Lounge, Tea/Coffee facilities, featured TV Holiday Ireland. Convenient Golf, Beaches, Car Ferry, Early Breakfasts.

| B&B PPS: | £17.50 | SNGL OCC. DBLE/TPL: | £25 | SNGL RM: | - |
| PART BRD: | - | % RED. CHILDREN: | - | DINNER: | - |

Rosslare 3km

Rosslare

Mrs Ann Kelly
DECCA HOUSE
**Rosslare,
Co Wexford**

TEL: **053 32410**   FAX: -

OPEN:	All Year except Christmas
NO. ROOMS:	5
ENSUITE:	3

V

Early breakfast. Location R740 (1km off main N25). Quiet area. Convenient Ferries. Access/Visa.

| B&B PPS: | £15/£17 | SNGL OCC. DBLE/TPL: £21.50/£23.50 | SNGL RM: | - |
| PART BRD: | - | % RED. CHILDREN: | - | DINNER: | - |

Rosslare Strand 3km

Rosslare

Mrs Cathy Stack
CILL DARA HOUSE
**Ford-of-Lyng Road, Rosslare,
Co Wexford**

TEL: **053 32459**   FAX: -

OPEN:	1st March-31st October
NO. ROOMS:	4
ENSUITE:	4

V

Tastefully restored old farmhouse. Peaceful location. Bedrooms with TV. Hairdryers and Electric Blankets. 10 mins to Ferry and Strand (R740).

| B&B PPS: | £17.50 | SNGL OCC. DBLE/TPL: | £24 | SNGL RM: | £20 |
| PART BRD: | - | % RED. CHILDREN: | 25% | DINNER: | - |

Rosslare Harbour 1km

Rosslare Harbour

Mrs Joan Barry
GLENVILLE
**St. Patricks Road, Rosslare Harbour,
Co Wexford**

TEL: **053 33142**   FAX: -

OPEN:	1st March-30th November
NO. ROOMS:	3
ENSUITE:	2

V

Detached, modern bungalow on N25, in rural setting. Close to Beaches (1 km). Golf Courses and Sea Angling.

| B&B PPS: | £17 | SNGL OCC. DBLE/TPL: | - | SNGL RM: | £17 |
| PART BRD: | - | % RED. CHILDREN: | 75% | DINNER: | - |

Rosslare Harbour 2km

Mrs Laura Boyce
LAURADALE
**Kilrane, Rosslare Harbour,
Co Wexford**

Rosslare Harbour

TEL: **053 33308**   FAX: -

OPEN:	April-October
No. ROOMS:	4
ENSUITE:	3

(V)

Modern bungalow .25 km off main road N25. 2km from Ferry & Rail Station. Quiet Area. Early Breakfast, Convenient Beaches, Golf.

| B&B PPS: | **£15/£17** | SNGL OCC. DBLE/TPL: | **£21.50/£23.50** | SNGL RM: | - |
| PART BRD: | - | % RED. CHILDREN: | 25% | DINNER: | - |

In Rosslare Harbour

Mrs Ann Brennan
LORANDA LODGE
**Ballygillane, Rosslare Harbour,
Co Wexford**

Rosslare Harbour

TEL: **053 33804**   FAX: -

OPEN:	All Year except Christmas
No. ROOMS:	3
ENSUITE:	1

(V)

Travel up village, supermarket on left, railway social club on right, next right, around double bend, house left. Ferry 1km

| B&B PPS: | **£15/£17** | SNGL OCC. DBLE/TPL: | **£21.50/£23.50** | SNGL RM: | - |
| PART BRD: | - | % RED. CHILDREN: | 50% | DINNER: | - |

Rosslare Harbour 1km

Mrs Cathleen Broderick
LYNDELL
**Kilrane, Rosslare Harbour,
Co Wexford**

Rosslare Harbour

TEL: **053 33316**   FAX: -

OPEN:	All Year except Christmas
No. ROOMS:	5
ENSUITE:	4

(V)

Well appointed bungalow, 100 ms.off N25. Early breakfast served. Tea/coffee making facilities in bedrooms. Golf and Beaches close by.

| B&B PPS: | **£15/£17** | SNGL OCC. DBLE/TPL: | **£21.50/£23.50** | SNGL RM: | - |
| PART BRD: | - | % RED. CHILDREN: | 25% | DINNER: | - |

Tagoat 1.5km

Mrs Catherine Browne
BROOMPARK
**Brittas, Tagoat, Rosslare Harbour,
Co Wexford**

Rosslare Harbour

TEL: **053 31340**   FAX: -

OPEN:	All Year except Christmas
No. ROOMS:	5
ENSUITE:	2

(V)

Georgian house near Golf, Fishing, Beaches. Early breakfast. 5 km from Ferry on N25.

| B&B PPS: | **£15/£17** | SNGL OCC. DBLE/TPL: | **£21.50/£23.50** | SNGL RM: | - |
| PART BRD: | - | % RED. CHILDREN: | 33% | DINNER: | - |

Rosslare Harbour 1km

Sue & Neil Carty
MARIANELLA
**Kilrane
Rosslare Harbour, Co Wexford**

Rosslare Harbour

TEL: **053 33139**   FAX: -

OPEN:	All Year
No. ROOMS:	6
ENSUITE:	4

(V)

Comfortable bungalow on N25. 1km Ferry Port. TV & Tea/Coffee facilities in all rooms. Early breakfast. Restaurants nearby.

| B&B PPS: | **£15/£17** | SNGL OCC. DBLE/TPL: | **£21.50/£23.50** | SNGL RM: | **£15/£16** |
| PART BRD: | - | % RED. CHILDREN: | 50% | DINNER: | - |

Kay Crean
OLD ORCHARD LODGE
Kilrane, Rosslare Harbour,
Co Wexford

	Rosslare Harbour		
OPEN:	1st January-31st December		
NO. ROOMS:	3		
ENSUITE:	2		V

TEL: **053 33468 / 087 472955**   FAX: -   -

2 mins to Ferry, Early Breakfast, Private Parking, beside good Restaurants. On quiet country road. Rooms with TV & Tea/coffee.

B&B PPS:	**£15/£17**	SNGL OCC. DBLE/TPL:	**£21.50/£23.50**	SNGL RM:	-
PART BRD:	-	% RED. CHILDREN:	-	DINNER:	-

Rosslare Harbour 1km

Mrs Mary Duggan
ELMWOOD
Rosslare Harbour,
Co Wexford

	Rosslare Harbour		
OPEN:	15th March-15th October		
NO. ROOMS:	3		
ENSUITE:	3		V

TEL: **053 33321**   FAX: -

Excellent recommendations. RAC acclaimed. Peaceful location 2 mins drive from Ferry. Signposted opposite church. Hairdryer, Tea/Coffee. Early Breakfast menu.

B&B PPS:	**£17**	SNGL OCC. DBLE/TPL:	**£23.50**	SNGL RM:	-
PART BRD:	-	% RED. CHILDREN:	**25%**	DINNER:	-

Rosslare Harbour 0.5km

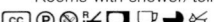

Anne Gleeson
WAYSIDE HOUSE
Ballygeary, Kilrane, Rosslare Harbour,
Co Wexford

	Rosslare Harbour		
OPEN:	31st March-31st October		
NO. ROOMS:	3		
ENSUITE:	3		V

TEL: **053 33475**   FAX: -

Country house, situated on quiet side road off N25. 1 km from Rosslare Port. Rooms with shower/toilet. Early breakfast.

B&B PPS:	**£17**	SNGL OCC. DBLE/TPL:	**£23.50**	SNGL RM:	-
PART BRD:	-	% RED. CHILDREN:	-	DINNER:	-

Rosslare Harbour 1.5km

Mrs Mary Goff
HILLCREST
Tagoat, Rosslare Harbour,
Co Wexford

	Rosslare Harbour		
OPEN:	1st April-31st October		
NO. ROOMS:	3		
ENSUITE:	3		V

TEL: **053 31178**   FAX: -

Highly recommended family home, with Landscaped gardens on N25. 4km Car Ferry. Early breakfast, Tea/coffee. Restaurants, Golf, Beaches nearby.

B&B PPS:	**£17**	SNGL OCC. DBLE/TPL:	**£23.50**	SNGL RM:	-
PART BRD:	-	% RED. CHILDREN:	**50%**	DINNER:	-

Rosslare Harbour 4km

Mrs Kathleen Lawlor
CARRAGH LODGE
Station Road, Rosslare Harbour,
Co Wexford

	Rosslare Harbour		
OPEN:	1st March-31st October		
NO. ROOMS:	3		
ENSUITE:	3		V

TEL: **053 33492**   FAX: -

Modern bungalow on quiet side road off N25. 3 minutes drive from Ferryport. TV, Tea & Coffee facilities.

B&B PPS:	**£17**	SNGL OCC. DBLE/TPL:	**£23.50**	SNGL RM:	-
PART BRD:	-	% RED. CHILDREN:	**50%**	DINNER:	-

Rosslare Harbour Village 1km

Mrs Carmel Lonergan
CLOVER LAWN
**Kilrane, Rosslare Harbour,
Co Wexford**

Rosslare Harbour

TEL: **053 33413**   FAX: -

OPEN:	**1st March-31st October**
NO. ROOMS:	4
ENSUITE:	2

(V)

Highly recommended comfortable home. Kilrane Village turn between pubs 3rd right. Ferry 1Km. Early Breakfast. Golf, Beaches, Restaurants, Rail nearby.

B&B PPS:	**£15/£17**	SNGL OCC. DBLE/TPL:	**£21.50/£23.50**	SNGL RM:	**£17**
PART BRD:	-	% RED. CHILDREN:	**50%**	DINNER:	-

Rosslare Harbour 1km

Brigid Murphy
ABRAE HOUSE
**Kilrane, Rosslare Harbour,
Co Wexford**

Rosslare Harbour

TEL: **053 33283**   FAX: **053 33283**

OPEN:	**All Year except Christmas**
NO. ROOMS:	3
ENSUITE:	3

(V)

Luxury home on main N25. Restaurants and Tourist Amenities within walking distance. 2 mins to Ferry. Early Breakfast.

B&B PPS:	**£17.50**	SNGL OCC. DBLE/TPL:	**£25**	SNGL RM:	-
PART BRD:	-	% RED. CHILDREN:	-	DINNER:	-

Wexford 17km

Mrs Dorothy O'Brien
BORO LODGE
**Kilrane, Rosslare Harbour,
Co Wexford**

Rosslare Harbour

TEL: **053 33610**   FAX: -

OPEN:	**5th January-20th December**
NO. ROOMS:	4
ENSUITE:	2

(V)

200ms off N25 at Kilrane. Quiet area 3mins drive Ferry, Rail. Convenient Golf, Beaches, Restaurant, Bus. Early breakfast. Private parking.

B&B PPS:	**£15/£17**	SNGL OCC. DBLE/TPL:	**£21.50/£23.50**	SNGL RM:	-
PART BRD:	-	% RED. CHILDREN:	-	DINNER:	-

Rosslare Harbour 1km

Mr & Mrs D O'Donoghue
LAUREL LODGE
**Rosslare Harbour,
Co Wexford**

Rosslare Harbour

TEL: **053 33291**   FAX: -

OPEN:	**All Year except Christmas**
NO. ROOMS:	4
ENSUITE:	4

(V)

Comfortable home on quiet road off Rosslare Harbour Village. 1 km from Ferry. Within walking distance of 4 Hotels.

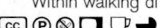

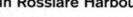

B&B PPS:	**£17**	SNGL OCC. DBLE/TPL:	**£23.50**	SNGL RM:	-
PART BRD:	-	% RED. CHILDREN:	**50%**	DINNER:	-

In Rosslare Harbour

Mrs Bernie Roche
PADUA
**Kilscoran, Tagoat, Rosslare Harbour,
Co Wexford**

Rosslare Harbour

TEL: **053 31373**   FAX: -

OPEN:	**All Year except Christmas**
NO. ROOMS:	3
ENSUITE:	3

(V)

Comfortable home on main Ferry Road. Warm welcome. Complementary Tea/Coffee. Choice of Early Breakfast. Convenient to all facilities.

B&B PPS:	**£17**	SNGL OCC. DBLE/TPL:	**£23.50**	SNGL RM:	-
PART BRD:	-	% RED. CHILDREN:	**25%**	DINNER:	-

Rosslare Harbour 2km

In Rosslare

Ms Una Stack
DUNGARA B&B
**Kilrane, Rosslare Harbour,
Co Wexford**

TEL: **053 33391**   FAX: -

Rosslare Harbour

OPEN:	**All Year**
NO. ROOMS:	4
ENSUITE:	4

 (V)

Comfortable home on main road. TV, Tea/Coffee facilities, Electric Blankets in bedrooms. Families welcome. Access/visa accepted, Early Breakfasts.

B&B PPS:	£17	SNGL OCC. DBLE/TPL:	£23.50	SNGL RM:	-
PART BRD:	-	% RED. CHILDREN:	50%	DINNER:	-

In Tagoat

Mrs Anne Walsh
HARBOUR LIGHTS
**Grahmorack, Tagoat,
Co Wexford**

TEL: **053 32295**   FAX: **053 32295**

Rosslare Harbour

OPEN:	**March-October**
NO. ROOMS:	4
ENSUITE:	4

(V)

Purpose built house, 1 km off N25 at Tagoat, Private parking, 5min drive to Ferry. Early breakfast. Close Golf Course, Beaches.

B&B PPS:	£17	SNGL OCC. DBLE/TPL:	£23.50	SNGL RM:	-
PART BRD:	-	% RED. CHILDREN:	25%	DINNER:	-

Rosslare Harbour 2km

Ms Siobhan Whitehead
KILRANE HOUSE
**Kilrane, Rosslare Harbour,
Co Wexford**

TEL: **053 33135**   FAX: **053 33739**

Rosslare Harbour

OPEN:	**All Year except Christmas**
NO. ROOMS:	6
ENSUITE:	6

(V)

Beautiful refurbished Georgian house. Retaining charm and original features. N25, 2 minutes drive Ferry. Tea making. Opposite Restaurant. Frommer Recommended.

B&B PPS:	£17/£18	SNGL OCC. DBLE/TPL:	£23.50/£25	SNGL RM:	-
PART BRD:	-	% RED. CHILDREN:	33%	DINNER:	-

Wexford 18km

Mrs Ann Wixted
ASGARD
**The Moorings, Rosslare Harbour,
Co Wexford**

TEL: **053 33602**   FAX: -

Rosslare Harbour

OPEN:	**All Year except Christmas**
NO. ROOMS:	4
ENSUITE:	3

(V)

Nearest B&B (600m) to Ferryport on main N25. Early Breakfast. Tea/coffee making, TV all bedrooms.

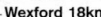

B&B PPS:	£15/£17	SNGL OCC. DBLE/TPL:	£21.50/£23.50	SNGL RM:	-
PART BRD:	-	% RED. CHILDREN:	25%	DINNER:	-

Wexford

James F Cahill
ARDRUADH MANOR
**Spawell Road, Wexford,
Co Wexford**

TEL: **053 23194**   FAX: -

Wexford

OPEN:	**1st January-24th December**
NO. ROOMS:	6
ENSUITE:	6

(V)

Elegant period house (1893) set in acre of private landscaped gardens in heart of old Viking Town - beside all amenities.

B&B PPS:	£17/£24	SNGL OCC. DBLE/TPL:	£25/£30.50	SNGL RM:	-
PART BRD:	-	% RED. CHILDREN:	-	DINNER:	-

Peter and Mary Caulfield
NEWTOWN HOUSE
**Newtown Road, Wexford,
Co Wexford**
TEL: **053 43253**   FAX: -

Wexford

OPEN:	2nd January-20th December
NO. ROOMS:	4
ENSUITE:	3

(V)

Luxurious family home on elevated site. Scenic view, convenient to Beaches, Golf, Fishing and Horseriding. Ideal tourists base for Wexford.

| B&B PPS: | **£16/£17** | SNGL OCC. DBLE/TPL: | **£22.50/£23.50** | SNGL RM: | **£22** |
| PART BRD: | - | % RED. CHILDREN: | **10%** | DINNER: | - |

Wexford 2.5km

Mrs Maria Doyle-Colfer
THE ROSE
**Camross, Foulksmills, Wexford,
Co Wexford**
TEL: **054 40524**   FAX: -

Wexford

OPEN:	Easter-30th September
NO. ROOMS:	5
ENSUITE:	2

(V)

Situated on N25, easy access, 25 mins Rosslare. Early Breakfast, Breakfast menu, conservatory, French spoken, Restaurants, pleasant walks. Refreshments on arrival.

| B&B PPS: | **£15/£17** | SNGL OCC. DBLE/TPL: | **£21.50/£23.50** | SNGL RM: | - |
| PART BRD: | - | % RED. CHILDREN: | **33%** | DINNER: | **£12** |

Wexford 18km

Mrs Angela Doocey
TOWNPARKS HOUSE
**Coolcotts, Wexford,
Co Wexford**
TEL: **053 45191**   FAX: -

Wexford

OPEN:	All Year except Christmas
NO. ROOMS:	5
ENSUITE:	5

(V)

Purpose-built Georgian house. (N25). 10mins walk town-centre. 15mins Rosslare ferries. Tea/Coffee facilities, Clock-Radios, Hairdryers. Early Breakfast.

| B&B PPS: | **£17.50/£20** | SNGL OCC. DBLE/TPL: | **£25/£30** | SNGL RM: | - |
| PART BRD: | - | % RED. CHILDREN: | **33.3%** | DINNER: | - |

In Wexford

Josie Kavanagh
HERITAGE VIEW
**Newtown Road, Wexford,
Co Wexford**
TEL: **053 45168**   FAX: -

Wexford

OPEN:	All Year except Christmas
NO. ROOMS:	5
ENSUITE:	5

(V)

Residence in scenic surroundings overlooking Heritage Park/River Slaney. Situated on N11/N25 2km from Wexford. Rosslare Harbour 15mins.

| B&B PPS: | **£17/£19** | SNGL OCC. DBLE/TPL: | **£23.50/£25.50** | SNGL RM: | - |
| PART BRD: | - | % RED. CHILDREN: | **12%** | DINNER: | - |

Wexford 2km

Paula & Stephen Kehoe
BAYFIELD HOUSE
**Saunderscourt, Ferrycarrig, Wexford,
Co Wexford**
TEL: **053 20071**   FAX: -

Wexford

OPEN:	7th January-20th December
NO. ROOMS:	3
ENSUITE:	3

(V)

Beautifully decorated home in stunning tranquil location overlooking Wexford Bay. National Heritage Park, Ferrycarrig Hotel & Riverside Restaurant nearby. 20 mins Ferries.

| B&B PPS: | **£18/£19.50** | SNGL OCC. DBLE/TPL: | **£25/£30** | SNGL RM: | - |
| PART BRD: | - | % RED. CHILDREN: | **33%** | DINNER: | - |

Wexford 5km

Wexford Town

Mrs Maureen Keogh
ELMLEIGH
Coolcots, Wexford Town,
Co Wexford

Tel: **053 44174**   Fax: -

Wexford		
OPEN:	**All Year**	
No. Rooms:	**4**	
Ensuite:	**3**	

Modern home, quiet residential area, TV, Tea/Coffee in rooms, Guest's Garden, Private Parking. Family rooms, convenient to Golf, Beaches, Ferry.

B&B PPS:	**£17**	Sngl Occ. Dble/Tpl:	**£23.50**	Sngl Rm:	**£18**
Part Brd:	-	% Red. Children:	**50%**	Dinner:	-

Wexford 3km

Ms Sarah I Lee
ROCKCLIFFE
Coolballow, Wexford,
Co Wexford

Tel: **053 43130**   Fax: -

Wexford		
OPEN:	**May-31st October**	
No. Rooms:	**4**	
Ensuite:	**2**	

Lovely landscaped garden. Ferry 15mins. Frommer Recommended. N25 from Rosslare, through roundabout towards Wexford. Junction left after "Farmers Kitchen".

B&B PPS:	**£15/£17**	Sngl Occ. Dble/Tpl:	**£21.50/£23.50**	Sngl Rm:	**£18**
Part Brd:	-	% Red. Children:	**20%**	Dinner:	-

Wexford 4km

Mrs Ann Meagher
TARA
Killeen, Ferrycarrig,
Co Wexford

Tel: **053 20133**   Fax: -

Wexford		
OPEN:	**All Year except Christmas**	
No. Rooms:	**4**	
Ensuite:	**2**	

Bungalow main N11, Walking distance Ferrycarrig Hotel, Oak Tavern Pub Restaurant, Heritage Park. 4 kms Wexford. 15 mins Rosslare Ferries. Early Breakfast.

B&B PPS:	**£15/£17**	Sngl Occ. Dble/Tpl:	**£21.50/£25**	Sngl Rm:	-
Part Brd:	-	% Red. Children:	**20%**	Dinner:	-

Wexford 4km

Nicholas & Kathleen Murphy
GLENHILL
Ballygoman, Barntown,
Co Wexford

Tel: **053 20015**   Fax: -

Wexford		
OPEN:	**All Year except Christmas**	
No. Rooms:	**3**	
Ensuite:	**3**	

Modern home in peaceful surroundings. Guaranteed hospitality on N25. (15 mins Rosslare Ferries.) Early breakfast. Private car park. Wexford 4km.

B&B PPS:	**£17/£21**	Sngl Occ. Dble/Tpl:	**£23.50/£27.50**	Sngl Rm:	-
Part Brd:	-	% Red. Children:	**40%**	Dinner:	-

In Wexford

Mrs Kathleen Nolan
DARRAL HOUSE
Spawell Road, Wexford,
Co Wexford

Tel: **053 24264**   Fax: -

Wexford		
OPEN:	**All Year except Christmas**	
No. Rooms:	**4**	
Ensuite:	**4**	

"Darral House" offers luxury accommodation. All rooms are tastefully decorated & Ensuite with Tea/Coffee making facilties & Televisions.

B&B PPS:	**£19/£22.50**	Sngl Occ. Dble/Tpl:	**£24/£27.50**	Sngl Rm:	-
Part Brd:	-	% Red. Children:	**50%**	Dinner:	-

David & Mary O'Brien
AUBURN HOUSE
**2 Auburn Tce, Redmond Road,
Wexford, Co Wexford**
TEL: **053 23605**   FAX: -

Wexford

OPEN:	2nd January-22nd December
NO. ROOMS:	5
ENSUITE:	4

Our elegantly restored townhouse offers superb accommodation. Bedrooms are spacious and charming, many enjoying a view of River Slaney.

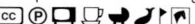

| B&B PPS: | **£18** | SNGL OCC. DBLE/TPL: | **£23** | SNGL RM: | - |
| PART BRD: | - | % RED. CHILDREN: | **50%** | DINNER: | - |

In Wexford

Nick & Eleanor O'Connor
TROON LODGE
**Ballycrane, Castlebridge, Wexford,
Co Wexford**
TEL: **053 59012**   FAX: **053 59200**   EMAIL: **troon@iol.ie**

Wexford

OPEN:	All Year except Christmas
NO. ROOMS:	4
ENSUITE:	3

Luxurious friendly home. Extensive gardens with Tennis Court. 5 minutes Curracloe Beach. 20 mins Rosslare. Power showers. All amenities nearby.

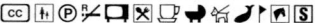

| B&B PPS: | **£18/£20** | SNGL OCC. DBLE/TPL: | **£24.50/£28** | SNGL RM: | **£16/£18** |
| PART BRD: | - | % RED. CHILDREN: | **50%** | DINNER: | |

Wexford 3km

Mrs Breda O'Grady
VILLA MARIA
**Ivy Lane, Coolcots, Wexford,
Co Wexford**
TEL: **053 45143**   FAX: -

Wexford

OPEN:	All Year except Christmas
NO. ROOMS:	4
ENSUITE:	3

Modern bungalow in private cul-de-sac. Convenient Heritage Park, Golf, Rosslare Ferry. Tea/Coffee facilities, early breakfast.

| B&B PPS: | **£15/£17** | SNGL OCC. DBLE/TPL: | **£23/£30** | SNGL RM: | - |
| PART BRD: | - | % RED. CHILDREN: | **50%** | DINNER: | - |

Wexford 1km

Margaret Roe
SHEEPWALK HOUSE
**Drinagh, Rosslare Road,
Co Wexford**
TEL: **053 58131**   FAX: **053 58131**

Wexford

OPEN:	6th January-18th December
NO. ROOMS:	3
ENSUITE:	3

Situated on Rosslare Road, ten minutes Ferry. Convenient to Restaurants, Pubs, Golf & Beaches. Tea/Coffee facilities. Early Breakfast, Visa/Access.

| B&B PPS: | **£17** | SNGL OCC. DBLE/TPL: | **£23.50** | SNGL RM: | **£21** |
| PART BRD: | - | % RED. CHILDREN: | **20%** | DINNER: | - |

Wexford 5km

Lynn Ruddock
THE BLUE DOOR
**18 Lr George St, Wexford,
Co Wexford**
TEL: **053 21047**   FAX: -

Wexford

OPEN:	1st January-22nd December
NO. ROOMS:	3
ENSUITE:	3

Quality Accommodation in an old Georgian Townhouse in the Town Centre - beside Shops, Pubs, Restaurants, all rooms ensuite with TV.

| B&B PPS: | **£20** | SNGL OCC. DBLE/TPL: | **£26.50** | SNGL RM: | - |
| PART BRD: | - | % RED. CHILDREN: | **50%** | DINNER: | - |

In Wexford

In Wexford

Mrs Catherine Saunderson
FARRANSEER HOUSE
Coolcots, Wexford,
Co Wexford
TEL: **053 44042**   FAX: -

Wexford

OPEN:	1st January-31st December
NO. ROOMS:	4
ENSUITE:	2

(V)

Spacious home in Wexford Town. Landscaped grounds. Convenient to local amenities. TV bedrooms and lounge.Tea/ Coffee facilities. Early Breakfast.

B&B PPS:	£16/£20	SNGL OCC. DBLE/TPL:	£22.50/£26.50	SNGL RM:	£18/£20
PART BRD:	£190	% RED. CHILDREN:	25%	DINNER:	£14

Wexford 3km

Mrs Christina Toomey
BEDFORD HOUSE
Ballymorris, Clonard, Wexford,
Co Wexford
TEL: **053 45643**   FAX: -

Wexford

OPEN:	All Year except Christmas
NO. ROOMS:	4
ENSUITE:	4

(V)

Situated on Duncannon New Line Road (R733) 0.5 kms off N25. 15 mins Rosslare Ferry. Early breakfast. Large family room.

B&B PPS:	£17	SNGL OCC. DBLE/TPL:	£23.50	SNGL RM:	-
PART BRD:	-	% RED. CHILDREN:	50%	DINNER:	£12

In Wexford Town

Mrs Margaret Wallace
KILDERRY
St Johns Road, Wexford Town,
Co Wexford
TEL: **053 23848**   FAX: **053 23848**

Wexford

OPEN:	1st March-30th November
NO. ROOMS:	3
ENSUITE:	2

(V)

Downtown Wexford. Rosslare ferries 15 minutes. Convenient to Golf, Heritage Park, Beaches. Clock-Radios, Hairdryers in bedrooms, Tea/Coffee facilities. Access/Visa.

B&B PPS:	£15.50/£20	SNGL OCC. DBLE/TPL:	£25/£33	SNGL RM:	-
PART BRD:	-	% RED. CHILDREN:	-	DINNER:	-

In Wexford Town

Mrs Maura Whitty
JOHNS GATE STREET HSE B&B
Wexford,
Co Wexford
TEL: **053 41124**   FAX: **053 41124**

Wexford

OPEN:	14th March-30th November
NO. ROOMS:	6
ENSUITE:	6

(V)

Downtown historical Wexford. Close to Arts Centre. Georgian Town House. All rooms ensuite, TV,Tea making. 15 mins car ferry.

B&B PPS:	£17/£20	SNGL OCC. DBLE/TPL:	-	SNGL RM:	-
PART BRD:	-	% RED. CHILDREN:	50%	DINNER:	-

RESERVATIONS

- Confirm phone bookings in writing without delay with agreed deposit.
- To avoid misunderstandings later, check rate on booking and clarify any additional changes which may apply to your booking.
- Give details of any special requirements.
- State clearly day, date of arrival and departure date.

The Gaeltacht
AN INTRODUCTION

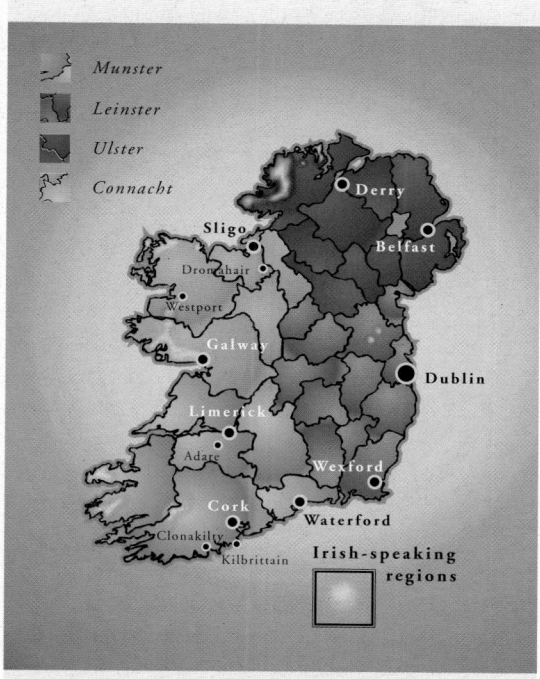

Munster
Leinster
Ulster
Connacht

Derry
Sligo
Belfast
Dromahair
Westport
Galway
Dublin
Limerick
Adate
Wexford
Cork
Clonakilty
Waterford
Kilbrittain
Irish-speaking regions

An Ghaeltacht

Tugtar an Ghaeltacht ar cheantair scaipthe in iarthuaisceart, iarthar agus iardheisceart na tíre ina bhfuil an Ghaeilge mar ghnáth-theanga labhartha an phobail. Iontú siúd tá fás agus forbairt ní amháin ar theanga na nGael ach ar gach gné den chultúr Gaelach, idir ceol, amhráin, sheanchas agus sean-nós. Tá buntáisti líonmhara bronnta ag an dúlra ar na dúichí seo go léir, agus tá éagsúlacht le fáil ag an gcuairteoir iontú, ó chanúint cheolmhar an deiscirt go glór na farraige sa tuaisceart. Tá gach saghas caitheamh aimsire le fáil iontú chomh maith.

The Gaeltacht

The Gaeltacht - what is it? In brief, it is the name given to several areas of Ireland, some large and some small, where Irish is the spoken language and where, by coordinated effort, Ireland's social, cultural and linguistic traditions are safeguarded and promoted.

Gaeltacht Areas

Nature has been extremely generous to the Gaeltacht areas. Situated in most cases along rugged, spectacular coastline, they are located in some of Ireland's most beautiful counties: Donegal, Mayo, Galway, Kerry, Cork and Waterford and inland, Co. Meath. For the carefree holiday-maker, casual visitor or language student, the Gaeltacht can be a rewarding and enjoyable experience.

Further Information

Further information on the Gaeltacht and its activities is available from:

Údarás na Gaeltachta, Na Forbacha, Gaillimh.

091-503100

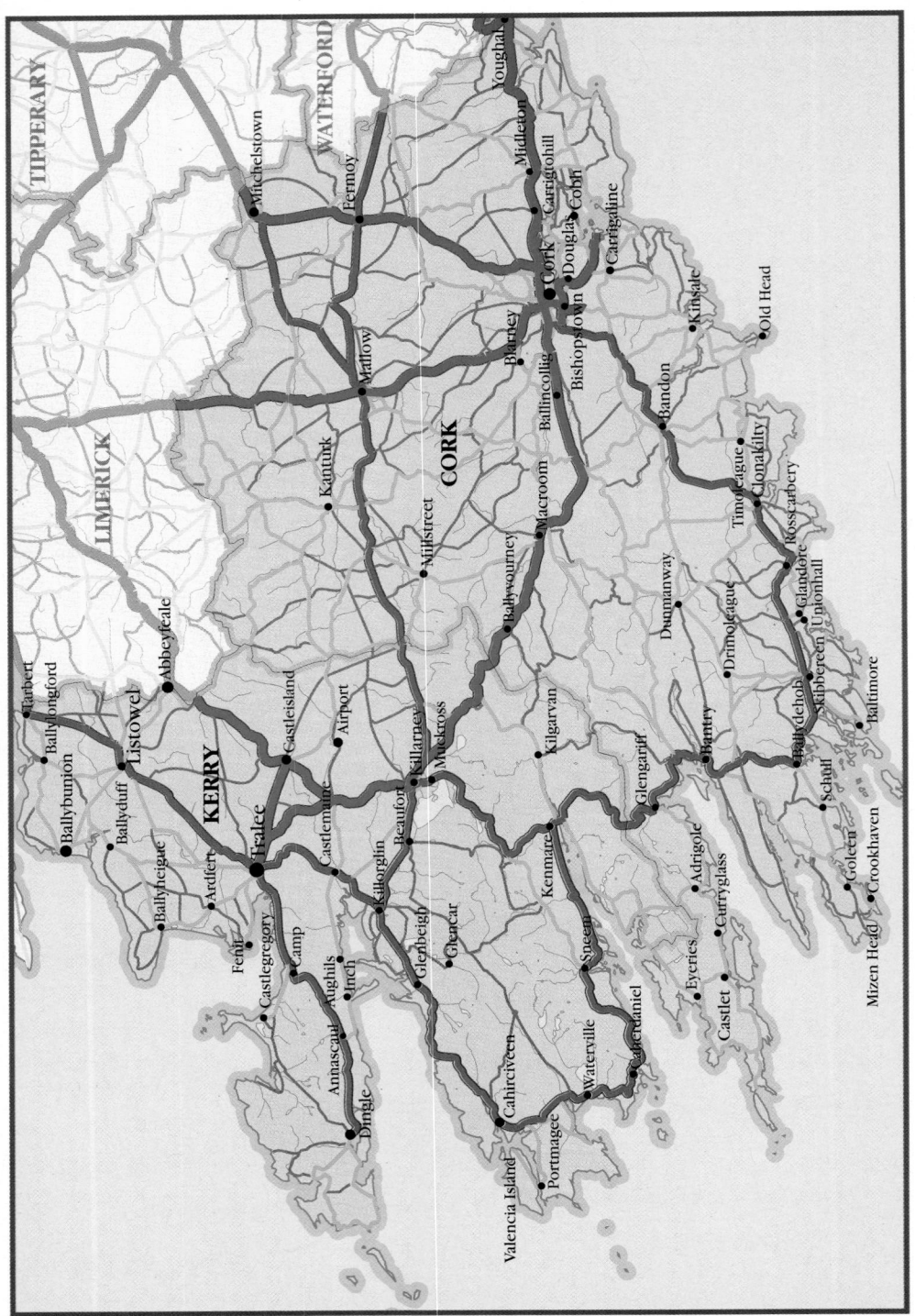

© ERA-Maptec

Located in the south-west corner of Ireland, the Cork and South Kerry region offers its visitors a great diversity of scenery, culture and leisure activities. The region claims some of the most varied and

spectacular scenery in the country. Here you will find the full range of holiday options to ensure a memorable, refreshing and very different holiday.

The South Western coastline, sculptured by the ice-age and influenced by the warm waters of the Gulf Stream, is steeped in ancient history and folklore from the East and West Cork coasts, The Beara and Dingle Peninsulas, and from the Ring of Kerry to the Lakes of Killarney and the Bandon, Lee and Blackwater Valleys.

Some of Ireland's best international festivals are hosted in the region and attractions for all the family, guarantees a fun filled holiday.

Area Representatives

CORK

Mrs. Colette Collins, Heather Lodge, Kerry Road, Tower, Blarney, Co. Cork. Tel: 021-381216. Fax: 021-381216

Mrs. Georgina Coughlan, Glebe House, Tay Road, Cobh, Co. Cork. Tel: 021-811373. Fax: 021-811373.

Mrs. Vera O'Byrne, Carrigcourt House, Carrigaline, Co. Cork. Tel: 021-371750. Fax: 021-371477.

KERRY

Mrs. Noreen Dineen, Manor House, 18 Whitebridge Manor, Ballycasheen, Killarney, Co. Kerry. Tel: 066-32716. Fax: 064-32716 (manual)

Mrs. Kay O'Keeffe, Cnoc Mhuire, Oakpark Road, Tralee, Co. Kerry. Tel: 066-26027.

Mrs. Fiona O'Sullivan, Mylestone House, Killowen Road, Kenmare, Co. Kerry. Tel: 064-41753.

 ## Tourist Information Offices

Cork City
Tel: (021) 273251

Blarney
Tel: (021) 381624

Killarney
Tel: (064) 31633

Skibbereen
Tel: (028) 21766

In Ballincollig

Mrs Rose Cotter
WESTFIELD HOUSE
West Village, Ballincollig, Co Cork

		Ballincollig
	OPEN:	All Year except Christmas
	NO. ROOMS:	3
	ENSUITE:	2

TEL: **021 871824**   FAX: -

Welcoming tea/coffee on arrival. Modern house, adjacent Ballincollig main Cork/Killarney N22. On bus route, convenient Blarney, Airport, Ferry.

B&B PPS:	£15/£18	SNGL OCC. DBLE/TPL:	£21.50/£25	SNGL RM:	25%
PART BRD:	-	% RED. CHILDREN:		DINNER:	-

Ballincollig 2km

Mrs Maureen Cronin
THE MILESTONE
Ovens, Ballincollig, Co Cork

		Ballincollig
	OPEN:	All Year except Christmas
	NO. ROOMS:	5
	ENSUITE:	5

TEL: **021 872562**   FAX: **021 872562**

AA QQQ Award. Cork/Killarney Road N22. Ballincollig 2 km. Tea/coffee/hairdrryer facilities. Highly commended home. Great base to tour from.

B&B PPS:	£17/£18	SNGL OCC. DBLE/TPL:	£23.50/£25	SNGL RM:	-
PART BRD:	-	% RED. CHILDREN:	25%	DINNER:	-

Ballincollig 11.5km

John & Elizabeth Plaice
MUSKERRY HOUSE
Farnanes, Co Cork

		Ballincollig
	OPEN:	All Year except Christmas
	NO. ROOMS:	6
	ENSUITE:	6

TEL: **021 336469**   FAX: **021 336469**

Cork/Killarney Road N22. All bedrooms with private bathroom. Convenient to Airport, Ferry. Early breakfast. Coarse Angling Facilities. Touring Itineraries planned.

B&B PPS:	£17/£18	SNGL OCC. DBLE/TPL:	£23.50/£25	SNGL RM:	-
PART BRD:	£190	% RED. CHILDREN:	25%	DINNER:	£13

In Ballydehob

Mrs Mary Coughlan
DUN AN OIR
Ballydehob, West Cork, Co Cork

		Ballydehob
	OPEN:	1st April-1st October
	NO. ROOMS:	3
	ENSUITE:	2

TEL: **028 37272**   FAX: -

Welcome to an Irish Family Home. Conveniently situated. Clean and comfortable friendly atmosphere. Interesting walks, wildlife. Local crafts and music.

B&B PPS:	£15/£17	SNGL OCC. DBLE/TPL:	£21.50/£23.50	SNGL RM:	-
PART BRD:	-	% RED. CHILDREN:	-	DINNER:	-

In Ballydehob

Mrs Ann Vaughan
LYNWOOD
Schull Road, Ballydehob, Co Cork

		Ballydehob
	OPEN:	March-October
	NO. ROOMS:	3
	ENSUITE:	3

TEL: **028 37124**   FAX: **028 37124**

Spacious Bungalow with tennis court. Tea/Coffee making facilities electric blankets, hairdryers and T.V. in all bedrooms. 300 mtrs from village.

B&B PPS:	£17/£18	SNGL OCC. DBLE/TPL:	£23.50/£24.50	SNGL RM:	-
PART BRD:	-	% RED. CHILDREN:	-	DINNER:	-

Ballyvourney

Nora Lucey
NORVILLE HOUSE
Ballymakeera, Macroom, Co Cork

OPEN:	All Year
NO. ROOMS:	3
ENSUITE:	-

TEL: **026 45486**   FAX: -

Luxury house (2min) off N22. Central to Killarney, Blarney and West Cork. Landscaped gardens with Picnic, Barbecue, Crazy Golf, Sandcastle.

| B&B PPS: | **£15** | SNGL OCC. DBLE/TPL: | **£21.50** | SNGL RM: | - |
| PART BRD: | - | % RED. CHILDREN: | **50%** | DINNER: | - |

Macroom 7km

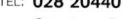

Baltimore

Mrs Margaret Harrington
CHANNEL VIEW
Baltimore, Co Cork

OPEN:	March-October
NO. ROOMS:	5
ENSUITE:	4

TEL: **028 20440**   FAX: -

Spacious Dormer Bungalow, Private Car Park overlooking the Bay. Sailing, Fishing, Island Trips, Diving, Scenic Walks, Golf, Tea/coffee facilities.

| B&B PPS: | **£16/£17** | SNGL OCC. DBLE/TPL: | **£22.50/£23.50** | SNGL RM: | - |
| PART BRD: | - | % RED. CHILDREN: | **30%** | DINNER: | - |

In Baltimore

Bandon

Mrs Anne Buckley
ST ANNE'S
Clonakilty Road, Bandon, Co Cork

OPEN:	All Year
NO. ROOMS:	5
ENSUITE:	5

TEL: **023 44239**   FAX: **023 44239**

Georgian house. Walled gardens. Near Town Centre. Convenient to Golf, Beaches, Fishing and Walking. Teamaking facilities. Airport 16 miles.

| B&B PPS: | **£17/£18** | SNGL OCC. DBLE/TPL: | **£23.50** | SNGL RM: | **£23.50** |
| PART BRD: | - | % RED. CHILDREN: | - | DINNER: | - |

Bandon 1km

Bandon

Mrs Carmel Nash
RIVERVIEW
7 Riverview Estate, Bandon, Co Cork

OPEN:	January-December
NO. ROOMS:	4
ENSUITE:	4

TEL: **023 41080**   FAX: -

Modern friendly home in quiet cul-de-sac on edge of town. Airport & Ferry 30 min drive. Golf, Tennis, Fishing, Beaches closeby.

| B&B PPS: | **£17/£18** | SNGL OCC. DBLE/TPL: | **£23.50** | SNGL RM: | - |
| PART BRD: | - | % RED. CHILDREN: | **10%** | DINNER: | - |

In Bandon

Bandon

Mrs Theresa O'Connor
ASHGROVE HOUSE
Castle Road, Bandon, Co Cork

OPEN:	1st January-15th December
NO. ROOMS:	3
ENSUITE:	3

TEL: **023 41033**   FAX: -

House on Golf Club Road, Patio back and front, 5 minutes walk Town, Golf Club. 6 miles to Beach. Tea on arrival.

| B&B PPS: | **£17** | SNGL OCC. DBLE/TPL: | **£23.50** | SNGL RM: | **£23.50** |
| PART BRD: | - | % RED. CHILDREN: | - | DINNER: | - |

Bandon 1km

Bantry 1km

Mrs Eileen Andrews
FERNDEENE
4 Slip Lawn, Bantry, Co Cork

TEL: 027 50146   FAX: -

Bantry

OPEN:	All Year except Christmas
NO. ROOMS:	4
ENSUITE:	3

Modern home in pleasant surroundings. 1km from Bantry Town (N71). Private car park and bicycle garage. Tea/coffee facilities in bedrooms.

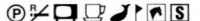

| B&B PPS: | £15/£17 | SNGL OCC. DBLE/TPL: | £21.50/£23.50 | SNGL RM: | £20 |
| PART BRD: | - | % RED. CHILDREN: | 50% | DINNER: | £15 |

Bantry 0.5km

Mrs Sheila Brennan
ELSLOO
Newtown, Bantry, Co Cork

TEL: 027 50471   FAX: -

Bantry

OPEN:	April-October
NO. ROOMS:	4
ENSUITE:	2

Situated on main Bantry/Glengarriff Route (N71) overlooking Bantry Bay. Minutes walk to all amenities. Tea/Coffee facilities. Bantry 0.5 km.

| B&B PPS: | £15/£17 | SNGL OCC. DBLE/TPL: | £21.50/£23.50 | SNGL RM: | £20.50 |
| PART BRD: | - | % RED. CHILDREN: | 50% | DINNER: | - |

Bantry 4km

Louise Casey
REENDONEGAN HOUSE
Reendonegan, Ballylickey, Bantry, Co Cork

TEL: 027 51455   FAX: 027 51455 (manual)

Bantry

OPEN:	May-September
NO. ROOMS:	3
ENSUITE:	2

Historic 18th century Georgian country house. overlooking Reendonegan Lough & Bantry Bay, private shoreline. Peaceful, tranquil setting. Off season by arrangement.

| B&B PPS: | £15/£17 | SNGL OCC. DBLE/TPL: | £22/£25 | SNGL RM: | - |
| PART BRD: | - | % RED. CHILDREN: | 50% | DINNER: | - |

In Ballylickey

Maeve Connolly
PIPIT COVE
Ballylickey, Bantry, Co Cork

TEL: 027 51594   FAX: 027 50545

Bantry

OPEN:	1st May-1st October
NO. ROOMS:	3
ENSUITE:	2

Situated off N71, 200m from the sea. Quiet garden setting with spectacular coastal scenery. Ideal touring base. Itineraries planned.

| B&B PPS: | £15/£17 | SNGL OCC. DBLE/TPL: | £21.50/£23.50 | SNGL RM: | - |
| PART BRD: | - | % RED. CHILDREN: | 20% | DINNER: | - |

Bantry 5km

Mrs Mary Cronin
COULIN
Gurteenroe, Bantry, Co Cork

TEL: 027 50020   FAX: -

Bantry

OPEN:	1st May-30th September
NO. ROOMS:	3
ENSUITE:	3

Spacious bungalow on main Bantry/Glengarriff Rd. N71. Beautiful view of sea, lake. TV tea making facilities in rooms. Electric Blankets.

| B&B PPS: | £17 | SNGL OCC. DBLE/TPL: | £23.50 | SNGL RM: | - |
| PART BRD: | - | % RED. CHILDREN: | - | DINNER: | - |

Bantry 3km

Mrs Genny Dooley
ATLANTIC VIEW
Gurteenroe, Bantry, Co Cork

Bantry	
OPEN:	All Year
NO. ROOMS:	3
ENSUITE:	1

TEL: **027 51221**　　FAX: -

Superb Sea and Mountain Views, secluded and peaceful modern bungalow in elevated position. Bantry/Glengarriff Road N71. Adjacent golf course.

B&B PPS:	**£15/£17**	SNGL OCC. DBLE/TPL:	**£21.50/£23.50**	SNGL RM:	-
PART BRD:	-	% RED. CHILDREN:	**25%**	DINNER:	-

Bantry 1km

Maggie Doyle
ATLANTIC SHORE
Newtown, Bantry, Co Cork

Bantry	
OPEN:	All Year
NO. ROOMS:	6
ENSUITE:	5

TEL: **027 51310**　　FAX: **027 51310**　　EMAIL: **divebantry@oal.com**

A spacious purpose built bungalow with a panaramic view of Bantry Bay.

B&B PPS:	**£17**	SNGL OCC. DBLE/TPL:	**£23.50**	SNGL RM:	**£14**
PART BRD:	-	% RED. CHILDREN:	**20%**	DINNER:	-

Bantry 1km

Mrs Phyllis Foley
ARD NA GREINE
Newtown, Bantry, Co Cork

Bantry	
OPEN:	1st April-30th November
NO. ROOMS:	4
ENSUITE:	3

TEL: **027 51169**　　FAX: -

Modern country home. Mature grounds,gardens. Peaceful location. 400 metres from N71. Ideal touring base West Cork/South Kerry/Hill walking.

B&B PPS:	**£15/£17**	SNGL OCC. DBLE/TPL:	**£23.50**	SNGL RM:	-
PART BRD:	-	% RED. CHILDREN:	**20%**	DINNER:	-

In Bantry

Mrs Brenda Harrington
LEYTON
23 Slip Lawn, Bantry, Co Cork

Bantry	
OPEN:	1st May-30th September
NO. ROOMS:	3
ENSUITE:	2

TEL: **027 50665**　　FAX: -

Modern home, quiet locality overlooking Bantry Town. Breakfast menu,Car Park, Bicycle Hire.Ideal touring base West Cork/Kerry. In Bantry.

B&B PPS:	**£15/£17**	SNGL OCC. DBLE/TPL:	**£21.50/£23.50**	SNGL RM:	-
PART BRD:	-	% RED. CHILDREN:	**20%**	DINNER:	-

In Bantry

Mrs Sheila Harrington
ELMWOOD HOUSE
6 Slip Lawn, Bantry, Co Cork

Bantry	
OPEN:	All Year
NO. ROOMS:	3
ENSUITE:	1

TEL: **027 50087**　　FAX: **027 50278**

Warm friendly home off main road.Tea/Cakes on arrival, town 5 minutes. Near all amenities, turf fire, Bicycle garage, Archivist.

B&B PPS:	**£15/£17**	SNGL OCC. DBLE/TPL:	**£21.50**	SNGL RM:	-
PART BRD:	-	% RED. CHILDREN:	**50%**	DINNER:	-

Mrs Tosca Kramer
THE MILL
Glengarrif Road, New Town, Bantry, Co Cork

TEL: **027 50278** FAX: **027 50278**

Bantry	
OPEN:	1st April-1st November
NO. ROOMS:	6
ENSUITE:	6

(V)

Spacious modern bungalow, ample parking on Bantry/Glengarriff Road (N71). 1 km town centre. Bicycle hire/repairs, laundry service, AA selected.

B&B PPS:	£17	SNGL OCC. DBLE/TPL:	£23.50/£25	SNGL RM:	-
PART BRD:	-	% RED. CHILDREN:	20%	DINNER:	-

Bantry 0.5km

Ms Mary C McCarthy
TIROROA
Gurteenroe, Near Ballylickey, Bantry, Co Cork

TEL: **027 50287** FAX: -

Bantry	
OPEN:	7th March-31st October
NO. ROOMS:	3
ENSUITE:	3

(V)

On Bantry/Glengariff road (N71. Panoramic View Lake, Sea, Mountains. Ideal for touring, private parking, tea making facilities in rooms.

B&B PPS:	£17	SNGL OCC. DBLE/TPL:	£23.50	SNGL RM:	-
PART BRD:	-	% RED. CHILDREN:	-	DINNER:	-

Bantry 4km

Mrs Sheila Maguire
SEA BREEZE
Caherdaniel, Bantry, Co Cork

TEL: **027 50267** FAX: **027 50267**

Bantry	
OPEN:	1st April-30th October
NO. ROOMS:	3
ENSUITE:	2

(V)

Bungalow with magnificent views of Bantry Bay and Beara Peninsula. Golf, Horseriding nearby. Ideal touring Cork/Kerry. Breakfast menu.

B&B PPS:	£14/£16	SNGL OCC. DBLE/TPL:	£20/£22	SNGL RM:	-
PART BRD:	£175	% RED. CHILDREN:	20%	DINNER:	-

Bantry 1km

Mrs Mary Milner
SHALOM
Newtown, Bantry, Co Cork

TEL: **027 50372** FAX: -

Bantry	
OPEN:	May-September
NO. ROOMS:	3
ENSUITE:	3

(V)

Luxury home, spacious garden, peaceful locality. Ideal touring base for West Cork and Kerry. Golf, Hill walking, Sailing and Fishing.

B&B PPS:	£17	SNGL OCC. DBLE/TPL:	£23.50	SNGL RM:	-
PART BRD:	-	% RED. CHILDREN:	20%	DINNER:	-

Bantry 1km

Mrs Cait Murray
ROCKLANDS
Gurteenroe, Bantry, Co Cork

TEL: **027 50212** FAX: -

Bantry	
OPEN:	10th January-20th December
NO. ROOMS:	3
ENSUITE:	3

(V)

Luxurious bungalow, Bantry - Glengarriff Rd N71. Magnificent views Bantry Bay, Lake, Sea, Mountains. Ideal touring base for West Cork/Kerry.

B&B PPS:	£17	SNGL OCC. DBLE/TPL:	£23.50	SNGL RM:	-
PART BRD:	£180	% RED. CHILDREN:	20%	DINNER:	£12

Bantry 4km

Bantry 3km

Mrs Kathleen O'Donovan
ASHLING
Cahir, Bantry, Co Cork

Bantry

OPEN:	1st May-30th September
NO. ROOMS:	4
ENSUITE:	3

TEL: **027 50616**   FAX: -

Modern bungalow off Bantry/Glengarrif Road. Spacious bedrooms overlooking sea and mountains. Near Golf Course. Credit Cards.

B&B PPS:	**£15/£17**	SNGL OCC. DBLE/TPL:	**£21.50/£23.50**	SNGL RM:	-
PART BRD:	-	% RED. CHILDREN:	**20%**	DINNER:	-

In Bantry

Mrs Breda O'Regan
SUNVILLE
Newtown, Bantry, Co Cork

Bantry

OPEN:	May-October
NO. ROOMS:	3
ENSUITE:	2

TEL: **027 50175**   FAX: -

Bungalow on main Bantry, Glengarriff Rd (N71). Minutes walk to town centre. Private car park. Close to all tourist amenities.

B&B PPS:	**£15/£17**	SNGL OCC. DBLE/TPL:	**£23.50**	SNGL RM:	-
PART BRD:	-	% RED. CHILDREN:	**50%**	DINNER:	-

Bantry 5km

John and Eileen O'Sullivan
FERNDALE
Ballickey, Bantry, Co Cork

Bantry

OPEN:	May-September
NO. ROOMS:	3
ENSUITE:	3

TEL: **027 50680**   FAX: -

Luxurious bungalow and peaceful garden surroundings off Bantry/Glengarriff Road (N71). Three minute walking distance to Pubs and Restaurants.

B&B PPS:	**£17**	SNGL OCC. DBLE/TPL:	**£23.50**	SNGL RM:	-
PART BRD:	-	% RED. CHILDREN:	**20%**	DINNER:	-

Bantry 1km

Mrs Margaret O'Sullivan
PARK VIEW
Newtown, Bantry, Co Cork

Bantry

OPEN:	All Year
NO. ROOMS:	4
ENSUITE:	2

TEL: **027 51174**   FAX: -

Modern home, ideal touring centre. On main Bantry Glengarriff (N71). Beaches, Golf, Fishing, Horse Riding convenient. Scenic drives. Choice of breakfast.

BUS NO: **8**

B&B PPS:	**£15/£17**	SNGL OCC. DBLE/TPL:	**£21.50**	SNGL RM:	**£18.50**
PART BRD:	-	% RED. CHILDREN:	**25%**	DINNER:	-

Bantry 2km

Mrs M V O'Sullivan
SORRENTO
Gouree More, Bantry, Co Cork

Bantry

OPEN:	April-October
NO. ROOMS:	3
ENSUITE:	2

TEL: **027 50335**   FAX: -

Modern bungalow on main Bantry/Glengariff Road. Golf Club, Riding, Fishing nearby. Overlooking lake and Bantry Bay.

BUS NO: **8**

B&B PPS:	**£15/£17**	SNGL OCC. DBLE/TPL:	**£21.50/£23.50**	SNGL RM:	-
PART BRD:	-	% RED. CHILDREN:	**20%**	DINNER:	-

81

Bantry 2km

Vincent and Margaret O'Sullivan
SONAMAR
Dromleigh South, Bantry, Co Cork

Bantry

OPEN:	1st May-30th September
NO. ROOMS:	5
ENSUITE:	3

TEL: **027 50502**   FAX: -

Distinctive bungalow with extensive gardens, overlooking town, unsurpassed view of Bantry Bay, Scenic Walks, quiet location. Signposted from the square.

B&B PPS:	**£15/£17**	SNGL OCC. DBLE/TPL:	**£21.50/£23.50**	SNGL RM:	-
PART BRD:	-	% RED. CHILDREN:	**20%**	DINNER:	-

Bantry

Ursula Schiesser
SHANGRI - LA
Glengarriff Road, Newtown/Bantry, Co Cork

Bantry

OPEN:	15th March-15th November
NO. ROOMS:	6
ENSUITE:	4

TEL: **027 50244**   FAX: **027 50244**

Bungalow with spectacular views of Bantry Bay. Spacious garden. Tea/Coffee making facilities. Credit Cards welcome, Golf.

B&B PPS:	**£16/£18**	SNGL OCC. DBLE/TPL:	**£22.50/£24.50**	SNGL RM:	-
PART BRD:	-	% RED. CHILDREN:	**20%**	DINNER:	**£12**

Bantry 1km

Mrs Joan Sweeney
HIGHFIELD
Newtown, Bantry, Co Cork

Bantry

OPEN:	May-October
NO. ROOMS:	4
ENSUITE:	3

TEL: **027 50791**   FAX: -

Situated on main Bantry/Glengarriff Road. Views of Sea and Mountains. Tea & coffee making facilities, electric blankets. Garage for bicycles.

BUS NO. **7**

B&B PPS:	**£15/£17**	SNGL OCC. DBLE/TPL:	**£21.50/£23.50**	SNGL RM:	-
PART BRD:	-	% RED. CHILDREN:	**50%**	DINNER:	-

Bantry 1km

Mrs Josephine Walsh
EDEN CREST
Newtown, Bantry, Co Cork

Bantry

OPEN:	1st March-30th November
NO. ROOMS:	4
ENSUITE:	3

TEL: **027 51110**   FAX: **027 51036**   EMAIL: **edencrest@tinet.ie**

On N71 Bantry/Glengariff Road, turn at Esso station. Comfortable, tranquil, scenic house, overlooking Bantry Bay, with Garden and parking.

B&B PPS:	**£16/£17**	SNGL OCC. DBLE/TPL:	**£22.50/£23.50**	SNGL RM:	-
PART BRD:	-	% RED. CHILDREN:	-	DINNER:	-

Helen Allcorn
Shournagh Road
Blarney, Co Cork

Blarney

OPEN:	1st May-31st October
NO. ROOMS:	3
ENSUITE:	1

TEL: **021 385577**   FAX: -

Spacious country home and gardens situated on the banks of the Shournagh River surrounded by woodlands and meadows. Antique furnishings.

B&B PPS:	**£15/£17**	SNGL OCC. DBLE/TPL:	**£21.50/£23.50**	SNGL RM:	**£17**
PART BRD:	-	% RED. CHILDREN:	**50%**	DINNER:	-

Blarney 2km

Blarney 1km

Mrs Veronica Annis-Sisk
YVORY HOUSE
Killowen, Blarney, Co Cork

Blarney

OPEN:	April-November
NO. ROOMS:	4
ENSUITE:	2

 V

TEL: **021 381128**   FAX: -

Superbly appointed luxury bungalow in landscaped gardens. Colour TV in bedrooms. Tea/Coffee facilities. Private parking. 1km west Blarney village.

B&B PPS:	£15/£18	SNGL OCC. DBLE/TPL:	£21.50/£24.50	SNGL RM:	-
PART BRD:	-	% RED. CHILDREN:	20%	DINNER:	-

Blarney 2km

Mrs Mary Buckley
LAURISTON
Coolowen, Blarney, Co Cork

Blarney

OPEN:	1st February-30th November
NO. ROOMS:	3
ENSUITE:	2

V

TEL: **021 381007**   FAX: -

Luxurious bungalow set in landscaped gardens. Tea/Coffee facilities, Hairdryers and TV in bedrooms. Golf and Pitch Putt nearby.

B&B PPS:	£15/£17	SNGL OCC. DBLE/TPL:	£21.50/£23.50	SNGL RM:	-
PART BRD:	-	% RED. CHILDREN:	50%	DINNER:	-

Blarney 1km

Mrs Philomena Bugler
LYNVARA
**Killard,
Blarney, Co Cork**

Blarney

OPEN:	1st April-15th November
NO. ROOMS:	3
ENSUITE:	2

V

TEL: **021 385429**   FAX: -

Country home off R617, walking distance to blarney castle and shops, Private parking, Heating, Garden, Tea/Coffee facilities, breakfast menu.

B&B PPS:	£15/£17	SNGL OCC. DBLE/TPL:	-	SNGL RM:	-
PART BRD:	-	% RED. CHILDREN:	25%	DINNER:	-

In Blarney

The Callaghan Family
BUENA VISTA
Station Road, Blarney, Co Cork

Blarney

OPEN:	All Year except Christmas
NO. ROOMS:	5
ENSUITE:	5

V

TEL: **021 385035**   FAX: -

Well established, AA listed, bungalow & garden, tranquil location. Walking distance Castle/Town. Breakfast menu. 3rd left from Blarney, on Cork side.

B&B PPS:	£17	SNGL OCC. DBLE/TPL:	£23.50	SNGL RM:	-
PART BRD:	-	% RED. CHILDREN:	25%	DINNER:	-

Blarney 4km

Colette Collins
HEATHER LODGE
Kerry Road, Tower, Blarney, Co Cork

Blarney

OPEN:	All Year except Christmas
NO. ROOMS:	3
ENSUITE:	2

V

TEL: **021 381216**   FAX: **021 381216**

 Enjoy warm friendly hospitality in our lovely home, overlooking peaceful, scenic countryside. 1 km off Blarney/Killarney Road (R 617). Private Parking.

B&B PPS:	£15/£17	SNGL OCC. DBLE/TPL:	£21.50/£23.50	SNGL RM:	-
PART BRD:	£180	% RED. CHILDREN:	40%	DINNER:	£12

In Blarney

Pat and Regina Coughlan
THE WHITE HOUSE
Shean Lower, Blarney, Co Cork

Blarney

OPEN:	All Year except Christmas
NO. ROOMS:	6
ENSUITE:	6

TEL: **021 385338**   FAX: -

Well heated luxurious home, overlooking Castle. A.A. listed. All rooms with Satellite TV, Tea/coffee facilities, hairdryers. Extensive breakfast menu.

B&B PPS:	**£17.50/£18**	SNGL OCC. DBLE/TPL:	**£24/£24.50**	SNGL RM:	-
PART BRD:	-	% RED. CHILDREN:	**25%**	DINNER:	-

Blarney 1.5km

Mrs Anne Cremin
ASHCROFT
Stoneview, Blarney, Co Cork

Blarney

OPEN:	1st March-30th November
NO. ROOMS:	4
ENSUITE:	2

TEL: **021 385224**   FAX: -

Luxurious well heated modern home overlooking Blarney Castle, and Golf Course. All rooms with TV, Hairdryers and Tea/Coffee facilities.

B&B PPS:	**£15/£17**	SNGL OCC. DBLE/TPL:	**£21.50/£23.50**	SNGL RM:	-
PART BRD:	-	% RED. CHILDREN:	**50%**	DINNER:	-

Blarney 1.5km

Fran & Tony Cronin
HILLVIEW HOUSE
Killard, Blarney, Co Cork

Blarney

OPEN:	All Year except Christmas
NO. ROOMS:	4
ENSUITE:	4

TEL: **021 385161**   FAX: -

Family run home. Peaceful rustic surroundings, relax in sun lounge. Private Car Park. Breakfast Menu, Babysitting, TV, Hairdryers, Tea/Coffee.

B&B PPS:	**£17**	SNGL OCC. DBLE/TPL:	**£23.50**	SNGL RM:	-
PART BRD:	-	% RED. CHILDREN:	**25%**	DINNER:	-

In Blarney

Mrs Margaret Cronin
ROSEMOUNT
The Square, Blarney, Co Cork

Blarney

OPEN:	1st April-1st November
NO. ROOMS:	5
ENSUITE:	2

TEL: **021 385584**   FAX: -

Modern two storey home in peaceful location. Landscaped garden, private car park. Two minutes walk to Castle, Shops, Restaurants, Entertainment.

B&B PPS:	**£15/£18**	SNGL OCC. DBLE/TPL:	**£21.50/£24.50**	SNGL RM:	-
PART BRD:	-	% RED. CHILDREN:	**20%**	DINNER:	-

Cork City 4km

Mrs Noreen Curran
EVERGREEN HOUSE
Rathpeacon, Blarney, Co Cork

Blarney

OPEN:	March-October
NO. ROOMS:	6
ENSUITE:	5

TEL: **021 305715/305714**   FAX: -

Warm friendly home, tranquil country setting, picturesque gardens, spacious rooms, breakfast menu. Rathpeacon exit off N20. Restaurant 5 min, Blarney 10 minutes.

B&B PPS:	**£15/£18**	SNGL OCC. DBLE/TPL:	**£21.50**	SNGL RM:	-
PART BRD:	-	% RED. CHILDREN:	**10%**	DINNER:	-

Blarney 1km

Mrs Monica Daly
AVONDALE LODGE
Killowen, Blarney, Co Cork

Blarney

OPEN:	1st April-31st October
NO. ROOMS:	3
ENSUITE:	3

TEL: **021 381736**   FAX: -

Warm friendly home in scenic farming location. Horseriding, Golf, Music, locally. Tea/coffee facilities, electric blankets, hairdryers. Private Parking. Blarney 1km.

B&B PPS:	**£15/£17.50**	SNGL OCC. DBLE/TPL:	**£22.50/£24**	SNGL RM:	-
PART BRD:	-	% RED. CHILDREN:	**25%**	DINNER:	-

In Blarney

Mrs. Mary Falvey
CUANAN HOUSE
12 Castle Close Road, Blarney, Co Cork

Blarney

OPEN:	1st March-17th December
NO. ROOMS:	3
ENSUITE:	-

TEL: **021 385329**   FAX: -

Comfortable modern house and warm welcome to our home. Superb eating, good music, excellent shopping, Blarney Castle within walking distance.

B&B PPS:	**£15**	SNGL OCC. DBLE/TPL:	**£21.50**	SNGL RM:	**£18**
PART BRD:	-	% RED. CHILDREN:	**33.3%**	DINNER:	-

In Blarney

Mrs Bridget Harrington
CURRAC BUI
30 Castle Close Drive, Blarney, Co Cork

Blarney

OPEN:	1st April-31st October
NO. ROOMS:	4
ENSUITE:	3

TEL: **021 385424**   FAX: -

Modern home, minutes walk from Blarney Castle, adjacent to bus route. Cork 7 km. Irish music/dancing arranged. Tea facilities available.

B&B PPS:	**£15/£17**	SNGL OCC. DBLE/TPL:	**£21.50/£23.50**	SNGL RM:	-
PART BRD:	-	% RED. CHILDREN:	**33.3%**	DINNER:	-

Cork City 6km

Mrs Eileen Hempel
EDELWEISS HOUSE
Leemount, Carrigrohane, Co Cork

Blarney

OPEN:	1st February-20th December
NO. ROOMS:	6
ENSUITE:	3

TEL: **021 871888**   FAX: **021 871888**

10 mins Cork City. Blarney 2 miles N22 Killarney Road. Take right turn. Signposted. Chef owner. Poster beds, TV, Hairdryers, Credit Cards.

B&B PPS:	**£15/£18**	SNGL OCC. DBLE/TPL:	**£21.50/£25**	SNGL RM:	-
PART BRD:	**£205**	% RED. CHILDREN:	**20%**	DINNER:	**£13**

In Blarney

Anne Hennessy
BLARNEY VALE HOUSE
Cork Road, Blarney, Co Cork

Blarney

OPEN:	1st April-31st October
NO. ROOMS:	4
ENSUITE:	4

TEL: **021 381511**   FAX: -

Luxurious home set on private grounds overlooking Blarney Village. Peaceful setting, friendly atmosphere. Rooms TV, hairdryers.Tea/coffee available. Breakfast menu.

B&B PPS:	**£17.50/£18**	SNGL OCC. DBLE/TPL:	**£24/£25**	SNGL RM:	-
PART BRD:	-	% RED. CHILDREN:	**25%**	DINNER:	-

In Blarney

Mrs Margaret Kearney
SUNVILLE
1 Castle Close Lawn, Blarney, Co Cork

Blarney

OPEN:	**1st April-1st November**
NO. ROOMS:	**3**
ENSUITE:	**2**

(V)

TEL: **021 381325** FAX: -

Modern comfortable home 5 mins walk to Castle, Restaurants, Shops, Entertainment, Adjacent to bus route and beautiful country walk. Tea/Coffee facilities.

B&B PPS:	**£15/£17**	SNGL OCC. DBLE/TPL:	**£23.50**	SNGL RM:	**£15/£16**
PART BRD:	-	% RED. CHILDREN:	**25%**	DINNER:	-

Blarney 5km

Mrs Cecilia Kiely
CLARAGH
Waterloo Road, Blarney, Co Cork

Blarney

OPEN:	**April-October**
NO. ROOMS:	**4**
ENSUITE:	**3**

(V)

TEL: **021 886308** FAX: -

Welcoming tray on arrival. Breakfast menu includes French toast. Electric blankets. Tea facilities in lounge. Blarney 10 minutes. Country walks.

B&B PPS:	**£15/£17**	SNGL OCC. DBLE/TPL:	**£21.50/£23.50**	SNGL RM:	-
PART BRD:	-	% RED. CHILDREN:	**10%**	DINNER:	-

Blarney 2km

Mrs Anne Lynch
THE GABLES
Stoneview, Blarney, Co Cork

Blarney

OPEN:	**March-November**
NO. ROOMS:	**3**
ENSUITE:	**3**

(V)

TEL: **021 385330** FAX: -

Comfortable Early-Victorian residence on two acres, overlooking Blarney Castle. Ideal touring base. Itineraries arranged. Homebaking/breakfast menu, electric blankets.

B&B PPS:	**£17**	SNGL OCC. DBLE/TPL:	**£24**	SNGL RM:	-
PART BRD:	-	% RED. CHILDREN:	**50%**	DINNER:	-

Blarney 1km

Robin & Claire Lyons
ELMGROVE
Shournagh Road, Blarney, Co Cork

Blarney

OPEN:	**All Year except Christmas**
NO. ROOMS:	**4**
ENSUITE:	**4**

(V)

TEL: **021 385136** FAX: -

Ideally situated just off Blarney/Killarney Road (R617). Close to all amenities, Golf, Horse Riding, Shopping, Restaurants. Home baking a speciality.

B&B PPS:	**£17/£18**	SNGL OCC. DBLE/TPL:	**£23.50/£24.50**	SNGL RM:	-
PART BRD:	-	% RED. CHILDREN:	**50%**	DINNER:	-

Blarney 3km

Mrs Marie McLoughney S.R.N
GREENWAY'S
**Woodside, Kerry Pike, Blarney
Co Cork**

Blarney

OPEN:	**1st March - 31st October**
NO. ROOMS:	**4**
ENSUITE:	**3**

(V)

TEL: **021 385383** FAX: -

Spacious home offering every comfort . From Blarney direction Killarney 1st Road left. Tea/Coffee facilities, TV bedrooms. City 4 miles. Breakfast choice.

B&B PPS:	**£15/£17**	SNGL OCC. DBLE/TPL:	**£21.50/£23.50**	SNGL RM:	**£18**
PART BRD:	-	% RED. CHILDREN:	**50%**	DINNER:	-

Blarney 1.5km

Phil & Liam Magnier
WATERLOO HOUSE
Waterloo, Blarney, Co Cork

	Blarney
OPEN:	All Year except Christmas
NO. ROOMS:	4
ENSUITE:	4

TEL: **021 381153**   FAX: -

Castle 1.5 km, Cork City 9 km. Safe private car park/garden. Fishing, Golfing, Driving Range, Horse Riding, Pitch and Putt nearby.

B&B PPS:	**£15/£17**	SNGL OCC. DBLE/TPL:	**£23.50/£25**	SNGL RM:	-
PART BRD:	-	% RED. CHILDREN:	15%	DINNER:	-

Blarney 1km

Mrs Caroline Morgan
KILLARNEY HOUSE
Station Road, Blarney, Co Cork

	Blarney
OPEN:	All Year except Christmas
NO. ROOMS:	6
ENSUITE:	6

TEL: **021 381841**   FAX: -

Purpose built luxury accommodation on 1 acre of landscaped gardens. Adjacent to Castle, Restaurants, Shops & Entertainment.

B&B PPS:	**£17.50/£18**	SNGL OCC. DBLE/TPL:	**£24/£25**	SNGL RM:	-
PART BRD:	-	% RED. CHILDREN:	20%	DINNER:	-

Blarney 1km

Mrs Janet Murphy Hallissey
PINE FOREST
Elmcourt, Blarney, Co Cork

	Blarney
OPEN:	All Year except Christmas
NO. ROOMS:	4
ENSUITE:	4

TEL: **021 385979**   FAX: -

Spacious bungalow situated in peaceful area with large Landscaped Garden, 1km from Blarney/Killarney Road (617). Breakfast menu available. Private Parking.

B&B PPS:	**£17**	SNGL OCC. DBLE/TPL:	**£23.50**	SNGL RM:	-
PART BRD:	-	% RED. CHILDREN:	25%	DINNER:	-

In Blarney

Mrs Mary O'Brien
FIRGROVE
1 Castle Close Villas, Blarney, Co Cork

	Blarney
OPEN:	March-November
NO. ROOMS:	3
ENSUITE:	2

TEL: **021 381403**   FAX: -

Well recommended quiet comfortable home. Friendly atmosphere. Minutes walk to Bus, Castle, Shops, Restaurants, Entertainment. Golf, Horseriding. Ideal touring base.

B&B PPS:	**£15/£18**	SNGL OCC. DBLE/TPL:	**£21.50/£24.50**	SNGL RM:	-
PART BRD:	-	% RED. CHILDREN:	20%	DINNER:	-

Blarney 6km

Mrs Ita O'Donovan
KNOCKAWN WOOD
Curraleigh, Inniscarra, Co Cork

	Blarney
OPEN:	All Year
NO. ROOMS:	4
ENSUITE:	3

TEL: **021 870284**   FAX: **021 870284**   EMAIL: **odknkwd@iol.ie**

Picturesque. Peaceful. Tea & scones on arrival. Dinner without notice. Frommer recommended. Inniscarra fishing. Ferry/Airport 30 minutes. 6km Blarney/Killarney Rd. (R618.

B&B PPS:	**£15/£17**	SNGL OCC. DBLE/TPL:	-	SNGL RM:	-
PART BRD:	**£180**	% RED. CHILDREN:	50%	DINNER:	£12

Blarney 3km

Anne & John O'Leary
ASHLEE LODGE
Tower, Blarney, Co Cork

Blarney	
OPEN:	All Year except Christmas
No. ROOMS:	6
ENSUITE:	5

TEL: **021 385346**   FAX: **021 385346**

(V)

Superbly appointed luxury bungalow. Blarney/Killarney road (R617). Quiet setting. Prize winning garden. Secure parking. Excellent cuisine, French, German spoken.

B&B PPS:	£16/£18	SNGL OCC. DBLE/TPL:		£25	SNGL RM:	-
PART BRD:	£195	% RED. CHILDREN:		25%	DINNER:	£15

Blarney 4km

Mrs Gertie O'Shea
TRAVELLERS JOY
Tower, Blarney, Co Cork

Blarney	
OPEN:	February-December
No. ROOMS:	3
ENSUITE:	2

TEL: **021 385541**   FAX: -

(V)

Blarney/Killarney, R617. Causin/Dillard recommended. Traditional music. Private parking. Prizewinning gardens. Quality Breakfasts. Ideal base for touring Cork/Kerry.

B&B PPS:	£15/£17	SNGL OCC. DBLE/TPL:	£21.50/£23.50	SNGL RM:	£18
PART BRD:	-	% RED. CHILDREN:	50%	DINNER:	£13

Blarney 3km

Chef Billie & Catherine Phelan
PHELAN'S WOODVIEW HOUSE
Tweedmount, Blarney, Co Cork

Blarney	
OPEN:	1st March-30th November
No. ROOMS:	8
ENSUITE:	7

TEL: **021 385197**   FAX: -

(V)

Enjoy Gourmet Cooking at Phelans, Seafood a speciality. TV in bedrooms. Tea/coffee facilities, Credit Cards. Frommer & Eye Witness Guides recommended.

B&B PPS:	£15/£18	SNGL OCC. DBLE/TPL:	£21.50/£24.50	SNGL RM:	£21
PART BRD:	-	% RED. CHILDREN:	25%	DINNER:	£15

Blarney 3km

Shiela & Michael Porter
SYLVAN MANOR TOWER,
Blarney, Co Cork

Blarney	
OPEN:	2nd January-22nd December
No. ROOMS:	4
ENSUITE:	4

TEL: **021 381977**   FAX: -

(V)

Purpose-built luxury accommodation. Warm friendly hospitality. Overlooking scenic countryside. Breakfast menu. Off Blarney/Killarney Road (R617). AA listed.

B&B PPS:	£17	SNGL OCC. DBLE/TPL:	£23.50	SNGL RM:	-
PART BRD:	-	% RED. CHILDREN:	20%	DINNER:	-

Blarney 5km

Noelle and Patrick Roche
CHIRIQUI
Canons Cross, Inniscarra, Co Cork

Blarney	
OPEN:	May-October
No. ROOMS:	4
ENSUITE:	4

TEL: **021 871061**   FAX: **021 871061 (Manual)**

(V)

Restful, comfortable, orthopaedic beds, electric blankets, hairdryers, warm, pressurised showers. Credit cards. Blarney-Killarney Rd R618. Satellite TV. Fishing facilities.

B&B PPS:	£18	SNGL OCC. DBLE/TPL:		£25	SNGL RM:	-
PART BRD:	-	% RED. CHILDREN:		50%	DINNER:	-

Blarney 3km

The Spillett Family
BREHON HOUSE
Killowen, Blarney, Co Cork

TEL: 021 385047　　FAX: -

Blarney

OPEN:	March-October
NO. ROOMS:	3
ENSUITE:	3

 (V)

Spacious bungalow set in scenic farming location overlooking open countryside. Private parking. Blarney 3 km. Riding Centre and Golf Courses nearby.

B&B PPS:	£17	SNGL OCC. DBLE/TPL:	£23.50/£25	SNGL RM:	-
PART BRD:	-	% RED. CHILDREN:	50%	DINNER:	-

Blarney 3km

Jim & Sinead Symons
ATHDARA
Kerry Road, Tower, Blarney Co Cork

TEL: 021 381143　　FAX: 021 381143

Blarney

OPEN:	1st Feburary-31st November
NO. ROOMS:	4
ENSUITE:	2

(V)

Bright spacious home 50 metres off Blarney/Killarney Rd (R617). Traditional Music, Restaurants, Golf/Fishing nearby. Hospitality assured. Groups welcome.

B&B PPS:	£15/£17	SNGL OCC. DBLE/TPL:	£21.50/£23.50	SNGL RM:	-
PART BRD:	£180	% RED. CHILDREN:	50%	DINNER:	£12

Blarney 2km

Mrs Olwen Venn
MARANATHA COUNTRY HOUSE
Tower, Blarney, Co Cork

TEL: 021 385102　　FAX: 021 385102

Blarney

OPEN:	April-November
NO. ROOMS:	5
ENSUITE:	4

(V)

Stroll through the beautiful private gardens and woodlands surrounding this lovely Victorian mansion. Spacious romantic bedrooms. Beautiful historic antiques throughout.

B&B PPS:	£19/£22.50	SNGL OCC. DBLE/TPL:	£23/£26.50	SNGL RM:	-
PART BRD:	-	% RED. CHILDREN:	50%	DINNER:	-

Carrigaline 5km

Tony & Catherine Deasy
RAFFEEN LODGE
Ringaskiddy Road, Monkstown, Co Cork

TEL: 021 371632　　FAX: 021 371632

Carrigaline/Ferryport/Airport Area

OPEN:	1st March-1st November
NO. ROOMS:	6
ENSUITE:	6

(V)

Highly recommended. Located on Cork/Ringaskiddy route (N28). Ideal touring base or first & last stop. Ferryport (5km), Airport (10km).

B&B PPS:	£17/£20	SNGL OCC. DBLE/TPL:	£23.50/£26.50	SNGL RM:	-
PART BRD:	-	% RED. CHILDREN:	20%	DINNER:	-

Carrigaline 1km

Mrs Vera O'Byrne
CARRIGCOURT HOUSE
Carrigaline, Co Cork

TEL: 021 371750　　FAX: 021 371477

Carrigaline/Ferryport/Cork Airport

OPEN:	All Year except Christmas
NO. ROOMS:	4
ENSUITE:	2

(V)

Tastefully decorated, spacious home with mature gardens and patio. Ideally situated for Ringaskiddy Ferry (3 mins) and Cork Airport (10 mins).

B&B PPS:	£15/£18	SNGL OCC. DBLE/TPL:	£21.50/£24.50	SNGL RM:	£17.50/£22.50
PART BRD:	-	% RED. CHILDREN:	50%	DINNER:	-

Carrigaline 1.5km

Gretta O'Grady
CHESTNUT LODGE
Carrigaline, Co Cork

TEL: **021 371382**   FAX: **021 372818**

Spacious luxurious home, peaceful surroundings, Golf, Angling, Horseriding, Cinema, Restaurants, Beaches closeby. Sun-lounge, patio. Ferryport 5km, Airport 10km.

Carrigaline/Cork Ferryport/Airport

OPEN:	All Year	
NO. ROOMS:	4	
ENSUITE:	4	(V)

B&B PPS:	£18/£22	SNGL OCC. DBLE/TPL:	£24.50/£28.50	SNGL RM:	-
PART BRD:	-	% RED. CHILDREN:	25%	DINNER:	-

Carrigaline 1km

Mrs Ann O'Leary
THE WILLOWS
Ballea Road, Carrigaline, Co Cork

TEL: **021 372669**   FAX: -

Split level house with gardens front and rear. Fishing, Golfing, Horse Riding, and Beaches 3km. Cork airport 6km. Ringaskiddy Ferry 5km.

Carrigaline/Cork Ferryport/Airport

OPEN:	All Year except Christmas	
NO. ROOMS:	5	
ENSUITE:	3	(V)

B&B PPS:	£15/£20	SNGL OCC. DBLE/TPL:	£21.50/£26.50	SNGL RM:	-
PART BRD:	-	% RED. CHILDREN:	33.3%	DINNER:	-

Carrigaline 5km

Dan & Anne O'Rahilly
ASHDALE HOUSE
Lower Shanbally, Ringaskiddy, Co Cork

TEL: **021 378681**   FAX: -

Situated on Cork/Ringaskiddy Route (N28). Ferryport 3 mins. Airport via South-Ring Road / N28 (12Kms). Early Breakfasts.

Carrigaline/Cork Ferryport/Airport

OPEN:	All Year except Christmas	
NO. ROOMS:	4	
ENSUITE:	4	(V)

B&B PPS:	£17/£18	SNGL OCC. DBLE/TPL:	£23.50/£25	SNGL RM:	-
PART BRD:	-	% RED. CHILDREN:	20%	DINNER:	-

Carrigtwohill 0.5km

Mrs Breda Hayes
CEDAR-VILLE
Carrigtwohill, Co Cork

TEL: **021 883246**   FAX: -

N25 Cork/Waterford/Rosslare road. Country home, Frommer recommended. Near excellent restaurants. Fota wildlife park. Jameson heritage, Trabolgon, Cobh. Parking.

Carrigtwohill

OPEN:	1st May-31st October	
NO. ROOMS:	4	
ENSUITE:	2	(V)

B&B PPS:	£15/£17	SNGL OCC. DBLE/TPL:	£21.50/£23.50	SNGL RM:	£21.50
PART BRD:	-	% RED. CHILDREN:	50%	DINNER:	-

Teresa Murray
ANNGROVE LODGE
Anngrove, Carrigtwohill, Co Cork

TEL: **021 883834**   FAX: -

Off N25, Cork/Rosslare Road. Peaceful scenic surroundings, landscaped gardens, play area. Convenient Fota Wildlife, Trabolgan, Jameson Heritage Centre, Golf.

Carrigtwohill

OPEN:	1st April-31st October	
NO. ROOMS:	4	
ENSUITE:	2	(V)

B&B PPS:	£15/£17	SNGL OCC. DBLE/TPL:	£21.50/£23.50	SNGL RM:	-
PART BRD:	£180	% RED. CHILDREN:	50%	DINNER:	£12

Carrigtwohill 2km

In Carrigtwohill

Miss Margot Seymour
DUN-VREEDA HOUSE
Carrigtwohill, Co Cork

Carrigtwohill

OPEN:	All Year
NO. ROOMS:	4
ENSUITE:	2

(V)

TEL: 021 883169   FAX: -

Off N25 Cork, Waterford/Rosslare Rd. at Carrigtwohill. Near Fota Wildlife, Cobh, Trabolgan, Midleton Heritage Centre. Little Island Golf. Snacks, meals.

| B&B PPS: | £15/£17 | SNGL OCC. DBLE/TPL: | £21.50/£23.50 | SNGL RM: | £18 |
| PART BRD: | £180 | % RED. CHILDREN: | 50% | DINNER: | £12 |

In Castletownbere

Mrs Mary Donegan
REALT-NA-MARA
Castletownbere, Co Cork

Castletownbere

OPEN:	All Year except Christmas
NO. ROOMS:	5
ENSUITE:	4

(V)

TEL: 027 70101   FAX: -

Friendly home, large gardens, Castletownbere/Glengarriff Road overlooking sea. near Beara Way Walking Route. Ideal Touring, Fishing, Golfing. Complimentary Tea/Coffee.

| B&B PPS: | £15/£17 | SNGL OCC. DBLE/TPL: | £21.50/£23.50 | SNGL RM: | - |
| PART BRD: | - | % RED. CHILDREN: | 33.3% | DINNER: | - |

Castletownbere 1km

Mrs Noralene McGurn
SEA BREEZE
Derrymihan, Castletownbere,
Beara Peninsula, Co Cork

Castletownbere

OPEN:	1st January-20th December
NO. ROOMS:	3
ENSUITE:	3

(V)

TEL: 027 70508   FAX: -

Newly decorated home situated in peaceful scenic location overlooking sea. On beautiful Ring of Beara route. Close Golf amenities etc.

| B&B PPS: | £17 | SNGL OCC. DBLE/TPL: | £23.50 | SNGL RM: | - |
| PART BRD: | - | % RED. CHILDREN: | 50% | DINNER: | £12 |

Ardgroom Village 5km

Mary & John Gerard O'Sullivan
SEA VILLA
Castletownberehaven Cst Rd, Ardgroom
Inward, Beara Peninsula, Co Cork

Castletownberehaven/Ardgroom

OPEN:	1st April-31st October
NO. ROOMS:	3
ENSUITE:	3

(V)

TEL: 027 74369   FAX: 027 74369

New luxurious acommodation in tranquil scenic location on Coast Road/Beara way. Breakfast menu. , TV, trouserpress, hairdryer. Visa/Mastercard.

| B&B PPS: | £17 | SNGL OCC. DBLE/TPL: | £23.50 | SNGL RM: | £21 |
| PART BRD: | - | % RED. CHILDREN: | 25% | DINNER: | - |

In Clonakilty

Tony & Noreen Driscoll
BAY VIEW HOUSE
Old Timoleague Road, Clonakilty,
Co Cork

Clonakilty

OPEN:	March-October
NO. ROOMS:	6
ENSUITE:	4

(V)

TEL: 023 33539   FAX: -

Beautifully decorated home. Prizewinning gardens, bright co-ordinated bedrooms. Relax in luxurious surroundings overlooking Bay, countryside, yet within 3 min walk towncentre.

| B&B PPS: | £15/£17 | SNGL OCC. DBLE/TPL: | £21.50/£23.50 | SNGL RM: | - |
| PART BRD: | - | % RED. CHILDREN: | 40% | DINNER: | - |

Mrs Clare Hayes
WYTCHWOOD
Emmet Square, Clonakilty, Co Cork

Clonakilty

OPEN:	All Year except Christmas
NO. ROOMS:	6
ENSUITE:	5

(V)

TEL: 023 33525   FAX: 023 33525   EMAIL: **wytchost@iol.ie**

Georgian house with walled garden in a quiet area. Le Guide du Routard recommended. Breakfast menu. Cycle hire and routes on premises.

B&B PPS:	**£18**	SNGL OCC. DBLE/TPL:	**£24.50**	SNGL RM:	**£20**
PART BRD:	-	% RED. CHILDREN:	25%	DINNER:	-

— Clonakilty

Mrs Ann Lehane
BALARD HOUSE
Ballymacowen, Clonakilty, Co Cork

Clonakilty

OPEN:	May-October
NO. ROOMS:	3
ENSUITE:	3

(V)

TEL: 023 33865   FAX: -

Modern bungalow in peaceful location on Kinsale/Clonakilty Road (R600). Restaurants, Beaches, Sailing, Golf & Horse-Riding within easy reach.

B&B PPS:	**£17**	SNGL OCC. DBLE/TPL:	**£23.50**	SNGL RM:	-
PART BRD:	**£200**	% RED. CHILDREN:	50%	DINNER:	**£13**

— Clonakilty 4km

Denise McCarthy-Walsh
BUSHMOUNT LODGE
Park Road, Clonakilty, Co Cork

Clonakilty

OPEN:	1st May-15th August
NO. ROOMS:	3
ENSUITE:	1

(V)

TEL: 023 33798   FAX: -

Elegant accommodation. Charming spacious home. Acre of secluded landscaped gardens. Romantic four-poster bedrooms. Extensive Breakfast menu. Located on by-pass.

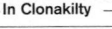 

B&B PPS:	**£20/£25**	SNGL OCC. DBLE/TPL:	-	SNGL RM:	**£20/£25**
PART BRD:	-	% RED. CHILDREN:	25%	DINNER:	-

— In Clonakilty

Noreen & David McMahon
NORDAV
off Western Road, (Fernhill Rd)
Clonakilty, Co Cork

Clonakilty

OPEN:	April-November
NO. ROOMS:	6
ENSUITE:	5

(V)

TEL: 023 33655   FAX: -

Award winning gardens, downstairs bedrooms (ensuite) self-catering facilities. 2 suites with fires one with verandah £25 P.P.S.

B&B PPS:	**£15/£19**	SNGL OCC. DBLE/TPL:	**£23.50/£25.50**	SNGL RM:	-
PART BRD:	-	% RED. CHILDREN:	-	DINNER:	-

— In Clonakilty

Mrs Breda Moore
SHALOM
Ballyduvane, Clonakilty, Co Cork

Clonakilty

OPEN:	March-October
NO. ROOMS:	3
ENSUITE:	2

TEL: 023 33473   FAX: -

Modern bungalow in rural setting on main Clonakilty - Skibbereen road (N71). 2 km Clonakilty Town, 6 km beautiful sandy Inchydoney Beach.

B&B PPS:	**£14/£15**	SNGL OCC. DBLE/TPL:	-	SNGL RM:	-
PART BRD:	-	% RED. CHILDREN:	-	DINNER:	-

— Clonakilty 2km

In Clonakilty

Angela O'Driscoll
AISLING HEIGHTS
Clogheen Meadows, Clogheen,
Clonakilty, West Cork, Co Cork

TEL: **023 33491**   FAX: -

Clonakilty

OPEN:	3rd January-20th December
No. ROOMS:	4
ENSUITE:	4

(V)

Newly built two storey house in nice area close to all amenities and within walking distance of town.

B&B PPS:	**£17**	SNGL OCC. DBLE/TPL:	**£23.50**	SNGL RM:	-
PART BRD:	-	% RED. CHILDREN:	**25%**	DINNER:	-

Clonakilty 3km

Mrs Nora O'Regan
ASSUMPTION HOUSE
Ballinascarthy, Clonakilty, Co Cork

TEL: **023 39268**   FAX: -

Clonakilty

OPEN:	1st March-31st October
No. ROOMS:	3
ENSUITE:	2

(V)

Warm welcoming home, in Ballinascarthy on N71. Freshly prepared wholesome food. Home cooking a speciality. Excellent location to Beaches & Day Tours.

B&B PPS:	**£15/£17**	SNGL OCC. DBLE/TPL:	**£21.50/£23.50**	SNGL RM:	**£21.50/£23.50**
PART BRD:	-	% RED. CHILDREN:	**25%**	DINNER:	-

Cobh 2km

Mrs Georgina Coughlan
GLEBE HOUSE
Tay Road, Cobh, Co Cork

TEL: **021 811373**   FAX: **021 811373**   EMAIL: **glebehouse@tinet.ie**

Cobh

OPEN:	1st April-31st October
No. ROOMS:	3
ENSUITE:	1

(V)

Comfortable friendly country home, sign posted after Fota Wildlife Park, or Cross River Ferry. Convenient Ringaskiddy Ferry Port. French spoken. Cobh 2 km.

B&B PPS:	**£15/£18**	SNGL OCC. DBLE/TPL:	**£21.50/£25**	SNGL RM:	-
PART BRD:	-	% RED. CHILDREN:	**20%**	DINNER:	-

Cobh 1.4km

Pat & Martha Hurley
HIGHLAND
Ballywilliam, Cobh, Co Cork

TEL: **021 813873**   FAX: **021 813873**

Cobh

OPEN:	1st March-31st October
No. ROOMS:	4
ENSUITE:	4

(V)

Modern home with panoramic views, close to Local and International Ferries. Fota Golf , Wildlife Park, Queenstown Story, Ground floor rooms.

B&B PPS:	**£18**	SNGL OCC. DBLE/TPL:	**£25**	SNGL RM:	-
PART BRD:	-	% RED. CHILDREN:	**50%**	DINNER:	-

Cobh 2km

Mrs Bernadette Maddox
TEARMANN
Ballynoe, Cobh, Co Cork

TEL: **021 813182**   FAX: **021 814011**

Cobh

OPEN:	1st March-31st October
No. ROOMS:	3
ENSUITE:	2

(V)

19th Century Traditional House. Premier guides recommended. Beautiful gardens for guests.Car Park. Convenient to Golf Courses & Heritage Centres. Ringaskiddy port.

B&B PPS:	**£15/£17.50**	SNGL OCC. DBLE/TPL:	**£21.50/£24**	SNGL RM:	-
PART BRD:	**£180**	% RED. CHILDREN:	**20%**	DINNER:	**£12**

Mrs Mary Bayer
WHITE LODGE
Airport Cross, Kinsale Road, Cork, Co Cork

Cork City/Airport Kinsale Road	
OPEN:	All Year except Christmas
No. Rooms:	4
Ensuite:	3

TEL: 021 961267   FAX: -

Peacefully situated villa overlooking Cork City. Airport 1 km, City 6 km. Enroute to Ferryport & West Cork. Friendly relaxed atmosphere.

B&B PPS:	£15/£17	SNGL OCC. DBLE/TPL:	£21.50/£23.50	SNGL RM:	£13/£15
PART BRD:	£180	% RED. CHILDREN:	50%	DINNER:	£12

Cork City 5km

Mrs Helena Higgins
HELENA
Kinsale Road, Ballygarvan, Co Cork

Cork City/Airport Kinsale Road	
OPEN:	1st April-31st October
No. Rooms:	3
Ensuite:	2

TEL: 021 888126   FAX: -

Modern bungalow on main Cork/Kinsale road, overlooking picturesque countryside, 5mins drive to Airport. Near Kinsale, Ferryport, Golf.

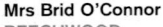

B&B PPS:	£16/£17.50	SNGL OCC. DBLE/TPL:	£22.50/£24	SNGL RM:	-
PART BRD:	-	% RED. CHILDREN:	10%	DINNER:	-

Cork 5km

Mrs Brid O'Connor
BEECHWOOD
Curra, Riverstick, Co Cork

Cork City/Airport Kinsale Road	
OPEN:	1st May-1st September
No. Rooms:	4
Ensuite:	3

TEL: 021 771456   FAX: -

Country home set in scenic and tranquil surroundings, off R600 (Airport/Kinsale Road). Convenient to Airport, Ferry Port and Kinsale.

B&B PPS:	£17/£17.50	SNGL OCC. DBLE/TPL:	£24	SNGL RM:	-
PART BRD:	-	% RED. CHILDREN:	10%	DINNER:	-

Kinsale 8km

Mrs Kathleen O'Mahony
FUCHSIA
Adamstown, Ballinhassig, Co Cork

Cork City/Airport Kinsale Road	
OPEN:	1st April-30th October
No. Rooms:	4
Ensuite:	2

TEL: 021 888198   FAX: -

Landscaped garden, books. Convenint Kinsale, Airport, Ferry port. Early breakfasts. (From Cork N27=R600) (West Cork N71=R613) Credit Cards.

B&B PPS:	£16/£17.50	SNGL OCC. DBLE/TPL:	£22.50/£24	SNGL RM:	-
PART BRD:	-	% RED. CHILDREN:	10%	DINNER:	-

Cork 8km

Mrs Breeda Savage
GREEN ISLE
Ballygarvan Village (Off Airport/Kinsale Road), Co Cork

Cork City/Airport Kinsale Road	
OPEN:	All Year except Christmas
No. Rooms:	3
Ensuite:	2

TEL: 021 888171   FAX: -

Country Home in Scenic Valley off Cork/Kinsale Road. Airport 2km. Near Kinsale. Ferryport 8km. Tea/Coffee in rooms. Visa.

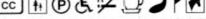

B&B PPS:	£16/£17.50	SNGL OCC. DBLE/TPL:	£22.50/£24	SNGL RM:	-
PART BRD:	-	% RED. CHILDREN:	20%	DINNER:	-

Cork City 10km

Cork City 2km

Mrs Kay O'Donovan
DUNDERG
38 Westgate Road, Bishopstown, Cork City, Co Cork

OPEN:	All Year except Christmas
NO. ROOMS:	3
ENSUITE:	1

TEL: 021 543078 FAX: **021 543078**

Quiet location 400m off N71 at Bishopstown Bar. Convenient to West Cork, Killarney, Ferry, Airport, University Hospital, UCC and FAS.

BUS NO: **5, 8**

B&B PPS:	**£15/£19**	SNGL OCC. DBLE/TPL:	**£21.50/£25.50**	SNGL RM:	**£17/£19**
PART BRD:	-	% RED. CHILDREN:	-	DINNER:	-

Cork City 2km

Mrs Eileen Stack
CAROLEVILLE
36 Beaumont Drive, Ballintemple, Blackrock, Co Cork

OPEN:	All Year except Christmas
NO. ROOMS:	3
ENSUITE:	3

TEL: 021 294321 FAX: -

Comfortable family home in residential area. TV/coffee/tea facilities in rooms. Private parking, Taxi, adjacent to Showgrounds. Airport. Car Ferry.

BUS NO: **2**

B&B PPS:	**£17**	SNGL OCC. DBLE/TPL:	-	SNGL RM:	**£22**
PART BRD:	-	% RED. CHILDREN:	**20%**	DINNER:	-

Cork City 2.5km

Mrs Barbara Ahern
BRANDON
Hillgrove Lawn, South Douglas Road, Cork City, Co Cork

OPEN:	All Year except Christmas
NO. ROOMS:	4
ENSUITE:	3

TEL: 021 893859 FAX: -

Detached house in quiet cul-de-sac. Convenient to Airport, Ferry, Bus, Swimming, Shopping, Restaurant, Golf. TV in bedrooms. Near O'Sullivans pharmacy.

BUS NO: **6**

B&B PPS:	**£15/£18**	SNGL OCC. DBLE/TPL:	**£21.50/£24.50**	SNGL RM:	-
PART BRD:	-	% RED. CHILDREN:	-	DINNER:	-

Cork 5km

Mrs Patricia Josephine Canniffe
KORLYM
Carrigaline Road, Douglas, Co Cork

OPEN:	1st April-31st October
NO. ROOMS:	4
ENSUITE:	2

TEL: 021 893858 FAX: -

Warm welcome. Home baking, complimentary tea, relax in spacious sun lounge. Ferryport/Airport 12 Km. Pubs, shopping 15 mins walk.

B&B PPS:	**£16/£18**	SNGL OCC. DBLE/TPL:	**£22.50/£24.50**	SNGL RM:	-
PART BRD:	-	% RED. CHILDREN:	-	DINNER:	-

Cork 3km

Mrs Catherine Edwards
RIVER VIEW
Douglas East, Cork, Co Cork

OPEN:	All Year except Christmas
NO. ROOMS:	3
ENSUITE:	3

TEL: 021 893762 FAX: -

Victorian 1890 home in Douglas village. near Barrys Pub. Convenient restaurants shopping centres, Churches, Airport, Ferry. Cable TV all bedrooms.

BUS NO: **7**

B&B PPS:	**£17/£20**	SNGL OCC. DBLE/TPL:	**£23.50**	SNGL RM:	-
PART BRD:	-	% RED. CHILDREN:	-	DINNER:	-

Cork 4km

Mrs Betty French
GLENMALURE
Carrigaline Road, Douglas, Co Cork

Cork City/Douglas Area

OPEN:	10th January-10th December
NO. ROOMS:	3
ENSUITE:	1

(V)

TEL: **021 894324**   FAX: -

Personal attention in comfortable home off N28. From Cork take second Douglas exit. From Ferryport, Douglas exit. Convenient Airport, Ferryport.

BUS NO: **7**

B&B PPS:	**£15/£18**	SNGL OCC. DBLE/TPL:	**£21.50/£24.50**	SNGL RM:	-
PART BRD:	-	% RED. CHILDREN:	**33.3%**	DINNER:	-

Cork City 4km

Mrs Elizabeth O'Shea + Family
FATIMA HOUSE
Grange Road, Douglas, Cork City, Co Cork

Cork City/Douglas Area

OPEN:	All Year
NO. ROOMS:	5
ENSUITE:	4

(V)

TEL: **021 362536**   FAX: **021 362536**

South ring road. Touchdown roundabout. Airport exit = N27 signposted. Sharp left Little Chef. Every convenience locally. House taxi. City buses.

BUS NO: **6, 7**

B&B PPS:	**£15/£20**	SNGL OCC. DBLE/TPL:	**£21.50/£26.50**	SNGL RM:	-
PART BRD:	-	% RED. CHILDREN:	-	DINNER:	-

Cork City 1km

Mrs Evelyn O'Sullivan
COOLFADDA HOUSE
Douglas Road, Cork City, Co Cork

Cork City/Douglas Area

OPEN:	All Year except Christmas
NO. ROOMS:	5
ENSUITE:	2

(V)

TEL: **021 363489**   FAX:

Route 609 Near St. Finbarrs Hospital. Ground floor accommodation. Tea facilities on request. Walking distance city centre, bus, train station.

BUS NO: **7, 7a, 6, 10**

B&B PPS:	**£15/£17.50**	SNGL OCC. DBLE/TPL:	**£21.50/£24.50**	SNGL RM:	-
PART BRD:	-	% RED. CHILDREN:	**33.3%**	DINNER:	-

Cork 3km

Mrs Ann Ryan
HILLCREST HOUSE
South Douglas Road, Cork, Co Cork

Cork City/Douglas Area

OPEN:	1st April-31st October
NO. ROOMS:	3
ENSUITE:	1

(V)

TEL: **021 891178**   FAX: -

Detached family home with large garden, south facing (bedroom overlooking garden). Close to Town & Ferry with Golf Course nearby.

BUS NO: **6**

B&B PPS:	**£15/£25**	SNGL OCC. DBLE/TPL:	**£21.50/£31.50**	SNGL RM:	-
PART BRD:	-	% RED. CHILDREN:	**30%**	DINNER:	-

Mrs Majorie Flynn
KENT HOUSE
47 Lower Glanmire Road, Cork City, Co Cork

Cork City/Lr Glanmire

OPEN:	All Year except Christmas
NO. ROOMS:	6
ENSUITE:	4

(V)

TEL: **021 504260**   FAX: -

Family run home adjacent to Railway Station and Bus Station. City Centre 5 mins walk.

B&B PPS:	**£16/£18**	SNGL OCC. DBLE/TPL:	**£22.50/£24.50**	SNGL RM:	-
PART BRD:	-	% RED. CHILDREN:	-	DINNER:	-

In Cork

Rhona Foley
NUMBER FORTY EIGHT
48 Lr Glanmire Road, Cork City, Co Cork

Cork City/Lower Glanmire Road

OPEN:	February-November
NO. ROOMS:	4
ENSUITE:	4

(V)

TEL: **021 505790**   FAX: -

Victorian Townhouse on Cork/ Dublin Road (N8).Adjacent Railway Station, walking distance City Centre/Bus Station. Homebaking. Early breakfast available.

B&B PPS:	£17	SNGL OCC. DBLE/TPL:	£23.50	SNGL RM:	-
PART BRD:	-	% RED. CHILDREN:	33%	DINNER:	-

In Cork City

Mrs Mary Foley
LISADELL HOUSE
Western Road, Cork City, Co Cork

Cork City/Western Road

OPEN:	All Year except Christmas
NO. ROOMS:	4
ENSUITE:	3

(V)

TEL: **021 546172**   FAX: -

Modern house on Cork's main tourist area, on the main road to Killarney & West Cork. Close to Airport, Car Ferry.

BUS NO: **8**

B&B PPS:	£15/£17	SNGL OCC. DBLE/TPL:	£21.50/£23.50	SNGL RM:	-
PART BRD:	-	% RED. CHILDREN:	25%	DINNER:	-

Cork City 2km

Mrs Rita O'Herlihy
55 WILTON GARDENS
off Wilton Road, Cork City, Co Cork

Cork City/Wilton University

OPEN:	All Year except Christmas
NO. ROOMS:	3
ENSUITE:	2

(V)

TEL: **021 541705**   FAX: -

Situated quiet park, off Wilton Road, convenient West Cork, Killarney roads, Airport, University, Hospital, College. Frommer recommended.

BUS NO: **8, 5**

B&B PPS:	£15/£17	SNGL OCC. DBLE/TPL:	£21.50	SNGL RM:	-
PART BRD:	-	% RED. CHILDREN:	20%	DINNER:	-

Cork City 2km

Mrs Siobhan Ryan
LABURNUM HOUSE
Denneny's Cross, Model Farm Road, Cork City, Co Cork

Cork City/Wilton University

OPEN:	1st February-22nd December
NO. ROOMS:	6
ENSUITE:	3

(V)

TEL: **021 541008**   FAX: -

Spacious home convenient to West Cork/Killarney Roads, Cork Universtiy Hospital, Airport, F.A.S, R.T.C, U.C.C.

BUS NO: **5, 8**

B&B PPS:	£15/£17	SNGL OCC. DBLE/TPL:	£21.50/£23.50	SNGL RM:	£15
PART BRD:	-	% RED. CHILDREN:	-	DINNER:	-

Cork City 2km

Michael and Patricia Flavin
ALBATROSS
Clogheen (near Clogheen Church), Blarney Road, Co Cork

Cork City

OPEN:	April-October
NO. ROOMS:	3
ENSUITE:	3

TEL: **021 392315**   FAX: -

Situated in peaceful area. 2 km city centre, 3 km Blarney. Convenient Cork City, Gaol, Tennis, Golf. Horseriding locally. An Irish welcome.

BUS NO: **2**

B&B PPS:	£18.50	SNGL OCC. DBLE/TPL:	£25	SNGL RM:	-
PART BRD:	-	% RED. CHILDREN:	-	DINNER:	-

Cork City 1km

Mrs Breeda Higgins
7 FERNCLIFF
Bellevue Park, St Lukes, Cork City, Co Cork

Cork City

OPEN:	1st March-31st December
NO. ROOMS:	4
ENSUITE:	-

 (V)

TEL: **021 508963**   FAX: **021 508963 (man)**

Victorian home, quiet cul-de-sac. Bus/Train Station/ City Centre, 1KM. Take left at T after Ambassador Hotel, then straight ahead.

BUS NO: **7, 8**

B&B PPS:	**£15**	SNGL OCC. DBLE/TPL:	**£21.50**	SNGL RM:	-
PART BRD:	-	% RED. CHILDREN:	**33.3%**	DINNER:	-

Cork 3km

Mrs Helen O'Driscoll
HAWTHORN
Dublin Pike, Whitescross, Cork, Co Cork

Cork City

OPEN:	March-November
NO. ROOMS:	3
ENSUITE:	-

(V)

TEL: **021 302899**   FAX: -

Family run home. Northside of city near Blackman Bar. Horseriding nearby. 15 minutes drive to Blarney and Cork.

BUS NO: **12**

B&B PPS:	**£16/£17**	SNGL OCC. DBLE/TPL:	**£22.50/£23.50**	SNGL RM:	-
PART BRD:	-	% RED. CHILDREN:	**10%**	DINNER:	-

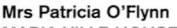
Cork City 1.5km

Mrs Patricia O'Flynn
MARIA VILLE HOUSE
Coolgarten Park, Magazine Road, Cork City, Co Cork

Cork City

OPEN:	May-September
NO. ROOMS:	5
ENSUITE:	3

(V)

TEL: **021 316508**   FAX: -

Family run home, quiet location. Convenient Airport, U.C.C. University Hospital. Restaurants, Pubs, Shopping 10 mins walk. Complimentary tea/coffee on arrival.

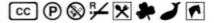 BUS NO: **5, 10**

B&B PPS:	**£15.50/£20**	SNGL OCC. DBLE/TPL:	-	SNGL RM:	-
PART BRD:	-	% RED. CHILDREN:	-	DINNER:	-

Crookhaven 0.5km

Maureen & James Newman
GALLEY COVE HOUSE
Crookhaven, West Cork, Co Cork

Crookhaven/Mizen Head

OPEN:	1st January-30th November
NO. ROOMS:	4
ENSUITE:	3

 (V)

TEL: **028 35137**   FAX: -

Friendly comfortable accommodation in peaceful scenic location. Overlooking Atlantic Ocean and Fastnet lighthouse. Near Mizen head and Barleycove. Excellent Breakfasts.

B&B PPS:	**£16/£19**	SNGL OCC. DBLE/TPL:	**£22.50/£25.50**	SNGL RM:	-
PART BRD:	-	% RED. CHILDREN:	-	DINNER:	-

Drimoleague 2km

Mrs Marian Collins
ROSELAWN HOUSE
Derrygrea, Drimoleague, Co Cork

Drimoleague/Skibbereen

OPEN:	1st March-1st November
NO. ROOMS:	3
ENSUITE:	2

(V)

TEL: **028 31369**   FAX: -

Elegant Country House on Cork/Bantry R586 Route. Local amenities. Skibbereen 12 km. Drimoleague 2 km. Homely atmosphere. Tea/coffee on arrival.

B&B PPS:	**£15/£17**	SNGL OCC. DBLE/TPL:	**£21.50/£23.50**	SNGL RM:	-
PART BRD:	**£180**	% RED. CHILDREN:	**50%**	DINNER:	**£12**

Joan Dinneen
CARRAIG HOUSE
Bantry Road, Dumanway, Co Cork

Dunmanway

OPEN:	April-October
NO. ROOMS:	4
ENSUITE:	4

TEL: **023 45667**   FAX: -

Relax, welcoming country home, private gardens, turf fire, adjacent swimming pool. Fresh air, Forest Walks, Fishing, Beaches, Pubs, Irish Music.

(V)

In Dunmanway

B&B PPS:	£17	SNGL OCC. DBLE/TPL:	£23.50	SNGL RM:	£22
PART BRD:	-	% RED. CHILDREN:	50%	DINNER:	-

Mrs. Patricia O'Leary
PALM RISE
Duntahane, Fermoy, Co Cork

Fermoy

OPEN:	All Year except Christmas
NO. ROOMS:	4
ENSUITE:	4

TEL: **025 31386**   FAX: -

Modern house in peaceful scenic surroundings close to Fishing, Leisure centre, Horseriding and Scenic Walks. Ideal touring base.

(V)

Fermoy 1km

B&B PPS:	£17	SNGL OCC. DBLE/TPL:	£23.50	SNGL RM:	-
PART BRD:	-	% RED. CHILDREN:	10%	DINNER:	-

Mrs Rita Barry-Murphy
COIS COILLE
Glengarriff, Co Cork

Glengarriff

OPEN:	1st April-31st October
NO. ROOMS:	6
ENSUITE:	6

TEL: **027 63202**   FAX: -

Warm hospitality in comfortable home overlooking Glengariff harbour. Award winning garden in quiet woodland setting. Extensive breakfast menu, home baking.

(V)

In Glengarriff

B&B PPS:	£17.50	SNGL OCC. DBLE/TPL:	£24	SNGL RM:	-
PART BRD:	-	% RED. CHILDREN:	20%	DINNER:	-

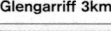

Mrs Kathleen Connolly
CARRAIG DUBH HOUSE
Droumgarriff, Glengarriff, Co Cork

Glengarriff

OPEN:	15th March-31st October
NO. ROOMS:	4
ENSUITE:	3

TEL: **027 63146**   FAX: -

Family home, 150m off main road, quiet, peaceful location , overlooking Harbour. Golf, Fishing, Walks nearby. Hairdriers in rooms. Extensive breakfast menu.

(V)

Glengarriff 3km

B&B PPS:	£15/£17	SNGL OCC. DBLE/TPL:	£21.50/£23.50	SNGL RM:	-
PART BRD:	-	% RED. CHILDREN:	20%	DINNER:	-

Mrs Ann Guerin
SEA FRONT
Glengarriff, Co Cork

Glengarrif

OPEN:	May-October
NO. ROOMS:	3
ENSUITE:	-

TEL: **027 63079**   FAX: -

Centrally situated, comfortable home on the waterfront. Convenient to Ferry for Garnish Island. Ideal Touring Centre.

(V)

In Glengarriff

B&B PPS:	£15	SNGL OCC. DBLE/TPL:	£21.50	SNGL RM:	-
PART BRD:	-	% RED. CHILDREN:	20%	DINNER:	-

In Glengarriff

Mrs Maureen MacCarthy
MAUREENS
**Glengarriff Village Home,
Glengarriff, Co Cork**
TEL: 027 63201 FAX: -

Glengarriff

OPEN:	All Year
NO. ROOMS:	5
ENSUITE:	3

Two storey house adjacent / picturesque village. Beside ancient Oak forest, sea, mountains, lakes and rivers. Opposite entrance to Garinish island.

B&B PPS:	£15/£17	SNGL OCC. DBLE/TPL:	£21.50/£23.50	SNGL RM:	£15/£17
PART BRD:	-	% RED. CHILDREN:	20%	DINNER:	-

In Glengarriff

Eileen & Imelda O'Sullivan
ISLAND VIEW HOUSE
Glengarriff, Co Cork
TEL: 027 63081 FAX: -

Glengariff

OPEN:	1st April-1st November
NO. ROOMS:	6
ENSUITE:	4

Comfortable home in quiet scenic area. 150 metres off main road. Most bedrooms overlooking Glengarriff Harbour. 10 minutes walk to town.

B&B PPS:	£15/£17	SNGL OCC. DBLE/TPL:	£21.50	SNGL RM:	-
PART BRD:	-	% RED. CHILDREN:	20%	DINNER:	-

In Goleen

Mrs Sue Hill
THE HERON'S COVE
The Harbour, Goleen, West Cork, Co Cork
TEL: 028 35225 FAX: 028 35422 EMAIL: suehill@tinet.ie

Goleen

OPEN:	All Year except Christmas
NO. ROOMS:	5
ENSUITE:	5

Comfortable rooms, good food, wine. Near Barleycove, Mizen Head. Hairdryers, electric blankets in rooms. Restaurant. Egon Ronay recommended. AA QQQQ.

B&B PPS:	£20/£30	SNGL OCC. DBLE/TPL:	-	SNGL RM:	£26.50
PART BRD:	£276	% RED. CHILDREN:	-	DINNER:	£19.50

Innishannon 3km

Mrs Kathleen Cummins
ELLAMORE
Ballymountain, Innishannon, Co Cork
TEL: 021 775807 FAX: -

Innishannon near Kinsale

OPEN:	1st April-30th September
NO. ROOMS:	3
ENSUITE:	3

Country residence, convenient to airport, ferryport. Follow signpost for Ballymountain house off N71 at innishannon bridge. Next house on left.

B&B PPS:	£17.50	SNGL OCC. DBLE/TPL:	£24	SNGL RM:	-
PART BRD:	-	% RED. CHILDREN:	50%	DINNER:	-

In Kanturk

Mrs Phyl Grace
HILLSIDE
Millview Road, Kanturk, Co Cork
TEL: 029 50241 FAX: -

Kanturk

OPEN:	21st April-30th September
NO. ROOMS:	5
ENSUITE:	3

A mature rambling garden welcomes you to this restful house. With pictures, old furnishings & books. Local Golf & Fishing.

B&B PPS:	£15/£17	SNGL OCC. DBLE/TPL:	£22/£27	SNGL RM:	-
PART BRD:	-	% RED. CHILDREN:	-	DINNER:	-

Kinsale 2km

Mrs Breda Ahern
JALNA
Pike Cross, Kinsale, Co Cork

Kinsale

OPEN:	All Year except Christmas
NO. ROOMS:	3
ENSUITE:	3

Ⓥ

TEL: **021 772692**   FAX: -

Luxurious modern bungalow set in country pastures. Spanish style interior and exterior. Conservatory opening on to patios and garden. Jacuzzi.

B&B PPS:	£17/£18.50	SNGL OCC. DBLE/TPL:	£23.50/£25	SNGL RM:	-
PART BRD:	-	% RED. CHILDREN:	25%	DINNER:	-

Kinsale 2km

Ms Jennifer Allen
SETANTA
1 Haven Hill, Summercove, Kinsale, Co Cork

Kinsale

OPEN:	1st May-1st October
NO. ROOMS:	3
ENSUITE:	3

Ⓥ

TEL: **021 772761**   FAX: -

Split-level bungalow, with views of Kinsale town & outer harbour. Spacious rooms with Satellite, TV. Breakfast menu. Personally run.

B&B PPS:	£17.50/£20	SNGL OCC. DBLE/TPL:	£25	SNGL RM:	-
PART BRD:	-	% RED. CHILDREN:	20%	DINNER:	-

Kinsale 1km

John & Eleanor Bateman
ROCKLANDS HOUSE
Compass Hill, Kinsale, Co Cork

Kinsale

OPEN:	All Year except Christmas
NO. ROOMS:	4
ENSUITE:	4

TEL: **021 772609**   FAX: **021 772609**

Set in 3 acres of woodland on a scenic walking trail. Rooms with Balconies, magnificent views of the Bandon river.

B&B PPS:	£18/£25	SNGL OCC. DBLE/TPL:	£25/£40	SNGL RM:	-
PART BRD:	-	% RED. CHILDREN:	25%	DINNER:	-

Kinsale 14km

Ms Patricia Blanchfield
BLANCHFIELD HOUSE
Rigsdale (Cork/Bandon Rd), Ballinhassig, Co Cork

Kinsale

OPEN:	10th March-30th October
NO. ROOMS:	6
ENSUITE:	2

Ⓥ

TEL: **021 885167**   FAX: **021 885805**

Period country residence on N 71, convenient to Airport, Ferry Port, Kinsale, Bandon. Private Salmon, Trout Fishing, Restaurant. AA QQ, Credit Cards.

B&B PPS:	£17/£22	SNGL OCC. DBLE/TPL:	£23.50/£28.50	SNGL RM:	-
PART BRD:	£224	% RED. CHILDREN:	33%	DINNER:	£15

Kinsale 10km

Mrs Gillian Bracken,
GLEBE COUNTRY HOUSE
Ballinadee Nr. Kinsale, Bandon, Co Cork

Kinsale

OPEN:	All Year
NO. ROOMS:	3
ENSUITE:	3

Ⓥ

TEL: **021 778294**   FAX: **021 778456**   EMAIL: **glebehse@indigo.ie**

Charming family run Georgian rectory. Close to the River Bandon Estuary and Kinsale. All rooms ensuite. AA. QQQQ. Major guides recommended.

B&B PPS:	£22.50/£27.50	SNGL OCC. DBLE/TPL:	£30/£37.50	SNGL RM:	-
PART BRD:	-	% RED. CHILDREN:	50%	DINNER:	£16.50

Mrs Ita Carey
ORCHARD COTTAGE
Farrangalway
Kinsale, Co Cork

Kinsale

Open:	1st March-1st November
No. Rooms:	4
Ensuite:	4

Tel: **021 772693**   Fax: -

Quiet Country Home adjacent to Kinsale's 18-hole Golf course. All rooms TV, C/Radios, Hairdryers, Tea/Coffee, AA QQQ. Airport Ferry 20 km.

B&B PPS:	£18	Sngl Occ. Dble/Tpl:	£25	Sngl Rm:	-
Part Brd:	-	% Red. Children:	25%	Dinner:	-

— Kinsale 3km —

Mrs Joan Chambers
ROSARIO
Sandycove, Kinsale, Co Cork

Kinsale

Open:	Easter-October
No. Rooms:	3
Ensuite:	1

Tel: **021 772810**   Fax: -

Secluded home on terraced gardens, overlooking peaceful cove and surrounded by superb sea views. "Guide du Routard" recommended.

B&B PPS:	£15/£17	Sngl Occ. Dble/Tpl:	£21.50/£23.50	Sngl Rm:	-
Part Brd:	-	% Red. Children:	20%	Dinner:	-

— Kinsale 2km —

Mrs Joan Collins
WATERLANDS
Cork Road, Kinsale, Co Cork

Kinsale

Open:	1st February-31st October
No. Rooms:	4
Ensuite:	4

Tel: **021 772318 / 088 2767917**   Fax: **021 774873**

Luxury accommodation , Breakfast Conservatory. Electric blankets h/dryers, c/radios, tea/coffee. Extensive breakfast. AA3Q. Highly recommended. Ideal touring base.Airport 20 mins.

B&B PPS:	£17/£19	Sngl Occ. Dble/Tpl:	£25/£28	Sngl Rm:	-
Part Brd:	-	% Red. Children:	33.3%	Dinner:	-

— Kinsale 1km —

Mrs Kathleen Cummins
BAY VIEW
Clasheen, Kinsale, Co Cork

Kinsale

Open:	1st May-30th September-
No. Rooms:	3
Ensuite:	3

Tel: **021 774054**   Fax: -

Comfortable modern house. View bay, Countryside from dining room, Hairdryers, C/radios in rooms. Breakfast menu. "Le guide du Routard" recommended.

B&B PPS:	£17	Sngl Occ. Dble/Tpl:	£25	Sngl Rm:	-
Part Brd:	-	% Red. Children:	-	Dinner:	-

— Kinsale 1km —

Mrs Mary Cummin's
CARRIGEEN
Gully Bridge, Kinsale, Co Cork

Kinsale

Open:	March-October
No. Rooms:	3
Ensuite:	2

Tel: **021 772687**   Fax: -

Modern, spacious, spilt-level bungalow. Outstanding Sea-Views. Scenic Walks, Yachting, Fishing, Golfing nearby.

B&B PPS:	£15/£18	Sngl Occ. Dble/Tpl:	£21.50/£24.50	Sngl Rm:	-
Part Brd:	-	% Red. Children:	20%	Dinner:	-

— Kinsale 2km —

Kinsale 2km

Mrs Mary Fitzgerald
ARD CUAIN
Forthill, Summercove, Kinsale, Co Cork

Kinsale

OPEN:	17th March-31st October
NO. ROOMS:	4
ENSUITE:	3

TEL: **021 772451**   FAX: -

Peaceful area overlooking Harbour and Charles Fort. Magnificent Coastal Walks. Frommer Guide Reccomended. Airport 20 min, Ferry 30 mins.

B&B PPS:	**£17.50**	SNGL OCC. DBLE/TPL:	**£25**	SNGL RM:	-
PART BRD:	-	% RED. CHILDREN:	**20%**	DINNER:	-

In Kinsale

Marian Fitzpatrick
SPRING COTTAGE
Barrick Hill, Kinsale, Co Cork

Kinsale

OPEN:	1st March-31st October
NO. ROOMS:	3
ENSUITE:	3

TEL: **021 774785**   FAX: -

Award winning traditional Irish Cottage overlooking Kinsale Town. 3 mins walk to Town Centre. Adjacent to all amenities. Fishing & Yachting.

B&B PPS:	**£18/£22**	SNGL OCC. DBLE/TPL:	**£27**	SNGL RM:	**£27**
PART BRD:	-	% RED. CHILDREN:	-	DINNER:	-

Kinsale 4km

Peggy & Eamonn Foley
FERNVILLE
Lower Cove, Kinsale, Co Cork

Kinsale

OPEN:	17th March-31st October
NO. ROOMS:	3
ENSUITE:	3

TEL: **021 774874**   FAX: -

First turn right after Charles Fort. Situated on Kinsale's outer Harbour. 2 mins from Beach and Coastal Walk. Sea views.

B&B PPS:	**£17.50/£20**	SNGL OCC. DBLE/TPL:	**£26.50**	SNGL RM:	-
PART BRD:	-	% RED. CHILDREN:	-	DINNER:	-

In Kinsale

Mrs Teresa Gray
ROCKVILLE
The Rock, Kinsale, Co Cork

Kinsale

OPEN:	1st March-1st November
NO. ROOMS:	3
ENSUITE:	3

TEL: **021 772791**   FAX: -

Modern well appointed spilt level home overlooking Kinsale Town and Harbour and within five minutes walk of town centre.

B&B PPS:	**£17**	SNGL OCC. DBLE/TPL:	**£23.50/£25**	SNGL RM:	-
PART BRD:	-	% RED. CHILDREN:	-	DINNER:	-

SYMBOLS

LOOK OUT FOR THESE SYMBOLS WHICH SHOULD BE DISPLAYED BY ALL MEMBERS OF TOWN & COUNTRY HOMES.

Kinsale 1km

Mrs M Griffin
HILLSIDE
Camp Hill, Kinsale, Co Cork

Kinsale

OPEN:	**All Year**
NO. ROOMS:	**6**
ENSUITE:	**5**

TEL: **021 772315**   FAX: -

Spacious home sea view, beautiful gardens situated on camp site Battle of Kinsale. Frommer recommended. 10 mins walk town. Guests conservatory.

| B&B PPS: | **£15/£18** | SNGL OCC. DBLE/TPL: | **£21.50/£24.50** | SNGL RM: | - |
| PART BRD: | - | % RED. CHILDREN: | **20%** | DINNER: | - |

Kinsale 1km

Orla Griffin
GRIFFIN'S RIVERSIDE HOUSE
Kippagh, Kinsale, Co Cork

Kinsale

OPEN:	**All Year**
NO. ROOMS:	**3**
ENSUITE:	**3**

TEL: **021 774917**   FAX: -

Panoramic ocean view. Luxury accommodatin relaxed friendly atmosphere. Hairdryers, Private Gardens, Car Park. All amenities walking distance. Golf, Fishing arranged.

| B&B PPS: | **£17/£18** | SNGL OCC. DBLE/TPL: | **£23.50/£24.50** | SNGL RM: | - |
| PART BRD: | - | % RED. CHILDREN: | **20%** | DINNER: | - |

Ballinspittle 1.5km

Mrs Kathleen Humberstone
WATERFALL HOUSE
Garrettstown, Kinsale, Co Cork

Kinsale

OPEN:	**1st March-1st November**
NO. ROOMS:	**4**
ENSUITE:	**4**

TEL: **021 778359**   FAX: **021 778359**

Modern house with Tennis Court. Walking distance, Atlantic Manor Hotel, Garrettstown strand. Old head views and rolling countryside. Pubs nearby.

| B&B PPS: | **£17** | SNGL OCC. DBLE/TPL: | - | SNGL RM: | **£20** |
| PART BRD: | - | % RED. CHILDREN: | **20%** | DINNER: | - |

Kinsale 3km

Mrs Joan Hurley
FOYLE
Acres, Kinsale, Co Cork

Kinsale

OPEN:	**1st March-31st October**
NO. ROOMS:	**4**
ENSUITE:	**4**

TEL: **021 772363**   FAX: -

Modern bungalow in rural setting, own garden. Situated on Coast Road, R600. Beaches, Golf, Fishing, Horseriding nearby. Airport/Ferryport 20km.

| B&B PPS: | **£17/£18** | SNGL OCC. DBLE/TPL: | **£23.50/£25** | SNGL RM: | - |
| PART BRD: | - | % RED. CHILDREN: | **25%** | DINNER: | - |

In Kinsale

Mrs Mary Hurley
SCEILIG HOUSE
Ard Brack, Kinsale, Co Cork

Kinsale

OPEN:	**January-December**
NO. ROOMS:	**3**
ENSUITE:	**2**

TEL: **021 772832**   FAX: -

Town house set in layered gardens overlooking Kinsale harbour. Seaview from bedrooms with private patio/balcony. Frommer and "La Guide" recommended.

| B&B PPS: | **£15/£22.50** | SNGL OCC. DBLE/TPL: | **£21.50/£30** | SNGL RM: | - |
| PART BRD: | - | % RED. CHILDREN: | **35%** | DINNER: | - |

Kinsale 2km

Mrs Nora Kelly
VALLEY-VIEW
Hospital Road, Coolvalanane, Kinsale, Co Cork

Kinsale

OPEN:	All Year
NO. ROOMS:	4
ENSUITE:	2

(V)

TEL: **021 772842** FAX: -

Spacious bungalow in scenic farming area. Overlooking open countryside, close to Beaches, Golf and Fishing. Airport, Ferry, half hour drive.

B&B PPS:	£15/£17	SNGL OCC. DBLE/TPL:	£21.50/£23.50	SNGL RM:	-
PART BRD:	-	% RED. CHILDREN:	50%	DINNER:	-

Kinsale 2km

Mrs Myrtle Levis
WALYUNGA
Sandycove, Kinsale, Co Cork

Kinsale

OPEN:	March-October
NO. ROOMS:	4
ENSUITE:	3

(V)

TEL: **021 774126** FAX: -

Bright spacious modern bungalow. Unique design, landscaped gardens, outstanding ocean & valley views, Sandy Beaches, Scenic Costal walks. Internationally acclaimed.

B&B PPS:	£17/£21	SNGL OCC. DBLE/TPL:	-	SNGL RM:	-
PART BRD:	-	% RED. CHILDREN:	20%	DINNER:	-

Kinsale 2km

Mrs Beta Lewis
THE BURROWS
Sandycove, Kinsale, Co Cork

Kinsale

OPEN:	1st March-1st November
NO. ROOMS:	3
ENSUITE:	1

(V)

TEL: **021 772012** FAX: -

Set in landscaped gardens, overlooking the sea. Beaches, Fishing, Sailing, Golf closeby. Beautiful scenic coastal walks.

B&B PPS:	£15/£17	SNGL OCC. DBLE/TPL:	£21.50/£23.50	SNGL RM:	-
PART BRD:	-	% RED. CHILDREN:	20%	DINNER:	-

In Kinsale

Anthony & Fiona McCarthy
SEA BREEZE
Featherbed Lane, Kinsale, Co Cork

Kinsale

OPEN:	All Year except Christmas
NO. ROOMS:	3
ENSUITE:	3

(V)

TEL: **021 774854** FAX: -

Dormer Bungalow with view of harbour from some bedrooms. 3 Mins walk town centre, private carpark, sailing, fishing and beaches nearby.

B&B PPS:	£17.50/£20	SNGL OCC. DBLE/TPL:	£25	SNGL RM:	-
PART BRD:	-	% RED. CHILDREN:	25%	DINNER:	-

In Kinsale

Brian & Ann McCarthy
ROCK VIEW
The Glen, Kinsale, Co Cork

Kinsale

OPEN:	All Year except Christmas
NO. ROOMS:	3
ENSUITE:	3

(V)

TEL: **021 773162** FAX: -

Attractive comfortable home. Located in the heart of award winning Kinsale town centre. Adjacent churches, museum, fishing beaches, golf and yachting.

B&B PPS:	£18.50/£20	SNGL OCC. DBLE/TPL:	£24	SNGL RM:	£24
PART BRD:	-	% RED. CHILDREN:	25%	DINNER:	-

Mr & Mrs Michael McCarthy
HILL TOP B&B
Sleaveen Heights, Kinsale, Co Cork

Kinsale

OPEN:	All Year except Christmas
No. ROOMS:	6
ENSUITE:	6

TEL: **021 772612**   FAX: -

Modern spacious bungalow, conservatory overlooking Kinsale Harbour and James's Fort. Close to Museum, Beaches, Golf, Yachting, Marina and Fishing. 3 mins from town.

B&B PPS:	**£17/£20**	SNGL OCC. DBLE/TPL:	**£25**	SNGL RM:	**£25**
PART BRD:	-	% RED. CHILDREN:	**25%**	DINNER:	-

In Kinsale

Mrs Tess McCarthy
CLUAIN ARD
Pike Cross, Farrenarougha, Kinsale, Co Cork

Kinsale

OPEN:	1st April-30th September-
No. ROOMS:	4
ENSUITE:	3

TEL: **021 774583**   FAX: -

Modern country home in a delightful rural setting on the outskirts of unique and historic Kinsale.

B&B PPS:	**£15.50/£17.50**	SNGL OCC. DBLE/TPL:	**£22/£24**	SNGL RM:	-
PART BRD:	-	% RED. CHILDREN:	**25%**	DINNER:	-

Kinsale 2km

Mrs Anne Maxwell
WOODGROVE HOUSE
Cappagh, Kinsale, Co Cork

Kinsale

OPEN:	1st February-31st October
No. ROOMS:	4
ENSUITE:	4

TEL: **021 772809**   FAX: **021 772809**

Luxurious accommodation with breakfast choice. Tea/coffee facilities. Beautiful spacious bedrooms with TV/hairdryer. Mature wooded gardens with car park.

B&B PPS:	**£17/£20**	SNGL OCC. DBLE/TPL:	**£25/£27**	SNGL RM:	-
PART BRD:	-	% RED. CHILDREN:	**25%**	DINNER:	-

In Kinsale

Mrs Caroline Murphy
STONEFIELD HOUSE
Kilcaw, Kinsale, Co Cork

Kinsale

OPEN:	1st March-31st October
No. ROOMS:	3
ENSUITE:	3

TEL: **021 772334**   FAX: -

Spacious Bungalow with Sea-View. Rooms ensuite with Satellite TV, Tea/Coffee making facilities. Airport 20 mins, Ferry 30 mins. Private parking.

B&B PPS:	**£17.50/£19**	SNGL OCC. DBLE/TPL:	**£25**	SNGL RM:	-
PART BRD:	-	% RED. CHILDREN:	**20%**	DINNER:	-

Kinsale 1km

Mrs Theresa Murphy
TESBEN HOUSE
Ballinspittle Road, Barrells Cross, Kinsale, Co Cork

Kinsale

OPEN:	1st March-31st October
No. ROOMS:	4
ENSUITE:	2

TEL: **021 778354**   FAX: -

Comfortable bungalow, picturesque view. Main tourist route, West Cork/Kerry. Old Head golf links, Horseriding, Beaches, Walks, Fishing, Ferryport. Airport 20KM.

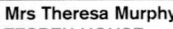

B&B PPS:	**£15/£18**	SNGL OCC. DBLE/TPL:	**£21.50/£24.50**	SNGL RM:	-
PART BRD:	-	% RED. CHILDREN:	**25%**	DINNER:	-

Kinsale 5km

Mrs Eileen O'Connell
DOONEEN
Ardcarrig, Bandon Road, Kinsale, Co Cork

Kinsale

OPEN:	All Year except Christmas
No. ROOMS:	4
ENSUITE:	3

Ⓥ

TEL: **021 772024**   FAX: -

Modern house in peaceful setting with views of inner and outer harbour. TV lounge. Private parking. Secluded gardens. Ensuite. Town area.

Ⓟ 🚶🎣🏠

B&B PPS:	£15/£17	SNGL OCC. DBLE/TPL:	£21.50/£25	SNGL RM:	-
PART BRD:	-	% RED. CHILDREN:	25%	DINNER:	

└ In Kinsale

Mrs K O'Donovan
Guardwell Street
Kinsale-, Co Cork

Kinsale

OPEN:	April-October
No. ROOMS:	5
ENSUITE:	3

Ⓥ

TEL: **021 772428**   FAX: -

Quaint old style family run home in historic town centre, adjacent Churches, Museum, Fishing, Beaches, Golf, Yachting. Tea making facilities.

👶 ☕ ♣ 🚶🎣

B&B PPS:	£15/£18	SNGL OCC. DBLE/TPL:	£21.50/£24.50	SNGL RM:	-
PART BRD:	-	% RED. CHILDREN:	25%	DINNER:	-

└ In Kinsale

Mrs Phil O'Donovan
ROSSBRIN
Harbour Heights, Cappagh, Kinsale, Co Cork

Kinsale

OPEN:	April-November
No. ROOMS:	3
ENSUITE:	3

TEL: **021 772112**   FAX: -

Elevated luxury bungalow in quiet residential park. Panoramic views. Close to Golf, Fishing, Horse Riding, Sailing, Swimming. Warm welcome with tea/coffee.

Ⓟ 🚫🎣🏠 Ⓢ

B&B PPS:	£17/£17.50	SNGL OCC. DBLE/TPL:	£25	SNGL RM:	-
PART BRD:	-	% RED. CHILDREN:	20%	DINNER:	-

└ In Kinsale

Betty & Pat O'Farrell
15 Main Street, Kinsale, Co Cork

Kinsale

OPEN:	All Year except Christmas
No. ROOMS:	4
ENSUITE:	3

Ⓥ

TEL: **021 774169**   FAX: **021 774169**

Town centre historical building, comfortable family home. French/German spoken. Convenient Sailing, Golfing, Fishing, Beaches, Restaurants, Historical sites, bicycle lock-up.

CC 👶 ☕ 🚶🎣🏠

B&B PPS:	£15/£20	SNGL OCC. DBLE/TPL:	-	SNGL RM:	-
PART BRD:	-	% RED. CHILDREN:	20%	DINNER:	-

└ In Kinsale

Mrs Mary O'Neill
SEA GULL HOUSE
Cork Street, Kinsale, Co Cork

Kinsale

OPEN:	March-November
No. ROOMS:	6
ENSUITE:	4

Ⓥ

TEL: **021 772240**   FAX: -

Next door to "Desmond Castle", wine museum built 1500. Near Beach, Fishing & Golf. Kinsale Gourmet Town. Groups welcome.

♣ 🎣🏠 Ⓢ

B&B PPS:	£17.50/£18.50	SNGL OCC. DBLE/TPL:	£24	SNGL RM:	£20
PART BRD:	-	% RED. CHILDREN:	20%	DINNER:	-

└ In Kinsale

Kinsale 5km

Mrs Sheila O'Regan
SIROCO
Ballyregan, Kinsale, Co Cork

		Kinsale	
	OPEN:	May-September	
	No. ROOMS:	3	
	ENSUITE:	-	**(V)**

TEL: **021 775129**   FAX: -

Modern bungalow in scenic surroundings, Innishannon 5 kms, Kinsale 5 kms, Beaches, Fishing, Yachting, Horse-Riding and Golf.

B&B PPS:	**£15**	SNGL OCC. DBLE/TPL:	**£21.50**	SNGL RM:	-
PART BRD:	-	% RED. CHILDREN:	**20%**	DINNER:	

Kinsale 4km

Mrs Claire O'Sullivan
RIVERMOUNT HOUSE
Knocknabinny, Barrells Cross, Kinsale, Co Cork

		Kinsale	
	OPEN:	1st February-5th November	
	No. ROOMS:	6	
	ENSUITE:	6	**(V)**

TEL: **021 778033**   FAX: **021 778225**

Award winning luxurious home overlooking the river. Spacious well appointed bedrooms. Superb decor. Extensive breakfast menu. AA QQQQ, RAC Highly Acclaimed.

B&B PPS:	**£17/£19**	SNGL OCC. DBLE/TPL:	**£23.50/£27**	SNGL RM:	-
PART BRD:	-	% RED. CHILDREN:	**20%**	DINNER:	

Mrs Phil Price
DANABEL
Sleaveen, Kinsale, Co Cork

		Kinsale	
	OPEN:	All Year except Christmas	
	No. ROOMS:	4	
	ENSUITE:	4	**(V)**

TEL: **021 774087**   FAX: -

Modern house, quiet area. Town 2 mins . Close walk Marina . Orthopaedic beds. Tea facilities. Frommer recommended. Harbour view from some bedrooms.

B&B PPS:	**£17/£20**	SNGL OCC. DBLE/TPL:	-	SNGL RM:	-
PART BRD:	-	% RED. CHILDREN:	-	DINNER:	-

In Kinsale

Mrs Ann Salter
CROSSWAYS
Ardbrack, Kinsale, Co Cork

		Kinsale	
	OPEN:	All Year except Christmas	
	No. ROOMS:	4	
	ENSUITE:	4	**(V)**

TEL: **021 772460**   FAX: -

Modern spacious home overlooking inner harbour. Town Centre 4 mins walk. Adjacent to Scenic Walks, Fishing, Pub Entertainment & Gourmet Restaurants.

B&B PPS:	**£17.50/£22**	SNGL OCC. DBLE/TPL:	**£25**	SNGL RM:	-
PART BRD:	-	% RED. CHILDREN:	**25%**	DINNER:	-

In Kinsale

Margo Searls
LANDFALL HOUSE
Cappagh, Kinsale, Co Cork

		Kinsale	
	OPEN:	All Year except Christmas	
	No. ROOMS:	4	
	ENSUITE:	4	**(V)**

TEL: **021 772575**   FAX: -

Luxury spacious house, Gardens. Panoramic views over River, Harbour and Town. 8 mins walk Town Centre. Scenic Walks, Beaches, Golf, Fishing.

B&B PPS:	**£18/£20**	SNGL OCC. DBLE/TPL:	**£25/£26.50**	SNGL RM:	-
PART BRD:	-	% RED. CHILDREN:	**25%**	DINNER:	-

June & Jack Sheehan
VILLA MARIA
Cork Road, Kinsale, Co Cork

Kinsale

OPEN:	1st March-November
NO. ROOMS:	5
ENSUITE:	5

TEL: 021 772627   FAX: -

Comfortable Villa, Scenic views, garden, quiet central location, bus route, Pub Entertainment. Golf, Beaches; Tea-making. Town 3 mins walk.

B&B PPS:	**£17/£18.50**	SNGL OCC. DBLE/TPL:	-	SNGL RM:	-
PART BRD:	-	% RED. CHILDREN:	**50%**	DINNER:	-

Macroom 9km

Sean & Margaret Moynihan
AN CUASAN
Coolavokig, Macroom, Co Cork

Macroom

OPEN:	May-October
NO. ROOMS:	6
ENSUITE:	5

TEL: 026 40018   FAX: -

Tranquil location on N22, Blarney/Killarney. Dilliard/Causin recommended. Breakfast menu. Landscaped gardens, downstairs accommodation. Walking, Fishing, Golf. Visa/ Access.

B&B PPS:	**£15/£17.50**	SNGL OCC. DBLE/TPL:	**£21.50/£24**	SNGL RM:	**£17.50**
PART BRD:	**£180**	% RED. CHILDREN:	**50%**	DINNER:	**£12**

Kathleen & Brendan Mulcahy
FOUNTAIN HOUSE
Cork Road, Macroom, Co Cork

Macroom

OPEN:	1st March-30th November
NO. ROOMS:	6
ENSUITE:	6

TEL: 026 41424   FAX: 026 41425

Lakeside, ground floor rooms. Gardens, private parking. Bicycle shed. Non-smoking rooms, central for Killarney, Bantry, Blarney, Kinsale. Fishing, Golf.

B&B PPS:	**£18**	SNGL OCC. DBLE/TPL:	**£24.50**	SNGL RM:	**£24**
PART BRD:	-	% RED. CHILDREN:	**25%**	DINNER:	-

Macroom 5km

Mrs Sheila Clifford
ARD - NA - LAOI
Opp Convent of Mercy, Bathview, Mallow, Co Cork

Mallow

OPEN:	1st March-31st October
NO. ROOMS:	4
ENSUITE:	4

TEL: 022 22317   FAX: -

Period residence, opposite Convent of Mercy. Mature gardens, in centre of town. Very private. Ideally situated for Fishing, Golfing, Swimming.

B&B PPS:	**£17**	SNGL OCC. DBLE/TPL:	**£23.50**	SNGL RM:	-
PART BRD:	-	% RED. CHILDREN:	**50%**	DINNER:	-

In Mallow

Mrs B Courtney
RATHMORE HOUSE
Fermoy Road, Mallow, Co Cork

Mallow

OPEN:	June-November
NO. ROOMS:	5
ENSUITE:	3

TEL: 022 21688   FAX: -

Peaceful setting beside Fermoy/Waterford Mitchelstown/Dublin road. Rosslare Ferryport route. Spacious grounds, parking. Home baking, tea/coffee in rooms.

B&B PPS:	**£15/£17**	SNGL OCC. DBLE/TPL:	-	SNGL RM:	**£17**
PART BRD:	-	% RED. CHILDREN:	**33%**	DINNER:	-

Mallow 2km

Mrs Mary Kiely
HILL TOP VIEW
Navigation Road, Mallow, Co Cork

Mallow

OPEN:	1st February-30th November
NO. ROOMS:	6
ENSUITE:	5

TEL: **022 21491**   FAX: **022 21491**

Country residence adjacent Racecourse/ Fishing, Golf/Horseriding nearby. Touring centre. TV,Tea/Coffee facilities, Hairdryers, Breakfast menu, Conservatory, Secluded gardens.

B&B PPS:	**£15/£17**	SNGL OCC. DBLE/TPL:	**£21.50/£23.50**	SNGL RM:	-
PART BRD:	-	% RED. CHILDREN:	33%	DINNER:	-

In Mallow

Mrs Eva Lane
PARK SOUTH
Doneraile, Mallow, Co Cork

Mallow

OPEN:	All Year
NO. ROOMS:	4
ENSUITE:	3

TEL: **022 25296**   FAX: -

Situated (1 km off n73) Dublin/Killarney, Cork/Ringaskiddy/Rosslare route. Fishing, Golf, Parks/Gardens, bicycle shed. Hot scones on arrival.

B&B PPS:	**£15/£17**	SNGL OCC. DBLE/TPL:	**£21.50/£23.50**	SNGL RM:	£15
PART BRD:	£190	% RED. CHILDREN:	50%	DINNER:	£14

Mallow 15km

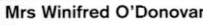

Mrs Winifred O'Donovan
OAKLANDS
Springwood
Off Killarney Road, Mallow, Co Cork

Mallow

OPEN:	1st March-1st November
NO. ROOMS:	4
ENSUITE:	4

TEL: **022 21127**   FAX: **022 21127**   EMAIL: **oaklands@tinet.ie**

A.A Q.Q.Q. Warm comfortable home, Peaceful location, safe parking, minutes to town, train, racecourse. 150 yards from N72/N20 roundabout. Signposted.

B&B PPS:	**£17**	SNGL OCC. DBLE/TPL:	**£23.50/£25**	SNGL RM:	-
PART BRD:	-	% RED. CHILDREN:	50%	DINNER:	-

In Mallow

Mrs M Walsh
RIVERSIDE HOUSE
Navigation Road, Mallow, Co Cork

Mallow

OPEN:	All Year except Christmas
NO. ROOMS:	4
ENSUITE:	4

TEL: **022 42761**   FAX: -

Country house in scenic surroundings overlooking Blackwater Valley, ideal base for touring on N72. Convenient Town Centre and Railway Station.

B&B PPS:	**£17**	SNGL OCC. DBLE/TPL:	-	SNGL RM:	-
PART BRD:	-	% RED. CHILDREN:	25%	DINNER:	-

In Mallow

Mrs Eileen Dowling
AMANDA
Cahermone, Midleton, Co Cork

Midleton

OPEN:	1st April-1st November
NO. ROOMS:	4
ENSUITE:	3

TEL: **021 631135**   FAX: -

On Midleton to Waterford/N25 Road. Near Jameson and Cobh Heritage Centre, Fota Wildlife, Trabolgan, Golf Courses. Restaurants nearby.

B&B PPS:	**£15/£17**	SNGL OCC. DBLE/TPL:	**£21.50/£23.50**	SNGL RM:	-
PART BRD:	-	% RED. CHILDREN:	50%	DINNER:	-

Midleton 1km

Midleton 6km

Mrs Margaret Harty
SWAN LAKE
Loughaderra, Midleton, Co Cork

Midleton

OPEN:	17th March-31st October
NO. ROOMS:	3
ENSUITE:	2

TEL: 021 667261   FAX: -

Overlooking Loughaderra Lake, 400 m off N 25, between Midleton and Castlemartyr. Convenient Midleton & Cobh, Heritage Centre, Ballymaloe Hse, Fota Wildlife.

B&B PPS:	£15/£17	SNGL OCC. DBLE/TPL:	£21.50/£23.50	SNGL RM:	£21.50/£23.50
PART BRD:	-	% RED. CHILDREN:	50%	DINNER:	

Midleton 0.5km

Mrs Mary Quinlan
SUNDOWN HOUSE
Kilmountain
Castlemartyr, Midleton, Co Cork

Midleton

OPEN:	1st April-1st November
NO. ROOMS:	4
ENSUITE:	2

TEL: 021 667375   FAX: -

0.5 km off Midleton to Waterford N 25, near Jameson Heritage Centre. Ballymaloe House, Blarney Castle, Deep Sea Angling/lake Fishing, Golf nearby.

B&B PPS:	£15/£17	SNGL OCC. DBLE/TPL:	£21.50/£23.50	SNGL RM:	-
PART BRD:	-	% RED. CHILDREN:	50%	DINNER:	-

In Midleton

Mrs Margaret Tobin
DECIES B&B
Castleredmond, Midleton, Co Cork

Midleton

OPEN:	April-November
NO. ROOMS:	5
ENSUITE:	2

TEL: 021 632645   FAX: -

Dormer Bungalow just off (N25). 0.5km from Midleton Town and Jameson Heritage Centre. Near Cobh Heritage Centre, Fota Wildlife Park.

B&B PPS:	£15/£17	SNGL OCC. DBLE/TPL:	£21.50/£23.50	SNGL RM:	£19
PART BRD:	-	% RED. CHILDREN:	50%	DINNER:	-

In Mitchelstown

Mrs Margaret Kiely
COOLACUNNA
Fermoy Road, Mitchelstown, Co Cork

Mitchelstown

OPEN:	1st April-31st October
NO. ROOMS:	3
ENSUITE:	2

TEL: 025 24170 / 086 2619900   FAX: -

Modern bungalow on own grounds on main Cork/Dublin Road, overlooking Galtee Mountains. Mitchelstown Caves nearby. 3 mins walk from town.

B&B PPS:	£15/£17	SNGL OCC. DBLE/TPL:	£21.50/£23.50	SNGL RM:	£16
PART BRD:	-	% RED. CHILDREN:	33%	DINNER:	-

Mitchelstown 6km

Mrs Ann Moher
CROUGHMORE
Mitchelstown, Co Cork

Mitchelstown

OPEN:	1st April-31st October
NO. ROOMS:	3
ENSUITE:	1

TEL: 025 24030/ 086 8126878   FAX: -

Beautiful residence between mountains, fishing rivers. Spacious, elegantly furnished and designed for guest privacy. Ideal for touring south.

B&B PPS:	£15/£17	SNGL OCC. DBLE/TPL:	£21.50/£23.50	SNGL RM:	-
PART BRD:	-	% RED. CHILDREN:	-	DINNER:	-

Mitchelstown 1km

Mrs Mary O'Connell
PALM LODGE
Limerick Road, R513, Mitchelstown, Co Cork

Mitchelstown

OPEN:	1st March-1st November
NO. ROOMS:	3
ENSUITE:	2

TEL: **025 24687**   FAX: -

Peaceful scenic home and gardens overlooking golf course/mountains/fishing. At centre of South via Dublin-Kerry-Rosslare. Restaurants nearby.

B&B PPS:	£15/£17	SNGL OCC. DBLE/TPL:	£21.50/£23.50	SNGL RM:	£17
PART BRD:	£180	% RED. CHILDREN:	33%	DINNER:	£13

In Rosscarbery

Mrs Helen Kelly
THE ORCHARD
Newtown, Rosscarbery, Co Cork

Rosscarbery

OPEN:	March-October
NO. ROOMS:	3
ENSUITE:	3

TEL: **023 48555**   FAX: -

Home in picturesque surroundings on N71. Close to all amenities. Location for relaxing holiday and ideal touring base. Warm welcome assured.

B&B PPS:	£17	SNGL OCC. DBLE/TPL:	£23.50	SNGL RM:	-
PART BRD:	-	% RED. CHILDREN:	-	DINNER:	-

Schull 1km

Mrs Nancy Brosnan
STANLEY HOUSE
Schull, Co Cork

Schull

OPEN:	March-October
NO. ROOMS:	4
ENSUITE:	4

TEL: **028 28425**   FAX: -

Modernised house, providing every comfort with spectacular views of sea and mountains. Set in beautiful garden, 1 km from Schull.

B&B PPS:	£17	SNGL OCC. DBLE/TPL:	£25	SNGL RM:	-
PART BRD:	-	% RED. CHILDREN:	10%	DINNER:	-

Mrs Marie McFarlane
HILLSIDE
Schull, Co Cork

Schull

OPEN:	1st April-30 th September
NO. ROOMS:	3
ENSUITE:	2

TEL: **028 28248**   FAX: -

Two-storey brick built house on one third of an acre with views of sea and mountain.

B&B PPS:	£15/£17	SNGL OCC. DBLE/TPL:	£22/£24	SNGL RM:	-
PART BRD:	-	% RED. CHILDREN:	-	DINNER:	-

Schull 1km

In Skibbereen

Mrs Cathy Gill
SUNNYSIDE
42 Mardyke Street, Skibbereen, Co Cork

Skibbereen Town

OPEN:	January-December
NO. ROOMS:	4
ENSUITE:	3

TEL: **028 21365**   FAX: -

Highly recommended, excellent breakfasts hospitality and comfort. Very peaceful, 1 minute - town centre and bus stop. Bicycle storage. Signposted on R595.

B&B PPS:	£15/£17	SNGL OCC. DBLE/TPL:	£21.50/£23.50	SNGL RM:	£17/£20
PART BRD:	-	% RED. CHILDREN:	50%	DINNER:	-

In Skibbereen

Mrs Josephine Griffin
GLENCAR
Cork Road, Skibbereen, Co Cork

Skibbereen

OPEN:	1st June-30th September
NO. ROOMS:	5
ENSUITE:	3

(V)

TEL: **028 21638**   FAX: -

Old style residence with large garden on the N71. Overlooking open countryside. Golf, Fishing, Tennis, Hill Walking and Beaches locally.

B&B PPS:	**£15/£17**	SNGL OCC. DBLE/TPL:	**£22**	SNGL RM:	**£22**
PART BRD:	-	% RED. CHILDREN:	-	DINNER:	-

Skibbereen 1.5km

Mrs Marguerite McCarthy
MARGUERITES
Baltimore Road, Coronea, Skibbereen, Co Cork

Skibbereen

OPEN:	All Year except Christmas
NO. ROOMS:	4
ENSUITE:	2

(V)

TEL: **028 21166**   FAX: -

Luxury accommodation in landscaped private grounds. Very peaceful, highly recommended. Ideal base for touring West Cork. Signposted on R595.

B&B PPS:	**£15/£17**	SNGL OCC. DBLE/TPL:	**£21.50/£23.50**	SNGL RM:	-
PART BRD:	-	% RED. CHILDREN:	**25%**	DINNER:	-

Mrs Hannah Murnane
LAKE VIEW
Shepperton, Skibbereen, Co Cork

Skibbereen

OPEN:	1st March-10th November
NO. ROOMS:	4
ENSUITE:	2

(V)

TEL: **028 33301**   FAX: -

Comfortable home on N71 overlooking beautiful Shepperton Lakes. All amenities locally. Bicycle shed, Electric blankets, Hairdryers, Breakfast menu.

Skibbereen 4km

B&B PPS:	**£15/£17**	SNGL OCC. DBLE/TPL:	**£21.50/£23.50**	SNGL RM:	**£15**
PART BRD:	**£180**	% RED. CHILDREN:	**50%**	DINNER:	**£12**

Skibbereen 1km

Mrs Hannah O'Cinneide
WOODVIEW
Off Baltimore Road, Skibbereen, Co Cork

Skibbereen

OPEN:	May-September
NO. ROOMS:	3
ENSUITE:	2

(V)

TEL: **028 21740**   FAX: -

Modern home within walking distance of town. Beaches, Tennis, Golf, Forest Walks, Fishing, Horseriding, Sailing nearby.

B&B PPS:	**£15/£17.50**	SNGL OCC. DBLE/TPL:	**£24**	SNGL RM:	-
PART BRD:	-	% RED. CHILDREN:	**50%**	DINNER:	-

Skibbereen 7km

Breda O'Driscoll
SANDYCOVE HOUSE
Castletownshend, Skibbereen, Co Cork

Skibbereen

OPEN:	1st January-20th December
NO. ROOMS:	4
ENSUITE:	4

(V)

TEL: **028 36223**   FAX: -

Seaside location with superb view of Cliffs and Ocean. Beautiful sandybeach adjacent. Ideal for Fishing, Swimming, Windsurfing, Cliffwalks.

B&B PPS:	**£17**	SNGL OCC. DBLE/TPL:	**£23.50**	SNGL RM:	**£17**
PART BRD:	**£185**	% RED. CHILDREN:	**50%**	DINNER:	**£12**

Skibbereen 1.5km

Mrs Eileen O'Driscoll
PALM GROVE
Coolnagurrane, Bantry Road, Skibbereen, Co Cork

Skibbereen

OPEN:	March-November
NO. ROOMS:	4
ENSUITE:	2

(V)

TEL: **028 21703**   FAX: -

Spacious bungalow overlooking Ilen River and open Countryside. Frommer recommended. Sports Centre, Beaches nearby, on R593.

B&B PPS:	**£15/£17**	SNGL OCC. DBLE/TPL:	**£21.50/£23.50**	SNGL RM:	-
PART BRD:	-	% RED. CHILDREN:	**25%**	DINNER:	-

Skibbereen 3km

Mrs Carolyn O'Neill
FERN LODGE
Baltimore Road, Skibbereen, Co Cork

Skibbereen

OPEN:	March-November
NO. ROOMS:	6
ENSUITE:	6

(V)

TEL: **028 22327**   FAX: -

Modern bungalow Peaceful rural setting on main Skibbereen / Baltimore Road. Lough Ine 2km Creagh gardens 1km. All amenities locally.

B&B PPS:	**£17**	SNGL OCC. DBLE/TPL:	**£23.50**	SNGL RM:	-
PART BRD:	-	% RED. CHILDREN:	**50%**	DINNER:	-

Skibbereen 1km

Mrs Carmel O'Sullivan
BALLYVALDON
Lurriga, Skibbereen, Co Cork

Skibbereen

OPEN:	1st May-20th September
NO. ROOMS:	3
ENSUITE:	1

(V)

TEL: **028 21507**   FAX: -

Modern house on own grounds. Facilities within easy access include Golf, Fishing, Tennis, Sailing. Beaches locally.

B&B PPS:	**£15/£17**	SNGL OCC. DBLE/TPL:	**£21.50/£23.50**	SNGL RM:	-
PART BRD:	-	% RED. CHILDREN:	-	DINNER:	-

In Skibbereen

Mrs K O'Sullivan
WHISPERING TREES
Baltimore Road, Skibbereen, Co Cork

Skibbereen

OPEN:	February-November
No. ROOMS:	5
ENSUITE:	5

(V)

TEL: **028 21376**   FAX: -

Modern house on own grounds in suburbs of Skibbereen. Tea/coffee making facilities. Golf, Fishing, Horseriding, Tennis, Beaches nearby. Credit Cards accepted.

B&B PPS:	**£17**	SNGL OCC. DBLE/TPL:	**£23.50**	SNGL RM:	-
PART BRD:	-	% RED. CHILDREN:	**50%**	DINNER:	-

In Skibbereen

Mrs Ann Williams
BORODALE
Coronea, Skibbereen, Co Cork

Skibbereen

OPEN:	May-October
No. ROOMS:	4
ENSUITE:	2

(V)

TEL: **028 21485**   FAX: -

Modern, comfortable, family run home. Peaceful select location. 3 minutes walk Skibbereen. Beaches, 18-hole Golf Course, Fishing, Horseriding, Sports facilities nearby.

B&B PPS:	**£15/£17**	SNGL OCC. DBLE/TPL:	**£21/£23.50**	SNGL RM:	-
PART BRD:	-	% RED. CHILDREN:	**50%**	DINNER:	-

Butlerstown 1km

Mrs Mary Holland
ATLANTIC SUNSET
Kilsillagh, Butlerstown, Bandon, Co Cork

Timoleague

OPEN:	1st January-20th December
No. ROOMS:	4
ENSUITE:	2

(V)

TEL: **023 40115**   FAX: -

First class accommodation overlooking Atlantic. Dunworley sandy beaches 1 km. Golf, Tennis, Boating locally. Frommer & French Guide recommended.

B&B PPS:	**£15/£17**	SNGL OCC. DBLE/TPL:	**£21.50/£23.50**	SNGL RM:	**£15**
PART BRD:	-	% RED. CHILDREN:	**20%**	DINNER:	-

Clonakilty 8km

Pat & Jo O'Donovan,
HARBOUR HEIGHTS
Timoleague, Bandon, Co Cork

Timoleague

OPEN:	1st January-31st December
No. ROOMS:	4
ENSUITE:	3

(V)

TEL: **023 46232**   FAX: -

Modern bungalow set in tranquil surroundings overlooking Timoleague Abbey, and Courtmacsherry Bay. Guest lounge, Conservatory. Breakfast menu. Private Car Park.

B&B PPS:	**£15/£17**	SNGL OCC. DBLE/TPL:	**£21.50/£23.50**	SNGL RM:	-
PART BRD:	**£190**	% RED. CHILDREN:	**50%**	DINNER:	**£15**

Clonakilty 10km

Mrs Catherine Ryan
PANORAMA B & B
Chapel Hill, Timoleague (Near Kinsale), West Cork, Co Cork

Timoleague

OPEN:	All Year except Christmas
No. ROOMS:	3
ENSUITE:	3

(V)

TEL: **023 46248**   FAX: -

Modern Bungalow, with panoramic view over famous Abbey / Courtmacsharry Bay. Indoor Leisure facilities, Tennis, Fishing, Golf, Horse Riding, Beaches nearby.

B&B PPS:	**£17/£20**	SNGL OCC. DBLE/TPL:	**£23.50/£26.50**	SNGL RM:	-
PART BRD:	-	% RED. CHILDREN:	**33%**	DINNER:	

In Union Hall

Adela A. Nugent
SHEARWATER
Keelbeg, Union Hall, Co Cork

Union Hall/Glandore

OPEN:	1st April-31st October
NO. ROOMS:	3
ENSUITE:	3

TEL: **028 33178**   FAX: -

"Shearwater" is situated overlooking Glandore Harbour and surrounding countryside. All bedrooms have sea views, the patio area offers outstanding scenery.

B&B PPS:	**£17**	SNGL OCC. DBLE/TPL:	**£23.50**	SNGL RM:	-
PART BRD:	-	% RED. CHILDREN:	**50%**	DINNER:	-

Skibbereen 10km

D & A O'Connell
ARDAGH HOUSE
Union Hall
West Cork, Co Cork

Union Hall

OPEN:	January-December
NO. ROOMS:	3
ENSUITE:	3

TEL: **028 33571**   FAX: **028 33571**

Beautiful 100 yr old authentically restored Farm house set within village. Extensive breakfast menu, Hairdryers, TV, Electric Blankets. Ideal touring base.

B&B PPS:	**£17**	SNGL OCC. DBLE/TPL:	**£25.50**	SNGL RM:	-
PART BRD:	-	% RED. CHILDREN:	**50%**	DINNER:	-

Youghal 4km

Mrs Kitty Bulman
KOALA HOUSE
Kennel, Youghal, Co Cork

Youghal

OPEN:	1st March-1st November
NO. ROOMS:	4
ENSUITE:	3

TEL: **024 92786**   FAX: -

N25,Rosslare - Cork route.Modern residence with large garden in rural setting.Private parking. Golf, fishing. Sandy beaches locally.

B&B PPS:	**£15/£17**	SNGL OCC. DBLE/TPL:	**£21.50/£23.50**	SNGL RM:	-
PART BRD:	-	% RED. CHILDREN:	-	DINNER:	-

Youghal 8km

Mrs Therese Cliffe
THE GABLES
Kinsalebeg, Youghal, Co Cork

Youghal

OPEN:	April-November
NO. ROOMS:	5
ENSUITE:	1

TEL: **024 92739**   FAX: -

N25 Cork/Rosslare Rd., close to Sandy Beaches, Fishing, Golf, Fota, Jameson, Heritage centre, Trabolgan, Ardmore, Tennis Court, private car park.

B&B PPS:	**£15/£17**	SNGL OCC. DBLE/TPL:	**£21.50/£23.50**	SNGL RM:	-
PART BRD:	-	% RED. CHILDREN:	**50%**	DINNER:	-

Youghal 2km

Mrs Anne Marie Coleman
SUAIN-ARAS
Ballyvergan, Cork Road (N25),
Youghal, Co Cork

Youghal

OPEN:	1st March-30th November
NO. ROOMS:	4
ENSUITE:	3

TEL: **024 92715**   FAX: -

Bungalow on N25 Cork/Rosslare Route. On 3 acres rural setting. Ground floor accommodation. TV lounge,Private Parking.Golf, Beaches nearby.

B&B PPS:	**£15/£17**	SNGL OCC. DBLE/TPL:	**£21.50/£23.50**	SNGL RM:	-
PART BRD:	-	% RED. CHILDREN:	**25%**	DINNER:	-

Mrs Nuala Connor
LAGILE LODGE
Killeagh, Youghal, Co Cork

Youghal

OPEN:	1st May-30th September
NO. ROOMS:	3
ENSUITE:	3

V

TEL: **024 95323**   FAX: -

Enjoy a stay among Animals, Wildlife on 10-acres Gardens, Paddocks 200m back off N25 in peaceful relaxed atmosphere. Breakfast menu.

B&B PPS:	£17/£20	SNGL OCC. DBLE/TPL:	-	SNGL RM:	-
PART BRD:	-	% RED. CHILDREN:	-	DINNER:	-

— Youghal 8km —

Maura Coughlan
CARN NA RADHARC
Ardsallagh, Youghal, Co Cork

Youghal

OPEN:	April-October
NO. ROOMS:	3
ENSUITE:	2

V

TEL: **024 92703**   FAX: -

2km off N25, Youghal Bridge. Magnificent views river, mountains, quiet cul-de-sac. Locally Beaches, PonyTrekking, Heritage Centres, Fota and Trabolgan.

B&B PPS:	£15/£17	SNGL OCC. DBLE/TPL:	£21.50/£23.50	SNGL RM:	-
PART BRD:	-	% RED. CHILDREN:	50%	DINNER:	-

— Youghal 6km —

Mrs Eileen Fogarty
BROMLEY HOUSE
Killeagh, Youghal, Co Cork

Youghal

OPEN:	March-October
NO. ROOMS:	4
ENSUITE:	4

V

TEL: **024 95235**   FAX: -

N25 Cork-Rosslare Rd. Golf, Beaches, Fishing nearby. Convenient to Fota, Cobh and Midleton Heritage Centres, Blarney. Private Parking.

B&B PPS:	£17	SNGL OCC. DBLE/TPL:	£23.50	SNGL RM:	-
PART BRD:	-	% RED. CHILDREN:	-	DINNER:	-

— Youghal 9km —

Mrs Phyllis Foley
ROSEVILLE
New Catherine St., Youghal, Co Cork

Youghal

OPEN:	20th January-20th December
NO. ROOMS:	5
ENSUITE:	5

V

TEL: **024 92571**   FAX: -

Attractive detached period residence situated within the "olde town" on the N25 Rosslare/Cork route - A warm welcome awaits you.

B&B PPS:	£17/£18	SNGL OCC. DBLE/TPL:	£23.50/£25	SNGL RM:	-
PART BRD:	-	% RED. CHILDREN:	33.3%	DINNER:	-

— In Youghal —

Mrs Eileen Gaine
AVONMORE HOUSE
South Abbey, Youghal, Co Cork

Youghal

OPEN:	All Year except Christmas
NO. ROOMS:	6
ENSUITE:	6

V

TEL: **024 92617**   FAX: -

Elegant 18th Century Georgian House at the entrance to Youghal Harbour within 3 min walk of Youghal's famous clock tower.

B&B PPS:	£18/£25	SNGL OCC. DBLE/TPL:	£20/£30	SNGL RM:	-
PART BRD:	-	% RED. CHILDREN:	25%	DINNER:	-

In Youghal

Mrs Mary Goggin
LEE HOUSE
29 Friar Street, Youghal, Co Cork

Youghal

OPEN:	All Year
NO. ROOMS:	5
ENSUITE:	4

TEL: **024 92292**   FAX: -

N25 Cork/Rosslare. Modern residence. In Youghal town. Two minutes walk to town centre. Private parking. Open all year.

B&B PPS:	£15/£20	SNGL OCC. DBLE/TPL:	-	SNGL RM:	£18/£20
PART BRD:	-	% RED. CHILDREN:	25%	DINNER:	-

Youghal 8km

Mrs Mary Mansfield
RIVERSIDE
Clashmore, Youghal, Co Cork

Youghal

OPEN:	1st March-30th September
NO. ROOMS:	3
ENSUITE:	3

TEL: **024 96135**   FAX: -

Modern Dormer in Heritage Village. 3 km off N25 between Dungarvan and Youghal. Locally; Sandy Beaches, Fishing, Golf, Fota Wildlife, Jameson.

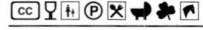

B&B PPS:	£17	SNGL OCC. DBLE/TPL:	£23.50	SNGL RM:	-
PART BRD:	-	% RED. CHILDREN:	50%	DINNER:	-

Youghal 6km

Mrs Carmel Tattan
TATTANS
Killeagh, Youghal, Co Cork

Youghal

OPEN:	1st March-31st October
NO. ROOMS:	5
ENSUITE:	4

TEL: **024 95173**   FAX: **024 95173**

N25 Cork/Rosslare Rd. 18th Century olde worlde premises. Convenient to Trabolgan, Fota, Golf, Fishing & Beaches. Private parking, spacious garden.

B&B PPS:	£17	SNGL OCC. DBLE/TPL:	£23.50	SNGL RM:	-
PART BRD:	£235	% RED. CHILDREN:	20%	DINNER:	£14

BOOKINGS

We recommend your first and last night is pre-booked. Your hosts will make a booking for you at your next selected home for the cost of the phone call. When travelling in high season (June, July, August), it is essential to pre-book your accommodation – preferably the evening before, or the following morning to avoid disappointment.

**SOME HOMES ARE CLOSED DURING THE WINTER.
WHEN TRAVELLING OFF-SEASON IT IS ADVISABLE TO CALL
AHEAD AND GIVE A TIME OF ARRIVAL TO ENSURE YOUR HOSTS
ARE AT HOME TO GREET YOU.**

Annascaul 2km

Mrs Kathleen O'Connor
FOUR WINDS
Annascaul, Co Kerry

Annascaul

Open:	All Year except Christmas
No. Rooms:	4
Ensuite:	3

Tel: **066 57168**   Fax: -

Recommended Dillard Causin Guide. Peaceful, scenic surroundings, walks, mountain climbing, beaches, fishing, lake/river. Golfing.

B&B PPS:	£15/£17	Sngl Occ. Dble/Tpl:	£21.50/£23.50	Sngl Rm:	-
Part Brd:	-	% Red. Children:	10%	Dinner:	-

In Ardfert

Katherine Higgins
ARDKEEL HOUSE
Ardfert, Co Kerry

Ardfert

Open:	All Year
No. Rooms:	3
Ensuite:	3

Tel: **066 34288**   Fax: -

Family run luxurious home, peaceful location off Ardfert-Fenit Road walking distance from bars, restaurants, near beach, Tralee golf course.

B&B PPS:	£17/£18	Sngl Occ. Dble/Tpl:	£23.50/£24.50	Sngl Rm:	-
Part Brd:	£180	% Red. Children:	33%	Dinner:	£13

In Ardfert

Mrs Bridie Sweeney
FAILTE
Tralee Road, Ardfert, Co Kerry

Ardfert

Open:	March-November
No. Rooms:	4
Ensuite:	3

Tel: **066 34278**   Fax: -

Luxurious bungalow. Tralee/Banna/Ballyheige road (R551) in historical Ardfert village near golf course, pitch & putt, beach, restaurant in village.

B&B PPS:	£17/£18	Sngl Occ. Dble/Tpl:	£23.50/£25	Sngl Rm:	-
Part Brd:	-	% Red. Children:	50%	Dinner:	-

Ballybunion 1km

Mrs Mary Beasley
THE 19TH GREEN
Golf Links Rd, Ballybunion, Co Kerry

Ballybunion

Open:	All Year except Christmas
No. Rooms:	4
Ensuite:	4

Tel: **068 27592**   Fax: **068 27830**

"Golfers Paradise". Opposite course. good seven iron to clubhouse. Luxurious accommodation. Green fee reductions. Breakfast from 6am. Drying room, hairdryers.

B&B PPS:	£18/£26	Sngl Occ. Dble/Tpl:	£25/£35	Sngl Rm:	-
Part Brd:	-	% Red. Children:	-	Dinner:	-

In Ballybunion

Maurice & Patricia Boyle
THE OLD COURSE
Golf Links Road, Ballybunion, Co Kerry

Ballybunion

Open:	1st May-15th October
No. Rooms:	3
Ensuite:	3

Tel: **068 27171**   Fax: -

Warm welcoming hospitality in luxurious, spacious modern home. Overlooking old course, green fee reduction. Early breakfasts, Car park, Drying facilities.

B&B PPS:	£18/£30	Sngl Occ. Dble/Tpl:	£25/£36.50	Sngl Rm:	-
Part Brd:	-	% Red. Children:	50%	Dinner:	-

In Ballybunion

Mrs Ray McCarthy
THE LINKS
Doon East, Ballybunion, Co Kerry

Ballybunion

OPEN:	1st April-1st October
NO. ROOMS:	3
ENSUITE:	3

(V)

TEL: **068 27687**   FAX: **068 27687**

Detached bungalow Luxurious accommodation overlooking sea & mountains. Green fee reductions. Early breakfast. Large car park. Near beach & golf.

B&B PPS:	£18	SNGL OCC. DBLE/TPL:	£25	SNGL RM:	£25
PART BRD:	-	% RED. CHILDREN:	50%	DINNER:	-

In Ballybunion

Mrs Anne McCaughey
DOON HOUSE
Doon Road, Ballybunion, Co Kerry

Ballybunion

OPEN:	1st April-1st November
NO. ROOMS:	3
ENSUITE:	3

(V)

TEL: **068 27411**   FAX: **068 27411**

Overlooking Ballybunion & Atlantic Ocean. Beautiful panoramic sea/mountain view. (Golfers home away from home). Green fee reductions. Early breakfasts.

B&B PPS:	£17/£25	SNGL OCC. DBLE/TPL:	£25/£31.50	SNGL RM:	£25
PART BRD:	-	% RED. CHILDREN:	-	DINNER:	--

Ballybunion 3km

Nora Quane
KILCONLY HOUSE
Coast Rd, Ballybunion, Co Kerry

Ballybunion

OPEN:	1st May-31st October
NO. ROOMS:	3
ENSUITE:	3

(V)

TEL: **068 27633**   FAX:

Situated on coast road north of Ballybunion. Close to golf, beaches and car ferry. Orthopaedic beds, breakfast menu, home baking.

B&B PPS:	£17	SNGL OCC. DBLE/TPL:	£23.50	SNGL RM:	-
PART BRD:	-	% RED. CHILDREN:	50%	DINNER:	-

Mrs Anne Leen
WAVE CREST
Cliff Road, Old Mill, Ballyheigue, Co Kerry

Ballyheigue

OPEN:	1st April-31st October
NO. ROOMS:	3
ENSUITE:	2

(V)

TEL: **066 33177**   FAX: -

Peaceful country setting. Spectacular scenery. Bedrooms overlooking bay on edge of Atlantic Ocean with Dingle mountain range on background.

B&B PPS:	£15/£17	SNGL OCC. DBLE/TPL:	£21.50/£23.50	SNGL RM:	-
PART BRD:	-	% RED. CHILDREN:	50%	DINNER:	-

In Ballyheigue

Ballylongford 2.5km

Patricia & Garrett Dee
CASTLE VIEW HOUSE
Carrig Island, Ballylongford, Co Kerry

Ballylongford

OPEN:	All Year except Christmas
NO. ROOMS:	6
ENSUITE:	6

(V)

TEL: **068 43304**   FAX: -

Modern house on scenic island facing historical Carrigafoyle Castle. Tarbert car ferry, golf nearby, scenic walks, angling, credit cards welcome.

B&B PPS:	£17	SNGL OCC. DBLE/TPL:	£23.50	SNGL RM:	-
PART BRD:	-	% RED. CHILDREN:	50%	DINNER:	£12

Caherdaniel 1km

Mrs Cathy Fitzmaurice
THE OLDE FORGE
Caherdaniel, Ring of Kerry, Co Kerry

Caherdaniel Ring of Kerry

OPEN:	All Year except Christmas
No. ROOMS:	6
ENSUITE:	6

TEL: **066 75140**   FAX: -

On Ring of Kerry. Access to sea. Horse riding, fishing, golf. Trips to Skelligs. Dillard Causin recommended. Kerry Way nearby.

B&B PPS:	**£17**	SNGL OCC. DBLE/TPL:	**£23.50**	SNGL RM:	-
PART BRD:	**£195**	% RED. CHILDREN:	**50%**	DINNER:	**£13**

Caherdaniel 1km

Donal & Monica Hunt
DERRYNANE BAY HOUSE
Caherdaniel, Co Kerry

Caherdaniel - Ring of Kerry

OPEN:	All Year except Christmas
No. ROOMS:	6
ENSUITE:	6

TEL: **066 75404/087 2343974**   FAX: **066 75436**

Superb accommodation, panoramic views over Derrynane Bay. Power showers. Breakfast menu. Golf, horse-riding, fishing, beaches nearby, adjacent Kerry Way. AA listed.

B&B PPS:	**£19**	SNGL OCC. DBLE/TPL:	**£24**	SNGL RM:	-
PART BRD:	**£205**	% RED. CHILDREN:	**33.3%**	DINNER:	**£13.50**

In Caherdaniel

Mrs Angela O'Sullivan
CAHERDANIEL
Ring of Kerry, Co Kerry

Caherdaniel Ring of Kerry

OPEN:	All Year except Christmas
No. ROOMS:	6
ENSUITE:	1

TEL: **066 75124**   FAX: -

Modern two storey house on Ring of Kerry. Horse riding, fishing, golf, mountain climbing, beaches. "access to Kerry Way".

B&B PPS:	**£15/£17**	SNGL OCC. DBLE/TPL:	**£21.50/£23.50**	SNGL RM:	**£17**
PART BRD:	-	% RED. CHILDREN:	**25%**	DINNER:	**£13**

Cahirciveen 4.5km

Mrs Caroline Coffey
BEGINIS
Laharn South, Portmagee Road, Cahirciveen, Co Kerry

Cahirciveen

OPEN:	All Year
No. ROOMS:	3
ENSUITE:	2

TEL: **066 72621**   FAX: -

Welcoming country home. Warm friendly hospitality. Delicious food. Beautiful harbour and island view. Low season reductions. Skelligs boat trips arranged.

B&B PPS:	**£15/£17**	SNGL OCC. DBLE/TPL:	**£21.50/£25**	SNGL RM:	-
PART BRD:	-	% RED. CHILDREN:	**25%**	DINNER:	-

Cahirciveen 3km

Mrs Irene Curran
HARBOUR HILL
Knockeens, Cahirciveen, Co Kerry

Cahirciveen

OPEN:	1st May-30th September
No. ROOMS:	3
ENSUITE:	2

TEL: **066 72844**   FAX: -

Peaceful hillside setting, panoramic views, harbour and islands off Ring of Kerry. Golf, fishing, horse-riding, Coastal walks, Skellig trips.

B&B PPS:	**£15/£17**	SNGL OCC. DBLE/TPL:	**£21.50/£23.50**	SNGL RM:	-
PART BRD:	-	% RED. CHILDREN:	**50%**	DINNER:	-

Mrs Eilis Dennehy
SEA BREEZE
Renard Road, Cahirciveen, Co Kerry

Cahirciveen

OPEN:	1st March-31st October
No. ROOMS:	6
ENSUITE:	4

Ⓥ

TEL: **066 72609** FAX: -

Country home, spectacular views sea, islands, castle, forts. Skellig trips, golf, seafood resturants, AA approved, breakfast menu, hairdryers, orthopaedic beds.

B&B PPS:	**£15/£17**	SNGL OCC. DBLE/TPL:	**£21.50/£23.50**	SNGL RM:	-
PART BRD:	-	% RED. CHILDREN:	**25%**	DINNER:	-

— Cahirciveen 0.5km

Mrs B Landers
SAN ANTOINE
Valentia Rd, Cahirciveen, Co Kerry

Cahirciveen

OPEN:	17th March-31st October
No. ROOMS:	7
ENSUITE:	7

Ⓥ

TEL: **066 72521** FAX: **066 72521**

"San Antoine". Set in peaceful landscaped gardens overlooking the bay. Sea sports, golf, horse riding, sandy beaches, scenic walks locally.

B&B PPS:	**£17**	SNGL OCC. DBLE/TPL:	**£23.50/£30**	SNGL RM:	-
PART BRD:	-	% RED. CHILDREN:	**30%**	DINNER:	-

— In Cahirciveen

Mary Landers
FRANSAL HOUSE
Foilmore, Caherciveen, Co Kerry

Cahirciveen

OPEN:	1st April-1st November
No. ROOMS:	3
ENSUITE:	3

Ⓥ

TEL: **066 72997** FAX: **066 72997**

Peaceful setting between river and mountains (Kerry Way). Boat, Fishing Trips arranged. Laundry service, near bus stop. Room only £12pps

B&B PPS:	**£17**	SNGL OCC. DBLE/TPL:	**£23.50**	SNGL RM:	-
PART BRD:	-	% RED. CHILDREN:	**33.3%**	DINNER:	**£13**

— Cahirciveen 6.5km

Ian & Ann Nugent
CUL DRAIOCHTA
Points Cross, Cahirciveen, Co Kerry

Cahirciveen

OPEN:	All Year
No. ROOMS:	3
ENSUITE:	3

Ⓥ

TEL: **066 73141** FAX: **066 72743**

Charming family home with magic scenery. On N70 Ring of Kerry. Superb base for all activities. Tea/coffee on arrival

B&B PPS:	**£17**	SNGL OCC. DBLE/TPL:	**£23.50/£24.50**	SNGL RM:	-
PART BRD:	**£180**	% RED. CHILDREN:	**30%**	DINNER:	**£12**

— Cahirciveen 1km

Marie O'Mahony
CASTLEVIEW
Valentia Road, Cahirciveen, Co Kerry

Cahirciveen

OPEN:	1st May-31st October
No. ROOMS:	4
ENSUITE:	-

Ⓥ

TEL: **066 72252** FAX: -

On Ring of Kerry. Access to sea, fishing, golf, horse riding, trips to Skelligs, coastal walks, scenic view from bedrooms.

B&B PPS:	**£15/£16**	SNGL OCC. DBLE/TPL:	**£21.50**	SNGL RM:	-
PART BRD:	-	% RED. CHILDREN:	**25%**	DINNER:	-

— In Cahirciveen

In Cahirciveen

Mrs Christina O'Neill
IVERAGH HEIGHTS
Carhan Rd, Cahirciveen, Co Kerry

Cahirciveen

Open:	All Year
No. Rooms:	4
Ensuite:	4

(V)

Tel: **066 72545**   Fax: -

Situated in peaceful gardens overlooking river. On Ring of Kerry road. Skellig trip arranged. Golf, fishing, entertainment locally. Itineraries planned.

B&B PPS:	£17	Sngl Occ. Dble/Tpl:	£23.50	Sngl Rm:	-
Part Brd:	-	% Red. Children:	20%	Dinner:	£12

In Cahirciveen

Eileen O'Shea
O'SHEAS'S B&B
Church St, Cahirciveen, Co Kerry

Cahirciveen

Open:	All Year
No. Rooms:	3
Ensuite:	3

(V)

Tel: **066 72402**   Fax: -

18th Century town house on Ring of Kerry. Fishing, golf, horse riding, sea sports, scenic walks, sandy beaches, archeological sites.

B&B PPS:	£17	Sngl Occ. Dble/Tpl:	£23.50	Sngl Rm:	-
Part Brd:	-	% Red. Children:	20%	Dinner:	-

In Cahirciveen

Gene & Aine Young
REENARD HOUSE
Reenard Road, Cahirciveen, Co Kerry

Cahirciveen

Open:	All Year
No. Rooms:	5
Ensuite:	5

(V)

Tel: **066 72752**   Fax: -

Luxurious, spacious purpose built home, unique location. 0.5km on Waterville side Cahirciveen. Relaxed friendly atmosphere. All rooms with sea view.

B&B PPS:	£17/£18	Sngl Occ. Dble/Tpl:	£23.50/£24.50	Sngl Rm:	-
Part Brd:	£190	% Red. Children:	50%	Dinner:	£14

Camp 4.5km

Mrs Fionnuala Fitzgerald
SUAN NA MARA
Lisnagree, Castlegregory Rd, Camp, Co Kerry

Camp/Castlegregory

Open:	1st March-30th November
No. Rooms:	6
Ensuite:	6

(V)

Tel: **066 39258**   Fax: **066 39258**

Beautifully appointed 'Laura Ashley' style home with mountain view, adjacent to glorious sandy beach. Extensive breakfast menu. Own pitch & putt.

B&B PPS:	£17/£22	Sngl Occ. Dble/Tpl:	£25/£38	Sngl Rm:	-
Part Brd:	-	% Red. Children:	25%	Dinner:	£16

Dingle 14km

Mrs Mary Ferriter
BEENOSKEE
Cappateige, Conor Pass Road, Castlegregory, Co Kerry

Castlegregory, Dingle Peninsula

Open:	All Year
No. Rooms:	4
Ensuite:	3

(V)

Tel: **066 39263**   Fax: **066 39263**

Warm hospitality. Spectacular uninterrupted seafront/sandy beaches. Decorated home. Orthopaedic beds. Breakfast menu. Homebaking. Guide Routard, Lonely Planet. 1KM W Stradbally

 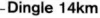

B&B PPS:	£15/£17	Sngl Occ. Dble/Tpl:	£21.50/£23.50	Sngl Rm:	-
Part Brd:	£180	% Red. Children:	50%	Dinner:	£13

Helen Healy
AISLING
Castlegregory, Co Kerry

Castlegregory Dingle Peninsula

OPEN:	**1st April-31st October**
NO. ROOMS:	5
ENSUITE:	2

TEL: **066 39134**   FAX: -

Long established, well appointed, spacious accommodation, two guest lounges, recommended in many guides. On 1 acre lawns, sandy beaches, turf fires. In Castlegregory village.

B&B PPS:	**£16/£18**	SNGL OCC. DBLE/TPL:	**£21/£23**	SNGL RM:	-
PART BRD:	-	% RED. CHILDREN:	**25%**	DINNER:	-

Tralee 26km

Mrs Mary Lynch
STRAND VIEW HOUSE
Kilcummin, Conor Pass Road,
Castlegregory, Co Kerry

Castlegregory Dingle Peninsula

OPEN:	**1st March-1st November**
NO. ROOMS:	4
ENSUITE:	4

TEL: **066 38131**   FAX: **066 39434**

Luxury accomodation on sea front overlooking Brandon Bay. Selected AA QQQQ Ideal touring base. Watersports, fishing, golf, 3KM west of Stradbally.

B&B PPS:	**£18/£20**	SNGL OCC. DBLE/TPL:	**£24.50/£26.50**	SNGL RM:	-
PART BRD:	-	% RED. CHILDREN:	**50%**	DINNER:	-

Stradbally 3km

Mrs Catherine Lyons
ORCHARD HOUSE
Castlegregory, Co Kerry

Castlegregory Dingle Peninsula

OPEN:	**April-October**
NO. ROOMS:	4
ENSUITE:	3

TEL: **066 39164**   FAX: -

Family home in idyllic village. 5 minutes walk from beach, convenient to water sports, golf, fishing, horse riding & mountain climbing.

B&B PPS:	**£17**	SNGL OCC. DBLE/TPL:	**£23.50**	SNGL RM:	-
PART BRD:	-	% RED. CHILDREN:	**50%**	DINNER:	-

Tralee 26km

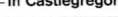

Mrs Maura Moriarty
THE FUCHSIA HOUSE
West Main Street, Castlegregory,
Co Kerry

Castlegregory / Dingle Peninsula

OPEN:	**All Year**
NO. ROOMS:	4
ENSUITE:	4

TEL: **066 39508**   FAX: -

New home with old Irish charm. Private parking, orthapaedic bed, power showers, beach five minutes, golf, fishing, mountain walks.

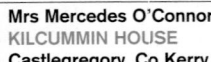

B&B PPS:	**£17/£20**	SNGL OCC. DBLE/TPL:	**£23.50/£27**	SNGL RM:	-
PART BRD:	-	% RED. CHILDREN:	**50%**	DINNER:	**£14.50**

In Castlegregory

Mrs Mercedes O'Connor
KILCUMMIN HOUSE
Castlegregory, Co Kerry

Castlegregory Dingle Peninsula

OPEN:	**1st April-15th November**
NO. ROOMS:	4
ENSUITE:	3

TEL: **066 39152**   FAX: -

This luxury country house set in peaceful scenic surroundings on the Dingle Peninsula, overlooking Kilcummin Beach. Home cooking our speciality.

B&B PPS:	**£17/£18**	SNGL OCC. DBLE/TPL:	**£23.50/£24.50**	SNGL RM:	-
PART BRD:	**£195**	% RED. CHILDREN:	**50%**	DINNER:	**£14**

Castlegregory 8km

Dingle 14km

Mrs Annette O'Mahony
THE SHORES COUNTRY HOUSE
Cappatigue, Conor Pass Road, Castlegregory, Co Kerry
TEL: **066 39196**   FAX: **066 39196**

Castlegregory Dingle Peninsula

OPEN:	17th March-30th November
NO. ROOMS:	3
ENSUITE:	2

(V)

Luxuriously decorated spacious "Laura Ashley" style rooms all with sea view. Breakfast/dinner menu. Recommended by guides, 1Km west Stradbally.

B&B PPS:	**£15/£20**	SNGL OCC. DBLE/TPL:	**£21.50/£26.50**	SNGL RM:	**£22/£25**
PART BRD:	**£225**	% RED. CHILDREN:	**33%**	DINNER:	**£15.50**

Stradbally

Mrs Agnes Reidy
GOULANE HOUSE
Stradbally, Conor Pass Road, Castlegregory, Co Kerry
TEL: **066 39174**   FAX: -

Castlegregory Dingle Peninsula

OPEN:	All Year
NO. ROOMS:	4
ENSUITE:	4

(V)

Outstanding Irish hospitality, beautiful views overlooking Brandon Bay, kettle available, restaurant 0.4 km, large room, breakfast choices, orthopaedic beds, numerous recommendations.

B&B PPS:	**£17**	SNGL OCC. DBLE/TPL:	**£23.50**	SNGL RM:	-
PART BRD:	-	% RED. CHILDREN:	**50%**	DINNER:	**£12**

Mrs Paula Walsh
SEA-MOUNT HOUSE
Cappatigue, Conor Pass Road, Castlegregory, Co Kerry
TEL: **066 39229**   FAX: -

Castlegregory / Dingle Peninsula

OPEN:	March-November
NO. ROOMS:	3
ENSUITE:	2

(V)

Outstanding views of the Ocean and long sandy beaches. Overlooking Brandon Bay. Mountainous background. Landscaped garden. Breakfast choices. Orthopaedic beds.

Stradbally 1km

B&B PPS:	**£15/£17**	SNGL OCC. DBLE/TPL:	**£21.50/£23.50**	SNGL RM:	-
PART BRD:	-	% RED. CHILDREN:	**50%**	DINNER:	-

Castleisland 4km

Mrs Eileen Cronin
GROTTO VIEW
Currow Village, Killarney, Co Kerry
TEL: **066 64646**   FAX: -

Castleisland

OPEN:	Easter/October
NO. ROOMS:	3
ENSUITE:	3

(V)

Modern home on edge of award winning village (off N23). Central for touring, Airport 2 km. Spacious rooms, Tea making facilities.

B&B PPS:	**£17**	SNGL OCC. DBLE/TPL:	**£23.50**	SNGL RM:	-
PART BRD:	**£180**	% RED. CHILDREN:	**50%**	DINNER:	**£12**

Castleisland 3km

Lilian Dillon
THE GABLES
Dooneen, Limerick Road, Castleisland, Co Kerry
TEL: **066 41060**   FAX: -

Castleisland

OPEN:	All Year except Christmas
NO. ROOMS:	4
ENSUITE:	3

(V)

High standard of accommodation in spacious, comfortable, country residence. Two triple rooms, Panoramic view, warm welcome, great breakfast, wonderful hospitality.

B&B PPS:	**£15/£17**	SNGL OCC. DBLE/TPL:	**£21.50/£23.50**	SNGL RM:	-
PART BRD:	**£180**	% RED. CHILDREN:	**50%**	DINNER:	**£12**

Mrs Eileen O'Connor
GLENBROOK HOUSE
Currow Village, Killarney, Co Kerry

Castleisland

OPEN:	All Year except Christmas
NO. ROOMS:	4
ENSUITE:	3

TEL: **066 64488**   FAX: -

Highly recommended home. Ideal for touring Kerry. Home cooking a speciality. Signposted off N23. Airport 1 km. Visa/Access/Mastercard Accepted.

Castleisland 3km

B&B PPS:	**£15/£18**	SNGL OCC. DBLE/TPL:	**£21.50/£24.50**	SNGL RM:	-
PART BRD:	**£200**	% RED. CHILDREN:	**50%**	DINNER:	**£13**

Mrs Joan Burke
MOUNTAIN VIEW
Ballinamona, Castlemaine, Co Kerry

Castlemaine

OPEN:	1st April-31st October
NO. ROOMS:	3
ENSUITE:	2

TEL: **066 67249**   FAX: -

Modern two storey new house with panoramic view, central for touring, Ring of Kerry and Dingle Peninsula. Access/Visa/Euro.

Castlemaine 1km

B&B PPS:	**£15/£17**	SNGL OCC. DBLE/TPL:	**£23.50**	SNGL RM:	**£19/£21**
PART BRD:	**£180**	% RED. CHILDREN:	**50%**	DINNER:	**£12**

Mrs Elizabeth O'Sullivan
CAHER HOUSE
Caherfilane, Castlemaine, Co Kerry

Castlemaine

OPEN:	1st April-31st October
NO. ROOMS:	6
ENSUITE:	5

TEL: **066 66126**   FAX: -

Comfortable residence overlooking Dingle Bay. Central for Ring of Kerry, Dingle, Killarney. Kerry County Airport 15 km between Castlemaine & Inch.

Castlemaine 4km

B&B PPS:	**£15/£17**	SNGL OCC. DBLE/TPL:	**£21.50/£23.50**	SNGL RM:	-
PART BRD:	**£180**	% RED. CHILDREN:	**50%**	DINNER:	**£12**

Mrs Eleanor Begley
CLOOSHMORE HOUSE
Clooshmore, Dingle, Co Kerry

Dingle

OPEN:	1st March-31st October
NO. ROOMS:	3
ENSUITE:	3

TEL: **066 51117**   FAX: -

Luxury home on the edge of Dingle Harbour, all rooms with hair-dryer, radio,T.V.,tea/coffee making facilities. Breakfast menu.

Dingle 2km

B&B PPS:	**£17/£18**	SNGL OCC. DBLE/TPL:	**£20/£22**	SNGL RM:	-
PART BRD:	-	% RED. CHILDREN:	-	DINNER:	-

Mrs Sheila Birmingham
BALLYMORE HOUSE
Ballymore, Ventry, Dingle Co Kerry

Dingle

OPEN:	1st May-30th September
NO. ROOMS:	7
ENSUITE:	5

TEL: **066 59050**   FAX: -

Spacious country home, overlooking sea. Peaceful location. Close to all amenities.

Dingle 4km

B&B PPS:	**£15/£17**	SNGL OCC. DBLE/TPL:	**£22/£24**	SNGL RM:	-
PART BRD:	-	% RED. CHILDREN:	**20%**	DINNER:	-

Dingle 10km

Mrs Kitty Brosnan
ABHAINN MHOR
Cloghane, Co Kerry

Dingle

OPEN:	1st April-31st October
NO. ROOMS:	4
ENSUITE:	3

TEL: **066 38211** FAX: -

Beside village. On Dingle way, foot of Brandon Mountain. Near Dingle, beaches, hill walking, guided walks, fishing, archaeology. Coeliac's welcome.

| B&B PPS: | **£17** | SNGL OCC. DBLE/TPL: | **£23.50** | SNGL RM: | **£17** |
| PART BRD: | **£185** | % RED. CHILDREN: | **50%** | DINNER: | **£12** |

Dingle 4.5km

Mrs Rita Brosnan
DROM HOUSE
Coumgaugh, Dingle, Co Kerry

Dingle

OPEN:	All Year except Christmas
NO. ROOMS:	3
ENSUITE:	3

TEL: **066 51134** FAX: -

Situated on Ballyferriter Road. All Rooms ensuite with TV, Clock/Radio, hairdryer & tea/coffee facilities. Playground for Children.

| B&B PPS: | **£17** | SNGL OCC. DBLE/TPL: | **£23.50** | SNGL RM: | - |
| PART BRD: | - | % RED. CHILDREN: | **50%** | DINNER: | - |

Dingle 1km

Mrs Camilla Browne
"RABHAN HOUSE"
Ladies Cross, Dingle, Co Kerry

Dingle

OPEN:	17th March-3rd November
NO. ROOMS:	4
ENSUITE:	4

TEL: **066 51259** FAX: -

Luxurious peaceful country home on main Slea Head Road, overlooking Dingle Bay and mountains. Tea/coffee, hairdryers, extensive breakfast menu.

| B&B PPS: | **£17** | SNGL OCC. DBLE/TPL: | **£23.50** | SNGL RM: | - |
| PART BRD: | - | % RED. CHILDREN: | - | DINNER: | - |

In Dingle

Mrs Eileen Carroll
MILESTONE
Milltown, Dingle, Co Kerry

Dingle

OPEN:	15th March-1st November
NO. ROOMS:	5
ENSUITE:	5

TEL: **066 51831** FAX: -

Quiet home overlooking Dingle Bay. All rooms with phone, TV, clock/radio, hairdryer, tea making facilities. Breakfast menu, private car park.

| B&B PPS: | **£17** | SNGL OCC. DBLE/TPL: | **£23.50** | SNGL RM: | - |
| PART BRD: | - | % RED. CHILDREN: | **20%** | DINNER: | - |

Dingle 4km

Mrs Mary Carroll
CEANN TRA HEIGHTS
Ventry, Dingle, Co Kerry

Dingle

OPEN:	April-November
NO. ROOMS:	4
ENSUITE:	4

TEL: **066 59866** FAX: -

Quiet country home overlooking Ventry Harbour in village. Seaview from rooms, tea making facilities, breakfast menu. Sandy beach, scenic walks.

| B&B PPS: | **£17** | SNGL OCC. DBLE/TPL: | **£23.50** | SNGL RM: | - |
| PART BRD: | - | % RED. CHILDREN: | **33.3%** | DINNER: | - |

Mrs Mary B Ui Chiobhain
ARD NA CARRAIGE
Carraig, Ballydavid, Dingle, Co Kerry

Dingle

Open:	1st May-1st October
No. Rooms:	4
Ensuite:	4

Tel: **066 55295**   Fax: -

Scenic Gaelic area, Gallarus Oratory, Kilmaolceadar. Traditional music. Close to beach, pubs restaurants, Dingle Way walk.

B&B PPS:	£17	Sngl Occ. Dble/Tpl:	£23.50	Sngl Rm:	-
Part Brd:	-	% Red. Children:	-	Dinner:	-

— Dingle 10km

Eileen Collins
KIRRARY
Avondale, Dingle, Co Kerry

Dingle

Open:	All Year except Christmas
No. Rooms:	3
Ensuite:	2

(V)

Tel: **066 51606**   Fax: **066 51606**

Family run, in quiet street, delightful gardens. Rent a bike. Turn right at roundabout, first left. Archaeology tours from house.

B&B PPS:	£15/£18	Sngl Occ. Dble/Tpl:	£24	Sngl Rm:	£23.50
Part Brd:	-	% Red. Children:	-	Dinner:	-

— In Dingle

Geraldine and Kevin Devane
Goat Street, Dingle, Co Kerry

Dingle

Open:	1st March-1st November
No. Rooms:	6
Ensuite:	5

Tel: **066 51193**   Fax: -

Town House overlooking Dingle Bay, within walking distance to all amenities. TV, Clock-radio, hairdryers, tea-coffee. Quiet location.

B&B PPS:	£15/£17	Sngl Occ. Dble/Tpl:	£21.50/£23.50	Sngl Rm:	-
Part Brd:	-	% Red. Children:	25%	Dinner:	-

— In Dingle

Mrs Breda Ferris
COIS CORRAIGH
Emila, Ballyferriter, Dingle Peninsula, Co Kerry

Dingle

Open:	1st May-30th September
No. Rooms:	5
Ensuite:	5

(V)

Tel: **066 56282**   Fax: **066 56005**

Family home convenient to beaches, golf course, restaurants. archeological sites nearby, Gallarus Oratory, Riase, Kilmaoulceadar.

B&B PPS:	£17	Sngl Occ. Dble/Tpl:	£23.50	Sngl Rm:	£17
Part Brd:	-	% Red. Children:	60%	Dinner:	-

— Ballyferriter 3km

Mrs Bridie Fitzgerald
DINGLE HEIGHTS
Ballinaboula, Dingle, Co Kerry

Dingle

Open:	March-October
No. Rooms:	4
Ensuite:	3

(V)

Tel: **066 51543**   Fax: -

Modern two storey house overlooking Dingle harbour. Private parking, Walking distance to town and all amenities.

B&B PPS:	£16/£17	Sngl Occ. Dble/Tpl:	£30	Sngl Rm:	-
Part Brd:	-	% Red. Children:	-	Dinner:	-

— In Dingle

Eleanor & Eamonn Fitzgerald
DINGLE VIEW
Conor Pass Road, Dingle, Co Kerry

Dingle

OPEN:	All Year except Christmas
NO. ROOMS:	4
ENSUITE:	4

TEL: **066 51662**   FAX: **066 51662**

New home overlooking Dingle Bay. Panoramic views. Superb location. Golf, horse riding, beaches. Near Dingle Way. Orthopaedic beds. Reduction low season.

B&B PPS:	£16/17	SNGL OCC. DBLE/TPL:	£23/£27	SNGL RM:	-
PART BRD:	-	% RED. CHILDREN:	-	DINNER:	-

— Dingle 1km

Beatrice Flannery
THE PLOUGH
Ventry, Dingle, Co Kerry

Dingle

OPEN:	1st March-30th September
NO. ROOMS:	3
ENSUITE:	3

TEL: **066 59727**   FAX: -

Warm friendly home in Ventry village. Walking distance to all amenities, panoramic sea/mountain views. Hairdryers, tea/coffee. Breakfast menu.

B&B PPS:	£17	SNGL OCC. DBLE/TPL:	£23.50	SNGL RM:	-
PART BRD:	-	% RED. CHILDREN:	-	DINNER:	-

— Dingle 4km

Marie Dolores Nic Gearalit
BOTHAR BUI
Ballydavid, Dingle, Co Kerry

Dingle

OPEN:	17th March-1st October
NO. ROOMS:	5
ENSUITE:	5

TEL: **066 55142**   FAX: -

Frommer Guide recommended. Breakfast menu. Home-cooking. Gaeilge agus Failte. Walkers & hill climbers paradise. Fishing, golf, archaeological sites nearby.

B&B PPS:	£17	SNGL OCC. DBLE/TPL:	£23.50	SNGL RM:	-
PART BRD:	£190	% RED. CHILDREN:	33%	DINNER:	£13

— Dingle 11km

Mrs Noirin Garvey Rohan
AN TOWERIN TRA
Baile Moir West, Ventry, Dingle, Co Kerry

Dingle

OPEN:	1st March-31st October
NO. ROOMS:	4
ENSUITE:	4

TEL: **066 59820**   FAX: -

Enjoy warm friendly hospitality in our tastefully decorated home. Magnificant sea views of Ventry harbour and Skellig Rocks. Home baking.

B&B PPS:	£17	SNGL OCC. DBLE/TPL:	£23.50	SNGL RM:	£23.50
PART BRD:	-	% RED. CHILDREN:	-	DINNER:	-

— Dingle 4km

Mrs Alice Hannafin,
AN SPEICE
Ballyferriter West, Dingle, Tralee, Co Kerry

Dingle

OPEN:	March-November
NO. ROOMS:	3
ENSUITE:	2

TEL: **066 56254**   FAX: -

Family bungalow on Slea Head Drive, walking distance Ballyferriter, near beaches, archeological sites, golf. sea and mountain view. Breakfast menu.

B&B PPS:	£16/£17	SNGL OCC. DBLE/TPL:	£22.50/£23.50	SNGL RM:	-
PART BRD:	-	% RED. CHILDREN:	50%	DINNER:	-

— In Ballyferriter

In Dingle

Mary & Michael Houlihan
ARD NA GREINE HOUSE
Spa Road, Dingle, Co Kerry

Dingle

OPEN:	**All Year**
NO. ROOMS:	4
ENSUITE:	4

(V)

TEL: **066 51113** FAX: **066 51898** EMAIL: **maryhoul@iol.ie**

AA 4 Q Quality Award, RAC acclaimed, Recommended 300 Best B&B's, Guide du Routard. Spacious rooms, orthopaedic beds, electric blankets, baths & extensive menu.

B&B PPS:	**£17/£19**	SNGL OCC. DBLE/TPL:	-	SNGL RM:	-
PART BRD:	-	% RED. CHILDREN:	-	DINNER:	-

Dingle 2km

Mary Huijgens-King
KING'S B&B
Ballinaboula, Dingle, Co Kerry

Dingle

OPEN:	**1st February-30th November**
NO. ROOMS:	5
ENSUITE:	5

(V)

TEL: **066 51745** FAX: -

Purpose built country home situated 2 kms. Dingle amid peaceful surroundings of hills, winding roads with cows, sheep And donkeys grazing nearby.

B&B PPS:	**£17**	SNGL OCC. DBLE/TPL:	**£23.50**	SNGL RM:	-
PART BRD:	-	% RED. CHILDREN:	**50%**	DINNER:	-

In Dingle

James & Hannah Kelliher
BALLYEGAN HOUSE
Upper John Street, Dingle, Co Kerry

Dingle

OPEN:	**All Year**
NO. ROOMS:	6
ENSUITE:	6

(V)

TEL: **066 51702** FAX: -

Home overlooking town/harbour. Peaceful restful accommodation in spacious rooms. Car parking. Minutes walk to town. TV lounge. AA recommended.

B&B PPS:	**£17/£18**	SNGL OCC. DBLE/TPL:	**£32**	SNGL RM:	-
PART BRD:	-	% RED. CHILDREN:	**25%**	DINNER:	-

Dingle 4km

Mrs Siobhan Kennedy
CLOONEEVIN
Ballymore, Ventry, Co Kerry

Dingle

OPEN:	**1st April-31st October**
NO. ROOMS:	4
ENSUITE:	4

TEL: **066 59916** FAX: -

Home with spacious bedrooms on Dingle/Ventry/Slea Head drive. Rural, peaceful setting. Ventry Beach/village 2km. Frommer guide listed.

B&B PPS:	**£15/£17**	SNGL OCC. DBLE/TPL:	**£17/£25**	SNGL RM:	-
PART BRD:	-	% RED. CHILDREN:	-	DINNER:	-

Dingle 8km

Angela Long
TIGH AN DUNA
Fahan, Slea Head, Ventry, Dingle, Co Kerry

Dingle

OPEN:	**1st May-1st October**
NO. ROOMS:	3
ENSUITE:	2

TEL: **066 59822** FAX: -

Country home near Slea Head. Bedrooms, diningroom overlooking Atlantic Ocean. Pre-historic sites, beaches, hill walking, restaurants locally. Breakfast menu. Personal attention.

B&B PPS:	**£15/£17**	SNGL OCC. DBLE/TPL:	**£21.50/£23.50**	SNGL RM:	-
PART BRD:	-	% RED. CHILDREN:	**50%**	DINNER:	-

Mrs Angela McCarthy
CILL BHREAC
Milltown, Dingle, Co Kerry

Dingle

OPEN:	March-November
NO. ROOMS:	5
ENSUITE:	5

TEL: 066 51358   FAX: -

Spacious home overlooking Dingle Bay, Mount Bandon. All rooms with radio, hairdryer, electric blankets. Tea facilities, satellite TV. Breakfast menu.

B&B PPS:	£17	SNGL OCC. DBLE/TPL:	£23.50	SNGL RM:	-
PART BRD:	-	% RED. CHILDREN:	25%	DINNER:	-

Dingle 1km

Tricia & Jim McCarthy
BALLYBEG HOUSE
Conor Pass Road, Dingle, Co Kerry

Dingle

OPEN:	1st March-30th November
NO. ROOMS:	4
ENSUITE:	3

TEL: 066 51569   FAX: -

Breathtaking views, town, harbour, Pass. Spacious rooms with satellite television, Orthopaedic beds, tea/coffee, electric blankets, clock radio. Extensive menu.

B&B PPS:	£17/£18	SNGL OCC. DBLE/TPL:	-	SNGL RM:	-
PART BRD:	-	% RED. CHILDREN:	-	DINNER:	-

Dingle 0.5km

Mrs Ann Manning
RIVERSIDE HOUSE
Emilough, Lispole, Dingle, Co Kerry

Dingle

OPEN:	1st May-1st October
NO. ROOMS:	4
ENSUITE:	3

TEL: 066 51807   FAX: -

Ground floor ensuite accommodation, sign posted on Tralee/Dingle Rd. Tea/coffee facilities in guest lounge, choice of breakfasts.

B&B PPS:	£15/£17	SNGL OCC. DBLE/TPL:	-	SNGL RM:	-
PART BRD:	-	% RED. CHILDREN:	33%	DINNER:	-

Dingle 4km

Mrs Ann Murphy
ARD-NA-MARA COUNTRY HSE
Ballymore, Ventry, Dingle, Co Kerry

Dingle

OPEN:	1st April-31st October
NO. ROOMS:	4
ENSUITE:	4

TEL: 066 59072   FAX: -

Elevated peaceful country home beside the sea overlooking Ventry Harbour. Rooms en-suite, breakfast menu. Complimentary tea/coffee

B&B PPS:	£17	SNGL OCC. DBLE/TPL:	£23.50	SNGL RM:	-
PART BRD:	-	% RED. CHILDREN:	50%	DINNER:	-

Dingle 4km

Mrs Mary Murphy
THE LIGHTHOUSE
The High Road, Ballinaboula, Dingle, Co Kerry

Dingle

OPEN:	1st Feburary-15th November
NO. ROOMS:	4
ENSUITE:	4

TEL: 066 51829   FAX: -

The Lighthouse offers magnificent views of Dingle Harbour. Quiet location, parking, minutes walk to town. Guest lounge, breakfast menu, Tea/Coffee.

B&B PPS:	£17	SNGL OCC. DBLE/TPL:	£23.50/£25	SNGL RM:	-
PART BRD:	-	% RED. CHILDREN:	50%	DINNER:	-

In Dingle

131

Anne & Pat Neligan
DUININ HOUSE
Conor Pass Road, Dingle, Co Kerry

Dingle

TEL: **066 51335**   FAX: **066 51335**

OPEN:	1st March-30th November
NO. ROOMS:	5
ENSUITE:	5

(V)

Superb location with magnificent views. Recommended by Frommer, Berlitz and "300 best B&Bs" Extensive breakfast menu. Luxurious guests conservatory/lounge.

B&B PPS:	£17/£18	SNGL OCC. DBLE/TPL:	-	SNGL RM:	-
PART BRD:	-	% RED. CHILDREN:	-	DINNER:	-

Dingle 1km

Mrs Margaret Noonan
CLUAIN MHUIRE HOUSE
Spa Road, Dingle, Co Kerry

Dingle

TEL: **066 51291**   FAX: -

OPEN:	All Year
NO. ROOMS:	4
ENSUITE:	4

(V)

4 Bedrooms with satellite TV. Tea/coffee facilities, electric blankets, hairdryer. Private large car park. Credit Cards. House well signposted.

B&B PPS:	£17	SNGL OCC. DBLE/TPL:	£23.50/£24	SNGL RM:	-
PART BRD:	-	% RED. CHILDREN:	20%	DINNER:	-

In Dingle

Mrs Kathleen O'Connor
SRAID EOIN HOUSE
John Street, Dingle, Co Kerry

Dingle

TEL: **066 51409**   FAX: **066 52156**

OPEN:	March-October
NO. ROOMS:	4
ENSUITE:	4

(V)

Newly refurbished house with spacious rooms, town centre, quiet location, within walking distance of all restaurants & bars. Family atmosphere.

B&B PPS:	£17/£18	SNGL OCC. DBLE/TPL:	£25/£30	SNGL RM:	-
PART BRD:	-	% RED. CHILDREN:	30%	DINNER:	-

In Dingle

Mrs Maureen O'Connor
ANGLERS REST
Ventry, Dingle Peninsula, Co Kerry

Dingle

TEL: **066 59947**   FAX: **066 59947**

OPEN:	1st April-31st October
NO. ROOMS:	5
ENSUITE:	3

(V)

Slea Head drive road, in Ventry Village, sandy beach, watersports, walking, fishing on own boat. Recommended Petra Tours. Leisure angling.

B&B PPS:	£15/£17	SNGL OCC. DBLE/TPL:	£21.50/£23.50	SNGL RM:	£23
PART BRD:	-	% RED. CHILDREN:	20%	DINNER:	-

Dingle 4km

Mrs Helen O'Neill
DOONSHEEN VIEW
High Road, Garfinny, Dingle, Co Kerry

Dingle

TEL: **066 51032**   FAX: -

OPEN:	April-September
NO. ROOMS:	3
ENSUITE:	3

(V)

Bungalow with fire safety certificate. Tranquil location, scenic views, close to beaches and popular walks. Ideal for touring Dingle Peninsula.

B&B PPS:	£17	SNGL OCC. DBLE/TPL:	£23.50	SNGL RM:	-
PART BRD:	-	% RED. CHILDREN:	50%	DINNER:	-

Dingle 2km

In Dingle

Mrs Mary O'Neill
John Street, Dingle, Co Kerry

Dingle

OPEN:	1st March-30th September
NO. ROOMS:	6
ENSUITE:	6

TEL: **066 51639**   FAX: -

Large comfortable home. Quiet location, 2 minutes walk to town centre,tea/coffee making facilities. Choice of breakfasts. Guest T.V. lounge.

B&B PPS:	£17	SNGL OCC. DBLE/TPL:	£25	SNGL RM:	-
PART BRD:	-	% RED. CHILDREN:	50%	DINNER:	-

Dingle 4km

Mrs Jacqueline O'Shea
TORANN NA DTONN
Ventry, Dingle, Co Kerry

Dingle

OPEN:	1st March-1st November
NO. ROOMS:	5
ENSUITE:	5

TEL: **066 59952**   FAX: -

Home beside Ventry village, on Slea Head drive, magnificent sea-view, sandy beach, watersports, fishing, hillwalking, horse riding, restaurants, golf.

B&B PPS:	£17	SNGL OCC. DBLE/TPL:	£23.50	SNGL RM:	£20
PART BRD:	-	% RED. CHILDREN:	33%	DINNER:	-

Dingle 5km

Eric and Eleanor Prestage
MOUNT EAGLE LODGE
Ventry, Dingle, Tralee, Co Kerry

Dingle

OPEN:	Easter/October
NO. ROOMS:	4
ENSUITE:	4

TEL: **066 59754**   FAX: **066 59754**

A lovely new house which has a commanding position overlooking Ventry harbour offering deluxe accommodation, spectacular views from bedrooms.

B&B PPS:	£17/£20	SNGL OCC. DBLE/TPL:	£23.50/£26.50	SNGL RM:	-
PART BRD:	-	% RED. CHILDREN:	20%	DINNER:	-

Mrs Mary Russell
RUSSELL'S B&B
The Mall, Dingle, Co Kerry

Dingle

OPEN:	All Year except Christmas
NO. ROOMS:	6
ENSUITE:	6

TEL: **066 51747**   FAX: **066 52331**   EMAIL: **maryr@iol.ie**

Detached house in town centre. Private parking, 1 minute walk to bus stop, restaurants etc . Recommended Guide du Routard, Reise.

B&B PPS:	£17/£19	SNGL OCC. DBLE/TPL:	£23/£29	SNGL RM:	-
PART BRD:	-	% RED. CHILDREN:	-	DINNER:	-

Dingle 1.5km

Brid Sheehy
BALLINVOWNIG
Dingle, Co Kerry

Dingle

OPEN:	March-October
NO. ROOMS:	3
ENSUITE:	3

TEL: **066 52104**   FAX: -

Excellent accommodation in quiet scenic location off main Tralee - Dingle Road. Convenient to all local amenities.

B&B PPS:	£17	SNGL OCC. DBLE/TPL:	£23.50	SNGL RM:	-
PART BRD:	-	% RED. CHILDREN:	50%	DINNER:	-

Dingle 1km

Mrs Mary Sheehy
SHEEHY'S
Milltown, Dingle, Co Kerry

	Dingle
OPEN:	1st March-1st November
NO. ROOMS:	4
ENSUITE:	2

TEL: **066 51453**   FAX: -

Peaceful home on the Brandon Creek road. Dingle 1Km. Close to all amenities. Private parking. Choices of breakfast. Irish speaking.

B&B PPS:	£15/£17	SNGL OCC. DBLE/TPL:	£21.50/£23.50	SNGL RM:	-
PART BRD:	-	% RED. CHILDREN:	50%	DINNER:	-

In Dingle

Mrs Josephine Walsh
THE TOWNHOUSE B&B
Main Street, Dingle, Co Kerry

	Dingle
OPEN:	All Year except Christmas
NO. ROOMS:	6
ENSUITE:	6

TEL: **066 51147**   FAX: **066 52044**

Luxurious townhouse. All rooms en-suite, hairdryer, clock/radio, satellite TV. Tea/coffee making facilities. Direct dial telephones. Breakfast menu.

B&B PPS:	£16.50/£20	SNGL OCC. DBLE/TPL:	-	SNGL RM:	£20/£30
PART BRD:	-	% RED. CHILDREN:	-	DINNER:	£15

Glenbeigh 1.2km

Mrs Doreen Caulfield
FOREST VIEW
Glenbeigh, Co Kerry

	Glenbeigh
OPEN:	Easter/October
NO. ROOMS:	3
ENSUITE:	3

TEL: **066 68140**   FAX: -

Comfortable family home in peaceful scenic area, with excellent forest views. Central Ring of Kerry location. Beaches, golflinks, horse riding nearby.

B&B PPS:	£17	SNGL OCC. DBLE/TPL:	£23.50	SNGL RM:	-
PART BRD:	-	% RED. CHILDREN:	40%	DINNER:	£14

Glenbeigh 1km

Della Doyle
GLENCURRAH HOUSE
Curraheen, Glenbeigh, Co Kerry

	Glenbeigh
OPEN:	1st March-31st October
NO. ROOMS:	4
ENSUITE:	4

TEL: **066 68133**   FAX: **066 68691**

On the Ring of Kerry. Peaceful scenic setting overlooking Dingle Bay. Adjacent to beaches, golf links, forest walks, horseriding.

B&B PPS:	£17/£19	SNGL OCC. DBLE/TPL:	£23.50/£25.50	SNGL RM:	-
PART BRD:	-	% RED. CHILDREN:	-	DINNER:	-

Glenbeigh 4km

Mrs Helena Fox
THE FOXTROT
Mountain Stage, Glenbeigh, Co Kerry

	Glenbeigh
OPEN:	May-September
NO. ROOMS:	4
ENSUITE:	4

TEL: **066 68417**   FAX: **066 68552**

Luxurious accommodation with magnificent scenery. Ajacent beaches, golf links, mountain and hill walking, horse riding, tennis, hand gliding. breakfast menu available.

B&B PPS:	£17.50	SNGL OCC. DBLE/TPL:	£24	SNGL RM:	-
PART BRD:	-	% RED. CHILDREN:	-	DINNER:	-

Glenbeigh 4km

Mrs Bridget McSweeney
HILLCREST HOUSE
Ballycleave, Glenbeigh, Co Kerry

Glenbeigh

OPEN:	April-October
NO. ROOMS:	4
ENSUITE:	2

TEL: **066 69165**   FAX: **066 69165**

On Glenbeigh - Killorglin road. Caragh Lake, Dooks golf links, fishing, beaches, mountains. "Red Fox" restaurant, Bog museum, Irish music nearby.

B&B PPS:	£15/£17	SNGL OCC. DBLE/TPL:	£21.50/£23.50	SNGL RM:	-
PART BRD:	-	% RED. CHILDREN:	50%	DINNER:	-

Glenbeigh 4.2km

Mrs Anne O'Riordan
MOUNTAIN VIEW
Mountain Stage, Glenbeigh, Kerry, Co Kerry

Glenbeigh

OPEN:	15th March-31st October
NO. ROOMS:	4
ENSUITE:	4

TEL: **066 68541**   FAX: **066 68541**

Quiet peaceful location with breathtaking views. 200mtrs off Ring of Kerry. adjacent to beaches, fishing, "Kerry Way", Low Season reductions.

B&B PPS:	£17	SNGL OCC. DBLE/TPL:	£23.50	SNGL RM:	-
PART BRD:	£180	% RED. CHILDREN:	50%	DINNER:	£12

Glenbeigh 1km

Mrs Noreen O'Toole
OCEAN WAVE
Glenbeigh, Co Kerry

Glenbeigh Ring of Kerry

OPEN:	1st March-31st October
NO. ROOMS:	6
ENSUITE:	6

TEL: **066 68249**   FAX: **066 68412**   EMAIL: **oceanwave@iol.ie**

Breathtaking views of Dingle Bay & Dooks golf links. Frommer recommended home on Ring of Kerry. Extensive breakfast menu.

B&B PPS:	£17.50/£20	SNGL OCC. DBLE/TPL:	£20/£25	SNGL RM:	-
PART BRD:	-	% RED. CHILDREN:	-	DINNER:	-

In Glenbeigh

Mrs Mary Riordan
BIRCHWOOD HOUSE
Station Road, Glenbeigh, Co Kerry

Glenbeigh

OPEN:	1st May-31st October
NO. ROOMS:	3
ENSUITE:	3

TEL: **066 68131**   FAX: **066 68592**

Hospitality and comfort awaits you in modern home, in peaceful scenic area. Adjacent to beaches, golf Links, horse riding, breathtaking walks.

B&B PPS:	£17	SNGL OCC. DBLE/TPL:	£23.50	SNGL RM:	-
PART BRD:	-	% RED. CHILDREN:	40%	DINNER:	-

Killorglin 15km

Michael & Joanne O'Grady
THE ROWAN TREE
Glencar, Co Kerry

Glencar

OPEN:	1st January-15th December
NO. ROOMS:	4
ENSUITE:	4

TEL: **066 60111**   FAX: -

Comfortable friendly family home situated in peaceful scenic country-side. Ideal base for hill walking, horse riding, fishing or golfing.

B&B PPS:	£17	SNGL OCC. DBLE/TPL:	£23.50	SNGL RM:	-
PART BRD:	-	% RED. CHILDREN:	20%	DINNER:	£13

L Inch 1km

Mrs Bunny Ashe
LOCH EALA
Inch, Annascaul, Co Kerry

Inch Dingle Peninsula

OPEN:	1st May-1st October
NO. ROOMS:	3
ENSUITE:	2

TEL: **066 58135**   FAX: -

Modern house, with sea and mountain views, on Killarney - Dingle road. fishing, hillwalking, bird sanctuary, surfing. Inch strand 2 Kms.

B&B PPS:	£15/£17	SNGL OCC. DBLE/TPL:	£21.50/£23.50	SNGL RM:	-
PART BRD:	-	% RED. CHILDREN:	25%	DINNER:	-

L Kenmare 1km

Mrs Hannah Boland
MUXNAW LODGE
Castletownbere Rd, Kenmare, Co Kerry

Kenmare

OPEN:	All Year
NO. ROOMS:	5
ENSUITE:	5

TEL: **064 41252**   FAX: -

Wonderful house built in 1801. Overlooking Kenmare Bay. Tennis court. Breakfast menu, many recommendations, RAC acclaimed, 300 best B+B's.

B&B PPS:	£19/£20	SNGL OCC. DBLE/TPL:	-	SNGL RM:	-
PART BRD:	-	% RED. CHILDREN:	-	DINNER:	£14

L Kenmare 1km

Mrs Bernadette Carraher -O'Sullivan
ANNAGRY HOUSE
Sneem Road, Kenmare, Co Kerry

Kenmare

OPEN:	All Year
NO. ROOMS:	6
ENSUITE:	6

TEL: **064 41283**   FAX: -

Quality accommodation, peaceful, beautiful view. Walking distance from town (N70). Spacious rooms with bath/shower. Variety breakfast menu a speciality.

B&B PPS:	£17	SNGL OCC. DBLE/TPL:	£23.50	SNGL RM:	-
PART BRD:	-	% RED. CHILDREN:	20%	DINNER:	-

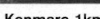

L Kenmare 1km

Mrs Anne Clifford
CHERRY HILL
Killowen, Kenmare, Co Kerry

Kenmare

OPEN:	1st May-14th September
NO. ROOMS:	3
ENSUITE:	2

TEL: **064 41715**   FAX: -

Spacious rooms, beautiful view of Kenmare River. Convenient to town/golf course.Ideal base touring Ring of Kerry/Beara. R569.

B&B PPS:	£15/£17	SNGL OCC. DBLE/TPL:	£22/£24	SNGL RM:	-
PART BRD:	-	% RED. CHILDREN:	25%	DINNER:	-

L In Kenmare

Toni & Tom Connor
ARDMORE HOUSE
Killarney Road, Kenmare, Co Kerry

Kenmare

OPEN:	1st March-30th November
NO. ROOMS:	6
ENSUITE:	6

TEL: **064 41406**   FAX: **064 41406**

Spacious home in quiet location adjoining farmlands. RAC acclaimed. Frommer recommended. Town Centre 5 mins walk. Golf arranged. Visa welcome.

B&B PPS:	£17/£18	SNGL OCC. DBLE/TPL:	£23.50/£25	SNGL RM:	-
PART BRD:	-	% RED. CHILDREN:	50%	DINNER:	-

Kenmare

Mrs Edel Dahm
ARD NA MARA
Pier Road, Kenmare, Co Kerry

Kenmare

OPEN:	All Year except Christmas
NO. ROOMS:	4
ENSUITE:	4

TEL: **064 41399**   FAX: **064 41399**

Family home with garden overlooking Kenmare Bay at the front & MacGillycuddy Reeks at the back 5 mins walk from town.

B&B PPS:	**£16**	SNGL OCC. DBLE/TPL:	**£20**	SNGL RM:	-
PART BRD:	-	% RED. CHILDREN:	**50%**	DINNER:	-

Kenmare 1km

Mrs B Dinneen
LEEBROOK HOUSE
Killarney Road, Kenmare, Co Kerry

Kenmare

OPEN:	1st April-1st November
NO. ROOMS:	4
ENSUITE:	4

(V)

TEL: **064 41521**   FAX: -

Luxurious house set in peaceful scenic surroundings. Located on N71 convenient to Kenmare Town. Ideal touring base Ring of Kerry/Beara.

B&B PPS:	**£17/£17.50**	SNGL OCC. DBLE/TPL:	**£23.50/£24**	SNGL RM:	-
PART BRD:	-	% RED. CHILDREN:	**25%**	DINNER:	-

Kenmare 1km

The Downing Family,
AVELOW HOUSE
Killarney Road, Kenmare, Co Kerry

Kenmare

OPEN:	Easter 31st October
NO. ROOMS:	4
ENSUITE:	4

(V)

TEL: **064 41473**   FAX: -

Comfortable home on Ring of Kerry road (N71). Convenient to golf, fishing, horse riding and sea sports.Town 1 km

B&B PPS:	**£17/£18**	SNGL OCC. DBLE/TPL:	**£23.50/£24.50**	SNGL RM:	-
PART BRD:	-	% RED. CHILDREN:	**10%**	DINNER:	-

In Kenmare

Mrs Marian Dwyer
ROCKCREST HOUSE
Gortamullen, Kenmare, Co Kerry

Kenmare

OPEN:	All Year
NO. ROOMS:	6
ENSUITE:	6

(V)

TEL: **064 41248**   FAX: -

Elegant home, spacious rooms with T.V. off N71 Killarney Rd. Quiet scenic location overlooking prehistoric Dolmen site and Kenmare river valley.

B&B PPS:	**£17/£18**	SNGL OCC. DBLE/TPL:	**£23.50/£25**	SNGL RM:	-
PART BRD:	-	% RED. CHILDREN:	**33%**	DINNER:	-

Kenmare 5km

Tony & Sheila Fahy
ROCKVILLA
Templenoe, Kenmare, Co Kerry

Kenmare

OPEN:	March-October
NO. ROOMS:	6
ENSUITE:	4

(V)

TEL: **064 41331**   FAX: **064 41331**

Modern two storey house. Rural setting near Templenoe Pier; Relaxed friendly atmosphere. Seafood a speciality.

B&B PPS:	**£15/£17**	SNGL OCC. DBLE/TPL:	**£21.50/£23.50**	SNGL RM:	**£15**
PART BRD:	**£190**	% RED. CHILDREN:	**20%**	DINNER:	**£13**

In Kenmare

Mrs Mary Fitzgerald
WHISPERING PINES
Glengarriff Road, Kenmare, Co Kerry

Kenmare

OPEN:	March-November
NO. ROOMS:	4
ENSUITE:	4

TEL: **064 41194**   FAX: -

Modernized Period home. Spacious gardens, 3 minutes walk to town, golf course and Kenmare Bay. Recommended Dillard Causin and Sullivan Guide.

| B&B PPS: | **£17/£18** | SNGL OCC. DBLE/TPL: | **£25** | SNGL RM: | - |
| PART BRD: | - | % RED. CHILDREN: | **50%** | DINNER: | - |

Kenmare 0.1km

Mrs Mary Hodnett
SILVERTREES
Lansdowne Lodge, Kenmare, Co Kerry

Kenmare

OPEN:	1st March-1st November
NO. ROOMS:	3
ENSUITE:	3

TEL: **064 41008**   FAX: -

Elegant home set in Rock garden, opposite golf course. spacious rooms, extensive breakfast menu. Ring of Kerry/Beara/Killarney lakes.

| B&B PPS: | **£17/£18** | SNGL OCC. DBLE/TPL: | **£22/£23** | SNGL RM: | - |
| PART BRD: | - | % RED. CHILDREN: | **25%** | DINNER: | - |

Kenmare 1km

Mrs Anne Kelly-Murphy
LABURNUM HOUSE
Gortamullen, Kenmare, Co Kerry

Kenmare

OPEN:	1st March-17th November
NO. ROOMS:	5
ENSUITE:	5

TEL: **064 41034**   FAX: **064 42168**   EMAIL: **murphyma@iol.ie**

Charming comfortable home. Scenic surroundings on Ring of Kerry N70 road. Convenient to all amenities. Walkers paradise. Host experienced guide.

| B&B PPS: | **£17/£18.50** | SNGL OCC. DBLE/TPL: | **£23.50/£25** | SNGL RM: | - |
| PART BRD: | - | % RED. CHILDREN: | **25%** | DINNER: | **£13** |

Kenmare 6km

Mrs Maureen McCarthy
HARBOUR VIEW
Castletowbere-Haven Road, Dauros, Kenmare, Co Kerry

Kenmare

OPEN:	1st March-31st October
NO. ROOMS:	4
ENSUITE:	2

TEL: **064 41755**   FAX: -

Luxurious seashore home overlooking Kenmare Bay (R571). Seafood. Rooms Tea./coffee facilities, satellite TV/video, hairdryer, electric blanket, AA QQQ award. Breakfast menu

| B&B PPS: | **£18.50** | SNGL OCC. DBLE/TPL: | **£26** | SNGL RM: | - |
| PART BRD: | **£230** | % RED. CHILDREN: | **20%** | DINNER: | **£16.50** |

Kenmare 0.3km

Mrs Rosita McCarthy
ARBUTUS HOUSE
Gortamullen Heights, Killarney Road, Kenmare, Co Kerry

Kenmare

OPEN:	1st May-30th September
NO. ROOMS:	3
ENSUITE:	3

TEL: **064 41059**   FAX: -

Peaceful scenic setting overlooking green pastures. Ideal touring base Ring of Kerry/Beara. All rooms TV, tea/coffee facilities, breakfast menu.

| B&B PPS: | **£18** | SNGL OCC. DBLE/TPL: | - | SNGL RM: | - |
| PART BRD: | - | % RED. CHILDREN: | - | DINNER: | - |

Margaret Moore
RIVERVILLE HOUSE
Gortamullen, Kenmare, Co Kerry

Kenmare

OPEN:	1st February-30th November
NO. ROOMS:	3
ENSUITE:	3

TEL: **064 41775**   FAX: -

Comfortable home, pine interior, overlooking Kenmare town and mountains. Non smoking. Ring Beara/Kerry touring base.Tea/coffee on arrival.

— In Kenmare —

B&B PPS:	£17	SNGL OCC. DBLE/TPL:	£22	SNGL RM:	-
PART BRD:	-	% RED. CHILDREN:	-	DINNER:	-

Mrs Carmel Moriarty
DRUID COTTAGE
Sneem Road, Kenmare, Co Kerry

Kenmare

OPEN:	March-November
NO. ROOMS:	3
ENSUITE:	2

TEL: **064 41803**   FAX: -

Classic stone residence, luxuriously renovated without losing old world charm. Antique furniture. Restful atmosphere. Wonderful views, complimentary tea/coffee.

— Kenmare 1km —

B&B PPS:	£15/£17.50	SNGL OCC. DBLE/TPL:	£24	SNGL RM:	-
PART BRD:	-	% RED. CHILDREN:	10%	DINNER:	--

Mrs Maura Murphy
ROSE COTTAGE
The Square, Kenmare, Co Kerry

Kenmare

OPEN:	All Year except Christmas
NO. ROOMS:	4
ENSUITE:	-

TEL: **064 41330**   FAX: **064 41355**

Old World Cottage with private gardens, having unique position of rural setting in Kenmare town.

— In Kenmare —

B&B PPS:	£16/£16.50	SNGL OCC. DBLE/TPL:	£22.50/£23	SNGL RM:	-
PART BRD:	-	% RED. CHILDREN:	-	DINNER:	£14

Tina O'Brien
CARA
Gort Na Dullagh, Kenmare, Co Kerry

Kenmare

OPEN:	1st March-31st October
NO. ROOMS:	3
ENSUITE:	2

TEL: **064 41634**   FAX: -

Modern bungalow in quiet scenic surroundings. 3 km from Kenmare. Ideal touring Beara Peninsula/ Ring of Kerry. Complimentary tea/coffee.

— Kenmare 3km —

B&B PPS:	£16/£18	SNGL OCC. DBLE/TPL:	£23.50/£24.50	SNGL RM:	-
PART BRD:	-	% RED. CHILDREN:	30%	DINNER:	-

Mrs Julia O'Connor
AN BRUACHAN
Killarney Road, Kenmare, Co Kerry

Kenmare

OPEN:	March-November
NO. ROOMS:	5
ENSUITE:	5

TEL: **064 41682**   FAX: -

Sheltered location on the N 71, 1KM from Kenmare. Own Riverfront containing fish pools. Choice of breakfast. Hill walking enthusiast.

— Kenmare 1km —

B&B PPS:	£17/£18.50	SNGL OCC. DBLE/TPL:	£23.50	SNGL RM:	-
PART BRD:	-	% RED. CHILDREN:	-	DINNER:	-

Kenmare

Anne O'Doherty
BRANDYLOUGHS
Lodge Wood, Kenmare, Co Kerry

Kenmare

OPEN:	April-October
NO. ROOMS:	4
ENSUITE:	4

TEL: 064 42147   FAX: -

Spacious quality country house, very quiet, opposite golf club entrance. Scenic mountain backdrop. 2 minutes walk to quality restaurants in town.

B&B PPS:	£20/£22	SNGL OCC. DBLE/TPL:	£25/£30	SNGL RM:	-
PART BRD:	-	% RED. CHILDREN:	-	DINNER:	-

Kenmare 5km

Mrs Lynne O'Donnell
O'DONNELLS OF ASHGROVE
Ashgrove,
Kenmare, Co Kerry

Kenmare

OPEN:	Easter/31st October
NO. ROOMS:	4
ENSUITE:	3

(V)

TEL: 064 41228   FAX: -

Beautiful country home in peaceful setting. many antiques. Guests welcomed as friends. German spoken. Recommended Dillard/Causin Guide. Brochure available.

B&B PPS:	£16/£18	SNGL OCC. DBLE/TPL:	£24/£26	SNGL RM:	-
PART BRD:	-	% RED. CHILDREN:	20%	DINNER:	-

Kenmare 12km

Mrs M O'Mahony
ARCHES
Blackwater Bridge, Kenmare, Co Kerry

Kenmare

OPEN:	March-October
NO. ROOMS:	5
ENSUITE:	5

(V)

TEL: 064 82030   FAX: -

Unrivalled view of Kenmare Bay. Ideal touring base. Main Ring road. Golfers haven, walking, horse riding, sea sports. Private parking.

B&B PPS:	£17/£17.50	SNGL OCC. DBLE/TPL:	£23.50/£25	SNGL RM:	£23/£24
PART BRD:	-	% RED. CHILDREN:	-	DINNER:	-

In Kenmare

Mrs Kathleen O'Shea
MELROSE
Gortamullen, Kenmare, Co Kerry

Kenmare

OPEN:	April-October
NO. ROOMS:	3
ENSUITE:	3

TEL: 064 41020   FAX: -

Family home in peaceful and scenic location overlooking Kenmare town. 5 minute walk to town. Central to all amenities.

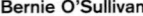

B&B PPS:	£17/£18	SNGL OCC. DBLE/TPL:	-	SNGL RM:	-
PART BRD:	-	% RED. CHILDREN:	10%	DINNER:	-

In Kenmare

Bernie O'Sullivan
CARRIGMORE HOUSE
Hospital Road, Kenmare, Co Kerry

Kenmare

OPEN:	1st March-31st October
NO. ROOMS:	3
ENSUITE:	3

(V)

TEL: 064 41563   FAX: -

Comfortable home spacious rooms. Scenic balcony views. Semi orthapaedic beds, hairdryers. 7 minutes walk town centre. Location a haven of rest.

B&B PPS:	£17/£18	SNGL OCC. DBLE/TPL:	£24.50	SNGL RM:	-
PART BRD:	-	% RED. CHILDREN:	10%	DINNER:	-

Kenmare 11km

Mrs Dympna O'Sullivan
FERN HEIGHT
Castletownberehaven Road (R571),
Lohart, Kenmare, Co Kerry

Kenmare

Open:	1st May-30th September	
No. Rooms:	4	
Ensuite:	3	(V)

Tel: 064 84248   Fax: 064 84271   Email: dympna@iol.ie

"A home from home" in peaceful area with sea, mountain and castle view.
Hospitality and excellent cuisine assured. Seafood, breakfast menu.

B&B PPS:	£15/£17	Sngl Occ. Dble/Tpl:	£21.50/£23.50	Sngl Rm:	-
Part Brd:	£200	% Red. Children:	20%	Dinner:	£14

Kenmare 3km

Mrs Edna O'Sullivan
MARINO HOUSE
Reen, Kenmare, Co Kerry

Kenmare

Open:	15th May-12th September	
No. Rooms:	6	
Ensuite:	1	(V)

Tel: 064 41154/41501   Fax:

Modernised 18th century residence, sea shore setting on Ring of Kerry Road.
Boating, fishing for guests. Frommer recommended.

B&B PPS:	£15/£17	Sngl Occ. Dble/Tpl:	£21.50/£23.50	Sngl Rm:	£17
Part Brd:	-	% Red. Children:	20%	Dinner:	

In Kenmare

Fiona & John O'Sullivan
MYLESTONE HOUSE
Killowen Road, Kenmare, Co Kerry

Kenmare

Open:	1st March-10th November	
No. Rooms:	5	
Ensuite:	5	(V)

Tel: 064 41753   Fax: -

Luxury residence opposite 18 hole golf course. Ideal touring base for Ring of
Kerry/Beara Peninsula. Galtee breakfast award commendation 1994.

B&B PPS:	£17/£18	Sngl Occ. Dble/Tpl:	£24/£26	Sngl Rm:	-
Part Brd:	-	% Red. Children:	20%	Dinner:	-

Kenmare 5km

Mrs Marian O'Sullivan
OAKFIELD
Castletownberehaven Rd., Dauros,
Kenmare, Co Kerry

Kenmare

Open:	1st May-30th September	
No. Rooms:	3	
Ensuite:	2	(V)

Tel: 064 41262   Fax: 064 41262

Experience hospitality and excellent cuisine in family run home near Kenmare Bay
and Waterfall. Breakfast choice. Seafood our speciality.

B&B PPS:	£15/£17	Sngl Occ. Dble/Tpl:	£21.50/£23.50	Sngl Rm:	-
Part Brd:	£200	% Red. Children:	20%	Dinner:	£14

In Kenmare

Mrs Ann Quill
ROSEWOOD HOUSE
Killowen Road, Kenmare, Co Kerry

Kenmare

Open:	1st May-30th September	
No. Rooms:	4	
Ensuite:	4	(V)

Tel: 064 41699   Fax: -

Residence opposite Kenmare 18 hole Golf course. Town centre two minutes.
Landscaped gardens. Excellent location for touring Cork/Kerry peninsula.

B&B PPS:	£17.50	Sngl Occ. Dble/Tpl:	£30	Sngl Rm:	-
Part Brd:	-	% Red. Children:	12.5%	Dinner:	-

Kenmare 2km

Mrs Eileen M Ryan
RIVER MEADOWS
Sneem Road, Kenmare, Co Kerry

Kenmare

OPEN:	1st March-30th November
NO. ROOMS:	4
ENSUITE:	3

TEL: **064 41306**   FAX: -

Set in rustic surroundings, private road leading to sea shore. Panoramic mountain views, 300mts off N70 Ring of Kerry Road.

| B&B PPS: | **£15/£17.50** | SNGL OCC. DBLE/TPL: | **£21.50/£24** | SNGL RM: | **£20** |
| PART BRD: | - | % RED. CHILDREN: | **10%** | DINNER: | - |

In Kenmare

Mrs Maureen Sayers
GREENVILLE
The Lodge, Kenmare, Co Kerry

Kenmare

OPEN:	1st February-30th November
NO. ROOMS:	3
ENSUITE:	3

TEL: **064 41769**   FAX: -

Detached modern house, opposite golf course. Full central heating. Town centre 1 min walk. Private parking. Landscaped gardens.

| B&B PPS: | **£17/£18** | SNGL OCC. DBLE/TPL: | - | SNGL RM: | - |
| PART BRD: | - | % RED. CHILDREN: | **33%** | DINNER: | - |

Kenmare 1km

Mrs Agnes Thornhill
FINNIHY LODGE
Killarney Road, Kenmare, Co Kerry

Kenmare

OPEN:	All Year except Christmas
NO. ROOMS:	4
ENSUITE:	2

TEL: **064 41198**   FAX: -

House in scenic woodland setting overlooking Finnihy River, ideally situated for touring West Cork and Kerry. Convenient to golf & fishing.

| B&B PPS: | **£30/£36** | SNGL OCC. DBLE/TPL: | - | SNGL RM: | **£20/£22** |
| PART BRD: | - | % RED. CHILDREN: | **20%** | DINNER: | - |

Kilgarvan 2km

Kelleher Family
WOODVIEW HOUSE
Kilgarvan, Co Kerry

Kilgarvan

OPEN:	15th May-15th September
NO. ROOMS:	3
ENSUITE:	-

TEL: **064 85363**   FAX: -

Modern family run home, beautifully located in scenic surroundings. Large rose garden. Private car park. Excellent hospitality.

| B&B PPS: | **£15** | SNGL OCC. DBLE/TPL: | **£21.50** | SNGL RM: | - |
| PART BRD: | **£180** | % RED. CHILDREN: | **25%** | DINNER: | **£12** |

Kenmare 20km

Mrs Joan McCarthy
SILLERDANE LODGE
Coolnoohill, Kilgarvan, Co Kerry

Kilgarvan

OPEN:	1st May-1st October
NO. ROOMS:	6
ENSUITE:	6

TEL: **064 85359**   FAX: -

Frommer recommended. Outdoor swimming pool in scenic surroundings, excellent cuisine, log fires. Electric blankets & tea making facilities all rooms.

| B&B PPS: | **£17** | SNGL OCC. DBLE/TPL: | **£23.50** | SNGL RM: | - |
| PART BRD: | **£190** | % RED. CHILDREN: | **25%** | DINNER: | **£13.50** |

Kilgarvan 1km

Mrs Mary MacDonnell
BIRCHWOOD
Churchground, Kilgarvan, Co Kerry

TEL: **064 85473**   FAX: **064 85570**

Kilgarvan

OPEN:	All Year except Christmas
NO. ROOMS:	3
ENSUITE:	3

Spacious home 1 acre, peaceful surroundings on R569. Central touring Ring of Kerry/Beara Peninsula. Fishing, golf arranged. AA QQQ recommended.

| B&B PPS: | £17 | SNGL OCC. DBLE/TPL: | £23.50 | SNGL RM: | - |
| PART BRD: | £180 | % RED. CHILDREN: | 50% | DINNER: | £12 |

Killarney 2km

Mrs Delia Adams
BRIDGE HOUSE
Coolgarrive, Tralee Road, Killarney, Co Kerry

TEL: **064 31425**   FAX: -

Killarney - Tralee Road

OPEN:	May-October
NO. ROOMS:	3
ENSUITE:	3

200 metres off Killarney - Limerick road. All credit cards accepted. Riding stables and golf course nearby. Golfers welcome, practice area.

| B&B PPS: | £17 | SNGL OCC. DBLE/TPL: | £23.50 | SNGL RM: | £21.50 |
| PART BRD: | - | % RED. CHILDREN: | - | DINNER: | - |

Killarney 8km

Mrs Margaret Blake
CHARLWOOD TOMIES
Beaufort, Killarney, Co Kerry

TEL: **064 44117**   FAX: -

Killarney/Beaufort

OPEN:	1st April-31st October
NO. ROOMS:	3
ENSUITE:	2

From Killarney left off Gap of Dungloe Road. Golfing, fishing, lake/river, mountaineering, horse riding, O'Sullivans Cascade all nearby. Peaceful.

| B&B PPS: | £15/£17 | SNGL OCC. DBLE/TPL: | £21.50/£23.50 | SNGL RM: | - |
| PART BRD: | - | % RED. CHILDREN: | 25% | DINNER: | - |

Killarney 1km

Mrs Eileen Brosnan
"CRYSTAL SPRINGS"
Ballycasheen Cross (Off Cork Road), Killarney, Co Kerry

TEL: **064 33272 / 064 35518**   FAX: **064 31188**

Killarney/Ballycasheen

OPEN:	All Year except Christmas
NO. ROOMS:	6
ENSUITE:	6

Luxury purpose built accommodation on riverbank (off N22). Rooms satellite TV/video. Tea makers, hairdryers, electric blankets. AA/frommer listed. Extensive menus.

| B&B PPS: | £17.50/£18.50 | SNGL OCC. DBLE/TPL: | £23.50/£25 | SNGL RM: | £22/£25 |
| PART BRD: | - | % RED. CHILDREN: | 25% | DINNER: | - |

In Killarney

Danny & Bridie Buckley
NABRODA HOUSE
Muckross Road, Killarney, Co Kerry

TEL: **064 31688**   FAX: -

Killarney/Muckross Road

OPEN:	March-October
NO. ROOMS:	5
ENSUITE:	5

Nabroda House, quality accommodation B&B. All rooms ensuite, TV and hairdryers. 5 mins walk from town centre on main Muckross road.

| B&B PPS: | £17/£18 | SNGL OCC. DBLE/TPL: | £23.50/£24.50 | SNGL RM: | - |
| PART BRD: | - | % RED. CHILDREN: | 50% | DINNER: | - |

Mrs Colleen Burke
BEENOSKEE
Dunrine, Tralee Rd., Killarney, Co Kerry

Killarney/Tralee Road

OPEN:	1st April-31st October
NO. ROOMS:	5
ENSUITE:	5

(V)

TEL: **064 32435**   FAX: **064 32435**

Limerick road (N22).Twice national excellence award winner. Landscaped garden. Tea facilities. Home baking, hairdryers. Visa/access/Mastercard. Tours arranged

B&B PPS:	£17	SNGL OCC. DBLE/TPL:	£23.50	SNGL RM:	-
PART BRD:	£180	% RED. CHILDREN:	50%	DINNER:	£12

— Killarney 5 km —

Mrs Philomena Burke
LISAVA
38 Scrahan Court, Ross Road, Killarney, Co Kerry

Killarney Town

OPEN:	April-October
NO. ROOMS:	3
ENSUITE:	2

(V)

TEL: **064 32634**   FAX: -

Modern house near town centre. Quiet area off Ross Road. Fifty metres from Esso station on Muckross road. Personal attention.

B&B PPS:	£15/£17	SNGL OCC. DBLE/TPL:	£21.50/£23.50	SNGL RM:	-
PART BRD:	-	% RED. CHILDREN:	-	DINNER:	-

— In Killarney —

Mrs Veronica Caesar
CAESAR'S
Lissyvigeen, Cork Road, Killarney, Co Kerry

Killarney

OPEN:	1st June/30th September
NO. ROOMS:	4
ENSUITE:	4

(V)

TEL: **064 31821**   FAX: -

Picturesque residence on N22.Superb location. Chosen and recommended by Irish Times Special Travel Correspondent on Cork / Kerry Ireland.

B&B PPS:	£17/£18	SNGL OCC. DBLE/TPL:	£23.50/£24.50	SNGL RM:	-
PART BRD:	-	% RED. CHILDREN:	25%	DINNER:	-

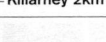
— Killarney 2km —

Mrs Eileen Carroll
THE MOUNTAIN DEW
3 Ross Road, Killarney, Co Kerry

Killarney Town

OPEN:	All Year
NO. ROOMS:	4
ENSUITE:	3

(V)

TEL: **064 33892**   FAX: **064 31332**

Modern house in quiet area, 2 mins walk town, rail/bus. Private car park. Tours arranged. Breakfast menu. In Killarney.

B&B PPS:	£15/£17	SNGL OCC. DBLE/TPL:	£21.50/£25	SNGL RM:	-
PART BRD:	-	% RED. CHILDREN:	50%	DINNER:	-

— In Killarney —

Mrs Marie Carroll
CEDAR HOUSE
Loreto Road (off Muckross Rd), Killarney, Co Kerry

Killarney Muckross Road

OPEN:	1st March-30th November
NO. ROOMS:	5
ENSUITE:	4

(V)

TEL: **064 32342**   FAX: **064 35156**

House ajacent Lakes, Muckross House, Gleneagle Complex, Ross golf club. Spacious bedrooms some with hairdryers.Tea facilities.in rooms. Tours arranged.

B&B PPS:	£18/£20	SNGL OCC. DBLE/TPL:	£24.50/£26.50	SNGL RM:	-
PART BRD:	-	% RED. CHILDREN:	25%	DINNER:	-

— Killarney 2km —

Killarney 5km

Mrs Eileen Casey
HOMEDALE
Dunrine, Tralee Road, Killarney, Co Kerry

TEL: **064 33855**   FAX: -

Killarney Tralee Road

OPEN:	12th March-31st October
NO. ROOMS:	3
ENSUITE:	3

Modern dormer bungalow. Rooms En suite. Tea/coffee making facilities. Friendly welcome. Ideal touring base. All tours arranged.

B&B PPS:	**£17**	SNGL OCC. DBLE/TPL:	**£23.50**	SNGL RM:	-
PART BRD:	-	% RED. CHILDREN:	**50%**	DINNER:	-

Killarney 5km

Mrs Mary Casey
DIRREEN HOUSE
Tralee - Limerick Road, Killarney N22, Co Kerry

TEL: **064 31676**   FAX: -

Killarney Tralee Road

OPEN:	15th March-1st November
NO. ROOMS:	4
ENSUITE:	4

Comfortable bedrooms TV, tea making facilities, hairdryers, breakfast menu, golf/tours arranged. Coach pick up/drop off from premises, view mountains.

B&B PPS:	**£17**	SNGL OCC. DBLE/TPL:	**£23.50**	SNGL RM:	-
PART BRD:	**£180**	% RED. CHILDREN:	**33.3%**	DINNER:	**£12**

Killarney 9km

Mrs Peggy Coffey
HOLLY GROVE
Gap of Dunloe, Beaufort, Killarney, Co Kerry

TEL: **064 44326**   FAX: -

Killarney Beaufort

OPEN:	March-October
NO. ROOMS:	4
ENSUITE:	3

Spacious bedrooms, 1 with 3 beds. Tea/coffee facilities. Pony riding, golf, fishing, climbing, music nearby. Ideal for touring Kerry/Dingle.

B&B PPS:	**£15/£17**	SNGL OCC. DBLE/TPL:	**£21.50/£23.50**	SNGL RM:	-
PART BRD:	**£180**	% RED. CHILDREN:	**50%**	DINNER:	**£12**

In Killarney

Mary & Avril Connell
ST ANTHONYS VILLA
Cork Road, Killarney, Co Kerry

TEL: **064 31534**   FAX: -

Killarney Cork Road Area

OPEN:	1st March-November
NO. ROOMS:	4
ENSUITE:	4

Home on Cork Road, walking distance from town. Continuously recommended in "Ireland on $45 a day". Ensuite rooms. Private parking.

B&B PPS:	**£17/£18**	SNGL OCC. DBLE/TPL:	**£23.50/£24.50**	SNGL RM:	-
PART BRD:	-	% RED. CHILDREN:	**50%**	DINNER:	-

Killarney 3km

Mrs Mary Counihan
VILLA MARIAS HOUSE
Aghadoe, Killarney, Co Kerry

TEL: **064 32307**   FAX: -

Killarney Aghadoe

OPEN:	1st April-31st October
NO. ROOMS:	3
ENSUITE:	2

Situated in panoramic tranquil setting. Excellent touring area. Golf, fishing and other amenities close by. Recommended by Dillard Causin guide.

B&B PPS:	**£15/£17**	SNGL OCC. DBLE/TPL:	**£21.50/£23.50**	SNGL RM:	-
PART BRD:	-	% RED. CHILDREN:	-	DINNER:	-

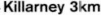

P & C Courtney
COURTMURPH HOUSE
Muckross Road, Killarney, Co Kerry

TEL: **064 34586**   FAX: **064 36630**

	Killarney Muckross Road		
OPEN:	April-October		
NO. ROOMS:	5		
ENSUITE:	5		

(V)

Spacious house, main tourist road. Rooms ensuite. Close to National Park, lakes & all amenities (golf, fishing, walking). Tours arranged.

B&B PPS:	£16/£18.50	SNGL OCC. DBLE/TPL:	£22.50	SNGL RM:	-
PART BRD:	-	% RED. CHILDREN:	50%	DINNER:	-

Killarney.2km

Mrs Eileen Cremin
MOUNTAIN VIEW
Gap of Dunloe, Beaufort, Co Kerry

TEL: **064 44212**   FAX: -

	Killarney Beaufort		
OPEN:	May-September		
NO. ROOMS:	3		
ENSUITE:	2		

(V)

Scenic area. Ideal for touring Ring of Kerry/Dingle. Horse riding, golf, fishing, hill walking, lakes nearby. Restaurant, Irish music 1km.

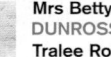

B&B PPS:	£15/£17	SNGL OCC. DBLE/TPL:	£21.50/£23.50	SNGL RM:	-
PART BRD:	-	% RED. CHILDREN:	50%	DINNER:	-

Killarney 8km

Mrs Betty Cronin
DUNROSS HOUSE
Tralee Road, Killarney, Co Kerry

TEL: **064 36322**   FAX: -

	Killarney/Tralee Road		
OPEN:	All Year except Christmas		
NO. ROOMS:	4		
ENSUITE:	4		

(V)

Luxurious home, Killarney 5km (N22). Rooms TV/tea-making. Adjacent to National Parks, lakes/golfing. Excellent location Ring Of Kerry/Dingle.

B&B PPS:	£17/£19	SNGL OCC. DBLE/TPL:	£23.50/£25.50	SNGL RM:	-
PART BRD:	£180	% RED. CHILDREN:	50%	DINNER:	£12.50

Killarney 5km

Mrs Lily Cronin
CRAB TREE COTTAGE
AND GARDENS, **Mangerton Road,**
Muckross, Killarney, Co Kerry

TEL: **064 33169/087 2385582**   FAX: -

	Killarney Muckross Road		
OPEN:	1st March-31st October		
NO. ROOMS:	4		
ENSUITE:	3		

(V)

Picturesque cottage in the midst of Killarney National Park and lakes. Award winning landscaped gardens. A paradise for nature lovers.

B&B PPS:	£17	SNGL OCC. DBLE/TPL:	£23.50	SNGL RM:	£17
PART BRD:	-	% RED. CHILDREN:	-	DINNER:	£14

Killarney 4km

Paula Cronin
CILL IDE
Muckross Church Rd, Muckross,
Killarney, Co Kerry

TEL: **064 33339**   FAX: -

	Killarney Muckross Road		
OPEN:	March-October		
NO. ROOMS:	4		
ENSUITE:	2		

(V)

Spacious bungalow, scenic, tranquil. guest sun lounge, TV, tea/coffee making facilities. Breakfast menu. Adjacent to Muckross House/ gardens, lakes.

B&B PPS:	£15/£18	SNGL OCC. DBLE/TPL:	£21.50/£23.50	SNGL RM:	-
PART BRD:	-	% RED. CHILDREN:	25%	DINNER:	-

Killarney 4km

Killarney 1.5km

Mrs Sheila Cronin
ASHWOOD HOUSE
Woodlawn Road, Killarney, Co Kerry

OPEN:	1st April-30th October
NO. ROOMS:	4
ENSUITE:	3

TEL: **064 31521** FAX: **064 35214**

Walking distance from Bus, Rail & all amenities. All tours arranged & leave from premises. Private car park, guest TV lounge.

B&B PPS:	£15/£17	SNGL OCC. DBLE/TPL:	£21.50/£23.50	SNGL RM:	-
PART BRD:	-	% RED. CHILDREN:	50%	DINNER:	-

Killarney 2km

Mrs Noreen Cudden
THE AMBER LANTERN
Fossa, Killarney, Co Kerry

Killarney Fossa

OPEN:	March-October
NO. ROOMS:	6
ENSUITE:	5

TEL: **064 31921** FAX: -

Well appointed home with balconies, opposite golf club, lakes. Ring of Kerry/Dingle road. Horse riding, Hill walking. Tours arranged.

B&B PPS:	£15/£17	SNGL OCC. DBLE/TPL:	£21.50/£23.50	SNGL RM:	-
PART BRD:	-	% RED. CHILDREN:	25%	DINNER:	-

Mrs Joan Culloty
PERPETUA
O'Sullivans Place, Off St. Anns Road, Killarney, Co Kerry

Killarney Town

OPEN:	April-October
NO. ROOMS:	3
ENSUITE:	3

Killarney

TEL: **064 33519** FAX: -

Luxury town house off main road. 3 mins to town centre. Bus & railway station. TV in bedrooms, breakfast menu, private parking.

B&B PPS:	£17	SNGL OCC. DBLE/TPL:	-	SNGL RM:	-
PART BRD:	-	% RED. CHILDREN:	-	DINNER:	-

Killarney 5km

Mrs Agnes Curran
ARBOUR VILLA
Golf Course Road, Fossa, Killarney, Co Kerry

OPEN:	Easter/November
NO. ROOMS:	4
ENSUITE:	4

TEL: **064 44334** FAX: -

Ring Kerry/golf course road, near lakes, Gap of Dunloe, fishing, horse riding, golf 2 km. Ideal walkers/climbers. Tours arranged.

B&B PPS:	£17/£22	SNGL OCC. DBLE/TPL:	£23.50/£28	SNGL RM:	-
PART BRD:	-	% RED. CHILDREN:	50%	DINNER:	£13

Killarney 2km

Hannah & Dan Daly
BROOKFIELD HOUSE
Coolgarrive, Aghadoe, Killarney, Co Kerry

Kilarney Aghadoe

OPEN:	March-November
NO. ROOMS:	6
ENSUITE:	6

TEL: **064 32077** FAX: -

Country residence, signposted 1km Killarney - Tralee - Limerick road N22. Convenient for touring Ring of Kerry, Dingle, Killarney. Best guides recommended.

B&B PPS:	£17	SNGL OCC. DBLE/TPL:	£23.50	SNGL RM:	-
PART BRD:	-	% RED. CHILDREN:	20%	DINNER:	£13

Killarney 3km

Mrs Deborah Devane
GLENMILL HOUSE
Nunstown, Aghadoe, Killarney, Co Kerry

TEL: 064 34391   FAX: -

Luxurious home with panoramic views lakes, golf course, McGillicuddy Reeks, National Park. Orthopaedic beds. Airport 15km. Adjacent to Aghadoe Heights Hotel

Killarney Aghadoe

OPEN:	17th March-31st October	
NO. ROOMS:	4	
ENSUITE:	4	

B&B PPS:	£17	SNGL OCC. DBLE/TPL:	£23.50	SNGL RM:	-
PART BRD:	-	% RED. CHILDREN:	25%	DINNER:	

Killarney 2km

Mrs Mary Devane
REEKS VIEW
Tullig, Killarney, Co Kerry

TEL: 064 33910   FAX: -

Luxurious bungalow off Killarney/Cork Road. Rooms with private shower/toilet. Ideal touring centre. Tours arranged. Signposted, Cork/Killarney roundabout N22.

Killarney Cork Road Area

OPEN:	April-November	
NO. ROOMS:	5	
ENSUITE:	4	

B&B PPS:	£15/£17	SNGL OCC. DBLE/TPL:	£21.50/£23.50	SNGL RM:	£17/£21
PART BRD:	£180	% RED. CHILDREN:	50%	DINNER:	£12

Killarney 2km

Mrs Noreen Dineen
MANOR HOUSE
18 Whitebridge Manor, Ballycasheen, Killarney, Co Kerry

TEL: 064 32716   FAX: 064 32716

Modern Georgian Style house in peaceful area. Fishing, golfing, swimming. National Park and lakes, cabaret and local tours arranged.

Killarney Cork Road Area

OPEN:	May-October	
NO. ROOMS:	4	
ENSUITE:	3	

B&B PPS:	£15/£17	SNGL OCC. DBLE/TPL:	£21.50/£23.50	SNGL RM:	-
PART BRD:	-	% RED. CHILDREN:	20%	DINNER:	-

Mrs Kathleen Doherty
WHITE HOUSE
Lissivigeen Cross, Killarney, Co Kerry

TEL: 064 32207   FAX: -

Warm country home, family run, on 2 acres. Peaceful scenic surroundings. Horse riding, golf, fishing locally. Tours arranged.

Killarney 2km

Killarney Cork Road Area

OPEN:	May-October	
NO. ROOMS:	4	
ENSUITE:	4	

B&B PPS:	£17	SNGL OCC. DBLE/TPL:	£23.50	SNGL RM:	£21
PART BRD:	£180	% RED. CHILDREN:	20%	DINNER:	£12

Killorglin 8km

Mrs Tess Doona
HOLLYBOUGH HOUSE
Cappagh, Kilgobnet, Beaufort, Co Kerry

TEL: 064 44255   FAX: -

Quiet scenic location central for Ring of Kerry, near Ireland's highest and most majestic mountains, The McGillycuddy Reeks. Visa accepted.

Killarney Beaufort

OPEN:	Easter/October	
NO. ROOMS:	4	
ENSUITE:	2	

B&B PPS:	£15/£17	SNGL OCC. DBLE/TPL:	£21.50/£23.50	SNGL RM:	-
PART BRD:	£180	% RED. CHILDREN:	20%	DINNER:	£12

Killarney 4km

Mrs Carmel Dore-O' Brien
TARA
**Gap of Dunloe Road, Fossa, Killarney,
Co Kerry**

Killarney Aghadoe Fossa

OPEN:	1st March-15th November
NO. ROOMS:	5
ENSUITE:	4

TEL: **064 44355/087 2386180** FAX: - EMAIL: **tarabnb@iol.ie**

Warm welcome. Quiet garden setting off N72. Golf (tee times), fishing (permits), climbing, walking, tours maps/advice. Menu, electric blankets, hairdryers.

B&B PPS:	£15/£17	SNGL OCC. DBLE/TPL:	£21.50/£23.50	SNGL RM:	-
PART BRD:	-	% RED. CHILDREN:	25%	DINNER:	-

In Killarney

Mrs Noreen Downing
ARDFALLEN HOUSE
Ross Road, Killarney, Co Kerry

Killarney Town

OPEN:	April October
NO. ROOMS:	3
ENSUITE:	3

TEL: **064 33632** FAX: -

Modern bungalow in quiet scenic area. 4 mins walk to town centre, bus/rail. Tours arranged.

B&B PPS:	£17	SNGL OCC. DBLE/TPL:	£23.50	SNGL RM:	-
PART BRD:	-	% RED. CHILDREN:	50%	DINNER:	-

Killarney 3km

Mrs Bridie Doyle
CLONFERT
Fossa, Killarney, Co Kerry

Killarney Fossa

OPEN:	15th March-31st October
NO. ROOMS:	4
ENSUITE:	4

TEL: **064 31459** FAX: -

Spacious family home Ring of Kerry/Dingle Road. Golf, fishing, riding 1 km. Orthopaedic beds. Golf and tours arranged. Breakfast menu.

B&B PPS:	£17	SNGL OCC. DBLE/TPL:	£23.50	SNGL RM:	-
PART BRD:	-	% RED. CHILDREN:	25%	DINNER:	-

In Killarney

Mrs Greta Doyle
ALGRET HOUSE
**80 Countess Grove, Off Countess Rd,
Killarney, Co Kerry**

Killarney Countess Road Area

OPEN:	2nd March-31st October
NO. ROOMS:	6
ENSUITE:	4

TEL: **064 32337** FAX: **064 32337**

Modern two storey home in quiet residental area. 5 min walk from town. Private car park. Tea/coffee making facilities, breakfast menu.

B&B PPS:	£15/£19	SNGL OCC. DBLE/TPL:	£23.50/£25.50	SNGL RM:	£21/£23
PART BRD:	-	% RED. CHILDREN:	25%	DINNER:	-

Killarney 1km

Mary Theresa & Derry Doyle
ELYOD HOUSE
Ross Road, Killarney, Co Kerry

Killarney Town

OPEN:	1st March 1st December
NO. ROOMS:	4
ENSUITE:	3

TEL: **064 36544** FAX: **064 31510**

Luxurious friendly home situated on verge of National Park, golf, lakes. 5 minutes from town centre, bus, rail. Tours arranged.

B&B PPS:	£17	SNGL OCC. DBLE/TPL:	£25	SNGL RM:	-
PART BRD:	-	% RED. CHILDREN:	10%	DINNER:	-

Mrs Sheila Falvey
FALSHEA HOUSE
Tralee Road, Killarney, Co Kerry

Killarney Tralee Road

TEL: 064 34871   FAX: -

Newly built house in scenic peaceful surroundings with private car park. Tours arranged. National award of excellence winner 1996.

	OPEN:	All Year except Christmas
	NO. ROOMS:	4
	ENSUITE:	4

| B&B PPS: | £17 | SNGL OCC. DBLE/TPL: | £23.50 | SNGL RM: | - |
| PART BRD: | £180 | % RED. CHILDREN: | 50% | DINNER: | £12 |

— Killarney 4km —

Mrs Theresa Ferris
ALPINE HEIGHTS
Gap of Dunloe, Killarney, Co Kerry

Killarney Beaufort

TEL: 064 44284   FAX: -

Bungalow in lake/mountain district. Traditional Irish music & step dancing. Ponies for hire, Fishing locally. 9-hole golf course.

	OPEN:	1st March 1st December
	NO. ROOMS:	4
	ENSUITE:	1

| B&B PPS: | £15/£17 | SNGL OCC. DBLE/TPL: | £21.50/£23.50 | SNGL RM: | - |
| PART BRD: | - | % RED. CHILDREN: | 50% | DINNER: | - |

— Killarney 6km —

Mrs Hannah Fitzgerald
GLENLOC HOUSE
Fossa, Killarney, Co Kerry

Killarney Fossa

TEL: 064 31880   FAX: -

On Ring of Kerry/Golf course road, near lakes, Gap of Dunloe, horse riding. Ideal for walkers & climbers. Tours arranged.

	OPEN:	1st April 31st October
	NO. ROOMS:	3
	ENSUITE:	3

| B&B PPS: | £17 | SNGL OCC. DBLE/TPL: | £23.50 | SNGL RM: | - |
| PART BRD: | - | % RED. CHILDREN: | 25% | DINNER: | - |

— Killarney 4km —

Mrs Anne Fleming
GLENDALE HOUSE
Dromadeesirt, Tralee Road, Killarney, Co Kerry

Killarney Tralee Road

TEL: 064 32152/34952   FAX: -

Luxurious house on Tralee Road (N22), Killarney 6 Kms. All rooms TV, tea/coffee making facilities, hair-dryers. Tours arranged.

	OPEN:	1st March 31st October
	NO. ROOMS:	6
	ENSUITE:	6

| B&B PPS: | £17 | SNGL OCC. DBLE/TPL: | £23.50 | SNGL RM: | £19 |
| PART BRD: | £195 | % RED. CHILDREN: | 33% | DINNER: | £13 |

— Killarney 6km —

Mrs Maureen Fleming
SHRAHEEN HOUSE
Ballycasheen (off N22), Killarney, Co Kerry

Killarney Cork Road Area

TEL: 064 31286   FAX: -

Luxurious home, off N 22. Satellite TV, tea/coffee facilities, hairdryer all rooms. Breakfast menu, AA & Frommer listed. Tours arranged.

	OPEN:	1st February-6th December
	NO. ROOMS:	6
	ENSUITE:	6

| B&B PPS: | £17.50/£18 | SNGL OCC. DBLE/TPL: | £24/£24.50 | SNGL RM: | - |
| PART BRD: | - | % RED. CHILDREN: | 25% | DINNER: | - |

— Killarney 2km —

Killarney 1km

Mrs Philomena Fleming
WHITE OAKS
16 Scrahan Court, Ross Road, Killarney, Co Kerry

Killarney Town

TEL: **064 31348** FAX: -

OPEN:	All Year
NO. ROOMS:	3
ENSUITE:	3

Luxurious townhouse in unrivalled locale. 7 min walk from town, rail facilities & bus. TV, tea making facilities, tours arranged.

| B&B PPS: | **£16/£17** | SNGL OCC. DBLE/TPL: | | £25 | SNGL RM: | - |
| PART BRD: | - | % RED. CHILDREN: | | 25% | DINNER: | - |

Killarney 5km

Maureen & Gene Fogarty
OSPREY
Lough Guitane Road, Muckross, Killarney, Co Kerry

Killarney Muckross Road

TEL: **064 33213** FAX: -

OPEN:	1st May 30th September
NO. ROOMS:	3
ENSUITE:	2

(V)

Overlooking lakes/mountains. National Park nearby. Landscaped gardens, peaceful area, homely atmosphere, Frommer Guide recommended, private parking, tours arranged.

| B&B PPS: | **£15/£17** | SNGL OCC. DBLE/TPL: | **£21.50/£23.50** | SNGL RM: | - |
| PART BRD: | - | % RED. CHILDREN: | 20% | DINNER: | - |

Mrs Mary Geaney
PINE CREST
Woodlawn Road, Killarney, Co Kerry

Killarney Muckross Road

TEL: **064 31721** FAX: -

OPEN:	15th January 15th December
NO. ROOMS:	6
ENSUITE:	6

(V)

Bungalow in scenic area, convenient to Lakes, National park, golf course, Airport, Ring of Kerry/Dingle, bus. Taxi from house.

Killarney 1km

| B&B PPS: | **£17/£18** | SNGL OCC. DBLE/TPL: | **£23.50/£24.50** | SNGL RM: | - |
| PART BRD: | - | % RED. CHILDREN: | 25% | DINNER: | - |

Mrs Moira Gorman
GORMAN'S
Tralee Road, Killarney, Co Kerry

Killarney Tralee Road

TEL: **064 33149** FAX: **064 33149**

OPEN:	1st January-23rd December
NO. ROOMS:	5
ENSUITE:	5

(V)

T.V's, Video, Tea facilities, all rooms, AA listed, breakfast menu, "former B. F. Garden prizewinners. Reductions low season, satellite TV, 5 Km Killarney.

Killarney 5km

| B&B PPS: | **£17** | SNGL OCC. DBLE/TPL: | **£23.50** | SNGL RM: | - |
| PART BRD: | **£180** | % RED. CHILDREN: | 33.3% | DINNER: | **£12** |

In Killarney

Louise Griffin
CHELMSFORD HOUSE
Muckross View, Dromhale, Killarney, Co Kerry

Killarney

TEL: **064 36402** FAX: **064 33883**

OPEN:	All Year except Christmas
NO. ROOMS:	3
ENSUITE:	3

(V)

Luxurious friendly home 5 mins walk to town. Awaken to magnificent Muckross view overlooking lakes/mountains, TV lounge, tours arranged.

| B&B PPS: | **£17/£20** | SNGL OCC. DBLE/TPL: | **£23.50/£26.50** | SNGL RM: | - |
| PART BRD: | - | % RED. CHILDREN: | - | DINNER: | - |

— In Killarney

Mrs Kathleen Guerin
IRISH COTTAGE
Muckross Road, Killarney, Co Kerry

Killarney Muckross Road

OPEN:	All Year
NO. ROOMS:	5
ENSUITE:	1

TEL: **064 32443**   FAX: -

Central location on main tourist road in mountain/lake district. Killarney town 5 minutes walk. Excellent cuisine. Private car park.

Ⓥ

B&B PPS:	£15/£17	SNGL OCC. DBLE/TPL:	£21.50/£23.50	SNGL RM:	-
PART BRD:	-	% RED. CHILDREN:	50%	DINNER:	-

— Killarney 1.5KM

Mary Guerin
BELLEVUE
1 Gortroe, Fossa, Killarney, Co Kerry

Killarney

OPEN:	15th March-31st October
NO. ROOMS:	3
ENSUITE:	3

TEL: **064 34621**   FAX: -

Dormer style, 1.5 km West of Killarney, Ring Kerry road, golf, horse riding, tours arranged. Rooms ensuite, TV, hairdryers, private parking.

Ⓥ

B&B PPS:	£18/£21	SNGL OCC. DBLE/TPL:	£25/£30	SNGL RM:	-
PART BRD:	-	% RED. CHILDREN:	50%	DINNER:	-

— Killarney 5km

Mrs Mary Howard
COMERAGH HOUSE
Tralee Road, Dunrine, Killarney, Co Kerry

Killarney Tralee Road

OPEN:	1st April-31st October
NO. ROOMS:	4
ENSUITE:	4

TEL: **064 34435**   FAX: -

Modern country home situated on N22. National award of excellence winner. Convenient base for ring of Kerry/Dingle. Airport 10 mins.

Ⓥ

B&B PPS:	£17/£19	SNGL OCC. DBLE/TPL:	£23.50/£25.50	SNGL RM:	-
PART BRD:	£180	% RED. CHILDREN:	50%	DINNER:	£12

— In Killarney

Catherine Howe
DUN-A-RI HOUSE
Ross Road, Killarney, Co Kerry

Killarney Ross Road

OPEN:	1st March-30th October
NO. ROOMS:	4
ENSUITE:	4

TEL: **064 36629**   FAX: -

Located in scenic peaceful area. Opposite Ross Castle holiday homes adjacent to Ross golf club, National Park. Breakfast menu, hairdryers.

Ⓥ

B&B PPS:	£17	SNGL OCC. DBLE/TPL:	£23.50	SNGL RM:	-
PART BRD:	-	% RED. CHILDREN:	50%	DINNER:	-

— Killarney 1km

Mrs Maureen Kearney
WOODBROOK HOUSE
Ballycasheen, Killarney, Co Kerry

Killarney Cork Road Area

OPEN:	April-October
NO. ROOMS:	4
ENSUITE:	4

TEL: **064 33904**   FAX: -

Modern new house within walking distance of Killarney town. Tours arranged. Golf, fishing and entertainment nearby. Complimentary tea on arrival.

Ⓥ

B&B PPS:	£17	SNGL OCC. DBLE/TPL:	£25	SNGL RM:	£20
PART BRD:	-	% RED. CHILDREN:	50%	DINNER:	-

Killarney 2km

Mr Tom Kearney
CILLCEARN HOUSE
Ballycasheen Road, Killarney, Co Kerry

OPEN:	All Year	
NO. ROOMS:	4	
ENSUITE:	3	

TEL: 064 35670   FAX: -

New luxurious home off N22, set in picturesque surroundings. Forest and river walks. Warm homely atmosphere, cable T.V lounge. Breakfast menu. Golf locally. Tours arranged.

B&B PPS:	£15/£18	SNGL OCC. DBLE/TPL:	£21.50/£24.50	SNGL RM:	-
PART BRD:	-	% RED. CHILDREN:	50%	DINNER:	£12

Killarney 1km

Mrs Nora Kelliher
HAZELWOOD
Park Rd Upper, Ballyspillane, Killarney, Co Kerry

Killarney Town

OPEN:	1st May-31st October	
NO. ROOMS:	4	
ENSUITE:	4	

TEL: 064 34363   FAX: -

Comfortable bungalow, 300m off N22, private parking, walking distance from town. Ideal touring base. Refreshments served on arrival tours arranged.

B&B PPS:	£17	SNGL OCC. DBLE/TPL:	£23.50	SNGL RM:	-
PART BRD:	£190	% RED. CHILDREN:	25%	DINNER:	£12

Killarney 6km

Mrs Catherine Kelly
INISFAIL
Beaufort, Co Kerry

Killarney Beaufort

OPEN:	1st April-31st October	
NO. ROOMS:	4	
ENSUITE:	3	

TEL: 064 44404   FAX: -

Warm welcome awaits you at our lovely home adjacent Gap of Dunloe, Carrauntoohil. Restaurant, entertainment, golf, fishing, horse riding close. Access/Visa.

B&B PPS:	£15/£17	SNGL OCC. DBLE/TPL:	£21.50/£23.50	SNGL RM:	-
PART BRD:	-	% RED. CHILDREN:	25%	DINNER:	-

Killarney 1km

Mr & Mrs William Kenny
SLIABH LAUCHRA HOUSE
Castlelough, Loretto Road, Killarney, Co Kerry

Killarney Muckross Road

OPEN:	April-September	
NO. ROOMS:	6	
ENSUITE:	6	

TEL: 064 32012   FAX: -

Tudor Style landscaped gardens. Adjacent to National Park, Lakes, Gleneagle Complex. Tours etc arranged. Peaceful atmosphere. Award winner (RAC, AA).

B&B PPS:	£17/£18	SNGL OCC. DBLE/TPL:	£23.50/£24.50	SNGL RM:	-
PART BRD:	-	% RED. CHILDREN:	-	DINNER:	-

In Killarney

Mrs Josephine King-Wiener
WIND-WAY TOWN HOUSE
New Road, Killarney, Co Kerry

Killarney Town

OPEN:	1st January-20th December	
NO. ROOMS:	6	
ENSUITE:	6	

TEL: 064 32835   FAX: -

New luxurious bungalow. Ideally located. 3 mins walk from town centre. Recommended in all best guides.

B&B PPS:	£17.50/£19	SNGL OCC. DBLE/TPL:	£25/£28	SNGL RM:	-
PART BRD:	-	% RED. CHILDREN:	25%	DINNER:	-

153

Killarney

Mrs Margaret Lanigan
CARAGH HOUSE
Scrahan Court, Ross Road, Killarney, Co Kerry

TEL: 064 34637   FAX: -

Killarney Town

OPEN:	1st April-30th September
NO. ROOMS:	3
ENSUITE:	3

Friendly home 2 mins walk town, rail, bus. Ideal touring centre. Beaches, golf, fishing, National Park, lakes, ponytrekking.

| B&B PPS: | £16.50 | SNGL OCC. DBLE/TPL: | - | SNGL RM: | - |
| PART BRD: | - | % RED. CHILDREN: | - | DINNER: | - |

Killarney 3km

Mrs Anne Leahy
"AVONDALE HOUSE"
Tralee Road, Killarney, Co Kerry

TEL: 064 35579   FAX: -

Killarney Tralee Road

OPEN:	All Year Except Christmas
NO. ROOMS:	5
ENSUITE:	5

Modern home 3Km Killarney, on Tralee - Limerick road (N22). Colour TV, tea/coffee making facilities, hairdryers, AA listed, electric blankets.

| B&B PPS: | £17/£17.50 | SNGL OCC. DBLE/TPL: | £23.50/£28 | SNGL RM: | - |
| PART BRD: | - | % RED. CHILDREN: | 33% | DINNER: | - |

In Killarney

Mrs Siobhan Leen
LEENS
22 Marian Terrace, Killarney, Co Kerry

TEL: 064 32819   FAX: -

Killarney Town

OPEN:	All Year except Christmas
NO. ROOMS:	4
ENSUITE:	2

Modern house in residential area. Follow pitch & putt sign at Lewis road, 1st left turn after junction, sign for house on the right.

| B&B PPS: | £15/£17 | SNGL OCC. DBLE/TPL: | £21.50/£23.50 | SNGL RM: | - |
| PART BRD: | - | % RED. CHILDREN: | 25% | DINNER: | - |

Killarney 5km

Cathy & Mike Lohan
LOHAN'S LODGE
Tralee Road, Killarney, Co Kerry

TEL: 064 33871   FAX: 064 33871

Killarney Tralee Road

OPEN:	1st March-5th November
NO. ROOMS:	5
ENSUITE:	5

All en-suite bedrooms with TV, electric blankets, tea facilities, hairdryers, breakfast menu. Reduction low season. Quality awards, AA4Q's, RAC highly acclaimed.

| B&B PPS: | £17/£17.50 | SNGL OCC. DBLE/TPL: | £25/£30 | SNGL RM: | - |
| PART BRD: | - | % RED. CHILDREN: | 33% | DINNER: | - |

In Killarney

Mrs Eileen Lucey
MARIAN HOUSE
Woodlawn Road, Killarney, Co Kerry

TEL: 064 31275   FAX: -

Killarney Muckross Road

OPEN:	All Year except Christmas
NO. ROOMS:	6
ENSUITE:	6

Modern house in quiet area 135 metres off main road. Walking distance form town. Private parking. Ideal location.

| B&B PPS: | £17/£17.50 | SNGL OCC. DBLE/TPL: | £23.50 | SNGL RM: | - |
| PART BRD: | - | % RED. CHILDREN: | 25% | DINNER: | - |

In Killarney

Mrs Joan Lucey
THE CASCADES
Muckross Rd., Killarney, Co Kerry

Killarney Muckross Road

OPEN:	1st April-31st October
NO. ROOMS:	4
ENSUITE:	4

TEL: **064 34306**   FAX: -

New luxurious home, 5 minutes walk from town centre, rail/bus. Carbaret, swimming, golf nearby. Tours arranged. Private parking.

B&B PPS:	£17	SNGL OCC. DBLE/TPL:	-	SNGL RM:	-
PART BRD:	-	% RED. CHILDREN:	-	DINNER:	-

In Killarney

Pauline Lyne
PARKFIELD HOUSE
Park Road, Killarney, Co Kerry

Killarney Town

OPEN:	March-November
NO. ROOMS:	6
ENSUITE:	6

TEL: **064 37022**   FAX: **064 37022**

New luxurious townhouse backing onto farmland, 5 minutes walk from the town centre. Complimentary afternoon tea on arrival. (off N22).

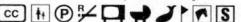

B&B PPS:	£17/£22	SNGL OCC. DBLE/TPL:	£25/£30	SNGL RM:	-
PART BRD:	-	% RED. CHILDREN:	50%	DINNER:	-

Killarney 4km

Mrs Eileen McAuliffe
MARLFIELD HOUSE
Lissivigeen (N72), Killarney, Co Kerry

Killarney Cork Road Area

OPEN:	June/September
NO. ROOMS:	4
ENSUITE:	4

TEL: **064 32129**   FAX: -

Modern two storey house 5 mins drive from Killarney, country surroundings on N72 road. All tours arranged from house. Horse riding, golf, fishing locally.

B&B PPS:	£17	SNGL OCC. DBLE/TPL:	£23.50	SNGL RM:	-
PART BRD:	-	% RED. CHILDREN:	10%	DINNER:	-

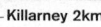
Killarney 2km

Mrs Kathleen McAuliffe
CARROWMORE HOUSE
Knockasarnett, Aghadoe, Killarney, Co Kerry

Killarney Aghadoe

OPEN:	April-October
NO. ROOMS:	5
ENSUITE:	5

TEL: **064 33520**   FAX: -

Warm welcoming family home, peaceful scenic surroundings off N22 Killarney - Tralee - Limerick Road. Ring of Kerry/Dingle. Local tour arranged

B&B PPS:	£17	SNGL OCC. DBLE/TPL:	£23.50	SNGL RM:	-
PART BRD:	-	% RED. CHILDREN:	25%	DINNER:	-

Killarney 5km

Mrs Bernie McCarthy
MCCARTHYS
Dunrine, Tralee Rd, Killarney, Co Kerry

Killarney Tralee Road

OPEN:	1st April-31st October
NO. ROOMS:	4
ENSUITE:	4

TEL: **064 31124**   FAX: -

Comfortable modern home on N22. In peaceful location. Local tours including walking and cycling arranged. National award of excellence winner.

B&B PPS:	£17	SNGL OCC. DBLE/TPL:	£23.50	SNGL RM:	-
PART BRD:	-	% RED. CHILDREN:	20%	DINNER:	£12

In Killarney

Mrs Kathleen McCarthy
SANCTA MARIA
53 Park Road Estate, Killarney, Co Kerry

Killarney Town

OPEN:	All Year
NO. ROOMS:	4
ENSUITE:	3

(V)

TEL: **064 32447** FAX: -

Comfortable house in residential area. Walking distance of town, close to all amenities. Private parking. Tours arranged. Complimentary tea arrival.

| B&B PPS: | **£15/£17** | SNGL OCC. DBLE/TPL: | **£21.50/£23.50** | SNGL RM: | - |
| PART BRD: | - | % RED. CHILDREN: | **25%** | DINNER: | - |

In Killarney

Joan McCarthy
THE HARP
Muckross Road, Killarney, Co Kerry

Killarney

OPEN:	All Year
NO. ROOMS:	4
ENSUITE:	4

(V)

TEL: **064 31272** FAX: -

Charming comfortable home, superb location, walking distance from town. Breakfast menu. Private parking.

| B&B PPS: | **£17/£17.50** | SNGL OCC. DBLE/TPL: | **£23.50/£24** | SNGL RM: | - |
| PART BRD: | **£180** | % RED. CHILDREN: | **25%** | DINNER: | **£12** |

Mrs Margaret McCarthy
CRICKET VIEW
7 Muckross Grove, Killarney, Co Kerry

Killarney Town

OPEN:	April-September
NO. ROOMS:	3
ENSUITE:	1

(V)

TEL: **064 32245** FAX: -

Modern two storey house in quiet area, 10 min walk to town centre. Family run, Tours arranged. Near Gleneagle Hotel.

(P)

| B&B PPS: | **£15/£17** | SNGL OCC. DBLE/TPL: | **£21.50/£23.50** | SNGL RM: | - |
| PART BRD: | - | % RED. CHILDREN: | **50%** | DINNER: | - |

Killarney 1km

Mrs Peggy McCarthy
DROMHALL HEIGHTS
Off Countess Road, Killarney, Co Kerry

Killarney Countess Road Area

OPEN:	1st March-30th November
NO. ROOMS:	3
ENSUITE:	2

(V)

TEL: **064 32662** FAX: -

Bungalow, magnificent view of mountain/lakes. Convenient to all amenities, town, bus and railway station. Single room. Private jaunting cars.

| B&B PPS: | **£15/£19** | SNGL OCC. DBLE/TPL: | **£21.50/£25.50** | SNGL RM: | **£21.50/£23.50** |
| PART BRD: | - | % RED. CHILDREN: | **10%** | DINNER: | - |

In Killarney

Killarney 6km

Mrs Betty McSweeney
HILTON HEIGHTS
Glebe, Tralee Road, Killarney, Co Kerry

Killarney Tralee Road

OPEN:	1st February-1st November
NO. ROOMS:	4
ENSUITE:	4

(V)

TEL: **064 33364** FAX: -

All ensuite rooms, hairdryers, all with TV, tea/coffee facilities. Sign for Hilton Heights on Tralee Rd. 5 km from Killarney.

| B&B PPS: | **£17** | SNGL OCC. DBLE/TPL: | **£23.50** | SNGL RM: | **£19** |
| PART BRD: | **£180** | % RED. CHILDREN: | **50%** | DINNER: | **£12** |

In Killarney

Miss Christine McSweeney
EMMERVILLE HOUSE
Muckross Drive, Off Muckross Rd (town end), Killarney, Co Kerry

Killarney Muckross Road

TEL: **064 33342**   FAX: -

OPEN:	1st January-31st December
NO. ROOMS:	4
ENSUITE:	4

(V)

Comfortable home in a quiet Cul-de-sac. 2 mins to town, Tea/coffee, hairdryers in rooms. T.V. lounge. Private parking. Reduction low season.

| B&B PPS: | £17 | SNGL OCC. DBLE/TPL: | £23.50 | SNGL RM: | £23.50 |
| PART BRD: | - | % RED. CHILDREN: | 25% | DINNER: | - |

In Killarney

Mrs Chriss Mannix
FLESK LODGE
Muckross Road, Killarney, Co Kerry

Killarney Muckross Road

TEL: **064 32135**   FAX: **064 32135**

OPEN:	All Year
NO. ROOMS:	6
ENSUITE:	6

(V)

Luxury bungalow, walking distance from town. All rooms ensuite. TV, hairdryers & tea/coffee making facilities.

| B&B PPS: | £16.50/£17 | SNGL OCC. DBLE/TPL: | £23/£23.50 | SNGL RM: | £19.50 |
| PART BRD: | £180 | % RED. CHILDREN: | 25% | DINNER: | £12 |

Killarney 6km

Anne & Neilius Moriarty
BROOKSIDE
Gortacollopa, Fossa, Killarney, Co Kerry

Killarney Fossa

TEL: **064 44187**   FAX: -

OPEN:	1st March-7th November
NO. ROOMS:	6
ENSUITE:	5

(V)

Award winning family home, farmland setting on Ring of Kerry near River Laune. Pastoral view, breakfast menu, advice on tours.

| B&B PPS: | £15/£17 | SNGL OCC. DBLE/TPL: | £21.50/£23.50 | SNGL RM: | - |
| PART BRD: | - | % RED. CHILDREN: | 25% | DINNER: | £12.50 |

Killarney 5km

Tim & Kathleen Moriarty
EAGLES REST
Lough Guittane Road, Muckross, Killarney, Co Kerry

Killarney Muckross Road

TEL: **064 35860**   FAX: -

OPEN:	1st April-31st October
NO. ROOMS:	4
ENSUITE:	4

(V)

Warm hospitality with magnificent view of lakes/mountains. Ideal for walking, fishing, golf. National Park 1Km, 1.5 KM off N71.

| B&B PPS: | £17 | SNGL OCC. DBLE/TPL: | £23.50 | SNGL RM: | - |
| PART BRD: | - | % RED. CHILDREN: | 50% | DINNER: | - |

Killarney 8km

Tim & Nora Moriarty
THE PURPLE HEATHER
Glencar Rd, Gap of Dunloe, Beaufort, Killarney, Co Kerry

Killarney Gap of Dunloe

TEL: **064 44266**   FAX: **064 44266**   EMAIL: **tnmorty@iol.ie**

OPEN:	March-October
NO. ROOMS:	6
ENSUITE:	5

(V)

Spacious home, breakfast consevatory with panoramic view, electric blanket, hairdryer, tea/coffee, pool room, tennis, restaurant, Irish music, golf 1 km.

| B&B PPS: | £15/£17 | SNGL OCC. DBLE/TPL: | £21.50/£23.50 | SNGL RM: | £17 |
| PART BRD: | £180 | % RED. CHILDREN: | 50% | DINNER: | £12 |

Killarney 3.5km

Eileen Moynihan
MAPLE LODGE
Fossa, Killarney, Co Kerry

Killarney Fossa

OPEN:	April-October
NO. ROOMS:	3
ENSUITE:	3

TEL: **064 36805** FAX: -

Luxury home with balcony, overlooking lakes and mountains. Near Hotel Europe, restaurants, golf, horseriding. Breakfast menu. TV lounge. Teamaking facilities.

B&B PPS:	£17	SNGL OCC. DBLE/TPL:	£23.50	SNGL RM:	-
PART BRD:	-	% RED. CHILDREN:	50%	DINNER:	-

Killarney 1km

Michael & Oonagh Moynihan
KYLEMORE
Ballydowney, Killarney, Co Kerry

Killarney

OPEN:	1st March-31st October
NO. ROOMS:	6
ENSUITE:	6

TEL: **064 31771** FAX: -

Modern home on Ring Of Kerry - golf course road (N72). Walking distance to Town. Horse riding. Hill walking nearby.

B&B PPS:	£17	SNGL OCC. DBLE/TPL:	£23.50	SNGL RM:	£20/£23
PART BRD:	-	% RED. CHILDREN:	50%	DINNER:	-

Killarney

Mrs. Patricia Moynihan
COIS AIRNE
55 Park Road Estate, Killarney, Co Kerry

Killarney Town

OPEN:	1st April-31st October
NO. ROOMS:	3
ENSUITE:	3

TEL: **064 33455** FAX: -

Family home,select residential area. Walking distance of town, railway ,bus station. TV, hairdryers in bedrooms. Breakfast menu. Off N22.

B&B PPS:	£17	SNGL OCC. DBLE/TPL:	£25	SNGL RM:	£25
PART BRD:	-	% RED. CHILDREN:	-	DINNER:	-

Killarney 2km

Mrs Eileen Murphy
GREEN ACRES
Fossa, Killarney, Co Kerry

Killarney Fossa

OPEN:	1st April-30th September
NO. ROOMS:	8
ENSUITE:	6

TEL: **064 31454** FAX: **064 31454**

Modern family home opposite Killarney golf and fishing Club. On Ring of Kerry road. Riding stables, Parkland, AA listed.

B&B PPS:	£15/£17	SNGL OCC. DBLE/TPL:	£21.50/£23.50	SNGL RM:	£20
PART BRD:	-	% RED. CHILDREN:	25%	DINNER:	-

Killarney 2km

Mrs Evelyn Murphy
CEDAR LODGE
Lissivigeen, Cork Road, Killarney, Co Kerry

Killarney Cork Road Area

OPEN:	All Year
NO. ROOMS:	6
ENSUITE:	6

TEL: **064 34754** FAX: **064 34754**

(N22) La-Routard/RAC recommended. Satellite TV, teamakers, hairdryers all rooms. Extensive breakfast menu. Free trout fishing River Flesk. Special offers.

B&B PPS:	£17/£17.50	SNGL OCC. DBLE/TPL:	£23.50/£25	SNGL RM:	-
PART BRD:	-	% RED. CHILDREN:	50%	DINNER:	-

Mrs Sheila Murphy
SERENIC VIEW
Coolcorcoran, Killarney, Co Kerry

Killarney/Tralee Road

OPEN:	1st May-30th September
NO. ROOMS:	4
ENSUITE:	4

TEL: **064 33434**   FAX: -

Ground floor ensuite accommodation sign posted on Killarney/Limerick Road. Quiet scenic area. Tea-making facilities, hairdryers, colour T.V's. Visa.

Killarney 2km

B&B PPS:	**£17**	SNGL OCC. DBLE/TPL:	**£23.50**	SNGL RM:	-
PART BRD:	-	% RED. CHILDREN:	**25%**	DINNER:	-

Vincent & Maureen Murphy
LAKELAND HAVEN
Fossa, Killarney, Co Kerry

Killarney Fossa

OPEN:	1st January-31st December
NO. ROOMS:	6
ENSUITE:	6

TEL: **064 35322**   FAX: -

Luxurious home. Ring of Kerry Road. Rooms with private verandah's overlooking lakes/mountains. Golf, riding stables, fishing, National Park nearby.

Killarney 3.5km

B&B PPS:	**£17.50**	SNGL OCC. DBLE/TPL:	**£24**	SNGL RM:	-
PART BRD:	-	% RED. CHILDREN:	**33%**	DINNER:	-

Mrs Ann Nash
NASHVILLE
Tralee Road, Killarney, Co Kerry

Killarney Tralee Road

OPEN:	1st February - 1st December
NO. ROOMS:	6
ENSUITE:	6

TEL: **064 32924**   FAX: -

Modern home on Tralee/Limerick Road N22. All rooms en-suite, colour TV, hairdryers, tea/coffee making facilities. AA listed.

Killarney 3km

B&B PPS:	**£16/£20**	SNGL OCC. DBLE/TPL:	**£22.50/£26.50**	SNGL RM:	**£18/£23**
PART BRD:	-	% RED. CHILDREN:	**33%**	DINNER:	**£13**

Mrs Triona Neilan
ROSSARNEY HOUSE
St Margaret's Road, Killarney, Co Kerry

Killarney Town

OPEN:	1st January-31st December
NO. ROOMS:	4
ENSUITE:	4

TEL: **064 34630**   FAX: -

A warm welcome to Rossarney townhouse. Personal attention. Complimentary tea/coffee. Orthopaedic beds. Golf, riding stables nearby. Reduction Low Season

In Killarney

B&B PPS:	**£17**	SNGL OCC. DBLE/TPL:	**£23.50**	SNGL RM:	-
PART BRD:	-	% RED. CHILDREN:	**25%**	DINNER:	-

Mrs Aileen O'Brien
COIS DARA
Rookery Road, Killarney, Co Kerry

Killarney Town

OPEN:	April-October
NO. ROOMS:	4
ENSUITE:	4

TEL: **064 35567**   FAX: **064 35567**   EMAIL: **coisdara@iol.ie**

Luxurious, non-smoking home in quiet area within walking distance of town. Fishing, walking, golf etc nearby. Private parking.

Killarney 1km

B&B PPS:	**£17**	SNGL OCC. DBLE/TPL:	**£25**	SNGL RM:	-
PART BRD:	-	% RED. CHILDREN:	-	DINNER:	-

— Killarney 2km —

Mrs Kathleen O'Brien
AVALON HOUSE
Gortroe, Killarney, Co Kerry

Killarney Fossa

OPEN:	1st May-31st October
NO. ROOMS:	4
ENSUITE:	3

(V)

TEL: **064 33156**   FAX: -

All the comforts of home, cul-de-sac, 100m off Ring of Kerry. Orthopaedic beds, menu, tea/coffee, golf, lakes, parks, tours.

B&B PPS:	**£15/£17**	SNGL OCC. DBLE/TPL:	**£21.50/£23.50**	SNGL RM:	-
PART BRD:	-	% RED. CHILDREN:	**33.3%**	DINNER:	-

— In Killarney —

Mrs Rosemary O'Connell
OAKLAWN
Muckross Drive, Off Muckross Road, Killarney, Co Kerry

Killarney Muckross Road

OPEN:	All Year except Christmas
NO. ROOMS:	3
ENSUITE:	3

(V)

TEL: **064 32616**   FAX: -

Luxury accommodation only minutes from town centre. Winner of prestigious "Killarney looking good competition" and best Town & Country Home.

B&B PPS:	**£17/£18**	SNGL OCC. DBLE/TPL:	**£23.50/£24.50**	SNGL RM:	-
PART BRD:	-	% RED. CHILDREN:	**25%**	DINNER:	-

— Killarney 1km —

Mrs Anne O'Connor
CLONALIS HOUSE
Countess Road, Killarney, Co Kerry

Killarney Countess Road Area

OPEN:	4th April-6th October
NO. ROOMS:	4
ENSUITE:	4

(V)

TEL: **064 31043**   FAX: **064 31043**

Recommended Dillard Causin Guide luxurious home, select residential location off Muckross Road and off N22 near town, lakes, golf. Tours arranged.

B&B PPS:	**£17/£17.50**	SNGL OCC. DBLE/TPL:	**£23.50/£24**	SNGL RM:	-
PART BRD:	-	% RED. CHILDREN:	-	DINNER:	-

— Killarney 3km —

Mrs Hannah O'Connor
TORC FALLS
Lough Guitane Road, Muckross, Killarney, Co Kerry

Killarney Muckross Road

OPEN:	March-October
NO. ROOMS:	5
ENSUITE:	5

(V)

TEL: **064 33566**   FAX: -

Spacious modern house. Quiet location, private parking. Central to National Park, Muckross House/Gardens, mountains, lakes, all amenities. Tours arranged.

B&B PPS:	**£17/£18**	SNGL OCC. DBLE/TPL:	**£23.50/£24.50**	SNGL RM:	-
PART BRD:	-	% RED. CHILDREN:	**25%**	DINNER:	-

— Killarney 1km —

Mrs Kathleen O'Connor
TOWER HOUSE
Muckross Road, Killarney, Co Kerry

Killarney Muckross Road

OPEN:	April-September
NO. ROOMS:	4
ENSUITE:	4

(V)

TEL: **064 33884**   FAX: -

Experience comfort and quality in our warm family run home on N71. Convenient to National Park, lakes. Advice on tours.

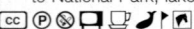

B&B PPS:	**£17/£18**	SNGL OCC. DBLE/TPL:	-	SNGL RM:	-
PART BRD:	-	% RED. CHILDREN:	-	DINNER:	-

Mrs Julianne O'Donnell
HYLANDS
Coolgarrive, Aghadoe, Killarney, Co Kerry

TEL: **064 34370**   FAX: -

Killarney Aghadoe

OPEN:	March-October
NO. ROOMS:	4
ENSUITE:	4

Modern home, quiet, scenic location, guest TV lounge, complimentary tea/coffee. Leaving Killarney, 1st left after roundabout off Tralee road (N22).

B&B PPS:	£17/£18	SNGL OCC. DBLE/TPL:	£23.50/£25	SNGL RM:	-
PART BRD:	-	% RED. CHILDREN:	33%	DINNER:	-

— Killarney 2km —

Mrs Bridie O'Donoghue
MUCKROSS DRIVE HOUSE
Muckross Drive, off Muckross Road, Killarney, Co Kerry

TEL: **064 34290**   FAX: -

Killarney Muckross Road

OPEN:	All Year
NO. ROOMS:	3
ENSUITE:	3

Purpose built B&B. Overlooking mountains,National Park. Minute walk town centre. Bus/rail, quiet location off Muckross road, tours arranged

B&B PPS:	£17/£17.50	SNGL OCC. DBLE/TPL:	£23.50/£24	SNGL RM:	-
PART BRD:	-	% RED. CHILDREN:	25%	DINNER:	-

— In Killarney —

Mrs Julia O'Donoghue
WOODLANDS
Ballydowney, Killarney, Co Kerry

TEL: **064 31467**   FAX: -

Killarney Fossa

OPEN:	All Year except Christmas
NO. ROOMS:	5
ENSUITE:	3

Friendly home walking distance town. Ring of Kerry road. riding stables, golf, fishing, lakes / National Park nearby. Ideal walkers/climbers.

B&B PPS:	£16/£17	SNGL OCC. DBLE/TPL:	£21.50/£23.50	SNGL RM:	£17/£20
PART BRD:	-	% RED. CHILDREN:	25%	DINNER:	-

— Killarney 1km —

Mrs Mary O'Donoghue
GLENCOOL HOUSE
Lissivigeen, Cork Road N22, Killarney, Co Kerry

TEL: **064 31315**   FAX: -

Killarney Cork Road Area

OPEN:	16th March-31st October
NO. ROOMS:	4
ENSUITE:	4

N22. Tea/coffee making facilities. All ensuite rooms with TV, Orthopaedic beds, breakfast menu. Tours arranged, golf, cabaret. Frommer recommended.

B&B PPS:	£17	SNGL OCC. DBLE/TPL:	£23.50	SNGL RM:	-
PART BRD:	-	% RED. CHILDREN:	25%	DINNER:	-

— Killarney 2km —

Mrs Phil O'Donohoe
MAYWOOD
Mill Road, Killarney, Co Kerry

TEL: **064 31263**   FAX: -

Killarney Muckross Road

OPEN:	1st April-30th September
NO. ROOMS:	5
ENSUITE:	3

Spacious, modern bungalow in scenic area near National Park. Golf, fishing, mountains, lakes nearby. Tours arranged.

B&B PPS:	£15/£17	SNGL OCC. DBLE/TPL:	£21.50/£23.50	SNGL RM:	-
PART BRD:	-	% RED. CHILDREN:	25%	DINNER:	-

— Killarney 1.5km —

— In Killarney

Mrs Betty O'Donovan
TIVOLI
Cork Road, Killarney, Co Kerry

Killarney Cork Road Area

OPEN:	1st May-20th September
NO. ROOMS:	4
ENSUITE:	3

TEL: **064 31450** FAX: -

Attractive modern home within walking distance of town centre, church, railway/bus station. Convenient to all amenities. Hairdryers all rooms.

B&B PPS:	£15/£17	SNGL OCC. DBLE/TPL:	£21.50/£23.50	SNGL RM:	-
PART BRD:	-	% RED. CHILDREN:	25%	DINNER:	-

— In Killarney

Mrs Eileen O'Grady
FORREST HILLS
Muckross Road, Killarney, Co Kerry

Killarney Muckross Road

OPEN:	All Year
NO. ROOMS:	6
ENSUITE:	4

TEL: **064 31844** FAX: -

Modern, well-heated home in scenic area, a few hundred yards from town centre. Spacious parking. Home cooking.

B&B PPS:	£15/£18	SNGL OCC. DBLE/TPL:	-	SNGL RM:	£20/£25
PART BRD:	-	% RED. CHILDREN:	50%	DINNER:	-

— Killarney 4km

Mrs Eileen O'Leary
THE SHADY NOOK
Crohane, Fossa, Killarney, Co Kerry

Killarney Fossa

OPEN:	1st May-30th September
NO. ROOMS:	3
ENSUITE:	3

TEL: **064 33351** FAX: -

Family home located in peaceful scenic area, convenient for touring Ring of Kerry/Dingle/lakes. Golf, fishing, horse riding .5km.

B&B PPS:	£17	SNGL OCC. DBLE/TPL:	£23.50	SNGL RM:	-
PART BRD:	£180	% RED. CHILDREN:	50%	DINNER:	£12

— Killarney

Mrs Evelyn O'Leary
KILBROGAN HOUSE
Muckross Road, Killarney, Co Kerry

Killarney Muckross Road

OPEN:	March - 31st October
NO. ROOMS:	4
ENSUITE:	4

TEL: **064 31444** FAX: -

On Ring of Kerry road adjacent Muckross House/National Park, mountains, lakes, Gleneagle Hotel. Log fires, home baking, Spacious parking. Tours arranged.

B&B PPS:	£17	SNGL OCC. DBLE/TPL:	-	SNGL RM:	£23.50
PART BRD:	-	% RED. CHILDREN:	50%	DINNER:	--

— Killarney 1km

Mrs Joan O'Mahoney
BRAMBLEWOOD HOUSE
Woodlawn Road, Killarney, Co Kerry

Killarney Town

OPEN:	1st May-30th September
NO. ROOMS:	3
ENSUITE:	3

TEL: **064 33648** FAX: -

Peaceful, secluded country setting, only 12 minutes walk town centre. Ideal for walkers, cyclists, anglers. Breakfast menu.

B&B PPS:	£17	SNGL OCC. DBLE/TPL:	£23.50	SNGL RM:	-
PART BRD:	-	% RED. CHILDREN:	-	DINNER:	-

— Killarney 2km —

Miss Noreen O'Mahoney
MYSTICAL ROSE
Woodlawn Road, Killarney, Co Kerry

Killarney Town

OPEN:	All Year
No. ROOMS:	6
ENSUITE:	6

TEL: **064 31453** FAX: -

Award winning guest home. Frommer Guide recommended. Beautiful country home convenient to mountain, lake district. All tours arranged.

Ⓟ✂🚶🏠Ⓢ

B&B PPS:	**£17/£18**	SNGL OCC. DBLE/TPL:	**£23.50/£24.50**	SNGL RM:	-
PART BRD:	-	% RED. CHILDREN:	**33.3%**	DINNER:	**£12**

— Killarney 1km —

Mrs Sheila O'Mahony
O'MAHONY'S
Cork Road, Killarney, Co Kerry

Killarney Town

OPEN:	1st March-30th November
No. ROOMS:	6
ENSUITE:	6

TEL: **064 32861** FAX: -

Warm comfortable home opposite Ryan Hotel. Rooms en suite, TV, hairdryers, breakfast menu, private parking. Walking distance town centre. Tours arranged.

cc Ⓟ✂☐☕🚶🏠

B&B PPS:	**£17**	SNGL OCC. DBLE/TPL:	**£23.50**	SNGL RM:	-
PART BRD:	-	% RED. CHILDREN:	**50%**	DINNER:	-

— Killarney 2km —

Mrs Norrie O'Neill
ALDERHAVEN COUNTRY HOME
Ballycasheen, Cork Road, Killarney, Co Kerry

Killarney Ballycasheen

OPEN:	15th March-1st December
No. ROOMS:	6
ENSUITE:	6

TEL: **064 31982** FAX:

Secluded Tudor house off N22. Private avenue, 5 acres woodlands, tranquil setting. Breakfast menu, hairdryers, tea/coffee in lounge. Tours arranged.

🚻Ⓟ☕🚶🏠

B&B PPS:	**£17/£17.50**	SNGL OCC. DBLE/TPL:	**£23.50/£24**	SNGL RM:	-
PART BRD:	-	% RED. CHILDREN:	**10%**	DINNER:	-

 In Killarney

Mrs Patricia O'Neill
LORENZO HOUSE
Lewis Road, Killarney Town, Killarney, Co Kerry

Killarney Town

OPEN:	1st April-31st October
No. ROOMS:	4
ENSUITE:	4

TEL: **064 31869** FAX: -

Modern town house, 3 minutes walk to town centre, bus and railway, national park, golf, riding stables nearby, tours arranged.

cc Ⓟ✂☕

B&B PPS:	**£17**	SNGL OCC. DBLE/TPL:	**£23.50**	SNGL RM:	-
PART BRD:	-	% RED. CHILDREN:	-	DINNER:	-

— Killarney 5km —

Sheila O'Neill
ALRAN HEIGHTS
Lough Guitane Road, Muckross, Killarney, Co Kerry

Killarney Muckross Road

OPEN:	May-September
No. ROOMS:	3
ENSUITE:	2

TEL: **064 32071** FAX: -

Set in quiet tranquil location with view of Mangerton Mountain. Adjacent to Killarney National Park, 1km off the N71.

🚻Ⓟ🚶🏠Ⓢ

B&B PPS:	**£15/£17**	SNGL OCC. DBLE/TPL:	**£21.50/£23.50**	SNGL RM:	-
PART BRD:	-	% RED. CHILDREN:	**50%**	DINNER:	-

Killarney 1km

Joan and Patrick O'Riordan
ST RITAS VILLA
Mill Road, Killarney, Co Kerry

Killarney Muckross Road

OPEN:	10th March-31st October
NO. ROOMS:	5
ENSUITE:	4

(V)

TEL: **064 31517**   FAX: -

Home adjacent to lakes, Muckross House, Gleneagle hotel. Tea/coffee served, Orthopaedic beds, hairdryers available. Tours arranged. Private parking.

B&B PPS:	£16/£18	SNGL OCC. DBLE/TPL:	£22.50/£24.50	SNGL RM:	-
PART BRD:	-	% RED. CHILDREN:	25%	DINNER:	-

Killarney 3km

Mrs Anne O'Rourke
SILVER SPRINGS
Tralee Road, Killarney, Co Kerry

Killarney Tralee Road

OPEN:	1st February-15th December
NO. ROOMS:	4
ENSUITE:	3

(V)

TEL: **064 31016**   FAX: -

Country home. 3km Killarney on Tralee - Limerick Rd N22. Bedrooms en-suite, with TV, hairdryers,Tea facilities.

B&B PPS:	£15/£17	SNGL OCC. DBLE/TPL:	£21.50/£23.50	SNGL RM:	£15/£18
PART BRD:	-	% RED. CHILDREN:	50%	DINNER:	£12

Killarney 1km

Mrs Kay O'Shea
SPRINGFIELD LODGE
Rookery Rd., Ballycasheen, Killarney, Co Kerry

Killarney Cork Road Area

OPEN:	1st March-31st October
NO. ROOMS:	3
ENSUITE:	3

(V)

TEL: **064 32944**   FAX: -

Modern friendly home. Warm welcome. Peaceful setting, private parking (off N22). Tea/coffee on arrival. Convenient to all amenities.Tours arranged.

B&B PPS:	£17/£17.50	SNGL OCC. DBLE/TPL:	£23.50/£24	SNGL RM:	-
PART BRD:	-	% RED. CHILDREN:	25%	DINNER:	-

Killarney 2km

Mrs Bernadette O'Sullivan
MUCKROSS LODGE
Muckross Road, Killarney, Co Kerry

Killarney Muckross Road

OPEN:	15th March-31st October
NO. ROOMS:	4
ENSUITE:	4

(V)

TEL: **064 32660**   FAX: **064 32660**

Adjacent to Muckross House/National Park/lakes. Spacious smoke-free bedrooms with TV, hairdryers, tea/coffee making facilities.

B&B PPS:	£17.50/£19	SNGL OCC. DBLE/TPL:	£25/£30	SNGL RM:	-
PART BRD:	-	% RED. CHILDREN:	-	DINNER:	-

In Killarney

Mrs Betty O'Sullivan
LISADEN
97 Countess Grove, Countess Road, Killarney, Co Kerry

Killarney Countess Road

OPEN:	March-October
NO. ROOMS:	4
ENSUITE:	4

(V)

TEL: **064 32006**   FAX: -

Bungalow in pleasant restful area off Countess Road, linking (N22/N71). 7 Minutes walk town centre bus/rail. Hairdryers available, tours arranged.

B&B PPS:	£17.50/£19.50	SNGL OCC. DBLE/TPL:	£24/£26	SNGL RM:	-
PART BRD:	-	% RED. CHILDREN:	25%	DINNER:	-

— Killorglin 8km —

Mrs Eileen O'Sullivan
KINGDOM VIEW
Glencar Road, Kilgobnet, Beaufort, Killarney, Co Kerry

Killarney Beaufort

OPEN:	1st February-30th November
NO. ROOMS:	6
ENSUITE:	5

TEL: **064 44343**   FAX: -

On Killarney/Glencar Road, slopes of McGilllcuddy Mountains. Spectacular countryside. Seafood speciality. Turf fire. Cot available. Traditional musicians in family.

B&B PPS:	**£15/£17**	SNGL OCC. DBLE/TPL:	**£21.50/£23.50**	SNGL RM:	-
PART BRD:	**£180**	% RED. CHILDREN:	**50%**	DINNER:	**£12**

— Killarney —

Mr Eugene A O'Sullivan
NORAVILLE HOUSE
St Margarets Road, Killarney, Co Kerry

Killarney Town

OPEN:	All Year
NO. ROOMS:	5
ENSUITE:	5

TEL: **064 36053**   FAX: -

Luxurious warm townhouse. Hairdryers, tea/coffee facilities in lounge. Tours arranged. Town 8 minutes walk. Owned by catering manager Reduction low season.

B&B PPS:	**£17**	SNGL OCC. DBLE/TPL:	**£23.50**	SNGL RM:	-
PART BRD:	-	% RED. CHILDREN:	**25%**	DINNER:	-

— Killarney 2km —

Jackie & Peggie O'Sullivan
SILVER BIRCH
Ballycasheen, Killarney, Co Kerry

Killarney Ballycasheen

OPEN:	May-October
NO. ROOMS:	4
ENSUITE:	4

TEL: **064 31550**   FAX: -

Modern two storey Georgian House. Peaceful area, Forest walks, fishing locally. Tours arranged. Hairdryers all rooms, breakfast menu, Off N22.

B&B PPS:	**£17**	SNGL OCC. DBLE/TPL:	**£23.50**	SNGL RM:	-
PART BRD:	-	% RED. CHILDREN:	-	DINNER:	-

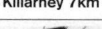

— Killarney 7km —

Mrs Mary O'Sullivan
LIOS-A-DUN
Pallas, Beaufort, Killarney, Co Kerry

Killarney Beaufort

OPEN:	1st May-30th September
NO. ROOMS:	3
ENSUITE:	2

TEL: **064 44119**   FAX: -

Family home warm welcome, "home from home feeling". Peaceful scenic area. Own putting green. Golf, fishing. Gap of Dunloe nearby.

B&B PPS:	**£15/£17**	SNGL OCC. DBLE/TPL:	**£21.50/£23.50**	SNGL RM:	-
PART BRD:	**£180**	% RED. CHILDREN:	**33.3%**	DINNER:	**£12**

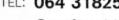

— In Killarney —

Maura O'Sullivan
MAR LODGE
St Annes Rd, Killarney, Co Kerry

Killarney

OPEN:	17th March-31st October
NO. ROOMS:	3
ENSUITE:	2

TEL: **064 31825**   FAX: -

Comfortable family run home. 3 mins walk to town centre, bus & train station. Fishing, walking, golf nearby. Advice on tours.

B&B PPS:	**£16/£17.50**	SNGL OCC. DBLE/TPL:	-	SNGL RM:	-
PART BRD:	-	% RED. CHILDREN:	-	DINNER:	-

Killarney 2km

Joan & Jerry Ryan
THE GROTTO
Fossa, Killarney, Co Kerry

Killarney

OPEN:	1st March-10th November
NO. ROOMS:	6
ENSUITE:	5

TEL: **064 33283**   FAX:

On Ring of Kerry/Dingle Road opposite lake and Killarney golf & fishing club. Tea facilities. Riding stables nearby. Tours arranged.

B&B PPS:	£15/£17	SNGL OCC. DBLE/TPL:	£21.50/£23.50	SNGL RM:	-
PART BRD:	-	% RED. CHILDREN:	25%	DINNER:	-

Killarney 2km

Mrs Hazel Scott
HAZELBROOK HEIGHTS
Aghadoe, Killarney, Co Kerry

Killarney Aghadoe

OPEN:	1st March-31st December
NO. ROOMS:	4
ENSUITE:	4

TEL: **064 34309**   FAX: -

Modern bungalow in scenic, peaceful area (off N22). Guest lounge, tea/coffee facilities, breakfast menu. Tours arranged, parking. Personal service.

B&B PPS:	£17/£18	SNGL OCC. DBLE/TPL:	£23.50/£25	SNGL RM:	-
PART BRD:	-	% RED. CHILDREN:	33.3%	DINNER:	-

Killarney 4km

Mrs Carmella Sheehy
LINN DUBH
Aghadoe, Killarney, Co Kerry

Killarney Aghadoe

OPEN:	March-November
NO. ROOMS:	5
ENSUITE:	4

TEL: **064 33828**   FAX: -

Overlooking lakes/mountains. Quiet scenic area. Causin/Dillard, Hachette Visa guide recommended. Orthopedic beds. Breakfast menu, tea facilities. Tours arranged.

B&B PPS:	£15/£17	SNGL OCC. DBLE/TPL:	£21.50/£26	SNGL RM:	-
PART BRD:	-	% RED. CHILDREN:	50%	DINNER:	-

Killarney 1km

Mrs Catherine Spillane
BEAUTY'S HOME
Cleeney, Tralee Road, Killarney, Co Kerry

Killarney Town

OPEN:	All Year except Christmas
NO. ROOMS:	6
ENSUITE:	3

TEL: **064 31567/ 064 31836**   FAX: **064 34077**

Luxurious Bungalow. Breakfast Buffet/Menu. TV, video, movie Channel, tea facilities. Electric blankets, Orthopaedic beds all rooms. Collection rail/bus station.

B&B PPS:	£15.50/£22	SNGL OCC. DBLE/TPL:	£24/£29	SNGL RM:	£21/£24
PART BRD:	-	% RED. CHILDREN:	20%	DINNER:	-

Killarney 0.3km

Beppie Tangney
KINVARA HOUSE
Muckross Road, Killarney, Co Kerry

Killarney Muckross Road

OPEN:	All Year except Christmas
NO. ROOMS:	4
ENSUITE:	3

TEL: **064 33358**   FAX: **064-33358**

Comfortable, friendly family run home 5 minutes walk to town, bus, rail. Convenient to all amenities. Tours arranged, Private jaunting cars.

B&B PPS:	£15/£17	SNGL OCC. DBLE/TPL:	£21.50/£25	SNGL RM:	-
PART BRD:	-	% RED. CHILDREN:	25%	DINNER:	-

Killarney 1km

Mrs Eileen Tarrant
MULBERRY HOUSE
Rookery Road, (Off Countess Road), Killarney, Co Kerry
Tel: **064 34112**   Fax: **064 32534**

Killarney Cork Road Area

Open:	1st February-1st December
No. Rooms:	5
Ensuite:	5

Ⓥ

Luxurious Country House backing onto farmland, unspoilt views of Killarneys Mountains (off N22). Near town, lakes, tea-makers, hairdryers, television. Frommer listed.

B&B PPS:	£17/£18	Sngl Occ. Dble/Tpl:	£23.50/£25	Sngl Rm:	-
Part Brd:	-	% Red. Children:	25%	Dinner:	-

Killarney 4km

Mrs Anne Teahan
FAIR HAVEN
Lissivigeen (N22), Cork Road, Killarney, Co Kerry
Tel: **064 32542**   Fax: -

Killarney Cork Road Area

Open:	May-October
No. Rooms:	5
Ensuite:	4

Ⓥ

Dillard/Causin Guide recommended. Warm country home on 2 acres. Peaceful, scenic area, with golf, fishing locally. All tours arranged.

B&B PPS:	£15/£17	Sngl Occ. Dble/Tpl:	£21.50/£23.50	Sngl Rm:	-
Part Brd:	-	% Red. Children:	20%	Dinner:	-

In Killarney

Mrs Mary Tuohy
FRIARY VIEW
Dennehy's, Bohereen, Killarney, Co Kerry
Tel: **064 32996**   Fax: -

Killarney Town

Open:	1st May-30th September
No. Rooms:	4
Ensuite:	4

Peaceful home in secluded area. Close to all amenities. Tours arranged. Minutes walk from town, small road beside Friary Church.

B&B PPS:	£17	Sngl Occ. Dble/Tpl:	-	Sngl Rm:	-
Part Brd:	-	% Red. Children:	50%	Dinner:	-

Killarney 2km

Mrs Agnes Walsh
WUTHERING HEIGHTS
Knockeenduff, Killarney, Co Kerry
Tel: **064 32756**   Fax: -

Killarney Tralee Road

Open:	All Year
No. Rooms:	4
Ensuite:	4

Bungalow in peaceful location signposted on Killarney/Limerick road (N22). Tea/coffee making facilities, Orthopaedic beds, electric blankets, hairdryer. Low season reduction.

B&B PPS:	£17	Sngl Occ. Dble/Tpl:	£23.50	Sngl Rm:	-
Part Brd:	£180	% Red. Children:	50%	Dinner:	£12

Killarney 1km

Mrs Anne Wrenn
THE WREN'S NEST
Woodhaven, Woodlawn Rd., Killarney, Co Kerry
Tel: **064 33580**   Fax: -

Killarney Muckross Road

Open:	All Year
No. Rooms:	4
Ensuite:	4

Ⓥ

Bungalow own grounds in pleasant restful area. Near lake, mountain district. Tours arranged. Tea making facilities. Hairdryers.Frommer recommended.

B&B PPS:	£17/£18	Sngl Occ. Dble/Tpl:	£23.50/£26	Sngl Rm:	-
Part Brd:	-	% Red. Children:	25%	Dinner:	£12

Killorglin 3km

Mrs Irma Clifford
FERN ROCK
Tinnahalla, Milltown, Co Kerry

TEL: **066 61848** FAX: -

Killorglin Ring of Kerry

OPEN:	10th January-1st December
NO. ROOMS:	4
ENSUITE:	3

(V)

Excellent accommodation (on N70 Tralee Rd) Superb view. Tours arranged. Golf .5 km, fishing, beaches close by. Frommer recommended.

B&B PPS:	£15/£17	SNGL OCC. DBLE/TPL:	£21.50/£23.50	SNGL RM:	-
PART BRD:	-	% RED. CHILDREN:	-	DINNER:	

In Killorglin

Mrs Marie Clifford
HILLCREST
Killarney Road, Killorglin, Co Kerry

TEL: **066 61552** FAX: **066 61996**

Killorglin Ring Of Kerry

OPEN:	May-September
NO. ROOMS:	5
ENSUITE:	5

(V)

Georgian styled residence, spectacular views of Irelands highest mountains. Orthopaedic Beds, electric blankets, TV, hairdryers, tea/coffee maker all rooms.

B&B PPS:	£17	SNGL OCC. DBLE/TPL:	£23.50	SNGL RM:	-
PART BRD:	-	% RED. CHILDREN:	50%	DINNER:	-

Killorglin 0.5km

Mrs Bridie Evans
ORGLAN HOUSE
Killarney Road, Killorglin, Co Kerry

TEL: **066 61540** FAX: -

Killorglin Ring of Kerry

OPEN:	April-October
NO. ROOMS:	4
ENSUITE:	3

(V)

Peaceful home, gardens overlooking river, town, mountains. Central for Ring of Kerry/Killarney/Dingle, near fishing, golf, beaches, hill walking.

B&B PPS:	£15/£17	SNGL OCC. DBLE/TPL:	£21.50/£23.50	SNGL RM:	-
PART BRD:	-	% RED. CHILDREN:	25%	DINNER:	

In Killorglin

Noreen Evans
LAUNE BRIDGE HOUSE
Killarney Rd., Killorglin, Co Kerry

TEL: **066 61161** FAX: -

Killorglin Ring Of Kerry

OPEN:	1st March-1st December
NO. ROOMS:	4
ENSUITE:	4

(V)

At the Bridge of Killorglin. Scenic location overlooking River. On the Ring of Kerry. Walking distance from high class restaurants.

B&B PPS:	£16/£17	SNGL OCC. DBLE/TPL:	£21/£22	SNGL RM:	-
PART BRD:	-	% RED. CHILDREN:	50%	DINNER:	-

Killorglin 2km

Mrs Christine Griffin
ARDRAHAN HOUSE
Ownagarry, Killorglin, Co Kerry

TEL: **066 62219** FAX: -

Killorglin

OPEN:	1st April-31st October
NO. ROOMS:	3
ENSUITE:	2

(V)

Bungalow on Glencar road, near mountains, seaside 10km, Caragh lake 7Km. Central for Ring of Kerry, Dingle, Killarney. Fishing, cyclists.

B&B PPS:	£15/£17	SNGL OCC. DBLE/TPL:	£21.50/£23.50	SNGL RM:	-
PART BRD:	£180	% RED. CHILDREN:	50%	DINNER:	-

In Killorgan

Mrs Angela Kelliher
IVERAGH HOUSE
Sunhill Road, Killorglin, Co Kerry

Killorgan Ring Of Kerry

OPEN:	All Year
NO. ROOMS:	4
ENSUITE:	3

(V)

TEL: **066 61305**   FAX: **066 61305**

Quality home, all bedrooms satellite TV, tea/coffee facilities, hairdryers, radio.
Superb views. Touring base Dingle/Kerry/Killarney, golf/fishing.

B&B PPS:	£15/£17	SNGL OCC. DBLE/TPL:	£21.50/£23.50	SNGL RM:	-
PART BRD:	£185	% RED. CHILDREN:	10%	DINNER:	£13

In Killorglin

Mrs Catherine Lyons
TORINE HOUSE
Sunhill Road, Killorglin, Ring of Kerry, Co Kerry

Killorgan Ring Of Kerry

OPEN:	1st March-1st December
NO. ROOMS:	6
ENSUITE:	6

(V)

TEL: **066 61352**   FAX: **066 61352**

Luxurious ensuite accommodation. Orthopaedic beds. Ten major golf courses nearby.
Central for Ring of Kerry, Killarney & Dingle. Guide du Routard recommended.

B&B PPS:	£17	SNGL OCC. DBLE/TPL:	£23.50	SNGL RM:	-
PART BRD:	£180	% RED. CHILDREN:	50%	DINNER:	£12

In Killorglin

Mrs Geraldine Mangan
RIVERSIDE HOUSE
Killorglin, Ring of Kerry, Co Kerry

Killorglin Ring Of Kerry

OPEN:	1st March-1st December
NO. ROOMS:	6
ENSUITE:	3

(V)

TEL: **066 61184**   FAX: -

Comfortable residence, magnificant view from rooms overlooking river, 18 hole golf
course, central Killarney, Ring/Kerry, Dingle, golfing, walking, route information.

B&B PPS:	£15/£18	SNGL OCC. DBLE/TPL:	£21.50/£24.50	SNGL RM:	-
PART BRD:	-	% RED. CHILDREN:	50%	DINNER:	-

In Killorglin

Mrs Marie Melia
ASHLING
Sunhill, Killorglin, Co Kerry

Killorglin Ring Of Kerry

OPEN:	16th March-31st October
NO. ROOMS:	3
ENSUITE:	1

(V)

TEL: **066 61226**   FAX: -

Family home, peaceful location, 2 mins walk town centre. Private Parking,
approved, central base Killarney, Ring of Kerry, Dingle, golf, walking.

B&B PPS:	£15/£17	SNGL OCC. DBLE/TPL:	£21.50/£23.50	SNGL RM:	-
PART BRD:	-	% RED. CHILDREN:	50%	DINNER:	-

Killorglin 3km

Mrs Eileen O'Connor
REEKS VIEW HOUSE
Tullig, Cromane Rd, Killorglin, Co Kerry

Killorglin Ring of Kerry

OPEN:	April-October
NO. ROOMS:	4
ENSUITE:	4

(V)

TEL: **066 61235**   FAX: **066 61235**

Home in scenic countryside. 1 km off Ring of Kerry Rd N70. Breakfast menu.
Orthopaedic beds, tea/coffee facilities. Ideal touring base.

B&B PPS:	£17	SNGL OCC. DBLE/TPL:	£23.50	SNGL RM:	-
PART BRD:	-	% RED. CHILDREN:	33.3%	DINNER:	-

Christina & Jerome O'Regan
O'REGANS COUNTRY HOME GDN
Bansha, Killorglin, Co Kerry

TEL: **066 61200** FAX: -

Killorglin Ring of Kerry

OPEN:	**All Year except Christmas**
NO. ROOMS:	**4**
ENSUITE:	**3**

(V)

Beautiful modern home on award winning gardens. Panoramic views, golf, fishing nearby. Home baking. Beaches, ideal touring base, hill walking.

B&B PPS:	**£15/£17**	SNGL OCC. DBLE/TPL:	**£21.50/£23.50**	SNGL RM:	-
PART BRD:	**£180**	% RED. CHILDREN:	-	DINNER:	**£13**

— Killorgan 1km —

Tommy & Kay Woods
PARK HOUSE
Laharn, Killorglin, Co Kerry

TEL: **066 61665** FAX: **066 62098**

Killorglin Ring of Kerry

OPEN:	**1st April-30th October**
NO. ROOMS:	**4**
ENSUITE:	**2**

(V)

Comfortable home on Ring of Kerry, overlooking mountains. Convenient for golf, fishing, touring, mountaineering and walking. Guide Du Routard recommended.

B&B PPS:	**£15/£17**	SNGL OCC. DBLE/TPL:	**£21.50/£23.50**	SNGL RM:	-
PART BRD:	-	% RED. CHILDREN:	**33%**	DINNER:	-

— Killorgan 0.5km —

Mrs Joan Carmody
PALMGROVE HOUSE
Tarbert Rd, Listowel, Co Kerry

TEL: **068 21857** FAX: -

Listowel

OPEN:	**1st April-31st October**
NO. ROOMS:	**5**
ENSUITE:	**3**

(V)

Comfortable home on main Tarbert road (N69). Car ferry 10 min. Complimentary tea/coffee on arrival. Private car park, comfort assured.

B&B PPS:	**£15/£20**	SNGL OCC. DBLE/TPL:	**£21.50/£26.50**	SNGL RM:	-
PART BRD:	-	% RED. CHILDREN:	**50%**	DINNER:	-

— Listowel 2.5km —

Mrs Mary Costello
ARAS MHUIRE
Ballybunion Road, Listowel, Co Kerry

TEL: **068 21515** FAX: -

Listowel

OPEN:	**1st January-31st December**
NO. ROOMS:	**4**
ENSUITE:	**4**

(V)

Location Ballybunion road near town. Reduction for more than 1 night. Room £12.50 p.p.s. Irish Independant recommended. Golf, beach, car ferry nearby.

B&B PPS:	**£17/£22**	SNGL OCC. DBLE/TPL:	**£23.50/£28.50**	SNGL RM:	**£17/£22**
PART BRD:	-	% RED. CHILDREN:	**50%**	DINNER:	-

— In Listowel —

Mrs Carmel Harnett
OAKWOOD
Cahirdown, Tarbert Road, Listowel, Co Kerry

TEL: **068 22020** FAX: -

Listowel

OPEN:	**All Year except Christmas**
NO. ROOMS:	**3**
ENSUITE:	**2**

(V)

Situated on N69 main Tarbert car ferry road. Orthpoaedic beds, electric blankets, tea facilities. Reduction for low season. Golf close by.

B&B PPS:	**£15/£20**	SNGL OCC. DBLE/TPL:	**£21.50/£26.50**	SNGL RM:	-
PART BRD:	-	% RED. CHILDREN:	**50%**	DINNER:	-

— Listowel 1km —

Listowel 1.5km

Mrs Teresa Keane
WHISPERING PINES
Bedford, Listowel, Co Kerry

Listowel

OPEN:	All Year
NO. ROOMS:	4
ENSUITE:	3

TEL: **068 21503**   FAX: -

Comfort assured in luxurious home in peaceful location on Ballylongford Road. Ballybunion and Listowel golf courses, Tarbert ferry, beaches 10 mins.

B&B PPS:	**£15/£19**	SNGL OCC. DBLE/TPL:	**£25.50**	SNGL RM:	-
PART BRD:	-	% RED. CHILDREN:	**25%**	DINNER:	**£14**

Listowel 1km

Mrs Noreen Lynch
LISGARVE
Ballylongford Road, Listowel, Co Kerry

Listowel

OPEN:	1st May-31st October
NO. ROOMS:	3
ENSUITE:	3

TEL: **068 21690**   FAX: -

Spacious luxury bungalow on quiet road, ensures maximum comfort and convenience for all guests. "Le Guide du Routard" recommended.

B&B PPS:	**£17/£22**	SNGL OCC. DBLE/TPL:	**£23.50/£28.50**	SNGL RM:	-
PART BRD:	-	% RED. CHILDREN:	-	DINNER:	-

Listowel 0.5km

Sean & Noreen Lyons
THE HAVEN
Tarbert Car Ferry Road,
Cahirdown, Listowel, Co Kerry

Listowel

OPEN:	All Year
NO. ROOMS:	5
ENSUITE:	5

TEL: **068 21992**   FAX: -

Purpose built to modern fire safety standards. 5 Minutes walk to town. Bedrooms with TV, hairdryers, teamaking facilities. Laundry facilities.

B&B PPS:	**£17**	SNGL OCC. DBLE/TPL:	**£23.50**	SNGL RM:	-
PART BRD:	-	% RED. CHILDREN:	**50%**	DINNER:	-

In Listowel

Mrs Breda Mahony
ASHFORD LODGE
Tarbert Road, Listowel, Co Kerry

Listowel

OPEN:	All Year
NO. ROOMS:	4
ENSUITE:	3

TEL: **068 21280**   FAX: -

On Tarbert car ferry road opposite golf course. Walking distance town centre. TV and tea facilities in bedrooms. Bicycle house.

B&B PPS:	**£15/£17**	SNGL OCC. DBLE/TPL:	**£21.50/£23.50**	SNGL RM:	-
PART BRD:	-	% RED. CHILDREN:	**50%**	DINNER:	-

In Listowel

Mrs Anne Moloney
GURTENARD HOUSE
Listowel, Co Kerry

Listowel

OPEN:	All Year except Christmas
NO. ROOMS:	4
ENSUITE:	3

TEL: **068 21137**   FAX: -

Georgian town house, built by Lord Listowel 1801. "Le Guide du Routard" recommended. Adjacent to town square. Private parking.

B&B PPS:	**£15/£19**	SNGL OCC. DBLE/TPL:	**£21.50/£25.50**	SNGL RM:	-
PART BRD:	-	% RED. CHILDREN:	**33.3%**	DINNER:	-

Mrs Nancy O'Neill
ASHGROVE HOUSE
Ballybunion Road, Listowel, Co Kerry

Listowel

OPEN:	April-October
No. ROOMS:	4
ENSUITE:	3

TEL: **068 21268**   FAX: **068 21268**

Country home adjoining farmlands. San Francisco News, Frommer Guide recommended. Orthopaedic beds, TV/hair-dryers rooms. Ballybunion golf course/ferry 10 mins.

B&B PPS:	**£17/£17.50**	SNGL OCC. DBLE/TPL:	**£23.50/£24**	SNGL RM:	-
PART BRD:	-	% RED. CHILDREN:	50%	DINNER:	-

Listowel 1km

Mrs Noreen Queally SRN
CLAREVILLE
Tarbert Road, Listowel, Co Kerry

Listowel

OPEN:	1st April-31st October
No. ROOMS:	4
ENSUITE:	4

TEL: **068 23723**   FAX: -

Attractive dormer bungalow, situated on main Tarbert car ferry road. Recommended by "Le Guide Du Routard". All orthopaedic beds.

B&B PPS:	**£17**	SNGL OCC. DBLE/TPL:	**£23.50**	SNGL RM:	-
PART BRD:	-	% RED. CHILDREN:	50%	DINNER:	-

Listowel 2km

Mrs Monica Quille
NORTH COUNTY HOUSE
67 Church St, Listowel, Co Kerry

Listowel

OPEN:	All Year
No. ROOMS:	8
ENSUITE:	6

TEL: **068 21238**   FAX: -

Centre of town. Luxurious family run home. Convenient to Ballybunion golf course (fee reduction). Tarbert car ferry. Ideal touring base.

B&B PPS:	**£15/£21**	SNGL OCC. DBLE/TPL:	**£21.50/£27**	SNGL RM:	**£19/£25**
PART BRD:	-	% RED. CHILDREN:	50%	DINNER:	-

In Listowel

Mrs Kathleen Stack
CEOL NA HABHANN
Tralee Road, Listowel, Co Kerry

Listowel

OPEN:	April-October
No. ROOMS:	4
ENSUITE:	3

TEL: **068 21345**   FAX: **068 21345**

Irish national Trust Award Winner. Thatched house on wooded river bank. Frommer Guide. Elsie Dillard recommended. Superior room £20 P.P.S.

B&B PPS:	**£15/£21**	SNGL OCC. DBLE/TPL:	**£21.50/£27.50**	SNGL RM:	-
PART BRD:	-	% RED. CHILDREN:	-	DINNER:	-

Listowel 1km

Mrs Majella Mangan
MANGAN'S COUNTRY HOME
Miltown, Killarney, Co Kerry

Killarney/Miltown

OPEN:	1st March-31st October
No. ROOMS:	3
ENSUITE:	2

TEL: **066 67502**   FAX: -

Hospitable, friendly country village. Central location Killarney/Dingle (R563). Enjoy Kerry Visual Arts Centre, walking, golfing, beaches, horse riding locally.

B&B PPS:	**£15/£17**	SNGL OCC. DBLE/TPL:	**£21.50/£23.50**	SNGL RM:	-
PART BRD:	-	% RED. CHILDREN:	33.3%	DINNER:	-

Killarney 17km

In Portmagee

Christina Murphy
THE WATERFRONT
Portmagee, Co Kerry

Portmagee

OPEN:	April-October
NO. ROOMS:	4
ENSUITE:	4

Ⓥ

TEL: **066 77208** FAX: -

At entrance Portmagee village on scenic Skellig Ring near bridge linking Valentia Island to mainland. Adjacent to Skellig Heritage Centre.

B&B PPS:	£17	SNGL OCC. DBLE/TPL:	£23.50	SNGL RM:	-
PART BRD:	-	% RED. CHILDREN:	50%	DINNER:	-

Sneem 6km

Mrs Evelyn Breen
CORAL BEACH
Sneem, Co Kerry

Sneem Ring Of Kerry

OPEN:	All Year except Christmas
NO. ROOMS:	3
ENSUITE:	2

Ⓥ

TEL: **064 45339/087 2397680** FAX: **(066) 75432**

Quiet peaceful location, between mountains and beach, overlooking Kenmare Bay. Open turf fire. Information on all amenities locally, available here.

B&B PPS:	£15/£20	SNGL OCC. DBLE/TPL:	£21.50/£26.50	SNGL RM:	-
PART BRD:	-	% RED. CHILDREN:	20%	DINNER:	-

Sneem

Mrs Gretta Drummond
ROCKVILLE HOUSE
Sneem, Co Kerry

Sneem Ring of Kerry

OPEN:	1st March-1st November
NO. ROOMS:	4
ENSUITE:	4

Ⓥ

TEL: **064 45135** FAX: -

Luxurious dormer bungalow set in private grounds. Kerry Way walking route, golf, fishing nearby. Bicycle shed. Breakfast menu.

B&B PPS:	£15/£16	SNGL OCC. DBLE/TPL:	£19/£20	SNGL RM:	-
PART BRD:	£185	% RED. CHILDREN:	30%	DINNER:	£13

In Sneem

Mrs. Noreen Drummond
BELLVIEW
Pier Road, Sneem, Co Kerry

Sneem Ring Of Kerry

OPEN:	All Year except Christmas
NO. ROOMS:	5
ENSUITE:	2

Ⓥ

TEL: **064 45389** FAX: -

Hospitable, friendly and tranquil residence situated on the Ring Of Kerry. Beaches, scenic walks, fishing, golfing, and tennis located nearby.

B&B PPS:	£15/£17	SNGL OCC. DBLE/TPL:	-	SNGL RM:	£17
PART BRD:	£180	% RED. CHILDREN:	25%	DINNER:	£12

Sneem 9km

Mrs Helen Foley
HILLSIDE HAVEN
Doon, Tahilla, Sneem, Killarney, Co Kerry

Sneem / Ring Of Kerry

OPEN:	1st April-30th October
NO. ROOMS:	4
ENSUITE:	4

Ⓥ

TEL: **064 82065** FAX: -

Spacious tastefully decorated bungalow, in mature gardens overlooking Kenmare Bay. Adjacent Kerry way walking route. Recommended for peace and tranquility.

B&B PPS:	£17/£18	SNGL OCC. DBLE/TPL:	£23.50/£24.50	SNGL RM:	-
PART BRD:	£180	% RED. CHILDREN:	25%	DINNER:	£13.50

Mrs Margaret Harrington
BANK HOUSE
North Square, Sneem, Killarney, Co Kerry

TEL: **064 45226**   FAX: -

Sneem - Ring of Kerry		
OPEN:	**March-November**	
NO. ROOMS:	4	
ENSUITE:	3	(V)

Georgian house with antiques and charm situated in heart Ireland's most picturesque village. Frommer and French guide recommended. Breakfast menu.

cc ❌ ☘ 🐾 🥄 🏠

B&B PPS:	**£15/£17**	SNGL OCC. DBLE/TPL:	**£21.50/£23.50**	SNGL RM:	-
PART BRD:	-	% RED. CHILDREN:	-	DINNER:	-

— Kenmare

Mrs Maura Hussey
AVONLEA HOUSE
Sportsfield Road, Sneem, Ring of Kerry, Co Kerry

TEL: **064 45221**   FAX: -   EMAIL: **avonlea@tinet.ie**

Sneem Ring of Kerry		
OPEN:	**1st April-30th November**	
NO. ROOMS:	5	
ENSUITE:	4	(V)

Perfect location, secluded spot beside village. Signposted. mountain/woodland surroundings. Frommer, Dillard/Causin, Routard recommended. Walks, golf, fishing, restaurants/pubs.

Ⓟ ᴿ ⚡ ☘ 🥄 🏠

B&B PPS:	**£15/£17**	SNGL OCC. DBLE/TPL:	-	SNGL RM:	-
PART BRD:	-	% RED. CHILDREN:	-	DINNER:	-

— In Sneem

Mrs Alice O'Sullivan
OLD CONVENT HOUSE
(WOODVALE), Pier Road, Sneem, Co Kerry

TEL: **064 45181**   FAX: **064 45181**

Sneem Ring of Kerry		
OPEN:	**All Year except Christmas**	
NO. ROOMS:	6	
ENSUITE:	6	(V)

Old World stone house (1865) beautifully situated on own grounds overlooking Sneem Estuary, mountains. Large Gardens with access to river.

Ⓟ ᴿ ⚡ 🍽 ☘ 🥄 🏠

B&B PPS:	**£17**	SNGL OCC. DBLE/TPL:	**£23.50**	SNGL RM:	-
PART BRD:	**£195**	% RED. CHILDREN:	**25%**	DINNER:	**£13**

— In Sneem

Mrs Phil Walsh
Oakhaven
Sallowglen, Tarbert, Co Kerry

TEL: **068 43208**   FAX: **068 43208**

Tarbert		
OPEN:	**April-October**	
NO. ROOMS:	3	
ENSUITE:	2	(V)

Modern bungalow on R551. Near car ferry, Ballybunion seaside & golf courses, Recommended Frommer Guide. Private parking. Near to Carraigfoyle Castle.

🔧 Ⓟ ᴿ ⚡ 🐾 🥄 🏠

B&B PPS:	**£15/£20**	SNGL OCC. DBLE/TPL:	**£21.50/£26.50**	SNGL RM:	-
PART BRD:	-	% RED. CHILDREN:	**50%**	DINNER:	-

— In Tarbert

Mrs Marion Barry
THE FAIRWAYS
Kerries, Fenit Road, Tralee, Co Kerry

TEL: **066 27691**   FAX: **066 27691**

Tralee		
OPEN:	**1st February-30th November**	
NO. ROOMS:	4	
ENSUITE:	4	(V)

Experience real comfort and quality. Breathtaking views, nearby tralee golf club, beaches, restaurants. Ideal touring/golfing base. Breakfast menu. Via R558.

cc 🔧 Ⓟ 🍽 🐾 🥄 🏠

B&B PPS:	**£17**	SNGL OCC. DBLE/TPL:	**£23.50**	SNGL RM:	-
PART BRD:	-	% RED. CHILDREN:	**35%**	DINNER:	-

— Tralee 2km

Geraldine & Michael Brooks
WOODBROOK HOUSE
Laharn, Tralee, Co Kerry

Tralee

OPEN:	2nd January-22nd December
NO. ROOMS:	4
ENSUITE:	4

(V)

TEL: **066 80078**   FAX: -

New two storey house on hill. All bedrooms on lower floor. Breakfast room, TV lounge upstairs all overlooking Tralee town,.

B&B PPS:	**£16/£20**	SNGL OCC. DBLE/TPL:	**£22.50/£26.50**	SNGL RM:	-
PART BRD:	-	% RED. CHILDREN:	**50%**	DINNER:	-

Tralee 3km

Mrs Patricia Canning
BRICRIU
20 Old Golf Links Road, Oakpark, Tralee, Co Kerry

Tralee

OPEN:	1st June-1st October
NO. ROOMS:	3
ENSUITE:	-

(V)

TEL: **066 26347**   FAX: -

Quiet area off N69 pass railway then 1st right, left, right again (10 mins walk) .Adjacent sports complex. Convenient golf. Beaches.

B&B PPS:	**£15/£18**	SNGL OCC. DBLE/TPL:	**£21.50/£25**	SNGL RM:	-
PART BRD:	**£180**	% RED. CHILDREN:	**10%**	DINNER:	**£12**

In Tralee

Hazel Costello
ARDROE HOUSE
Oakpark Road, Tralee, Co Kerry

Tralee

OPEN:	26th May-26th September
NO. ROOMS:	4
ENSUITE:	2

(V)

TEL: **066 26050**   FAX: -

Period town house. Convenient to bus/train depot. sports complex, golf, horse riding, beaches, walks and mountains. Ideal touring base.(N69)

B&B PPS:	**£15/£17**	SNGL OCC. DBLE/TPL:	**£20/£22**	SNGL RM:	-
PART BRD:	-	% RED. CHILDREN:	**50%**	DINNER:	-

In Tralee

Mrs Eileen Curley
MOUNTAIN VIEW HOUSE
Ballinorig West, Tralee, Co Kerry

Tralee

OPEN:	All Year except Christmas
NO. ROOMS:	6
ENSUITE:	4

(V)

TEL: **066 22226**   FAX: -

Own grounds. Close all amenities. Ideal golf/touring base. Approaching Tralee on N21, turn right just before roundabout. Frommer recommended.

B&B PPS:	**£15/£18**	SNGL OCC. DBLE/TPL:	**£21.50/£23.50**	SNGL RM:	-
PART BRD:	-	% RED. CHILDREN:	**25%**	DINNER:	-

Tralee 2km

Mrs Diana Curtin
AMBLESIDE HOUSE
Tonevane, Tralee, Co Kerry

Tralee Dingle Road Area

OPEN:	1st April-30th September
NO. ROOMS:	3
ENSUITE:	2

(V)

TEL: **066 23960**   FAX: -

Nestled peacefully in mountainside overlooking Bay Vale of Tralee. Adjacent to Dingle Way mountain walk. Blennerville Windmill, beaches, golf, Aquadome.

B&B PPS:	**£15/£19**	SNGL OCC. DBLE/TPL:	**£21.50/£25.50**	SNGL RM:	-
PART BRD:	-	% RED. CHILDREN:	**25%**	DINNER:	-

Tralee 4km

Mrs Gail Daly
ASHDALE
Fenit Road, Tralee, Co Kerry

Tralee Fenit Road

OPEN:	1st April-31st October
NO. ROOMS:	3
ENSUITE:	3

TEL: **066 28927**   FAX: **066 28927**

Luxurious home on R558 overlooking Slieve Mish Mountains. Ideal base for golfing, fishing, touring. Beaches, sailing and excellent restaurants nearby.

B&B PPS:	**£17/£22**	SNGL OCC. DBLE/TPL:	**£23.50/£28.50**	SNGL RM:	-
PART BRD:	-	% RED. CHILDREN:	-	DINNER:	-

— Tralee 2km

Mrs Gertie Deady
GURRANE
50 Derrylea, Tralee, Co Kerry

Tralee

OPEN:	1st January-24th December
NO. ROOMS:	4
ENSUITE:	2

TEL: **066 24734**   FAX: -

Modern two storey house on route N69 on Listowel Tarbert ferry road, adjacent golf, rail, bus station. Tralee superb attractions.

B&B PPS:	**£15/£18**	SNGL OCC. DBLE/TPL:	**£21.50/£24.50**	SNGL RM:	-
PART BRD:	**£180**	% RED. CHILDREN:	**20%**	DINNER:	**£12**

— Tralee 1.5km

Mrs Hannah Devane
EASTCOTE
34 Oakpark Demesne, Tralee, Co Kerry

Tralee

OPEN:	All Year except Christmas
NO. ROOMS:	3
ENSUITE:	2

TEL: **066 25942**   FAX: -

Select accommodation, in peaceful location. All facilities in rooms. Ideal touring base, 200 meters off N69 route, Tarbert ferry road.

B&B PPS:	**£16/£17**	SNGL OCC. DBLE/TPL:	**£22.50/£23.50**	SNGL RM:	**£17**
PART BRD:	-	% RED. CHILDREN:	-	DINNER:	-

— Tralee 1km

Mrs Maura Dowling
LEESIDE
Oakpark, Tralee, Co Kerry

Tralee

OPEN:	All Year except Christmas
NO. ROOMS:	3
ENSUITE:	3

TEL: **066 26475**   FAX: -

On N69 Tarbert ferry route. Convenient bus/rail. Antique Irish country furniture. TV's. Recommended Lets Go Ireland 1997. Orthopaedic Beds.

B&B PPS:	**£17**	SNGL OCC. DBLE/TPL:	**£23.50**	SNGL RM:	**£19**
PART BRD:	-	% RED. CHILDREN:	**40%**	DINNER:	-

— In Tralee

Mrs K Dunne
OAKDENE
53 Derrylea, Oakpark Road, Tralee, Co Kerry

Tralee

OPEN:	All Year except Christmas
NO. ROOMS:	4
ENSUITE:	3

TEL: **066 25934**   FAX: -

Situated on Tralee/Listowel road N69. Convenient to train, bus, airport, pitch & putt, golf, beaches.

B&B PPS:	**£15/£17**	SNGL OCC. DBLE/TPL:	**£21.50/£23.50**	SNGL RM:	-
PART BRD:	-	% RED. CHILDREN:	**25%**	DINNER:	-

— Tralee 1.5km

Mrs Bridie Fitzgerald
SEA VIEW HOUSE
Annagh, Main Dingle Road, Blennerville, Tralee, Co Kerry

TEL: **066 21830**   FAX: -

Tralee Dingle Road Area
OPEN: **1st June-31st August**
NO. ROOMS: **5**
ENSUITE: **5**   (V)

Bungalow in picturesque surroundings, beneath Slieve Mish mountain. Overlooking Tralee Bay. Ideal touring base. Convenient to beaches, angling, golf, aquadome, windmill.

| B&B PPS: | £18/£20 | SNGL OCC. DBLE/TPL: | £24.50/£26.50 | SNGL RM: | - |
| PART BRD: | - | % RED. CHILDREN: | - | DINNER: | - |

— Tralee 5km —

Mrs Ann Gleeson
ROSEDALE LODGE
Oakpark Road, Tralee, Co Kerry

TEL: **066 25320**   FAX: -

Tralee
OPEN: **March-November**
NO. ROOMS: **3**
ENSUITE: **3**   (V)

Welcome to Rosedale Lodge on Tralee - Listowel road N69. Tarbert ferry route. Personal supervision. Ideal touring base. Walking distance of town.

| B&B PPS: | £17 | SNGL OCC. DBLE/TPL: | £23.50 | SNGL RM: | - |
| PART BRD: | - | % RED. CHILDREN: | - | DINNER: | - |

— Tralee 1km —

Mrs Catherine Gleeson
BROOKDALE
Castlemaine Rd., Tralee, Co Kerry

TEL: **066 25063**   FAX: -

Tralee
OPEN: **1st April-1st November**
NO. ROOMS: **3**
ENSUITE: **3**   (V)

Dormer bungalow on Killorglin/Ring of Kerry Rd (N70). Ideally located for beaches, golf, fishing and horse riding. Complimentary tea/Coffee

| B&B PPS: | £17 | SNGL OCC. DBLE/TPL: | £23.50 | SNGL RM: | - |
| PART BRD: | - | % RED. CHILDREN: | 25% | DINNER: | - |

— Tralee 1km —

Mrs Majella Griffin
RONNOCO
Knockanish, Spa, Tralee, Co Kerry

TEL: **066 36436**   FAX: -

Tralee Fenit Road Area
OPEN: **All Year except Christmas**
NO. ROOMS: **4**
ENSUITE: **3**   (V)

Scenic location R558 Tralee Fenit /Barron road. Minutes drive beaches, sailing, fishing, Tralee golf links, seafood restaurants. Ideal golfing/touring base.

| B&B PPS: | £16/£18 | SNGL OCC. DBLE/TPL: | £22.50/£24.50 | SNGL RM: | - |
| PART BRD: | - | % RED. CHILDREN: | 10% | DINNER: | - |

— Tralee 2.5km —

Mrs Mary Hannafin
SHANGRI-LA
The Spa, Tralee, Co Kerry

TEL: **066 36214**   FAX: -

Tralee Fenit Road Area
OPEN: **All Year**
NO. ROOMS: **5**
ENSUITE: **3**   (V)

Secluded country residence overlooking Tralee Bay. Walk to beach, pub & restaurant. Golf courses nearby. Ideal golfing/touring base.

| B&B PPS: | £15/£18 | SNGL OCC. DBLE/TPL: | £21.50/£24.50 | SNGL RM: | - |
| PART BRD: | - | % RED. CHILDREN: | - | DINNER: | £13 |

— Tralee 4km —

Mrs Mary Healy
ASHMOOR
Mounthawk, Caherslee, Tralee, Co Kerry

Tralee

OPEN:	April-October
NO. ROOMS:	3
ENSUITE:	2

(V)

TEL: **066 24471**   FAX: -

Comfortable dormer bungalow. 10 minutes walk town centre. Ideal touring base, with golf, sailing, beaches, restaurants nearby. Tea/coffee, TV, bedrooms.

B&B PPS:	£15/£18	SNGL OCC. DBLE/TPL:	£21.50/£24.50	SNGL RM:	£19/£21
PART BRD:	-	% RED. CHILDREN:	25%	DINNER:	-

Tralee 1km

Mrs Sheila Horgan
ALVERNA
26 Liosdara, Oakpark, Tralee, Co Kerry

Tralee

OPEN:	2nd January-22nd December
NO. ROOMS:	5
ENSUITE:	2

(V)

TEL: **066 26970**   FAX: -

Quiet area off N69, 5 min walk railway/bus depot, golf, beaches. Turn right after sports centre 4th house on left.

B&B PPS:	£15/£18	SNGL OCC. DBLE/TPL:	£21.50/£24.50	SNGL RM:	£21.50/£23.50
PART BRD:	-	% RED. CHILDREN:	50%	DINNER:	-

Tralee 1km

Mrs Sheila Kerins
BALLINGOWAN HOUSE
Mile Height, Killarney Road, Tralee, Co Kerry

Tralee

OPEN:	1st March-30th November
NO. ROOMS:	4
ENSUITE:	4

(V)

TEL: **066 27150**   FAX: **066 20325**

All rooms with TV, tea/coffee facilities. Frommer Guide/AA recommended. Approaching Tralee on N21/N22 on left before McDonalds.

B&B PPS:	£17	SNGL OCC. DBLE/TPL:	£23.50	SNGL RM:	-
PART BRD:	-	% RED. CHILDREN:	30%	DINNER:	-

Tralee 2km

Mrs Eileen Lynch
ST ENDAS
Oakpark, Tralee, Co Kerry

Tralee

OPEN:	All Year except Christmas
NO. ROOMS:	4
ENSUITE:	3

(V)

TEL: **066 26494**   FAX: -

Town house convenient sports complex, Aquadome, golf, beaches, greyhound racing. 5 mins railway station. Private parking. Ideal touring base. N69.

B&B PPS:	£15/£17	SNGL OCC. DBLE/TPL:	£21.50/£23.50	SNGL RM:	-
PART BRD:	-	% RED. CHILDREN:	50%	DINNER:	-

In Tralee

Helen Lyons
KNOCKBRACK
Oakpark Road, Tralee, Co Kerry

Tralee

OPEN:	17th March-31st October
NO. ROOMS:	3
ENSUITE:	3

(V)

TEL: **066 27375**   FAX: -

Bright comfortable family home in residential area. Convenient golf, theatre and greyhound track. Situated on Listowel (car ferry) road N69.

B&B PPS:	£17/£18	SNGL OCC. DBLE/TPL:	£23.50/£24.50	SNGL RM:	-
PART BRD:	-	% RED. CHILDREN:	20%	DINNER:	-

Tralee 1km

Ms Helena McElligott
CLOGHERBRIEN HOUSE
Clogherbrien, Tralee, Co Kerry

Tralee

OPEN:	7th January-20th December
NO. ROOMS:	3
ENSUITE:	3

TEL: **066 28708** FAX: - -

New house, Orthopaedic beds, high-powered showers, strictly non-smoking residence. Situated R551 Ardfert/Ballyheigue road. Convenient beaches, golf course, aquadome.

B&B PPS:	£17/£20	SNGL OCC. DBLE/TPL:	£23.50/£26.50	SNGL RM:	-
PART BRD:	-	% RED. CHILDREN:	25%	DINNER:	-

— Tralee 3km —

Mrs Joan McGarry
CLOONCAIRN
The Spa, Tralee, Co Kerry

Tralee Fenit Road Area

OPEN:	All Year except Christmas
NO. ROOMS:	4
ENSUITE:	3

TEL: **066 36236** FAX: -

Scenic location overlooking Tralee Bay and mountains. 5 min walk to seashore, bar, restaurant. Adjacent to golf links. Ideal touring base.

B&B PPS:	£17/£18	SNGL OCC. DBLE/TPL:	£23.50/£24.50	SNGL RM:	-
PART BRD:	-	% RED. CHILDREN:	-	DINNER:	-

— Tralee 3.5km —

Mrs Mary McGrath
KERRIA
Listellick North, Ballybunion Road,
Tralee, Co Kerry

Tralee

OPEN:	6th April-20th October
NO. ROOMS:	4
ENSUITE:	2

TEL: **066 24451** FAX: - -

Beautifully located bungalow (R556 Tralee/Abbeydorney and Ballybunion Road). Magnificent views of Tralee Bay, Slieve Mish Mountains. Complimentary tea/coffee.

B&B PPS:	£15/£17	SNGL OCC. DBLE/TPL:	£21.50/£23.50	SNGL RM:	-
PART BRD:	-	% RED. CHILDREN:	25%	DINNER:	-

— Tralee 3km —

Mrs Juliette O'Callaghan
GREEN GABLES
1 Clonmore Villas, Ballymullen Road,
Tralee, Co Kerry

Tralee

OPEN:	All Year except Christmas
NO. ROOMS:	4
ENSUITE:	3

TEL: **066 23354** FAX: **066 23354** -

Listed Victorian period town house. Town centre location adjacent County Library, Town Park on N70. 5 min walk bus/train station.

B&B PPS:	£15/£17	SNGL OCC. DBLE/TPL:	£21.50/£23.50	SNGL RM:	£16/£19
PART BRD:	-	% RED. CHILDREN:	33%	DINNER:	-

— In Tralee —

Mrs Noreen O'Callaghan
ST ANNE'S
11 Caherwisheen, Ballyard,
Tralee, Co Kerry

Tralee / Ballyard Area

OPEN:	12th March-1st November
NO. ROOMS:	5
ENSUITE:	4

TEL: **066 22029** FAX: -

Spacious peaceful home 400 metres off Dingle/Ring of Kerry (N70). 3 mins drive town centre. TV, tea/coffee making facilities.

B&B PPS:	£15/£17	SNGL OCC. DBLE/TPL:	£21.50/£23.50	SNGL RM:	-
PART BRD:	-	% RED. CHILDREN:	25%	DINNER:	-

— Tralee 1km —

L Tralee 2km

Anne O'Connell
ANNANDALE HOUSE
Laharn, Tralee, Co Kerry

Tralee

OPEN:	All Year except Christmas
NO. ROOMS:	4
ENSUITE:	4

(V)

TEL: **066 22424** FAX: **066 22424**

Modern house overlooking Tralee on Listowel - Tralee Road. N69. Convenient to bus, train, golf, sports complex, beaches, TV/music lounge.

B&B PPS:	**£17**	SNGL OCC. DBLE/TPL:	**£23.50**	SNGL RM:	-
PART BRD:	-	% RED. CHILDREN:	**50%**	DINNER:	-

L Tralee 2km

Mrs Rose O'Connell
BARNAKYLE
Clogherbrien, Tralee, Co Kerry

Tralee

OPEN:	1st March-31st October
NO. ROOMS:	5
ENSUITE:	5

(V)

TEL: **066 25048** FAX: **066 25048**

Situated on R551 Ardfert/Ballyheigue road. Convenient to beaches, sailing, horse riding, golf, Siamsa Tire, aqua dome, caves and restaurants.

B&B PPS:	**£17/£19**	SNGL OCC. DBLE/TPL:	**£23.50/£25.50**	SNGL RM:	-
PART BRD:	-	% RED. CHILDREN:	**50%**	DINNER:	-

L Tralee 1km

Mrs Joan O'Connor
SKEHANAGH LODGE
Skehanagh, Castlemaine Road, Tralee, Co Kerry

Tralee

OPEN:	April-November
NO. ROOMS:	5
ENSUITE:	4

(V)

TEL: **066 24782** FAX: **066 24782**

Spacious bungalow on Ring of Kerry Rd, N70. Tea making facilities, TV in bedrooms. Le Routard recommended. Ideal touring base

B&B PPS:	**£15/£17**	SNGL OCC. DBLE/TPL:	**£21.50/£23.50**	SNGL RM:	-
PART BRD:	-	% RED. CHILDREN:	**25%**	DINNER:	-

L In Tralee

Philomena O'Connor
ROSELAWN LODGE
Rathass, Tralee, Co Kerry

Tralee

OPEN:	1st January-20th December
NO. ROOMS:	4
ENSUITE:	4

(V)

TEL: **066 24875** FAX: -

Comfortable suburban bungalow, spacious car park. Situated on N21. Central base for touring Kerry. Convenient to all tourist attractions.

B&B PPS:	**£17**	SNGL OCC. DBLE/TPL:	**£23.50**	SNGL RM:	**£20**
PART BRD:	-	% RED. CHILDREN:	**25%**	DINNER:	-

L Tralee 2km

Ita O'Donnell
AHAROE
Blennerville, Tralee, Co Kerry

Tralee Dingle Road Area

OPEN:	17th March-31st October
NO. ROOMS:	4
ENSUITE:	4

(V)

TEL: **066 23108** FAX: -

Quiet location off Tralee/Dingle Road at Blennerville. Overlooking Blennerville Windmill, Steam-Train, Old Ship Canal. Panoramic view Slieve Mish Mountain.

B&B PPS:	**£17**	SNGL OCC. DBLE/TPL:	**£23.50**	SNGL RM:	-
PART BRD:	-	% RED. CHILDREN:	**25%**	DINNER:	-

Mrs. Kay O'Keeffe
CNOC MHUIRE
Oakpark Road, Tralee, Co Kerry

Tralee

OPEN:	All Year except Christmas
NO. ROOMS:	3
ENSUITE:	2

(V)

TEL: **066 26027**   FAX: -

On car ferry N69 road. Golf, angling, beaches nearby. Electric blankets, Tea making facilities. AA listed, Theatre tickets arranged.

B&B PPS:	£15/£17	SNGL OCC. DBLE/TPL:	-	SNGL RM:	-
PART BRD:	-	% RED. CHILDREN:	20%	DINNER:	-

— Tralee 1km

Rose O'Keeffe
ASHVILLE HOUSE
Ballyard, Tralee, Co Kerry

Tralee Ballyard

OPEN:	All Year
NO. ROOMS:	6
ENSUITE:	6

(V)

TEL: **066 23717**   FAX: -

Architect designed house, country setting off Dingle Road (N86). Tralee 2 minutes drive. TV, tea/coffee, hairdryers, power showers. Breakfast menu.

B&B PPS:	£17	SNGL OCC. DBLE/TPL:	£23.50	SNGL RM:	-
PART BRD:	-	% RED. CHILDREN:	-	DINNER:	-

— Tralee 1km

Mrs Mary O'Neill
BEECH GROVE
Oakpark, Tralee, Co Kerry

Tralee

OPEN:	All Year except Christmas
NO. ROOMS:	4
ENSUITE:	3

(V)

TEL: **066 26788**   FAX: **066 26788**

On car ferry road N69. Near railway/bus station, sports complex, town centre. Secure car park. Siamse tickets, tours arranged.

B&B PPS:	£15/£17	SNGL OCC. DBLE/TPL:	£21.50/£23.50	SNGL RM:	£21.50/£23.50
PART BRD:	-	% RED. CHILDREN:	50%	DINNER:	

— Tralee 1km

Mrs Helen O'Shea
CLUAIN MOR HOUSE
Boherbee, Tralee, Co Kerry

Tralee

OPEN:	All Year except Christmas
NO. ROOMS:	5
ENSUITE:	4

(V)

TEL: **066 25545**   FAX: -

On 1 acre garden: 5 mins rail station, aquadome. Golf, angling, beaches nearby. Tea making facilities. TV room for guests. TV bedrooms.

B&B PPS:	£15/£17	SNGL OCC. DBLE/TPL:	£22/£23.50	SNGL RM:	£18/£20
PART BRD:	-	% RED. CHILDREN:	25%	DINNER:	-

— In Tralee

Mrs Lena O'Sullivan
KNOCKANISH HOUSE
The Spa, Tralee, Co Kerry

Tralee Fenit Road Area

OPEN:	1st April-1st November
NO. ROOMS:	6
ENSUITE:	5

(V)

TEL: **066 36268/086 8120837**   FAX: -

Luxurious home overlooking Tralee Bay. Golfing groups welcome. Nearby Tralee 18 hole golf course, restaurants & beaches. Ideal golfing/touring base.

B&B PPS:	£16/£18	SNGL OCC. DBLE/TPL:	£22.50/£24.50	SNGL RM:	-
PART BRD:	-	% RED. CHILDREN:	20%	DINNER:	-

— Tralee 3km

Tralee 6km

Malcolm & Phyl Perlman
KESWICK LODGE
Curraheen, Tralee, Co Kerry

Tralee Dingle Road Area

OPEN:	All Year except Christmas
NO. ROOMS:	4
ENSUITE:	4

(V)

TEL: **066 28751**   FAX: -

Country home on N86 overlooking Tralee Bay and Slieve Mish mountains. Tralee 6 Km. Ideal for Dingle, Killarney and Kerry Ring.

B&B PPS:	£17	SNGL OCC. DBLE/TPL:	£23.50	SNGL RM:	. -
PART BRD:	-	% RED. CHILDREN:	20%	DINNER:	-

Tralee 4km

Mrs Marie Rolls
KILCOE HOUSE
Knockanish West, Spa, Tralee, Co Kerry

Tralee Fenit Road Area

OPEN:	1st April-31st October
NO. ROOMS:	4
ENSUITE:	3

(V)

TEL: **066 36363**   FAX: -

Modern luxury bungalow overlooking Tralee Bay. Golf, beaches, sailing, fishing & seafood restaurants nearby. Ideal golf/touring base.

B&B PPS:	£15/£18	SNGL OCC. DBLE/TPL:	£21.50/£24.50	SNGL RM:	-
PART BRD:	-	% RED. CHILDREN:	50%	DINNER:	-

Blennerville 1.5km

Mrs Margaret Ryle
CRANA-LI
Curragraigue, Blennerville,
Tralee, Co Kerry

Tralee Dingle Road Area

OPEN:	May-30th September
NO. ROOMS:	5
ENSUITE:	3

(V)

TEL: **066 24467**   FAX:

Spacious bungalow in peaceful location near Blennerville Windmill. Mountain walks/beaches, horse riding nearby. Conservatory overlooking landscaped garden. Breakfast menu.

B&B PPS:	£15/£17	SNGL OCC. DBLE/TPL:	£21.50/£23.50	SNGL RM:	-
PART BRD:	-	% RED. CHILDREN:	30%	DINNER:	-

Tralee 2km

Mrs Gillian Slye
CARRAIG
Manor East, Killarney Rd.,
Tralee, Co Kerry

Tralee Killarney Road Area

OPEN:	All Year except Christmas
NO. ROOMS:	3
ENSUITE:	2

(V)

TEL: **066 24840/087 571638**   FAX: -

Luxury dormer bungalow in secluded garden setting. Attractive bedrooms. Large triple/family room. On N21 - 22. Easy access to scenic routes.

B&B PPS:	£15/£19	SNGL OCC. DBLE/TPL:	£21.50/£25.50	SNGL RM:	-
PART BRD:	-	% RED. CHILDREN:	50%	DINNER:	-

Tralee 1.5km

Mrs Joan Smith
BRIANVILLE
Clogherbrien
Fenit Road, Tralee, Co Kerry

Tralee Fenit Road Area

OPEN:	All Year
NO. ROOMS:	5
ENSUITE:	4

TEL: **066 26645**   FAX: -

Luxurious modern bungalow. Scenic view of mountains. 18 hole golf links, seafood restaurants nearby. Hairdryers, tea/coffee facilities in rooms.

B&B PPS:	£16/£17	SNGL OCC. DBLE/TPL:	-	SNGL RM:	-
PART BRD:	-	% RED. CHILDREN:	50%	DINNER:	-

Mrs Kathleen Tierney
LOCK GATES
Lohercannon, Tralee, Co Kerry

Tralee

OPEN:	1st May-31st October
NO. ROOMS:	3
ENSUITE:	2

TEL: **066 25114**   FAX: -

Overlooking Slieve Mish Mountains, Windmill and Canal. walking routes, Steam train nearby.Right turn at Blennerville bridge on Tralee Canal Road.

B&B PPS:	£15/£17	SNGL OCC. DBLE/TPL:	£21.50/£23.50	SNGL RM:	-
PART BRD:	-	% RED. CHILDREN:	25%	DINNER:	-

— Tralee 2km

Tim & Mary Walshe
THE WILLOWS
5 Clonmore Terrace, Moyderwell, Tralee, Co Kerry

Tralee

OPEN:	7th January-23rd December
NO. ROOMS:	4
ENSUITE:	3

TEL: **066 23779**   FAX: **066 23779**

Georgian Town House, with old world charm. Tastefully deocorated, centrally located. Tea/coffee facilities, Breakfast menu. Ideal touring base.

B&B PPS:	£15/£18	SNGL OCC. DBLE/TPL:	£21.50/£24.50	SNGL RM:	-
PART BRD:	-	% RED. CHILDREN:	50%	DINNER:	-

— In Tralee

Mary Lane
SHEALANE HOUSE
Corha-Mor, Valentia Island, Co Kerry

Valentia Island

OPEN:	All Year except Christmas
NO. ROOMS:	3
ENSUITE:	3

TEL: **066 76354/ 087 2338591**   FAX: -

Peaceful setting on road bridge entrance adjacent to Skellig Experience Centre. Skellig trips, fishing, walking arranged. Restaurants, traditional music nearby.

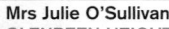

B&B PPS:	£17/£20	SNGL OCC. DBLE/TPL:	£23.50/£26.50	SNGL RM:	£18/£22
PART BRD:	-	% RED. CHILDREN:	25%	DINNER:	-

— Portmagee 1km

Mrs Julie O'Sullivan
GLENREEN HEIGHTS
Knightstown Road, Valentia Island, Co Kerry

Valentia Island

OPEN:	1st April-1st November
NO. ROOMS:	3
ENSUITE:	2

TEL: **066 76241**   FAX: -

Spectacular view sea/mountains. Orthopaedic beds. Breakfast menu, local seafood. Scenic walks, trips to Skellig arranged. Bridge and car ferry.

B&B PPS:	£15/£17	SNGL OCC. DBLE/TPL:	£21.50/£23.50	SNGL RM:	-
PART BRD:	£180	% RED. CHILDREN:	50%	DINNER:	£12

— Knightstown 2km

Mrs Breda Barry
GOLF LINKS VIEW
Murreigh, Waterville, Co Kerry

Waterville

OPEN:	1st March-31st October
NO. ROOMS:	4
ENSUITE:	4

TEL: **066 74623**   FAX: **066 74623**

AA QQQ recommended, Comfortable ensuite rooms, nice views. TV, tea/coffee making facilities. Fishing, golf course, beach, riding school nearby.

B&B PPS:	£17	SNGL OCC. DBLE/TPL:	£23.50	SNGL RM:	-
PART BRD:	£180	% RED. CHILDREN:	25%	DINNER:	£12

— Waterville 1km

In Waterville

Mrs Abbie Clifford
CLIFFORDS B&B
Waterville,Co Kerry

Waterville

OPEN:	1st March-30th November
NO. ROOMS:	6
ENSUITE:	5

 (V)

TEL: **066 74283**   FAX: -

Family run home beside Sea, Ring of Kerry. fishing, golfing, pony riding, bicycle hire locally. Good seafood restaurants nearby. Private parking.

B&B PPS:	£15/£17	SNGL OCC. DBLE/TPL:	£21.50/£23.50	SNGL RM:	-
PART BRD:	-	% RED. CHILDREN:	25%	DINNER:	-

Waterville 1km

Mrs Kathleen Coffey
HILLVIEW
Ballybrack, Waterville, Co Kerry

Waterville

OPEN:	1st March-31st October
NO. ROOMS:	5
ENSUITE:	4

(V)

TEL: **066 74621**   FAX: **066 74621**

Modern house in quiet location. Enjoy hillwalking, cycling or fishing. Private carpark. TV, coffee/tea in rooms.

B&B PPS:	£17	SNGL OCC. DBLE/TPL:	£23.50	SNGL RM:	£17
PART BRD:	£180	% RED. CHILDREN:	25%	DINNER:	-

 Waterville 4km

Mrs Patricia Curran
ATLANTIC VIEW
Toor, Waterville, Co Kerry

Waterville

OPEN:	May-September
NO. ROOMS:	3
ENSUITE:	2

(V)

TEL: **066 74335**   FAX: **066 74335**

Family run country home overlooking picturesque Ballinskelligs Bay and the Atlantic Ocean. Enjoy quiet country walks, fishing, golf, horse riding locally.

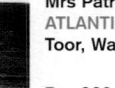

B&B PPS:	£15/£17	SNGL OCC. DBLE/TPL:	£21.50/£23.50	SNGL RM:	-
PART BRD:	-	% RED. CHILDREN:	-	DINNER:	-

In Waterville

Mrs Angela Grady
O'GRADY'S TOWNHOUSE
Spunkane, Waterville, Co Kerry

Waterville

OPEN:	17th March-31st October
NO. ROOMS:	6
ENSUITE:	5

 (V)

TEL: **066 74350**   FAX: **066 74730**

AA 3Q quality award, RAC acclaimed situated on Northern approach, paralled N70. Spacious rooms, some with sea views, Orthopaedic beds.

B&B PPS:	£15/£17	SNGL OCC. DBLE/TPL:	£21.50/£23.50	SNGL RM:	-
PART BRD:	-	% RED. CHILDREN:	25%	DINNER:	-

In Waterville

Mrs Cirean Morris
KLONDYKE HOUSE
New Line Road, Waterville, Co Kerry

Waterville

OPEN:	All Year
NO. ROOMS:	6
ENSUITE:	5

(V)

TEL: **066 74119**   FAX: **066 74666**

Detached residence. AA listed, overlooking Waterville Championship golf course, Atlantic Ocean. Trips to Skellig Rock, fishing Lough Currane, golf arranged.

B&B PPS:	£15/£17	SNGL OCC. DBLE/TPL:	£21.50/£23.50	SNGL RM:	£16/£21
PART BRD:	-	% RED. CHILDREN:	25%	DINNER:	-

Cahirciveen 18Km

Nora Murphy
ASHLING HOUSE
Main Street, Waterville, Co Kerry

Waterville

OPEN:	**April-October**
NO. ROOMS:	**5**
ENSUITE:	**4**

(V)

TEL: **066 74247**   FAX: **-**

Modern two-storey house situated on Main Street overlooking Ballinskellig Bay. Sandy beaches, fishing, golf, horse riding, mountain walking, swimming.

B&B PPS:	**£15/£17**	SNGL OCC. DBLE/TPL:	**£21.50/23.50**	SNGL RM:	**£15**
PART BRD:	**-**	% RED. CHILDREN:	**25%**	DINNER:	**-**

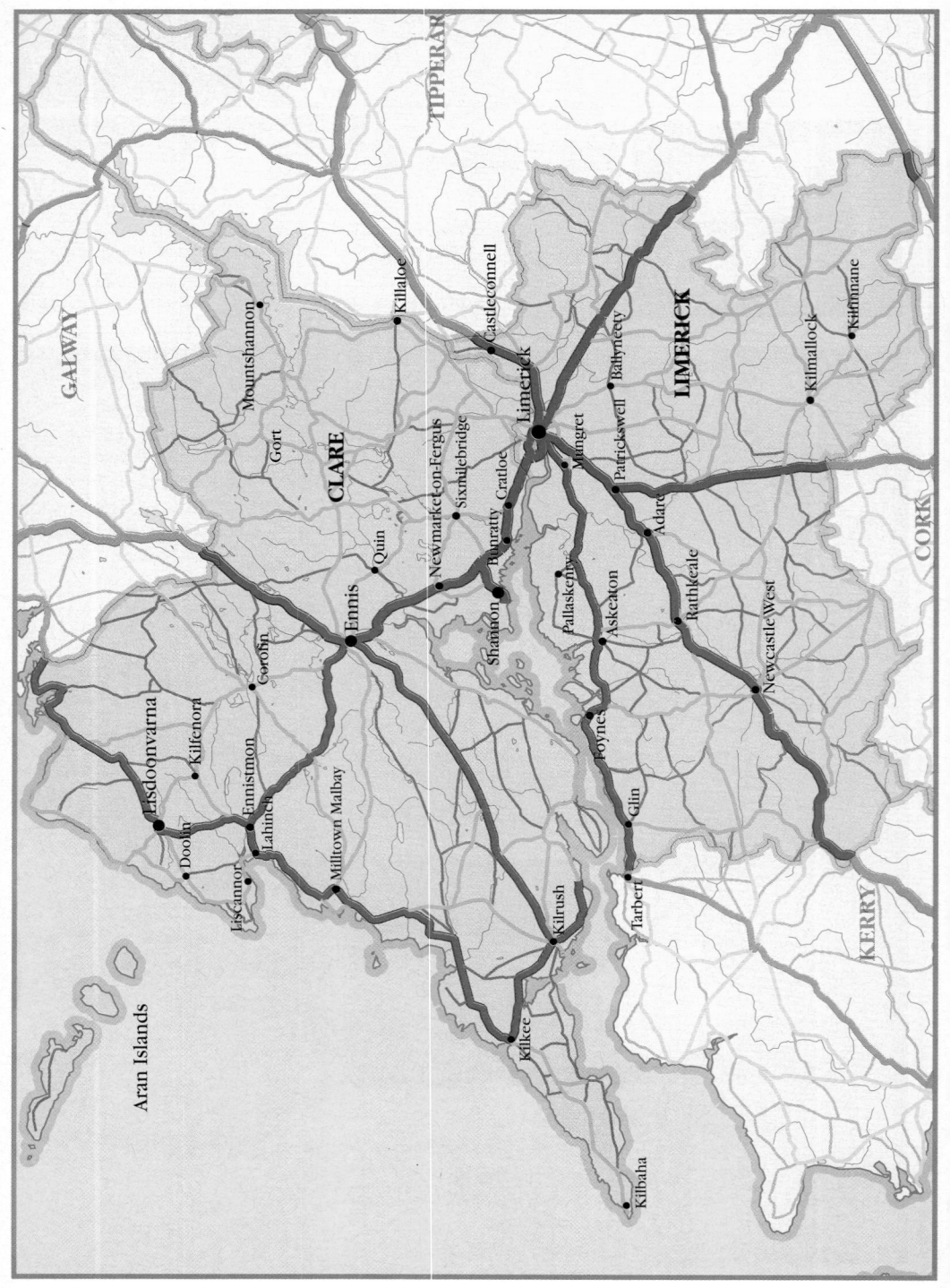

© ERA-Maptec

Ireland's Shannon Region

The Shannon Region comprise counties Clare Limerick, North Tipperary, North Kerry and South Offaly. It is a particularly beautiful part of Ireland and is dominated by water. The Shannon river, the longest river in Ireland or the UK flows through its centre and gives the Region its name. Shannon's Lough Derg - Ireland's pleasure lake - touches on three counties, Clare, Tipperary and Galway. The Region also boasts hundreds of smaller lakes and many rivers.

The Shannon Region has a dramatic Atlantic coastline, with beautiful beaches and a purity of air that refreshes the Region and invigorates the visitor.

Though the Shannon Region is compact , only 100 miles (166 Kms), from end to end, there is tremendous diversity in its scenery from the Slieve Bloom mountains to lakelands, golden beaches, the awesome Cliffs of Moher and the Burren District.

The Region offers great visitor attractions and night-time entertainment options and is also perfect for the activity enthusiast interested in golfing, angling, horse riding, walking, cycling or water based activities.

Area Representatives

CLARE
Mrs. Mary Corcoran, Grange, Wood Road, Cratloe, Co. Clare.
Tel: 061-357389

Mrs. Bernie Cosgrove, St. Judes, Coast Road, Lisdoonvarna,
Co. Clare. Tel: 065-74108

Mrs. Fiona Staunton, Teach Rua, Coor, Edenvale, Ennis, Co. Clare.
Tel: 065-40499.

LIMERICK
Mrs. Mary Dundon, Foxhollow House, Croom Road, Adare,
Co. Limerick.
Tel: 061-396776. Fax: 061-396776.

Mrs. Carole O'Toole, Glen Eagles, 12 Vereker Gardens, Ennis Road,
Limerick, Co. Limerick.
Tel: 061-455521. Fax: 061-455521 (manual)

i Tourist Information Offices

Ennis
Tel: (065) 28366

Limerick City
Tel: (061) 317522

Tralee
Tel: (066) 21288

Shannon Airport
Tel: (061) 471664

Bunratty

Mrs Mary Browne
BUNRATTY LODGE
Bunratty, Co Clare

	Bunratty
OPEN:	March-November
NO. ROOMS:	6
ENSUITE:	6

TEL: **061 369402**   FAX: **061 369363**

Between Castle, Durty Nelly's, Birnbaum/ Erdvig/Frommer/Sullivan Recommended. Breakfast award. Televisions/hairdryers/coffee. Well heated rooms. Airport 10 minutes.

B&B PPS:	**£18.50**	SNGL OCC. DBLE/TPL:	**£33**	SNGL RM:	-
PART BRD:	-	% RED. CHILDREN:	**20%**	DINNER:	-

Bunratty

Bunratty

Mrs Trish Cronin
BRIAR LODGE
Hill Road, Bunratty, Co Clare

	Bunratty
OPEN:	1st March-30th November
NO. ROOMS:	6
ENSUITE:	6

TEL: **061 363388**   FAX: -

Bunratty Castle/Dirty Nelly's 1 Mile. Airport 10 Minutes. Tea/Coffee, Hairdryers, curling irons, rooms. Turn at corner Fitzpatricks hotel. 1 Mile right.

B&B PPS:	**£17**	SNGL OCC. DBLE/TPL:	**£24**	SNGL RM:	-
PART BRD:	-	% RED. CHILDREN:	**25%**	DINNER:	-

Bunratty 1.5km

Bunratty

Mrs. Patricia Darcy
BUNRATTY HEIGHTS
Bunratty, Co Clare

	Bunratty
OPEN:	All Year except Christmas
NO. ROOMS:	4
ENSUITE:	4

TEL: **061 369324**   FAX: -

Morning guests welcome. Airport 10 minutes. Tea/coffe, colour T.V. Take road between Bunratty Castle and Durty Nelly's, 1 km.

B&B PPS:	**£17**	SNGL OCC. DBLE/TPL:	**£23.50**	SNGL RM:	**£16**
PART BRD:	-	% RED. CHILDREN:	**25%**	DINNER:	-

Shannon 6km

Bunratty

T. M. Dennehy
TUDOR LODGE
Hill Road, Bunratty, Co Clare

	Bunratty
OPEN:	March-October
NO. ROOMS:	5
ENSUITE:	5

TEL: **061 362248**   FAX: **061 362569**

Tudor style residence in Sylvan setting. All rooms have private facilities. Bunratty Castle 5 mins walk. Shannon Airport 10 mins drive.

B&B PPS:	**£17.50/£19**	SNGL OCC. DBLE/TPL:	**£25**	SNGL RM:	-
PART BRD:	-	% RED. CHILDREN:	**20%**	DINNER:	-

In Bunratty

Bunratty

Ms Peg Donoghue
CASTLEVIEW
Hill Road, Bunratty, Co Clare

	Bunratty
OPEN:	1st April-31st October
NO. ROOMS:	4
ENSUITE:	2

TEL: **061 364408**   FAX: -

Two storey Country home in picturesque surroundings located 200 metres Bunratty, road between Fitzpatricks' Hotel , Antique Shop/Conference Centre. Airport 10 mins.

B&B PPS:	**£18**	SNGL OCC. DBLE/TPL:	**£25**	SNGL RM:	-
PART BRD:	-	% RED. CHILDREN:	**10%**	DINNER:	-

In Bunratty

Shannon 8km

Mrs. Anne Fuller
LEAVALE
Moyhill, Bunratty, Cratloe, Co Clare

Bunratty

OPEN:	1st April-31st October
NO. ROOMS:	3
ENSUITE:	2

(V)

TEL: **061 357439**   FAX: -

1 mile from Bunratty Castle on N18. Airport 10 minutes. Tea/Coffee facilities. Clock radio, hairdryer, orthopaedic beds, visitors garden.

B&B PPS:	£15/£17	SNGL OCC. DBLE/TPL:	£21.50/23.50	SNGL RM:	-
PART BRD:	-	% RED. CHILDREN:	25%	DINNER:	

In Bunratty

Mrs Margaret Garry
ROCKFIELD HOUSE
Hill Road, Bunratty, Co Clare

Bunratty

OPEN:	All Year except Christmas
NO. ROOMS:	6
ENSUITE:	6

(V)

TEL: **061 364391**   FAX: **061 364391**

Overlooking River. Surrounded by Folk Park. 2 minutes Bunratty Castle & Durty Nelly's. Hairdryer in rooms. Recommended Dillard Causin.

B&B PPS:	£17	SNGL OCC. DBLE/TPL:	£26	SNGL RM:	-
PART BRD:	-	% RED. CHILDREN:	-	DINNER:	-

Bunratty 3km

Teresa Grady
BUNRATTY ARMS
Bunratty, Sixmilebridge, Co Clare

Bunratty

OPEN:	1st February-31st October
NO. ROOMS:	4
ENSUITE:	4

(V)

TEL: **061 369256**   FAX: **061 369256**

R471 off N18 at Hurlers Cross 1 mile, or take road between Castle & Durty Nelly's, at end turn right.

B&B PPS:	£17	SNGL OCC. DBLE/TPL:	£23.50	SNGL RM:	-
PART BRD:	-	% RED. CHILDREN:	20%	DINNER:	-

Mrs Sheila Hanrahan
THE CROOKED CHIMNEY
Hurlers Cross, Bunratty, Co Clare

Bunratty

OPEN:	1st January-20th December
NO. ROOMS:	5
ENSUITE:	5

(V)

TEL: **061 364696**   FAX: **061 364696**   EMAIL: **bikeirl@iol.ie**

Off the main road (N18). Purpose built house, 3 miles Shannon Airport, 2 miles Bunratty. Private gardens for guest viewing.

B&B PPS:	£17	SNGL OCC. DBLE/TPL:	£23.50/£25	SNGL RM:	£16/£22
PART BRD:	-	% RED. CHILDREN:	10%	DINNER:	-

Shannon 3km

Shannon 2km

Mrs Maureen McCabe
BUNRATTY HILLSIDE
Clonmoney North, Bunratty, Co Clare

Bunratty

OPEN:	1st March-15th November
NO. ROOMS:	6
ENSUITE:	4

(V)

TEL: **061 364330**   FAX: **061 364330**   EMAIL: **fbb@iol.ie**

Morning guests welcome. Dillard/Causin recommended. Tea/coffee facilities. Airport 10 mins Bunratty 2 km, off N18 at Sixmilebridge R471.

B&B PPS:	£15/£17	SNGL OCC. DBLE/TPL:	£21.50/£23.50	SNGL RM:	-
PART BRD:	-	% RED. CHILDREN:	20%	DINNER:	-

Bunratty 1km

Mrs Imelda McCarthy
INNISFREE
Bunratty, Co Clare

Bunratty

OPEN:	1st March-30th November
NO. ROOMS:	4
ENSUITE:	3

TEL: **061 369773**   FAX: -

Airport 10 mins. Road between Castle/Durty Nelly's. Ground floor rooms, tea/coffee facilities, Hairdryers. Frommer Readers recommended. Breakfast menu.

(V)

B&B PPS:	**£15/£17**	SNGL OCC. DBLE/TPL:	**£21.50/£25**	SNGL RM:	-
PART BRD:	-	% RED. CHILDREN:	**25%**	DINNER:	-

In Bunratty

Paula McInerney
RIVERSIDE B&B
Clonmoney West, Bunratty, Co Clare

Bunratty

OPEN:	All Year
NO. ROOMS:	3
ENSUITE:	3

TEL: **061 364148**   FAX: -

New custom built B&B on main dual carriage-way to Shannon. 0.5km to Bunratty, breakfast menu. Shannon Airport 7 mins.

(V)

B&B PPS:	**£17**	SNGL OCC. DBLE/TPL:	**£23.50**	SNGL RM:	-
PART BRD:	-	% RED. CHILDREN:	**20%**	DINNER:	-

Shannon 6km

Mrs Mary McKenna
GALLOW'S VIEW
Bunratty East, Co Clare

Bunratty

OPEN:	15th February/15th December
NO. ROOMS:	5
ENSUITE:	5

TEL: **061 369125**   FAX: -

Road between Castle/Durty Nellies, through car park 6th house on right. Frommer recommended. Airport 10 mins. TV, hairdryers, tea/coffee.

(V)

B&B PPS:	**£17**	SNGL OCC. DBLE/TPL:	**£25**	SNGL RM:	-
PART BRD:	-	% RED. CHILDREN:	**20%**	DINNER:	-

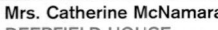

Bunratty 1.5km

Mrs. Catherine McNamara
DEERFIELD HOUSE
Sixmilebridge, Deerpark, Bunratty, Co Clare

Bunratty

OPEN:	30th April-30th October
NO. ROOMS:	3
ENSUITE:	3

TEL: **061 369262**   FAX: -

Situated peaceful country setting. Road between Bunratty Castle, Durty Nelly's. Airport 10 mins. Right at end road, first left, 5th house

(V)

B&B PPS:	**£17**	SNGL OCC. DBLE/TPL:	**£23.50**	SNGL RM:	-
PART BRD:	-	% RED. CHILDREN:	**50%**	DINNER:	-

Bunratty 2km

Mrs Margaret Mulkeen
HILL VIEW
Hill Road, Bunratty, Co Clare

Bunratty

OPEN:	All Year except Christmas
NO. ROOMS:	3
ENSUITE:	3

TEL: **061 364824**   FAX: **061 364824**

From Airport left at Hurlers Cross Limerick Road. N18 .25 mile turn right. From Bunratty take Hill Road 1 mile.

(V)

B&B PPS:	**£17**	SNGL OCC. DBLE/TPL:	**£23.50**	SNGL RM:	-
PART BRD:	-	% RED. CHILDREN:	**20%**	DINNER:	-

Mrs Majella Mullane
ASHFORD HOUSE
Cloghlea, Bunratty, Sixmilebridge, Co Clare

Bunratty

OPEN:	1st March-31st October
NO. ROOMS:	3
ENSUITE:	3

 (V)

TEL: 061 369600   FAX: 061 369907   EMAIL: mullanej@iol.ie

Luxurious home. All rooms have separate exit door. TV, hairdryer, clock radio. Take road between Castle and Durty Nellies.

B&B PPS:	£17	SNGL OCC. DBLE/TPL:	£24	SNGL RM:	-
PART BRD:	-	% RED. CHILDREN:	20%	DINNER:	-

— Shannon Town 8km —

Mrs Anne Nash
CLOVER HILL LODGE
Bunratty, Co Clare

Bunratty

OPEN:	1st April-31st October
NO. ROOMS:	4
ENSUITE:	4

(V)

TEL: 061 369039   FAX: 061 360520

Between Castle, Durty Nelly's. Luxury home. AA. Internet recommended. Breakfast menu. TV/hairdryers all rooms. Orthopaedic beds. Airport 10 minutes.

B&B PPS:	£17	SNGL OCC. DBLE/TPL:	£26	SNGL RM:	-
PART BRD:	-	% RED. CHILDREN:	20%	DINNER:	-

— Bunratty 1.5km —

Concepta O'Connor
PARK HOUSE
Folk Park Road, Bunratty, Co Clare

Bunratty

OPEN:	1st April-31st October
NO. ROOMS:	6
ENSUITE:	6

(V)

TEL: 061 369902   FAX: -

Purpose built luxurious home. Spacious bedrooms with TV's, hairdryers, clock radios. Breakfast menu. Airport 10 mins. Bunratty Castle 2 mins.

B&B PPS:	£17	SNGL OCC. DBLE/TPL:	£23.50	SNGL RM:	-
PART BRD:	-	% RED. CHILDREN:	25%	DINNER:	-

— Shannon 6km —

Mrs Marie Therese Quinn
CASTLESIDE
Bunratty East, Bunratty, Co Clare

Bunratty

OPEN:	1st March-25th November
NO. ROOMS:	4
ENSUITE:	-

(V)

TEL: 061 369390   FAX: -

Country home, situated 1 mile Bunratty Castle, Folk Park. Take Winery road from Castle Car park, third B/B on right.

B&B PPS:	£15	SNGL OCC. DBLE/TPL:	£21.50	SNGL RM:	-
PART BRD:	-	% RED. CHILDREN:	25%	DINNER:	-

— Bunratty 1.5km —

Mrs Mary Rohan
BUNRATTY VILLA
Bunratty East, Bunratty, Co Clare

Bunratty

OPEN:	1st March-31st October
NO. ROOMS:	5
ENSUITE:	5

(V)

TEL: 061 369241   FAX: 061 369241

Convenient Shannon-Limerick, 10 minutes walk Bunratty Castle. Take road between Bunratty Castle and Durty Nelly's, first house on right

B&B PPS:	£17	SNGL OCC. DBLE/TPL:	£23.50	SNGL RM:	-
PART BRD:	-	% RED. CHILDREN:	25%	DINNER:	-

— Shannon 6km —

Bunratty 2km

Sheila Tiernan
ASHGROVE HOUSE
Bunratty, Co Clare

Bunratty

OPEN:	All Year except Christmas
NO. ROOMS:	4
ENSUITE:	4

 (V)

TEL: **061 369332**   FAX: -

3 mins drive Bunratty Castle/Folk Park. 10 mins Shannon Airport . 3 mins drive Durty Nellies. Private entrances, road between Castle & Durty Nellies.

B&B PPS:	£17/£17.50	SNGL. OCC. DBLE/TPL:	£23.50/£25	SNGL RM:	-
PART BRD:	-	% RED. CHILDREN:	25%	DINNER:	-

Bunratty 1km

Mrs Eileen Woulfe
SHANNON VIEW
Bunratty, Co Clare

Bunratty

OPEN:	17th March-30th November
NO. ROOMS:	6
ENSUITE:	6

(V)

TEL: **061 364056**   FAX: **061 364056**

Bungalow on N 18 Shannon - Limerick road. Galtee breakfast winner. Tea/coffee making facilities in all rooms. Guests lounge.

B&B PPS:	£17.50	SNGL. OCC. DBLE/TPL:	£24	SNGL RM:	-
PART BRD:	-	% RED. CHILDREN:	-	DINNER:	-

Kinvara 4km

Mrs Anne Martin
VILLA MARIA
Leagh South, Burren, Co Clare

Burren

OPEN:	Easter-October
NO. ROOMS:	5
ENSUITE:	3

(V)

TEL: **065 78019**   FAX: -

Overlooking Galway Bay. Quiet area Panoramic Burren setting. Information on Burren available, Irish Music, excellent seafood locally. Smoke free home.

BUS NO:

B&B PPS:	£15/£17	SNGL. OCC. DBLE/TPL:	£21.50/£23.50	SNGL RM:	-
PART BRD:	£180	% RED. CHILDREN:	20%	DINNER:	£12

In Corofin Village

Mrs Maura Clancy
RIVERBANK HOUSE
Bridge Street, Corofin, Co Clare

Corofin

OPEN:	All Year except Christmas
NO. ROOMS:	3
ENSUITE:	3

(V)

TEL: **065 37060**   FAX: **065 37060**

"A resting place for weary travellers." Four poster beds/open fireplaces/hairdryers/electric blankets/laundry service/breakfast menu. Airport 45 Minutes.

B&B PPS:	£17	SNGL. OCC. DBLE/TPL:	£23.50	SNGL RM:	-
PART BRD:	-	% RED. CHILDREN:	25%	DINNER:	-

In Corofin

Mrs Mary Cleary
LAKEFIELD LODGE
Ennis Road, Corofin, Co Clare

Corofin

OPEN:	1st April-31st October
NO. ROOMS:	4
ENSUITE:	4

(V)

TEL: **065 37675**   FAX: **065 37299**

On periphery of Burren national park, heart of Lake District. Cliffs of Moher, Shannon Airport 30 minutes. Traditional music. Tea/Coffee facilities.

B&B PPS:	£17/£17.50	SNGL. OCC. DBLE/TPL:	£24/£25	SNGL RM:	-
PART BRD:	£195	% RED. CHILDREN:	33%	DINNER:	£14

Corofin 1.5km

Mary & Michael Corbett
KILLEEN HOUSE
Killeen, Corofin, Co Clare

Corofin

OPEN:	**1st April-31st October**
NO. ROOMS:	3
ENSUITE:	2

(V)

TEL: **065 37329** FAX: -

Luxury accommodation, tea/coffee on arrival, private TV lounge. Close Burren National Park, Ailwee Caves, Cliffs of Moher, fishing locally.

B&B PPS:	**£15/£17**	SNGL OCC. DBLE/TPL:	**£21.50/£23.50**	SNGL RM:	-
PART BRD:	-	% RED. CHILDREN:	**33%**	DINNER:	-

Corofin 1.5km

Mrs Theresa Fogarty
COTTAGE VIEW
Kilnaboy, Corofin, Ennis, Co Clare

Corofin

OPEN:	**3rd April-23rd October**
NO. ROOMS:	3
ENSUITE:	2

(V)

TEL: **065 37662** FAX: -

Spacious modern bungalow overlooking Lake Inchiquin on edge of Burren. Ideal touring base. Home cooked meals, open fire in lounge.

B&B PPS:	**£15/£17**	SNGL OCC. DBLE/TPL:	**£21.50/£23.50**	SNGL RM:	£17
PART BRD:	£180	% RED. CHILDREN:	**50%**	DINNER:	£12

Corofin 3km

Thomas and Rita Kierce
BURREN HOUSE
Kilnaboy, Corofin, Co Clare

Corofin

OPEN:	**17th March-31st October**
NO. ROOMS:	3
ENSUITE:	2

(V)

TEL: **065 37143** FAX: -

Spacious house with Burren countryside views on R476 route. Convenient to Lake District, Burren National Park. Tea/Coffee facilities

B&B PPS:	**£15/£17**	SNGL OCC. DBLE/TPL:	**£21.50/23.50**	SNGL RM:	-
PART BRD:	-	% RED. CHILDREN:	**25%**	DINNER:	£13

Limerick 6km

Mrs Mary Corcoran
GRANGE
Wood Road, Cratloe, Co Clare

Cratloe near Bunratty

OPEN:	**All Year**
NO. ROOMS:	4
ENSUITE:	2

(V)

TEL: **061 357389** FAX: - EMAIL: **alfie@iol.ie**

Off N18 at Limerick Inn. Hotel, Airport 15 minutes, Limerick 8 minutes. Morning guests welcome. Frommer, Lonely Planet recommended. Electric blankets.

B&B PPS:	**£15/£17**	SNGL OCC. DBLE/TPL:	**£21.50/£23.50**	SNGL RM:	-
PART BRD:	£180	% RED. CHILDREN:	**20%**	DINNER:	£12

Bunratty 2km

Mrs. Carmel O'Ryan
SUNNYBANK
Ballymorris, Cratloe, Co Clare

Cratloe near Bunratty

OPEN:	**1st April-31st October**
NO. ROOMS:	4
ENSUITE:	3

(V)

TEL: **061 357108** FAX: -

House 400 yards Limerick - Shannon road at Ballymorris. Comfortable T.V lounge with peat fires. Traditional music, Bunratty 1.5 mile

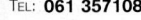

B&B PPS:	**£15/£17**	SNGL OCC. DBLE/TPL:	**£21.50/£23.50**	SNGL RM:	-
PART BRD:	-	% RED. CHILDREN:	**25%**	DINNER:	-

Limerick City 8km

Anne Phelan
KEELWOOD HOUSE
Cratloe, Co Clare

	Cratloe

OPEN:	All Year except Christmas	
NO. ROOMS:	3	
ENSUITE:	3	

TEL: **061 357496**   FAX: **061 357496**

House set in private woodlands, ideally located for touring Bunratty, Clare, Limerick Region. 2km off N18, Limerick Inn, traditional music.

B&B PPS:	£17	SNGL OCC. DBLE/TPL:	£23.50	SNGL RM:	-
PART BRD:	-	% RED. CHILDREN:	25%	DINNER:	-

Limerick 9km

Michael and Joan Quinn
CRATLOE HEIGHTS
Ballymorris, Cratloe, Co Clare

	Cratloe near Bunratty

OPEN:	1st May-1st November	
NO. ROOMS:	3	
ENSUITE:	1	

TEL: **061 357253**   FAX: -

Bungalow with panoramic view. "Lonely Planet" recommended. 500 yds off N18. Shannon 10 minutes, Limerick 10 minutes. Horse riding. Ringfort. Collection old machinery

B&B PPS:	£15/£17	SNGL OCC. DBLE/TPL:	£21.50/£23.50	SNGL RM:	£20/£22
PART BRD:	-	% RED. CHILDREN:	25%	DINNER:	-

Lisdoonvarna 2km

Mrs Kathleen Cullinan
HARBOUR VIEW
Doolin, Co Clare

	Doolin

OPEN:	20th February-31st October	
NO. ROOMS:	4	
ENSUITE:	4	

TEL: **065 74154**   FAX: -

Home, beautiful setting. Ideal for visiting the Burren, Cliffs of Moher and the Aran Islands. Airport 1 hour. Hairdryers, electric blankets.

B&B PPS:	£17	SNGL OCC. DBLE/TPL:	£23.50	SNGL RM:	-
PART BRD:	-	% RED. CHILDREN:	-	DINNER:	£13

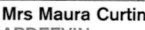

Doolin 4km

Mrs Maura Curtin
ARDEEVIN
Caherkinalla, Doolin, Co Clare

	Doolin

OPEN:	1st May-30th September	
NO. ROOMS:	4	
ENSUITE:	3	

TEL: **065 74094**   FAX: -

Family bungalow, 2KM off R478 signposted at Statoil shop on Cliffs of Moher Road. Burren, Aran Ferry, panoramic view, peaceful.

B&B PPS:	£15/£17	SNGL OCC. DBLE/TPL:	£21.50/£23.50	SNGL RM:	-
PART BRD:	-	% RED. CHILDREN:	33%	DINNER:	-

In Doolin

Susan Daly
DALY'S HOUSE
Doolin, Co Clare

	Doolin

OPEN:	All Year	
NO. ROOMS:	4	
ENSUITE:	4	

TEL: **065 74242**   FAX: **065 74668**

Situated 150 yards from Doolin Village. Panoramic views of the Sea and Cliffs of Moher. Family run traditional B&c

B&B PPS:	£17	SNGL OCC. DBLE/TPL:	-	SNGL RM:	£20
PART BRD:	-	% RED. CHILDREN:	50%	DINNER:	-

Doolin 2km

Brid and Val Egan
ATLANTIC SUNSET HOUSE
Cliffs of Moher Road, Doolin, Co Clare

OPEN:	1st January-23rd December	
NO. ROOMS:	6	
ENSUITE:	6	

(V)

TEL: **065 74080**   FAX: -

Warm hospitable home near Cliffs of Moher, Burren, Aran Ferry, traditional music. Peat fires. Hairdryers. Elsie Dillard recommended. Airport 1hr.

B&B PPS:	**£17**	SNGL OCC. DBLE/TPL:	**£23.50**	SNGL RM:	-
PART BRD:	-	% RED. CHILDREN:	**20%**	DINNER:	**£12**

Doolin Village

Mrs Maeve Fitzgerald
CHURCHFIELD
Doolin, Co Clare

Doolin

OPEN:	1st January-20th December	
NO. ROOMS:	6	
ENSUITE:	5	

(V)

TEL: **065 74209**   FAX: **065 74622**

House at Doolin P.O. Rooms with view of Cliffs of Moher, sea and countryside. Traditional music, Burren. Frommer recommended. Breakfast menu.

B&B PPS:	**£15/£18**	SNGL OCC. DBLE/TPL:	**£22.50/£26**	SNGL RM:	-
PART BRD:	-	% RED. CHILDREN:	**33.3%**	DINNER:	**£12**

In Doolin

John D Flanagan
BALLYVARA HOUSE
Ballyvara, Doolin, Co Clare

Doolin

OPEN:	All Year except Christmas	
NO. ROOMS:	4	
ENSUITE:	4	

(V)

TEL: **065 74467**   FAX: **065 74868**   EMAIL: **bvara@iol.ie**

19th Century Farm cottage remodelled by owner, traditional music, Burren. Cliffs Moher, Aran Ferries. Quiet setting on R479. Airport 1 hr.

B&B PPS:	**£17/£20**	SNGL OCC. DBLE/TPL:	**£23.50/£27**	SNGL RM:	-
PART BRD:	-	% RED. CHILDREN:	**50%**	DINNER:	-

Lisdoonvarna 7km

Mrs Caitriona J Garrahy
RIVERFIELD HOUSE
Doolin, Co Clare

Doolin

OPEN:	All Year	
NO. ROOMS:	4	
ENSUITE:	3	

(V)

TEL: **065 74113**   FAX: -

Century-old reconstructed home. Five minutes walking to all pubs and restaurants. Family room, Credit Cards, Airport 1 hour. Family run.

B&B PPS:	**£15/£17**	SNGL OCC. DBLE/TPL:	**£21.50/£23.50**	SNGL RM:	-
PART BRD:	-	% RED. CHILDREN:	**25%**	DINNER:	-

Doolin

Mrs Darra Hughes
SEA VIEW HOUSE
Fisher Street, Doolin, Co Clare

Doolin

OPEN:	All Year except Christmas	
NO. ROOMS:	4	
ENSUITE:	4	

(V)

TEL: **065 74826**   FAX: -

Luxury accommodation overlooking Atlantic Ocean., warm friendly welcome, extensive breakfast menu. Walking distance to pubs, restaurants, Aran Ferry. Airport 1 hr.

B&B PPS:	**£17/£18**	SNGL OCC. DBLE/TPL:	-	SNGL RM:	-
PART BRD:	-	% RED. CHILDREN:	**20%**	DINNER:	-

Lisdoonvarna 6km

Marian & Martin McDonagh
GLASHA MEADOWS
Glasha, Doolin, Co Clare

Doolin	
OPEN:	All Year except Christmas
NO. ROOMS:	6
ENSUITE:	6

TEL: **065 74443**   FAX: -

Modern bungalow situated on Coast Road. 1.5 km. from Doolin village. Six bedrooms ensuite with private car park and T.V. lounge.

B&B PPS:	£17	SNGL OCC. DBLE/TPL:	£23.50	SNGL RM:	-
PART BRD:	-	% RED. CHILDREN:	30%	DINNER:	-

Lisdoonvarna 6km

Miss Ann Mitchell
BURREN WAY COTTAGE
Doolin, Co Clare

Doolin	
OPEN:	1st March-10th November
NO. ROOMS:	3
ENSUITE:	-

TEL: **065 74516**   FAX: -

Warm welcome to traditional cosy cottage with turf fire, electric blankets, Orthopaedic beds & extensive breakfast menu. Shannon Airport 1 Hr

B&B PPS:	£16	SNGL OCC. DBLE/TPL:	£22.50	SNGL RM:	£20.50
PART BRD:	-	% RED. CHILDREN:	20%	DINNER:	-

In Doolin

Mary Jo O'Connell
SEASCAPE B&B
Roadford, Doolin, Co Clare

Doolin	
OPEN:	All Year
NO. ROOMS:	4
ENSUITE:	4

TEL: **065 74451**   FAX: -

Located on a quiet cul-de-sac in the heart of Doolin. Close to pubs, Burren, Cliffs of Moher, Aran Islands ferries.

B&B PPS:	£17/£18	SNGL OCC. DBLE/TPL:	£23.50/£28	SNGL RM:	-
PART BRD:	-	% RED. CHILDREN:	33%	DINNER:	-

Doolin Village 2km

Mr Frank Roche
WESTFIELD HOUSE
Carnane, Doolin, Co Clare

Doolin	
OPEN:	1st April-30th September
NO. ROOMS:	4
ENSUITE:	4

TEL: **065 74192**   FAX: **065 74192**

Warm, comfortable, modern bungalow. Situated in scenic peaceful location on R 478. Traditional music, Aran Ferry. Orthopaedic beds, good food.

B&B PPS:	£17	SNGL OCC. DBLE/TPL:	£23.50	SNGL RM:	-
PART BRD:	-	% RED. CHILDREN:	50%	DINNER:	-

Doolin 3km

John and Anne Sims
ISLAND VIEW
Cliffs of Moher Road, Doolin, Co Clare

Doolin	
OPEN:	April-October
NO. ROOMS:	4
ENSUITE:	3

TEL: **065 74346**   FAX: **065 74844**   EMAIL: **lisdoon@iol.ie**

"Lonely Planet", "Le Guide du Routard" recommended. Warm welcome, Breakfast menu, Orthopaedic beds. Transport to pubs. Tea/scones on arrival.

B&B PPS:	£15/£17	SNGL OCC. DBLE/TPL:	£21.50/£23.50	SNGL RM:	-
PART BRD:	£190	% RED. CHILDREN:	33%	DINNER:	£13

Ennis 1km

Mrs Margaret Barry
EYREDEMESNE
Beechpark, Ennis, Co Clare

Ennis

OPEN:	1st April-30th September
NO. ROOMS:	4
ENSUITE:	4

TEL: **065 29863** FAX: -

Luxury hospitable family home on one acre of landscaped gardens, adjacent Golf Course, Showgrounds on main Milltown-Malbay Road.

B&B PPS:	£17	SNGL OCC. DBLE/TPL:	£23.50	SNGL RM:	-
PART BRD:	-	% RED. CHILDREN:	33.3%	DINNER:	-

In Ennis Town

Mrs Martina Brennan
CLONEEN
Clonroad, Ennis, Co Clare

Ennis

OPEN:	April-October
NO. ROOMS:	3
ENSUITE:	1

TEL: **065 29681** FAX: -

Town centre, bus station, 5 minutes walk. Convenient to Airport, Craggaunowen, Burren. Spacious garden. Clonroad leads to Quin and Tulla

B&B PPS:	£15/£17	SNGL OCC. DBLE/TPL:	£21.50/£23.50	SNGL RM:	-
PART BRD:	-	% RED. CHILDREN:	20%	DINNER:	-

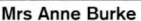
Ennis 2km

Mrs Anne Burke
CASA MARIA
Loughville, Lahinch Road, Ennis, Co Clare

Ennis

OPEN:	Easter-31st October
NO. ROOMS:	3
ENSUITE:	2

TEL: **065 20395** FAX: -

Easy access, friendly, opposite Statoil station on N85 route. Cliffs, Burren, Ennis, 3 minutes drive. Shannon 25 minutes. Extensive parking.

B&B PPS:	£15/£17	SNGL OCC. DBLE/TPL:	£21.50/£23.50	SNGL RM:	-
PART BRD:	-	% RED. CHILDREN:	20%	DINNER:	-

Ennis 2km

Mrs Phinula Cahill
RICMAR
Rockmount, Ennis, Co Clare

Ennis

OPEN:	All Year
NO. ROOMS:	4
ENSUITE:	3

TEL: **065 20242** FAX: -

Family home on own grounds. Golf courses in area, Fishing nearby. Shannon, Cliffs of Moher half hour drive.

B&B PPS:	£15/£17	SNGL OCC. DBLE/TPL:	£21.50	SNGL RM:	-
PART BRD:	£180	% RED. CHILDREN:	20%	DINNER:	£13

Ennis 2km

Mrs Bernie Canny
SUNVILLE
Claureen, Lahinch Road, Ennis, Co Clare

Ennis

OPEN:	All Year except Christmas
NO. ROOMS:	5
ENSUITE:	1

TEL: **065 28661** FAX: -

Bungalow. TV lounge, Open fire. Route N85 to Cliffs of Moher, Burren. 20 mins Shannon Airport, medieval banquets, traditional music.

B&B PPS:	£15/£17	SNGL OCC. DBLE/TPL:	£21.50	SNGL RM:	-
PART BRD:	-	% RED. CHILDREN:	-	DINNER:	-

Ennis 1.5km

Mrs Josephine Clune		**Ennis**	
CLARE MANOR HOUSE			
Clare Road, Ennis, Co Clare		Open: **All Year**	
		No. Rooms: **6**	
		Ensuite: **6**	

Tel: **065 20701**   Fax: -

On N18 route, morning guests welcome. Shannon 20 mins drive, convenient to Bunratty, Burren, Cliffs of Moher, golf, fishing.

B&B PPS:	£17/£17.50	Sngl Occ. Dble/Tpl:	£23.50/£24	Sngl Rm:	-
Part Brd:	-	% Red. Children:	-	Dinner:	£18

Ennis 1km

Mrs Mary Connole		**Ennis**	
SHANLEE			
Lahinch Road, Ennis, Co Clare		Open: **All Year**	
		No. Rooms: **4**	
		Ensuite: **2**	(V)

Tel: **065 40270**   Fax: -

Modern comfortable home, 20 minutes, Shannon Airport. Convenient Burren, Cliffs of Moher, golf, fishing, traditional music, banquets. Morning guests welcome.

B&B PPS:	£15/£17	Sngl Occ. Dble/Tpl:	£21.50/£23.50	Sngl Rm:	£17/£18
Part Brd:	-	% Red. Children:	50%	Dinner:	£12

Ennis 2km

Mrs Teresa Crowe		**Ennis**	
SHALOM			
Ballybeg, Killadysert Road, Ennis, Co Clare		Open: **1st May-1st October**	
		No. Rooms: **3**	
		Ensuite: **2**	

Tel: **065 29494**   Fax: -

Easy accesable home-all rooms on ground floor, two with spacious private bathrooms. Quiet setting, convenient to Town and attractions.

B&B PPS:	£15/£17	Sngl Occ. Dble/Tpl:	-	Sngl Rm:	£20
Part Brd:	-	% Red. Children:	50%	Dinner:	-

In Ennis

Judy Dowling		**Ennis**	
SYCAMORE			
Tulla Road, Ennis, Co Clare		Open: **1st March-30th November**	
		No. Rooms: **3**	
		Ensuite: **3**	(V)

Tel: **065 21343**   Fax: -

Luxurious accommodation 6 mins walk town centre. TV/radio/tea/coffee in bedrooms. 20 mins Shannon Airport. Ideal touring base.

B&B PPS:	£17	Sngl Occ. Dble/Tpl:	£23.50	Sngl Rm:	-
Part Brd:	-	% Red. Children:	25%	Dinner:	-

Ennis 2km

Mrs Mary Finlay		**Ennis**	
CLONRUSH			
Lahinch Road, Ennis, Co Clare		Open: **1st February-1st November**	
		No. Rooms: **6**	
		Ensuite: **4**	(V)

Tel: **065 29692**   Fax: -

Easy to find, hard to leave, ideal touring base, Cliffs of Moher, Burren, Bunratty Castle, golf, beaches. 20 minutes Airport.

B&B PPS:	£16/£17	Sngl Occ. Dble/Tpl:	£22.50/£23.50	Sngl Rm:	£15/£22
Part Brd:	-	% Red. Children:	50%	Dinner:	-

The Finn Family

Ennis

Ennis 1km

DRUIMIN
Golf Links Road, Ennis, Co Clare

OPEN:	1st April-30th September	
NO. ROOMS:	4	
ENSUITE:	4	

TEL: **065 24183**   FAX: **065 24183**

Tranquil setting beside Golf Club on R474, with Peat Fire and Award Winning Breakfasts. We like it here, so will you.

B&B PPS:	**£17**	SNGL OCC. DBLE/TPL:	**£23.50**	SNGL RM:	-
PART BRD:	-	% RED. CHILDREN:	-	DINNER:	-

Mrs Mary Finucane

Ennis

Ennis 1km

MOYVILLE
Lahinch Road, Ennis, Co Clare

OPEN:	March-November	
NO. ROOMS:	4	
ENSUITE:	4	

TEL: **065 28278**   FAX: **065 28278**

Spacious comfortable home on N85 to the Burren. Cliffs of Moher. Golf, fishing, entertainment locally. Electric blankets, hairdryers in rooms.

B&B PPS:	**£17**	SNGL OCC. DBLE/TPL:	**£23.50**	SNGL RM:	-
PART BRD:	-	% RED. CHILDREN:	**33%**	DINNER:	**£12**

Maureen Flynn

Ennis

Ennis 1km

AISLING GHEAL
St Flannan's Cross, Limerick Road, Ennis, Co Clare

OPEN:	All Year	
NO. ROOMS:	6	
ENSUITE:	6	

TEL: **065 23810**   FAX: **065 29399**

Purpose built guesthouse. Six luxury ensuite bedrooms with all facilities. Ideally located just off main Limerick - Galway Rd, close Airport.

B&B PPS:	**£17/£18**	SNGL OCC. DBLE/TPL:	**£23.50/£25**	SNGL RM:	-
PART BRD:	-	% RED. CHILDREN:	**33%**	DINNER:	-

Sean & Teresa Grogan

Ennis

Ennis 4km

ST PATRICK'S
Corebeg, Doora, Ennis, Co Clare

OPEN:	All Year	
NO. ROOMS:	3	
ENSUITE:	2	

TEL: **065 40122**   FAX: **065 40122 (man)**

Quiet scenic area Ideal location for Knappogue, Bunratty, Cragganowen, Burren, Cliffs of Moher, golfing, fishing, traditional music. Morning visitors welcome.

B&B PPS:	**£15/£17**	SNGL OCC. DBLE/TPL:	**£21.50/£23.50**	SNGL RM:	-
PART BRD:	**£180**	% RED. CHILDREN:	**20%**	DINNER:	**£12**

Mrs Geraldine Halloran

Ennis

Ennis 6km

ROSEHAVEN
Ennis Rd, Ruan, Ennis, Co Clare

OPEN:	All Year	
NO. ROOMS:	3	
ENSUITE:	2	

TEL: **065 37867**   FAX: **065 37933**

In Ruan Village. From Ennis turn off N18 at Ballyalla Fishing, Burren 4KM, Cliffs/Caves, tea/coffee facilities.

B&B PPS:	**£15/£17**	SNGL OCC. DBLE/TPL:	**£21.50/£23.50**	SNGL RM:	-
PART BRD:	**£184**	% RED. CHILDREN:	**33.3%**	DINNER:	**£12**

In Ennis

Mrs. Maura Healy
BROOKVILLE HOUSE
Tobartaoscan, Off Limerick Road, Ennis, Co Clare

Ennis

OPEN:	1st March-30th November
NO. ROOMS:	3
ENSUITE:	2

(V)

TEL: 065 29802   FAX: -

Tranquil location, garden. Bus station, town 10 mins walk, adjacent West Co. Hotel, Golf courses. Airport, Cliffs, Castles 30 mins.

B&B PPS:	£16/£18	SNGL. OCC. DBLE/TPL:	£22.50/£24.50	SNGL RM:	£20
PART BRD:	-	% RED. CHILDREN:	20%	DINNER:	£12

Ennis 1km

Liz & Peter Houlihan
GLENCAR HOUSE
Galway Rd., Ennis, Co Clare

Ennis

OPEN:	All Year except Christmas
NO. ROOMS:	6
ENSUITE:	6

(V)

TEL: 065 22348   FAX: 065 22348

Situated on Galway Rd (N18). 1 km from Ennis Town Centre, 20 m from Auburn Lodge Hotel. 20 min Shannon Airport. Convenient Burren.

B&B PPS:	£17	SNGL. OCC. DBLE/TPL:	£23.50	SNGL RM:	£20
PART BRD:	-	% RED. CHILDREN:	50%	DINNER:	-

Ennis 2.5km

Mary Keary
RYE HILL
Roslevan, Tulla Road, Ennis, Co Clare

Ennis

OPEN:	1st January-20th December
NO. ROOMS:	6
ENSUITE:	6

(V)

TEL: 065 24313   FAX: -

Family run business, peaceful area, convenient to Shannon Airport, Foodstore, Filling Station on site. Visa/Access accepted. All rooms ensuite.

B&B PPS:	£17/£19.50	SNGL. OCC. DBLE/TPL:	£23.50/£26	SNGL RM:	£19.50
PART BRD:	-	% RED. CHILDREN:	50%	DINNER:	£12

In Ennis

John & Kathleen Kenneally
WILLBROOK HOUSE
Tulla Road, Ennis, Co Clare

Ennis

OPEN:	All Year
NO. ROOMS:	3
ENSUITE:	2

(V)

TEL: 065 20782   FAX: -

12 minutes walk town. Early morning callers welcome. Convenient Restaurants, Pubs, Cliffs of Moher, Medieval Banquets, Shannon Airport (20 mins).

B&B PPS:	£15/£17	SNGL. OCC. DBLE/TPL:	£21.50/£23.50	SNGL RM:	-
PART BRD:	-	% RED. CHILDREN:	50%	DINNER:	-

Ennis

Mrs Joan Kilcawley
CAMELOT
Kilrush Road, Ennis, Co Clare

Ennis

OPEN:	1st April-30th September
NO. ROOMS:	4
ENSUITE:	2

(V)

TEL: 065 24093   FAX: -

"Spend a shining moment in Camelot" on Killimer Car Ferry Rd., walking distance of town. Route 68. Convenient to Airport.

B&B PPS:	£15/£17	SNGL. OCC. DBLE/TPL:	-	SNGL RM:	-
PART BRD:	-	% RED. CHILDREN:	20%	DINNER:	-

Ennis 1km

Mrs Maureen Langan
ST ANNES
Limerick Road, Ennis, Co Clare

OPEN:	1st March-12th December
No. ROOMS:	3
ENSUITE:	3

TEL: **065 28501**   FAX: -

On (N18), Airport 20 mins. Adjacent West Co. Hotel. Convenient Cliffs of Moher, Burren, golf, tea/facilities, T.V. hairdryers, bedrooms.

B&B PPS:	**£17**	SNGL OCC. DBLE/TPL:	**£23.50**	SNGL RM:	-
PART BRD:	-	% RED. CHILDREN:	-	DINNER:	-

In Ennis

Mrs Sheelagh Lynch
ARDLANN
6 Fernhill, Galway Road, Ennis, Co Clare

Ennis

OPEN:	All Year except Christmas
No. ROOMS:	3
ENSUITE:	1

TEL: **065 40173**   FAX: -

Quiet cul-de-sac on Galway road, 2 mins town centre, swimming, tennis, golf. TV, tea/coffee facilities in rooms.

B&B PPS:	**£16/£18.50**	SNGL OCC. DBLE/TPL:	**£22.50/£25**	SNGL RM:	-
PART BRD:	-	% RED. CHILDREN:	**25%**	DINNER:	-

Ennis 5km

Tom & Rita Meaney
ASHLEIGH HOUSE
Barefield, Ennis, Co Clare

Ennis

OPEN:	April-October
No. ROOMS:	4
ENSUITE:	4

TEL: **065 27187**   FAX: **065 27331**   EMAIL: **tommeaney@tinet.ie**

Ennis/Galway Rd. Shannon Airport 30 mins. Ideal touring base. Convenient to Burren, Cliffs of Moher, Castle banquets, golf & fishing.

B&B PPS:	**£17**	SNGL OCC. DBLE/TPL:	**£23.50**	SNGL RM:	-
PART BRD:	**£180**	% RED. CHILDREN:	**50%**	DINNER:	**£12**

The Meere Family
FOUR WINDS
Limerick Road, Ennis, Co Clare

In Ennis

Ennis

OPEN:	15th March-15th October
No. ROOMS:	5
ENSUITE:	4

TEL: **065 29831**   FAX: -

Large home on main Airport road (N18). Private car park at rear. Golf, Pitch/Putt nearby. 5 mins town centre.

B&B PPS:	**£15/£17**	SNGL OCC. DBLE/TPL:	**£21.50/£23.50**	SNGL RM:	-
PART BRD:	-	% RED. CHILDREN:	**33%**	DINNER:	-

Mrs Valerie Morris
CARRAIG MHUIRE
Barefield, Ennis, Co Clare

Ennis 5km

Ennis

OPEN:	All Year except Christmas
No. ROOMS:	5
ENSUITE:	3

TEL: **065 27106**   FAX: **065 27375**

Warm hospitality always. AA/RAC and other high recommendations. Situated N18 Ennis/Galway Road. Ideal touring base. Convenient to Airport.

B&B PPS:	**£15/£17**	SNGL OCC. DBLE/TPL:	**£21.50/£23.50**	SNGL RM:	**£19**
PART BRD:	**£180**	% RED. CHILDREN:	**50%**	DINNER:	**£12**

Ennis 1.5km

Normoyle Family
OAKLEY B/B
10 Woodlawn, Lahinch Road, Ennis, Co Clare

Ennis

TEL: **065 29267/088 2712221**   FAX: -

OPEN:	1st May-31st October
No. ROOMS:	4
ENSUITE:	2

(V)

Spacious home 100 metres off main road, quiet location. Cliffs of Moher, Burren, Bunratty Castle, Golf, Fishing. Airport 20 mins.

| B&B PPS: | £15/£17 | SNGL OCC. DBLE/TPL: | £21.50/£23.50 | SNGL RM: | £20 |
| PART BRD: | - | % RED. CHILDREN: | 20% | DINNER: | £12 |

Ennis 2km

Rita O'Brien
LOUGHVILLE HOUSE
Loughville, Lahinch Road, Ennis, Co Clare

Ennis

TEL: **065 20345**   FAX: **065 20345**   -

OPEN:	April-October
No. ROOMS:	3
ENSUITE:	2

(V)

Pink house with balcony. Route N85, Cliffs of Moher, Burren. Ennis 2 km, Shannon 20 km. Golf, Fishing, Music. Guaranteed welcome.

| B&B PPS: | £15/£17 | SNGL OCC. DBLE/TPL: | £21.50/£23.50 | SNGL RM: | - |
| PART BRD: | - | % RED. CHILDREN: | 33% | DINNER: | - |

Ennis 1.5km

Mrs Mareaid O'Connor
VILLA NOVA
1 Woodlawn
Lahinch Road, Ennis, Co Clare

Ennis

TEL: **065 28570**   FAX: -

OPEN:	1st April-31st October
No. ROOMS:	4
ENSUITE:	2

(V)

Bungalow on N85. Restauarant and Pub with music 2 mins walk. Shannon 25 mins. Fishing, Golf, Cliffs of Moher nearby.

| B&B PPS: | £15/£17 | SNGL OCC. DBLE/TPL: | £21.50/£23.50 | SNGL RM: | - |
| PART BRD: | - | % RED. CHILDREN: | - | DINNER: | £12 |

Ennis 2km

Mrs Teresa O'Donohue
SANBORN HOUSE
Edenvale, Kilrush Road, Ennis, Co Clare

Ennis

TEL: **065 24959**   FAX: -

OPEN:	All Year
No. ROOMS:	4
ENSUITE:	4

(V)

Spacious neo-Georgian house in peaceful, scenic surroundings, Kilrush/car ferry Road. Convenient Airport, Burren, Banquets. Early guests welcome. Frommer recommended.

| B&B PPS: | £17 | SNGL OCC. DBLE/TPL: | £23.50 | SNGL RM: | - |
| PART BRD: | - | % RED. CHILDREN: | 50% | DINNER: | - |

Ennis 1km

Mrs Kathleen O'Loughlin
ARD NA GREINE HOUSE
Showgrounds Road, Ennis, Co Clare

Ennis

TEL: **065 40783**   FAX: **065 40783**

OPEN:	31st March-30th September
No. ROOMS:	3
ENSUITE:	3

(V)

Overlooking town, walking distance Golf, Tennis, Swimming, Traditional Music. Burren Beach, Airport within 30 mins. Warm friendly family home.

| B&B PPS: | £17 | SNGL OCC. DBLE/TPL: | £23.50 | SNGL RM: | - |
| PART BRD: | - | % RED. CHILDREN: | 20% | DINNER: | - |

Ennis 3km

Mrs Monica O'Loughlin
MASSABIELLE
Off Quin Road, Ennis, Co Clare

OPEN:	1st May-15th October
NO. ROOMS:	5
ENSUITE:	4

TEL: 065 29363   FAX: 065 29363

Recommended by "Frommer", "Sullivan", "Best B&B's" Guides. Friendly, relaxed family home in peaceful rural setting with Landscaped Gardens, Tennis Court.

B&B PPS:	£15/£17	SNGL OCC. DBLE/TPL:	£21.50/£23.50	SNGL RM:	-
PART BRD:	-	% RED. CHILDREN:	20%	DINNER:	-

Ennis 1km

Mary O'Sullivan
OGHAM HOUSE
3 Abbey Court, Clare Road, Ennis, Co Clare

Ennis

OPEN:	All Year except Christmas
NO. ROOMS:	3
ENSUITE:	2

TEL: 065 24878   FAX: -

Enjoy our warm hospitality in comfortable home. N18 route opposite West County Hotel. Convenient to Bunratty, Cliffs Moher, Burren, Golf.

B&B PPS:	£17/£18	SNGL OCC. DBLE/TPL:	£23.50/£24.50	SNGL RM:	-
PART BRD:	-	% RED. CHILDREN:	25%	DINNER:	-

Ennis 1km

Mrs Brigid Pyne
KILMOON HOUSE
Kildysart Road, Off Limerick Rd., Ennis, Co Clare

Ennis

OPEN:	1st April-30th September
NO. ROOMS:	3
ENSUITE:	2

TEL: 065 28529   FAX: -

Spacious home in peaceful environment, 20 mins from Shannon Airport. Convenient to Bunratty Castle, Knappogue, Burren and Cliffs of Moher.

B&B PPS:	£15/£17	SNGL OCC. DBLE/TPL:	£21.50/£23.50	SNGL RM:	-
PART BRD:	-	% RED. CHILDREN:	50%	DINNER:	-

Ennis 10km

Mrs Joan Quinn
LISDUFF
off Limerick Road, Ballynacally, Ennis, Co Clare

Ennis

OPEN:	10th April-5th October
NO. ROOMS:	3
ENSUITE:	3

TEL: 065 38488   FAX: -

Overlooking Shannon Estuary, on coast road (R473) to Car Ferry. Convenient Airport, Scenic walks, Breakfast menu, Complimentry tea on arrival.

B&B PPS:	£17	SNGL OCC. DBLE/TPL:	£23.50	SNGL RM:	-
PART BRD:	£180	% RED. CHILDREN:	50%	DINNER:	£12.50

Ennis

T J & Pauline Roberts
CARBERY HOUSE
Kilrush Road/Car Ferry Rd., Ennis, Co Clare

Ennis

OPEN:	April-October
NO. ROOMS:	4
ENSUITE:	3

TEL: 065 24046   FAX: -

Route 68, morning visitors welcome. Orthopaedic beds, electric blankets, hospitality trays, hairdryers. Continental breakfast - reduced rate. Frommer recommended. Convenient Airport.

B&B PPS:	£15/£17	SNGL OCC. DBLE/TPL:	£21.50/£23.50	SNGL RM:	-
PART BRD:	-	% RED. CHILDREN:	10%	DINNER:	-

Mrs Fiona Staunton
TEACH RUA
Coor, Edenvale, Ennis, Co Clare

Ennis

OPEN:	15th April-25th September
NO. ROOMS:	3
ENSUITE:	3

(V)

TEL: 065 40499   FAX: -

Spacious dormer bungalow, peaceful scenic area, 3 km Ennis on Kilrush/car ferry road. Golf within 2km. Ideal touring base.

Ennis 3km

B&B PPS:	£17	SNGL OCC. DBLE/TPL:	£23.50	SNGL RM:	-
PART BRD:	£180	% RED. CHILDREN:	30%	DINNER:	-

Mrs Ina Troy
HAZELDENE
Barefield, Ennis, Co Clare

Ennis

OPEN:	1st January-20th December
NO. ROOMS:	5
ENSUITE:	5

(V)

TEL: 065 27212 / 087 2326787   FAX: -

Ennis/Galway road. Morning guests welcome. Airport 30mins distance. T.V in bedrooms. Convenient Cliffs of Moher. Banquets, Golf, Fishing.

Ennis 5km

B&B PPS:	£17	SNGL OCC. DBLE/TPL:	£23.50	SNGL RM:	£17
PART BRD:	£180	% RED. CHILDREN:	33.3%	DINNER:	£12

Mrs Kathleen Cahill
STATION HOUSE
Ennis Road, Ennistymon, Co Clare

Ennistymon

OPEN:	All Year except Christmas
NO. ROOMS:	6
ENSUITE:	6

(V)

TEL: 065 71149   FAX: 065 71709

Spacious home, tea facilities, hair dryers, telephone, TV bedrooms. Cliffs of Moher, Burren, Golf, Fishing, Ponytrekking, Guide Du Routard recommended.

Ennistymon

B&B PPS:	£17	SNGL OCC. DBLE/TPL:	£23.50	SNGL RM:	-
PART BRD:	-	% RED. CHILDREN:	-	DINNER:	-

Mrs Mary Clair
DE CLAR
Circular Rd., Ennistymon, Co Clare

Ennistymon

OPEN:	1st April-31st October
NO. ROOMS:	3
ENSUITE:	2

(V)

TEL: 065 71277   FAX: -

Family run home. Tea, Coffee Makers and Hairdryers in bedrooms. Convenient to Airport, Car Ferry, Cliffs, Burren, Golf, Fishing nearby.

Ennistymon

B&B PPS:	£15/£17	SNGL OCC. DBLE/TPL:	£21.50/£23.50	SNGL RM:	-
PART BRD:	-	% RED. CHILDREN:	-	DINNER:	-

Maureen Scales
CALLURA LODGE
Callura East, Ennistymon, Co Clare

Ennistymon

OPEN:	March-October
NO. ROOMS:	4
ENSUITE:	2

(V)

TEL: 065 71640   FAX: -

Modern bungalow situated on the main Burren route. Cliffs of Moher, Golf, Aillwee Caves, Pony Trekking, Fishing nearby.

Ennistymon 1.5km

B&B PPS:	£15/£17	SNGL OCC. DBLE/TPL:	£21.50/£23.50	SNGL RM:	-
PART BRD:	-	% RED. CHILDREN:	50%	DINNER:	-

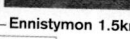

Mr John D MacNamara
ADMIRAL'S REST
Fanore (Coast Rd)., Co Clare

Fanore

OPEN:	Easter-30th October
NO. ROOMS:	9
ENSUITE:	9

 (V)

TEL: **065 76105**   FAX: **065 76161**

Overlooking Galway Bay, Aran Islands & Connemara The breathless beauty of the Burren abounds in this unique haven. Restaurant adjoining.

B&B PPS:	**£17**	SNGL OCC. DBLE/TPL:	**£23.50**	SNGL RM:	**£21**
PART BRD:	-	% RED. CHILDREN:	**50%**	DINNER:	**£16**

Lisdoonvarna 16km

Mrs Geraldine Howley
CARRAIG LIATH
Kilfenora, Co Clare

Kilfenora

OPEN:	March- November
NO. ROOMS:	4
ENSUITE:	2

(V)

TEL: **065 88075**   FAX: -

Bungalow in peaceful surroundings, ideal touring centre for exploring the Burren, Interpretative Centre in village. Traditional music, Restaurants, warm welcome.

B&B PPS:	**£15/£17**	SNGL OCC. DBLE/TPL:	**£21.50/£23.50**	SNGL RM:	-
PART BRD:	**£180**	% RED. CHILDREN:	**50%**	DINNER:	**£12**

In Kilfenora

Mary Fitzpatrick
MONTERAY
Kilrush Road, Kilkee, Co Clare

Kilkee

OPEN:	1st May-30thSeptember
NO. ROOMS:	4
ENSUITE:	4

(V)

TEL: **065 56244**   FAX: -

Situated on the N67, 1.5km from Kilkee, with a secure car parking area

B&B PPS:	**£18**	SNGL OCC. DBLE/TPL:	**£24.50**	SNGL RM:	-
PART BRD:	-	% RED. CHILDREN:	-	DINNER:	

Kilkee 1.5km

Mrs Patsy Flanagan
HARBOUR LODGE
6 Marine Parade, Kilkee, Co Clare

Kilkee

OPEN:	15th March-31st October
NO. ROOMS:	4
ENSUITE:	3

(V)

TEL: **065 56090**   FAX: -

Town Home across road from Beach in scenic area, adjacent all amenities. Recommended by "The Irish Bed & Breakfast Book".

B&B PPS:	**£15/£17**	SNGL OCC. DBLE/TPL:	**£21.50/£23.50**	SNGL RM:	-
PART BRD:	-	% RED. CHILDREN:	-	DINNER:	-

In Kilkee

Mrs Breda Haugh
DUNEARN
West End, Kilkee, Co Clare

Kilkee

OPEN:	15th March-15th November
NO. ROOMS:	4
ENSUITE:	4

(V)

TEL: **065 56545**   FAX: -

Lovely period home modernised and elgantly furnished overlooking Atlantic & Kilkee's wonderful Cliffs & Bay. Fishing, Swimming, Diving, Walking, Golf.

B&B PPS:	**£17**	SNGL OCC. DBLE/TPL:	**£23.50**	SNGL RM:	-
PART BRD:	-	% RED. CHILDREN:	**50%**	DINNER:	-

In Kilkee

In Kilkee

Mrs Maureen Haugh
DUGGERNA HOUSE
West End, Kilkee, Co Clare

Kilkee

OPEN:	1st May-1st October
NO. ROOMS:	4
ENSUITE:	4

TEL: **065 56152**   FAX: -

On seafront overlooking the Duggerna rocks. Scenic surroundings. Golf, Fishing, Scuba Diving, Pitch and Putt. Ideal Touring Centre. Frommer Recommendation.

B&B PPS:	£17	SNGL OCC. DBLE/TPL:	£23.50	SNGL RM:	-
PART BRD:	-	% RED. CHILDREN:	-	DINNER:	-

In Kilkee

Mary Hickie
BAYVIEW
O'Connell Street, Kilkee, Co Clare

Kilkee

OPEN:	All Year except Christmas
NO. ROOMS:	8
ENSUITE:	8

TEL: **065 56058**   FAX: -

Enjoy warm friendly hospitality in our tastefully decorated home. Magnificent view of Kilkee Bay, Cliffs. Central all amenities, Breakfast menu.

B&B PPS:	£17/£18	SNGL OCC. DBLE/TPL:	£23.50/£24.50	SNGL RM:	£23.50
PART BRD:	-	% RED. CHILDREN:	-	DINNER:	

n Kilkee

Diana Martin
WESTCLIFF HOUSE
West End, Kilkee, Co Clare

Kilkee

OPEN:	17th March-31stOctober
NO. ROOMS:	6
ENSUITE:	4

TEL: **065 56108**   FAX: -

Modernised Seafront home, spacious rooms. Scenic Area; Cork, Kerry, Galway within touring distance.

B&B PPS:	£15/£17	SNGL OCC. DBLE/TPL:	£21.50/£26	SNGL RM:	£17
PART BRD:	-	% RED. CHILDREN:	70%	DINNER:	-

Kilkee

Mrs Katherine O'Connor
JOURNEY'S END
East End, Kilkee, Co Clare

Kilkee

OPEN:	March-November
NO. ROOMS:	3
ENSUITE:	3

TEL: **065 56449**   FAX: -

Detached Dormer Bungalow. Situated on Seafront. Spacious Bedrooms with sea view. Tea/coffee facilities. Breakfast room/conservatory with Panoramic views Bay.

B&B PPS:	£16/£17	SNGL OCC. DBLE/TPL:	£21/£23.50	SNGL RM:	-
PART BRD:	-	% RED. CHILDREN:	10%	DINNER:	-

In Kilkee

Miss Margaret Prendergast
KINCORA
O'Connell Street, Kilkee, Co Clare

Kilkee

OPEN:	May-October
NO. ROOMS:	6
ENSUITE:	6

TEL: **065 56107**   FAX: -

Showers and toilets in all rooms. Bath in two rooms. Tea making facilities in all rooms.

B&B PPS:	£17	SNGL OCC. DBLE/TPL:	£23.50	SNGL RM:	£17
PART BRD:	-	% RED. CHILDREN:	-	DINNER:	-

In Kilkee

Mrs Emily Troy
WEST WINDS
Geraldine Place, Kilkee, Co Clare

Kilkee

OPEN:	1st March-1st November
NO. ROOMS:	4
ENSUITE:	2

(V)

TEL: **065 56498**   FAX: -

Family run home near seafront. Convenient to Golf, Diving, Swimming. Electric blankets, Orthopaedic beds.

| B&B PPS: | £15/£17 | SNGL OCC. DBLE/TPL: | £21.50/£23.50 | SNGL RM: | - |
| PART BRD: | - | % RED. CHILDREN: | 20% | DINNER: | - |

Killaloe 2km

Mrs Patricia Byrnes
RATHMORE HOUSE
Ballina, Killaloe, Co Clare

Killaloe

OPEN:	1st April-31st.October
NO. ROOMS:	6
ENSUITE:	4

(V)

TEL: **061 379296**   FAX: -

Family home R494, close river Shannon on lough Derg. Scenic area, Fishing, walking, cycling, water sports. Convenient Limerick City, Bunratty, Shannon.

| B&B PPS: | £15/£17 | SNGL OCC. DBLE/TPL: | £21.50/£23.50 | SNGL RM: | - |
| PART BRD: | - | % RED. CHILDREN: | 25% | DINNER: | - |

Celine King
SHANNARRA
Killaloe, Co Clare

Killaloe

OPEN:	1st February-30th November
NO. ROOMS:	3
ENSUITE:	3

(V)

TEL: **061 376548**   FAX: -

Comfortable family run accommodation 7 km north of Killaloe on Scarriff road. Scenic views. Convenient to Music Pubs, Restaurants, Watersport & Hillwalking.

| B&B PPS: | £17/£18 | SNGL OCC. DBLE/TPL: | £23.50/£24.50 | SNGL RM: | - |
| PART BRD: | - | % RED. CHILDREN: | 10% | DINNER: | - |

Killaloe 7km

Michael & Mary Clarke
BRUACH NA COILLE
Killimer Road, Kilrush, Co Clare

Kilrush

OPEN:	All Year except Christmas
NO. ROOMS:	4
ENSUITE:	2

(V)

TEL: **065 52250**   FAX: -

Situated on N67. Opposite Woodlands on Killimer Car-Ferry Road (8K). Frommer and AA recommended. Fresh juices with variety of breakfasts.

| B&B PPS: | £15/£17 | SNGL OCC. DBLE/TPL: | £21.50/£23.50 | SNGL RM: | - |
| PART BRD: | - | % RED. CHILDREN: | 50% | DINNER: | - |

Kilrush 1km

Sean & Mary Cotter
THE CENTRAL
46 Henry Street, Kilrush, Co Clare

Kilrush

OPEN:	All Year
NO. ROOMS:	4
ENSUITE:	4

(V)

TEL: **065 51332**   FAX: **065 51332**

Family run attractive Georgian Town House on N67 Route - Shannon Car Ferry - 7 kms. Central to all amenities. Breakfast menu.

| B&B PPS: | £17 | SNGL OCC. DBLE/TPL: | £23.50 | SNGL RM: | - |
| PART BRD: | - | % RED. CHILDREN: | 50% | DINNER: | £12 |

Kilkee 10km

Mrs Eithna Hynes
HILLCREST
Doonbeg Road, Kilrush, Co Clare

Kilrush

OPEN:	All Year except Christmas
No. ROOMS:	4
ENSUITE:	4

TEL: **065 51986**   FAX: -

Attractive spacious bungalow, guest conservatory. TV, Hairdryers, Tea/coffee making facilities. Extensive breakfast menu. Kilrush 1km. Quiet location.

B&B PPS:	£17	SNGL OCC. DBLE/TPL:	£23.50	SNGL RM:	-
PART BRD:	-	% RED. CHILDREN:	50%	DINNER:	£12

Kilrush 1km

Imy Kerrigan
COIS-NA-SIONNA
Ferry Junction, Killimer, Kilrush, Co Clare

Kilrush

OPEN:	All Year
No. ROOMS:	4
ENSUITE:	4

TEL: **065 53073**   FAX: -

Beautiful home on the Shannon with panoramic sea-view. N67. Ferry 2 mins. Travel agents vouchers. Touring base Clare, Kerry.

B&B PPS:	£17	SNGL OCC. DBLE/TPL:	£23.50	SNGL RM:	-
PART BRD:	-	% RED. CHILDREN:	50%	DINNER:	-

Kilrush 9km

Mrs Alyson O'Neill
OLD PAROCHIAL HOUSE
Cooraclare, Kilrush, Co Clare

Kilrush

OPEN:	April-October
No. ROOMS:	4
ENSUITE:	2

TEL: **065 59059**   FAX: **065 51006**   EMAIL: **oldparochial@webheads.ie**

Welcome to Period home (C1872), Rural hideaway overlooking Village (400m) ON (R483), Gardens, Pitch, Putt. Tea arrival. Seafood Pubs/Coast nearby.

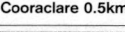

B&B PPS:	£16/£18	SNGL OCC. DBLE/TPL:	£23/£25	SNGL RM:	-
PART BRD:	-	% RED. CHILDREN:	50%	DINNER:	-

Cooraclare 0.5km

Mrs Joanne Barrett
EDENLANDIA
School Road, Lahinch, Co Clare

Lahinch

OPEN:	1st March-30th November
No. ROOMS:	3
ENSUITE:	3

TEL: **065 81361**   FAX: **065 81361**   EMAIL: **xbarrett@iol.ie**

Frommer recommended in panoramic setting off N67. Golfers 19th. Tee times arranged. Green fee concession. Tea/coffee, hairdryer all rooms.

B&B PPS:	£17	SNGL OCC. DBLE/TPL:	£24	SNGL RM:	-
PART BRD:	-	% RED. CHILDREN:	-	DINNER:	-

Lahinch 1km

Mrs Brid Fawl
MULCARR HOUSE
Ennistymon Road, Lahinch, Co Clare

Lahinch

OPEN:	Easter-27th October
No. ROOMS:	4
ENSUITE:	3

TEL: **065 81123**   FAX: -

Smoke free home, walking distance to Beach, Golf Course. Convenient Cliffs of Moher, Doolin, Burren. Tea making facilities. Hair Dryers.

B&B PPS:	£15/£17	SNGL OCC. DBLE/TPL:	£21.50/£23.50	SNGL RM:	-
PART BRD:	-	% RED. CHILDREN:	20%	DINNER:	-

In Lahinch

In Lahinch

Mrs Anita Gallery
TUDOR LODGE
Ennistymon Road, Lahinch, Co Clare

Lahinch

OPEN:	10th March-31st October
NO. ROOMS:	4
ENSUITE:	4

TEL: **065 81270 / 088 2786330** FAX:

Comfortable house, personally run. Overlooking Golf Courses. Tea/Coffee making facilities in bedrooms. Early breakfasts if required. Continental breakfast-reduced rate.

B&B PPS:	£17	SNGL OCC. DBLE/TPL:	£23.50	SNGL RM:	£17
PART BRD:	-	% RED. CHILDREN:	-	DINNER:	

Lahinch 1km

Mrs Ann Hanrahan
GLENVILLE
School Road, Lahinch, Co Clare

Lahinch

OPEN:	April-30th September
NO. ROOMS:	4
ENSUITE:	3

TEL: **065 81094** FAX: **065 81094**

Bungalow off Miltown Malbay/Ferry road (N 67). Panoramic view of Bay. Tranquil area, convenient to Cliffs of Moher, Doolin, Burren.

B&B PPS:	£15/£17	SNGL OCC. DBLE/TPL:	£21.50/£23.50	SNGL RM:	-
PART BRD:	-	% RED. CHILDREN:	25%	DINNER:	-

In Lahinch

Edel Kenny
CRAGLEA LODGE
Cregg, Lahinch, Co Clare

Lahinch

OPEN:	All Year except Christmas
NO. ROOMS:	3
ENSUITE:	2

TEL: **065 81450** FAX: **065 81450** EMAIL: **klahinch@iol.ie**

Bungalow - with a view of the sea In off the Road, quiet area TV lounge for guest only.

B&B PPS:	£15/£17	SNGL OCC. DBLE/TPL:	£21.50/£23.50	SNGL RM:	-
PART BRD:	-	% RED. CHILDREN:	20%	DINNER:	-

Lahinch 1km

Annie O'Brien
LE BORD DE MER
Cregg, Lahinch, Co Clare

Lahinch

OPEN:	March-November
NO. ROOMS:	3
ENSUITE:	3

TEL: **065 81454** FAX: **065 81454**

Breathtaking Ocean View, Lahinch Championship Golf, French speaking, beside Beach. Ideal base Cliffs of Moher, Burren, Aran Islands, Routard recommended.

B&B PPS:	£17	SNGL OCC. DBLE/TPL:	£23.50	SNGL RM:	-
PART BRD:	-	% RED. CHILDREN:	50%	DINNER:	-

Lahinch 1km

Mrs Frances Sarma
NAZIRA
School Road, Lahinch, Co Clare

Lahinch

OPEN:	March-30th November
NO. ROOMS:	3
ENSUITE:	3

TEL: **065 81362** FAX: -

Architect designed, commanding magnificent views of Bay, Golf Courses, beautiful scenic countryside. Peaceful setting. Recommended in Dillard Causin Guide.

B&B PPS:	£17/£17.50	SNGL OCC. DBLE/TPL:	£23.50/£24	SNGL RM:	-
PART BRD:	-	% RED. CHILDREN:	20%	DINNER:	-

Mrs Margaret Skerritt
MOHER VIEW
Ennistymon Road, Lahinch, Co Clare

Lahinch

OPEN:	April-October
NO. ROOMS:	3
ENSUITE:	3

TEL: **065 81206** FAX: -

Elevated dormer bungalow overlooking golf course. Convenient to Cliffs of Moher, Doolin, Burren, tea/coffee making facilities.

| B&B PPS: | **£17** | SNGL OCC. DBLE/TPL: | | SNGL RM: | - |
| PART BRD: | - | % RED. CHILDREN: | **25%** | DINNER: | - |

Lahinch 1km

Joseph & Ita Slattery
SEAFIELD LODGE
Ennistymon Road, Lahinch, Co Clare

Lahinch

OPEN:	Easter-31st October
NO. ROOMS:	4
ENSUITE:	4

TEL: **065 81594** FAX: -

Elevated Dormer Bungalow on N67, 5 mins walk Lahinch, Beach Golf Course. All rooms TV, Radio, & Electric Blankets, Hairdryers.

| B&B PPS: | **£17** | SNGL OCC. DBLE/TPL: | **£23.50** | SNGL RM: | - |
| PART BRD: | - | % RED. CHILDREN: | **25%** | DINNER: | - |

In Lahinch

Mrs Marian White
"SEA BREEZE"
Carrowgar, Miltown Malbay Road, Lahinch, Co Clare

Lahinch

OPEN:	1st May-30th September
NO. ROOMS:	3
ENSUITE:	3

TEL: **065 81073** FAX: -

Bungalow on N67, Coast Road from Lahinch to Killimer Car-ferry. Convenient Cliffs of Moher, Burren, trips to Aran Islands.

| B&B PPS: | **£17** | SNGL OCC. DBLE/TPL: | **£23.50** | SNGL RM: | - |
| PART BRD: | - | % RED. CHILDREN: | **25%** | DINNER: | - |

Lahinch 2km

Noel and Agnes Andrews
CARRAIG HOUSE
Liscannor, Co Clare

Liscannor

OPEN:	All Year except Christmas
NO. ROOMS:	6
ENSUITE:	6

TEL: **065 81260** FAX: -

Spacious house, quiet scenic surroundings. Views of Bay and Cliffs from bedrooms. Tea/coffee making facilities. Close to Golf, Fishing.

| B&B PPS: | **£17** | SNGL OCC. DBLE/TPL: | **£23.50** | SNGL RM: | - |
| PART BRD: | - | % RED. CHILDREN: | **25%** | DINNER: | - |

In Liscannor

Patrick and Eilis Blake
SEA HAVEN
Liscannor, Co Clare

Liscannor

OPEN:	All Year except Christmas
NO. ROOMS:	6
ENSUITE:	6

TEL: **065 81385** FAX: **065 81417**

Spacious dormer bungalow with sea views on main Lahinch Cliffs of Moher road. Tea/coffee facilities, breakfast menu, orthopaedic beds.

| B&B PPS: | **£17** | SNGL OCC. DBLE/TPL: | **£23.50** | SNGL RM: | - |
| PART BRD: | **£180** | % RED. CHILDREN: | **25%** | DINNER: | **£12** |

In Liscannor

In Liscannor

Kevin & Ann Thynne
SEAMOUNT
Liscannor, Co Clare

Liscannor

OPEN:	17th March-31st October	
NO. ROOMS:	4	
ENSUITE:	4	

TEL: **065 81367**   FAX: -

Family run home on road to "Famous Cliffs of Moher". In quiet secluded landscaped garden adjacent to Pubs, Fishing, Restaurants.

B&B PPS:	£17	SNGL OCC. DBLE/TPL:	£23.50	SNGL RM:	-
PART BRD:	-	% RED. CHILDREN:	50%	DINNER:	-

In Lisdoonvarna

Mrs Eileen Barrett
MARCHMONT
Lisdoonvarna, Co Clare

Lisdoonvarna

OPEN:	All Year except Christmas	
NO. ROOMS:	4	
ENSUITE:	4	

TEL: **065 74050**   FAX: **065 74050**

Town House, Car Park. TV Lounge, Hairdryers rooms. Tea/Coffee facilities. Bicycle lock-up. Lets Go and Rick Steves recommended.

B&B PPS:	£17/£18	SNGL OCC. DBLE/TPL:	£23.50/£24.50	SNGL RM:	-
PART BRD:	-	% RED. CHILDREN:	25%	DINNER:	-

Lisdoonvarna 1km

Mrs Bernie Cosgrove
ST JUDES
Coast Road, Lisdoonvarna, Co Clare

Lisdoonvarna

OPEN:	1st May-31st October	
NO. ROOMS:	4	
ENSUITE:	4	

TEL: **065 74108**   FAX: -

Elevated site, on N67 Doolin Road. Burren, Cliffs of Moher, Doolin, closeby. Electric Blankets, Hairdryers, Bicycle Shed, (1) three bedded room.

B&B PPS:	£17	SNGL OCC. DBLE/TPL:	£23.50/£25	SNGL RM:	-
PART BRD:	-	% RED. CHILDREN:	25%	DINNER:	-

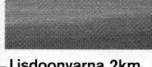

Lisdoonvarna 2km

Mrs Monica Droney
CROSSWINDS
Lisdoonvarna, Co Clare

Lisdoonvarna

OPEN:	April-October	
NO. ROOMS:	3	
ENSUITE:	2	

TEL: **065 74469**   FAX: -

Situated on Cliffs of Moher Rd, (R478). 10 mins drive Doolin, Island Ferries, Burren & Lisdoonvarna Walking distance to nightly entertainment.

B&B PPS:	£15/£17	SNGL OCC. DBLE/TPL:	£21.50/£23.50	SNGL RM:	-
PART BRD:	-	% RED. CHILDREN:	40%	DINNER:	-

In Lisdoonvarna

Mrs Mary Finn
ST ENDA'S
Church Street, Lisdoonvarna, Co Clare

Lisdoonvarna

OPEN:	March-October	
NO. ROOMS:	3	
ENSUITE:	2	

TEL: **065 74066**   FAX: -

Five minutes walking Town Centre. Leading to main Galway Road. Welcoming tea/coffee and home baking. Ideal base for Burren.

B&B PPS:	£15/£17	SNGL OCC. DBLE/TPL:	£21.50/£23.50	SNGL RM:	£15/£17
PART BRD:	£180	% RED. CHILDREN:	50%	DINNER:	£12

Lisdoonvarna 0.5km

Vera Fitzpatrick
FERMONA HOUSE
Bog Road, Lisdoonvarna, Co Clare

Lisdoonvarna

OPEN:	1st March-1st November	
NO. ROOMS:	5	
ENSUITE:	5	(V)

TEL: **065 74243**   FAX: -

Modern bungalow, landscaped gardens, near famous Spa Wells. 8 minutes walk to bus stop, town centre. Early breakfasts, Home baking. Bicycle shed.

B&B PPS:	**£17/£18**	SNGL. OCC. DBLE/TPL:	**£23.50/£24.50**	SNGL RM:	-
PART BRD:	-	% RED. CHILDREN:	**33%**	DINNER:	-

Lisdoonvarna 1km

Mrs Ann Green
HILLTOP
Doolin Road, Lisdoonvarna, Co Clare

Lisdoonvarna

OPEN:	1st May-31st October	
NO. ROOMS:	3	
ENSUITE:	3	(V)

TEL: **065 74134**   FAX: -

Comfortable home within walking distance of Village. Convenient to Doolin, Cliffs of Moher, Burren. Traditional music. One large family room.

B&B PPS:	**£17**	SNGL. OCC. DBLE/TPL:	**£23.50**	SNGL RM:	-
PART BRD:	-	% RED. CHILDREN:	**33%**	DINNER:	-

In Lisdoonvarna

Oliver & Deirdre McNamara
DEISE
Bog Road, Lisdoonvarna, Co Clare

Lisdoonvarna

OPEN:	1st April-1st November	
NO. ROOMS:	4	
ENSUITE:	4	(V)

TEL: **065 74360**   FAX: **065 74360**   EMAIL: **olde @ iol.ie**

19th Century Cottage restored to high standard of comfort. Cliffs of Moher, Lahinch, Doolin, Aran Islands and The Burren closeby.

B&B PPS:	**£17/£20**	SNGL. OCC. DBLE/TPL:	**£23.50/£27**	SNGL RM:	**£17/£20**
PART BRD:	-	% RED. CHILDREN:	**50%**	DINNER:	-

Lisdoonvarna 1km

Mrs Cathleen O'Connor
RONCALLI
Doolin Road, Lisdoonvarna, Co Clare

Lisdoonvarna

OPEN:	10th April-31st October	
NO. ROOMS:	3	
ENSUITE:	2	(V)

TEL: **065 74115**   FAX: -

7 mins walk village on N67. Quiet location. "Lets Go" recommended. Adjacent Burren, Cliffs of Moher, Aran Ferry, Traditional Music. Bicycle lockup.

B&B PPS:	**£15/£17**	SNGL. OCC. DBLE/TPL:	**£21.50/£23.50**	SNGL RM:	-
PART BRD:	-	% RED. CHILDREN:	**50%**	DINNER:	-

In Lisdoonvarna

Mrs Joan O'Flaherty
GOWLAUN
St Brendan's Road, Lisdoonvarna, Co Clare

Lisdoonvarna

OPEN:	April-October	
NO. ROOMS:	3	
ENSUITE:	3	(V)

TEL: **065 74369**   FAX: -

Peaceful home on landscaped gardens. 5 Mins walk from town bus stop. Bedrooms ensuite, tea making facilities, safe parking. Quiet location.

B&B PPS:	**£17**	SNGL. OCC. DBLE/TPL:	**£23.50**	SNGL RM:	-
PART BRD:	-	% RED. CHILDREN:	**40%**	DINNER:	-

Lisdoonvarna 1km

Anne & Denis O'Loughlin
BURREN BREEZE
The Wood Cross, Lisdoonvarna, Co Clare

Lisdoonvarna

OPEN:	All Year except Christmas
NO. ROOMS:	6
ENSUITE:	6

TEL: **065 74263 / 088 563983** FAX: **065 74820** EMAIL: **Burrenbb@iol.ie**

Bath and shower, tea/coffee, TV, hairdryers in rooms. Near Doolin. Local information. Junction N67/R477 on Doolin Road. Credit Cards.

B&B PPS:	**£12.50/£13.50**	SNGL OCC. DBLE/TPL:	**£15/£25**	SNGL RM:	-
PART BRD:	**£170**	% RED. CHILDREN:	**50%**	DINNER:	**£11**

In Lisdoonvarna

The Petty Family
SUNVILLE
Off Doolin Road, Lisdoonvarna, Co Clare

Lisdoonvarna

OPEN:	All Year
NO. ROOMS:	4
ENSUITE:	4

TEL: **065 74065** FAX: **065 74065**

Situated off N67, Cliffs of Moher, Doolin ferry. Burren, Golf closeby. Frommer Recommended. Electric Blankets, Hairdryers, Tea/Coffee Facilities.

B&B PPS:	**£17/£18**	SNGL OCC. DBLE/TPL:	**£24/£25**	SNGL RM:	-
PART BRD:	**£190**	% RED. CHILDREN:	**33%**	DINNER:	**£14**

Lisdoonvarna 1km

Mrs. Helen Stack
ORE-A-TAVA HOUSE
Lisdoonvarna, Co Clare

Lisdoonvarna

OPEN:	March-October
NO. ROOMS:	6
ENSUITE:	6

TEL: **065 74086** FAX: **065 74547**

Bungalow in quiet setting on N67. Rooms with T.V, telephone, hairdryers. Fax & photocopying available.

B&B PPS:	**£17/£18**	SNGL OCC. DBLE/TPL:	**£23.50**	SNGL RM:	-
PART BRD:	-	% RED. CHILDREN:	**33.3%**	DINNER:	-

Lisdoonvarna 1km

Mrs Irene Vaughan
WOODHAVEN
Doolin Coast Road, Lisdoonvarna, Co Clare

Lisdoonvarna

OPEN:	All Year
NO. ROOMS:	4
ENSUITE:	4

TEL: **065 74017** FAX: -

Situated off N 67 in scenic, peaceful surroundings. Traditional music. Near Doolin ferry and Cliffs of Moher. Electric Blankets, Hairdryers.

B&B PPS:	**£17**	SNGL OCC. DBLE/TPL:	**£23.50**	SNGL RM:	-
PART BRD:	-	% RED. CHILDREN:	**25%**	DINNER:	-

Miltown Malbay 4km

Mrs Rita Harrison
GLOR NA MARA
Spanish Point, Miltown Malbay, Co Clare

Miltown Malbay

OPEN:	29th May-30th September
NO. ROOMS:	3
ENSUITE:	3

TEL: **065 84589** FAX: **065 84589**

Coastline. Tranquil, non-smoking home. 1 hour airport, 30 mins ferry. Breakfast menu. Cliff walks, Golf, Fishing, Beaches, Restaurants. Traditional Music.

B&B PPS:	**£17**	SNGL OCC. DBLE/TPL:	-	SNGL RM:	-
PART BRD:	-	% RED. CHILDREN:	**25%**	DINNER:	-

Mary Hughes
AN GLEANN
Ennis Road, Miltown Malbay, Co Clare

Miltown Malbay

OPEN:	All Year except Christmas
No. ROOMS:	4
ENSUITE:	4

(V)

TEL: **065 84281** FAX: -

Friendly family run home, rooms ensuite TV, Tea/Coffee. Close all amenities. Located 1km Ennis Road. Recommended "New York Times".

B&B PPS:	£15/£17	SNGL. OCC. DBLE/TPL:	-	SNGL RM:	-
PART BRD:	-	% RED. CHILDREN:	50%	DINNER:	-

Miltown Malbay 1km

Katie & John McInerney
ATLANTIC STAR
Spanish Point, Miltown Malbay, Co Clare

Miltown Malbay

OPEN:	All Year
No. ROOMS:	6
ENSUITE:	6

(V)

TEL: **065 84782** FAX: -

Modern spacious house on main N67 road to/from Killimer Car Ferry. Opposite Golf course. 400 metres from sandy beach.

B&B PPS:	£17	SNGL. OCC. DBLE/TPL:	£23.50	SNGL RM:	-
PART BRD:	£180	% RED. CHILDREN:	50%	DINNER:	£12

Miltown Malbay 1km

Howe Family
OAK HOUSE
Mountshannon, Co Clare

Mountshannon

OPEN:	1st April-1st Novermber
No. ROOMS:	3
ENSUITE:	-

TEL: **061 927185** FAX: -

Country home, panoramic view, overlooking Lough Derg. Private Beach, Boats, excellent facilities for Fishermen. Ideal base for touring. 200m village.

B&B PPS:	£15	SNGL. OCC. DBLE/TPL:	£21.50	SNGL RM:	-
PART BRD:	-	% RED. CHILDREN:	25%	DINNER:	-

In Mountshannon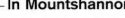

Mrs Colette Waterstone
DERG LODGE
Mountshannon, Co Clare

Mountshannon

OPEN:	All year except Christmas
No. ROOMS:	4
ENSUITE:	1

(V)

TEL: **061 927180** FAX: **061 927180 (man)**

Luxury Accommodation. Boat hire, Angling information. Excellent Restaurants & Pubs, Pony Trekking, Pitch & Putt, Golf, Walking, Swimming & Cycling.

B&B PPS:	£15/£17	SNGL. OCC. DBLE/TPL:	£21.50/£23.50	SNGL RM:	-
PART BRD:	£180	% RED. CHILDREN:	-	DINNER:	£12

In Mountshannon

Colette Gilbert
FERGUS LODGE
Ennis Road, Newmarket on Fergus, Co Clare

Newmarket-on-Fergus

OPEN:	All Year
No. ROOMS:	4
ENSUITE:	2

(V)

TEL: **061 368351** FAX: -

On N18, beside Texaco filling station. Shannon Airport, Bunratty, Knappogue, 10 minutes.Dromoland Castle and Clare Inn Hotel 2 minutes.

B&B PPS:	£15/£17	SNGL. OCC. DBLE/TPL:	£23/£25	SNGL RM:	-
PART BRD:	£180	% RED. CHILDREN:	20%	DINNER:	£12

Ennis 12km

Newmarket-on-Fergus 2km

Mrs Maureen Hogan
GOLF VIEW
Ennis Road, Latoon Cross, Newmarket on Fergus, Co Clare

Newmarket-on-Fergus

OPEN:	All Year except Christmas
NO. ROOMS:	4
ENSUITE:	3

TEL: **061 368095**   FAX: **065 28624**

New House on N18, overlooking Dromoland Castle, Clare Inn Golf course. Shannon Airport, Castles, Ennis 10 mins. All rooms ground floor.

B&B PPS:	£17/£18	SNGL OCC. DBLE/TPL:	-	SNGL RM:	-
PART BRD:	-	% RED. CHILDREN:	10%	DINNER:	-

Newmarket-on-Fergus 2km

Mrs Sheila Ryan
THE DORMER
Lisduff, Newmarket-On-Fergus, Co Clare

Newmarket-on-Fergus

OPEN:	April-October
NO. ROOMS:	3
ENSUITE:	2

TEL: **061 368354**   FAX: **061 368354**   -

Situated in peaceful rural setting, Airport side of Newmarket-On-Fergus N18. Shannon Airport, Bunratty 15 mins. Fine Restaurants locally.

B&B PPS:	£15/£17	SNGL OCC. DBLE/TPL:	£21.50/£23.50	SNGL RM:	-
PART BRD:	-	% RED. CHILDREN:	50%	DINNER:	-

Quin 1 km

Mrs. Ita Lee
MARLEE HOUSE
Ennis Road, Quin, Co Clare

Quin

OPEN:	1st April-15th October
NO. ROOMS:	3
ENSUITE:	2

TEL: **065 25686**   FAX: -

Bungalow, scenic view, ideal first, last stop. Airport, Bunratty 20 mins. Knappogue, Craggaunowen, Dromoland, Golf. Clare Inn Hotel 5 mins.

B&B PPS:	£15/£17	SNGL OCC. DBLE/TPL:	£21.50/£23.50	SNGL RM:	-
PART BRD:	£180	% RED. CHILDREN:	25%	DINNER:	£12

In Quin

Mrs Joan Murphy
ROOSKA HOUSE
Quin, Co Clare

Quin

OPEN:	1st April-31st October
NO. ROOMS:	4
ENSUITE:	2

TEL: **065 25661**   FAX: -

Modern house in village. Convenient Quin Abbey, Knappogue and Craggaunowen. Shannon Airport 30 mins, Ennis 15 mins, Limerick 30 mins.

B&B PPS:	£15/£17	SNGL OCC. DBLE/TPL:	£21.50/£23.50	SNGL RM:	-
PART BRD:	£180	% RED. CHILDREN:	33.3%	DINNER:	£12

Ennis 11km

Mrs Marguerite O'Donovan
BALLYMARKHAM HOUSE
Knappogue Rd., Quin, Co Clare

Quin

OPEN:	1st April-31st October
NO. ROOMS:	3
ENSUITE:	2

TEL: **065 25726**   FAX: -

Two storey Georgian house on mature elevated landscaped grounds, in peaceful rural setting. The nearest B & B to Knappogue Castle.

B&B PPS:	£15/£17	SNGL OCC. DBLE/TPL:	£21.50/£23.50	SNGL RM:	-
PART BRD:	£180	% RED. CHILDREN:	33%	DINNER:	£12

Shannon 7km

Mr John Boland
FORT LACH
Drumline, Newmarket-on-Fergus,
Co Clare
TEL: **061 364003**   FAX: **061 364059**

Shannon

OPEN:	All Year except Christmas
NO. ROOMS:	4
ENSUITE:	4

(V)

Modern house, rural setting, 500 yds. off N18 Shannon, Airport, Bunratty, Golf, Horse Riding, Fishing 10 mins. Ideal Touring centre.

B&B PPS:	**£17**	SNGL. OCC. DBLE/TPL:	**£23.50**	SNGL. RM:	-
PART BRD:	-	% RED. CHILDREN:	20%	DINNER:	-

Shannon 4km

Mrs Kathleen Collins
VALHALLA
Urlanbeg, Newmarket-on-Fergus,
Shannon, Co Clare
TEL: **061 368293**   FAX: **061 368660**

Shannon

OPEN:	All Year except Christmas
NO. ROOMS:	3
ENSUITE:	3

(V)

Situated on Newmarket-on-Fergus/Shannon Road R472. 1km off N18. Ideal first last stop. Morning guests welcome. Bunratty and Shannon 10 minutes.

B&B PPS:	**£17**	SNGL. OCC. DBLE/TPL:	-	SNGL. RM:	-
PART BRD:	-	% RED. CHILDREN:	33%	DINNER:	-

Shannon 4km

Mrs Geraldine Enright
TRADAREE
Drumline, Newmarket-on-Fergus,
Co Clare
TEL: **061 364386**   FAX: -

Shannon

OPEN:	March-October
NO. ROOMS:	3
ENSUITE:	-

(V)

Old style dormer bungalow - 100 m off N18 to Ennis. Bunratty Castle, Shannon Airport 5 mins. Morning guests welcome.

B&B PPS:	**£15/£15.50**	SNGL. OCC. DBLE/TPL:	**£21.50**	SNGL. RM:	**£19**
PART BRD:	-	% RED. CHILDREN:	25%	DINNER:	-

Shannon 5km

Mrs Phil Fleming
KNOCKNAGOW
Leimaneighmore, Newmarket-on-
Fergus, Co Clare
TEL: **061 368685**   FAX: **061 368685**

Shannon

OPEN:	All Year except Christmas
NO. ROOMS:	4
ENSUITE:	4

(V)

Purpose built home, 2km from N18 / R472 (Shannon/Newmarket on Fergus Road). Early Guests welcome. Convenient Shannon Airport, 8KM, Bunratty, Knappogue castles.

B&B PPS:	**£17**	SNGL. OCC. DBLE/TPL:	**£23.50**	SNGL. RM:	-
PART BRD:	-	% RED. CHILDREN:	50%	DINNER:	-

Shannon 3km

Mrs Nora Glennon
EMMERDALE
Drumline, Newmarket-on-Fergus,
Co Clare
TEL: **061 364217**   FAX: -

Shannon

OPEN:	1st April-31st October
NO. ROOMS:	3
ENSUITE:	3

(V)

Modern, rust brick dormer bungalow situated adjacent N18, opposite World Aviation Park, within 5 mins of Bunratty, Shannon Airport.

B&B PPS:	**£17**	SNGL. OCC. DBLE/TPL:	**£23.50**	SNGL. RM:	-
PART BRD:	-	% RED. CHILDREN:	20%	DINNER:	-

In Shannon

Mrs Brede Lohan
35 Tullyglass Crescent
Shannon, Co Clare

Shannon

OPEN:	All Year except Christmas
NO. ROOMS:	6
ENSUITE:	6

(V)

TEL: **061 364268** FAX: -

Home overlooking river Shannon. Cul-de-sac. Airport terminal 1.5 miles. Banquets 10 mins drive. Leisure Centre, Swimming Pool, Sauna 200yds.

B&B PPS:	£18	SNGL OCC. DBLE/TPL:	£24.50	SNGL RM:	£23
PART BRD:	-	% RED. CHILDREN:	20%	DINNER:	£18

In Shannon

Mrs Kay Moloney
MOLONEY'S B&B
21 Coill Mhara, Shannon, Co Clare

Shannon

OPEN:	3rd January-22nd December
NO. ROOMS:	4
ENSUITE:	2

(V)

TEL: **061 364185** FAX: -

Home situated 5 mins from Airport Terminal. Shannon Town Centre 400 yds. Third road on left after Texaco filling station.

B&B PPS:	£15/£17	SNGL OCC. DBLE/TPL:	-	SNGL RM:	-
PART BRD:	-	% RED. CHILDREN:	20%	DINNER:	-

Shannon Town 2km

Mrs Mary Mooney
THE KYRENIA
Drumline, Newmarket-on-Fergus,
Co Clare

Shannon

OPEN:	1st March-31st October
NO. ROOMS:	3
ENSUITE:	3

(V)

TEL: **061 364137** FAX: -

Spacious modern home on N18. 5 mins Shannon Airport, Bunratty Castle. Cable TV Morning guests welcome. Early breakfast.

B&B PPS:	£17	SNGL OCC. DBLE/TPL:	£23.50	SNGL RM:	-
PART BRD:	-	% RED. CHILDREN:	20%	DINNER:	-

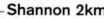

Shannon 2km

Mrs Betty Nally
IVORY LODGE
Drumline, Newmarket on Fergus,
Co Clare

Shannon

OPEN:	All Year except Christmas
NO. ROOMS:	4
ENSUITE:	3

(V)

TEL: **061 364039** FAX: -

Purpose built home, Drumline, 100m off N18. Airport/Bunratty 8 mins. TV, Hairdryer, Tea/Coffee in rooms. Morning guests welcome.

B&B PPS:	£17	SNGL OCC. DBLE/TPL:	-	SNGL RM:	-
PART BRD:	-	% RED. CHILDREN:	20%	DINNER:	-

Shannon 3km

Mrs Wiestawa O'Brien
TARA GREEN
Ballycally/ Aerospace Rd, Newmarket-
on-Fergus, Co Clare

Shannon

OPEN:	All Year except Christmas
NO. ROOMS:	5
ENSUITE:	4

(V)

TEL: **061 363789** FAX: **061 363789** EMAIL: **tarag@iol.ie**

3 miles Shannon Airport. Welcome to Irish/Polish home. Organic garden. Home cooking. At Shannon roundabouts follow sign for Ballycally.

B&B PPS:	£15/£22	SNGL OCC. DBLE/TPL:	£21.50/£28.50	SNGL RM:	-
PART BRD:	£180	% RED. CHILDREN:	-	DINNER:	£15

In Shannon

Mary O'Loughlin
AVALON
11 Ballycaseymore Hill, Shannon Town, Co Clare

		Shannon
OPEN:	All Year except Christmas	
NO. ROOMS:	3	
ENSUITE:	2	(V)

TEL: **061 362032** FAX: **061 362032** EMAIL: **avalon5@iol.ie**

Home overlooking Shannon, quiet cul-de-sac. 5 min drive to Airport. Near Bunratty, Ennis, Limerick. Turn left at Old Lodge Pub.

B&B PPS:	£15/£17	SNGL OCC. DBLE/TPL:	£21.50/£23.50	SNGL RM:	-
PART BRD:	-	% RED. CHILDREN:	50%	DINNER:	-

Shannon 5km

Mrs Fidelma Ryan
MAPLE VIEW
Urlanmore, Newmarket on Fergus, Co Clare

		Shannon
OPEN:	All Year except Christmas	
NO. ROOMS:	3	
ENSUITE:	2	(V)

TEL: **061 368062** FAX: -

10 mins drive from Shannon Airport R472. Morning guests welcome, Shops, Restaurants 2 km. Bunratty Castle 5 mins drive.

B&B PPS:	£15/£17.50	SNGL OCC. DBLE/TPL:	£21.50/£24	SNGL RM:	-
PART BRD:	-	% RED. CHILDREN:	33.3%	DINNER:	-

Shannon 2km

Geraldine E Ryan
HILLCREST
Clonlohan, Newmarket-on-Fergus, Co Clare

		Shannon
OPEN:	15th January-15th December	
NO. ROOMS:	5	
ENSUITE:	2	(V)

TEL: **061 364158** FAX: -

Family home R472 off N18. Central local amenities, Golf, Fishing, Horseriding, Bunratty - Overlooking Airport. Morning guests welcome. Early Breakfasts.

B&B PPS:	£16/£17	SNGL OCC. DBLE/TPL:	£21.50/£23.50	SNGL RM:	£15
PART BRD:	-	% RED. CHILDREN:	50%	DINNER:	-

Shannon 4km

Mrs Kathleen Ryan
ARDREE
Monument Cross, Newmarket-on-Fergus, Co Clare

		Shannon
OPEN:	1st April-15th October	
NO. ROOMS:	3	
ENSUITE:	1	(V)

TEL: **061 368256** FAX: - EMAIL: **ardree@indigo.ie**

Off Shannon/Newmarket Road R472, 2km from N18. Morning guests welcome. Golf, Horse Riding, Fishing. Bunratty & Shannon 10 mins.

B&B PPS:	£15/£17	SNGL OCC. DBLE/TPL:	£21.50/£23.50	SNGL RM:	-
PART BRD:	-	% RED. CHILDREN:	20%	DINNER:	-

Shannon 1km

Mrs Mary Tobin
SHANNONSIDE
Clonlohan, Shannon/Newmarket Road, Newmarket-on-Fergus, Co Clare

		Shannon
OPEN:	All Year	
NO. ROOMS:	7	
ENSUITE:	6	(V)

TEL: **061 364191** FAX: **061 362069**

Morning guests welcome, early breakfasts available. 5 mins drive Shannon Airport on R472. Frommer recommended. Convenient Bunratty, Knappogue. Scenic area

B&B PPS:	£15/£17	SNGL OCC. DBLE/TPL:	£21.50/£23.50	SNGL RM:	-
PART BRD:	£180	% RED. CHILDREN:	50%	DINNER:	-

Mrs Ann Benson — Adare

In Adare

RIVERSDALE
Station Road, Adare, Co Limerick

OPEN: March-December
NO. ROOMS: 3
ENSUITE: 1

TEL: 061 396751   FAX: -

Modern friendly comfortable home, 3 mins walk to Churches, Hotels, Restaurants. Refreshments on arrival. Shannon Airport 30 mins. In Adare.

B&B PPS:	£15/£17	SNGL OCC. DBLE/TPL:	£21.50/£23.50	SNGL RM:	-
PART BRD:	-	% RED. CHILDREN:	-	DINNER:	-

Mary Boyle — Adare

Adare 3km

KNOCKREAD HOUSE
Croom Road, Adare, Co Limerick

OPEN: 1st April-1st November
NO. ROOMS: 3
ENSUITE: 1

TEL: 061 396935   FAX: -

A family run B/B, enjoy home comforts, wooded countryside, green pastures, country Walks, 5 mins drive Adare. Woodlands Hotel 1km.

B&B PPS:	£15.50/£17.50	SNGL OCC. DBLE/TPL:	£22/£24	SNGL RM:	-
PART BRD:	-	% RED. CHILDREN:	50%	DINNER:	-

Chris & Ursula Bromell — Adare

Adare 3km

CURRAGOUR HOUSE
Mount Earl, Adare, Co Limerick

OPEN: All Year except Christmas
NO. ROOMS: 3
ENSUITE: 3

TEL: 061 396705   FAX: -

Luxurious modern home just 3km from the beautiful village of Adare. Tranquil setting. Golf, Fishing, Horseriding nearby. Baby facilities. Tea/coffee.

B&B PPS:	£17	SNGL OCC. DBLE/TPL:	£23.50	SNGL RM:	-
PART BRD:	-	% RED. CHILDREN:	25%	DINNER:	-

Mrs. Patsy Davis — Adare

Croagh 1.5km

CLONSHIRE MILL
Croagh, Co Limerick

OPEN: 1st May-30th September
NO. ROOMS: 3
ENSUITE: -

TEL: 069 64200   FAX: -

19th century house on 2 1/2 acres, Gardens, Orchards, warm welcome, Donkeys, Pets, Stables available. Clonshire Equestrian Centre 3 minutes.

B&B PPS:	£15	SNGL OCC. DBLE/TPL:	£21.50	SNGL RM:	£15
PART BRD:	£180	% RED. CHILDREN:	50%	DINNER:	£12

Ms Anne Donegan — Adare

WESTFIELD HOUSE
Graigue, Adare, Co Limerick

OPEN: April-October
NO. ROOMS: 3
ENSUITE: 3

TEL: 061 396539   FAX: -

Luxurious home woodland surroundings. Off N21. Airport 30 mins. Ballymaloe Breakfast menu. Golfers Haven/Touring Base. Highly recommended. Personal attention guaranteed.

Adare 1km

B&B PPS:	£17	SNGL OCC. DBLE/TPL:	£23.50	SNGL RM:	-
PART BRD:	-	% RED. CHILDREN:	25%	DINNER:	-

└ In Adare

Miss Catherine Donegan O'Neill
BERKELEY LODGE
Station Road, Adare, Co Limerick
061 396857

Adare

OPEN:	All Year
NO. ROOMS:	6
ENSUITE:	5

(V)

TEL: **061 396857**   FAX: **061 396857**

Superb B+B, Hairdryers, Breakfast Menu. Hospitality first class. Walking distance Hotels/Restaurants/Churches/Heritage Centre.Turn at Roundabout (Shannon 40 mins)

B&B PPS:	**£17.50**	SNGL OCC. DBLE/TPL:	**£25**	SNGL RM:	-
PART BRD:	-	% RED. CHILDREN:	-	DINNER:	-

└ Adare 2km

Mrs Mary Dundon
FOXHOLLOW HOUSE
Croom Road, Adare, Co Limerick

Adare

OPEN:	All Year
NO. ROOMS:	4
ENSUITE:	4

(V)

TEL: **061 396776**   FAX: **061 396776**

AA QQQQ. Luxury quality Country House, Landscaped gardens, Peaceful Countryside, Breakfast Menu. Many recommendations. TV, Hairdryer, Tea/coffee in bedrooms.

B&B PPS:	**£18.50/£20**	SNGL OCC. DBLE/TPL:	**£25/£26.50**	SNGL RM:	-
PART BRD:	-	% RED. CHILDREN:	**50%**	DINNER:	-

└ In Adare

Mrs Geraldine Fitzgerald
SCEILIG HOUSE
Killarney Road, Adare, Co Limerick

Adare

OPEN:	All Year
NO. ROOMS:	5
ENSUITE:	4

(V)

TEL: **061 396627**   FAX: -

Welcoming family home in Adare. Convenient Hotels, Restaurants, Leisure Amenities, Pitch and Putt at rear. Ideal Touring Base. Shannon 30 minutes.

B&B PPS:	**£15/£17**	SNGL OCC. DBLE/TPL:	**£21.50/£23.50**	SNGL RM:	-
PART BRD:	-	% RED. CHILDREN:	**33.3%**	DINNER:	-

└ In Adare

Mrs Agnes Fitzpatrick
ADARE LODGE
Kildimo Road, Adare, Co Limerick

Adare

OPEN:	All Year
NO. ROOMS:	6
ENSUITE:	6

(V)

TEL: **061 396629**   FAX: **061 395060**

Highly recommended AA QQQQ award. TV, Tea & Coffee in rooms. Adjacent Dunraven Arm's Hotel. Golf, Horseriding, Churches. Shannon Airport 30 mins.

B&B PPS:	**£20/£22.50**	SNGL OCC. DBLE/TPL:	**£30/£35**	SNGL RM:	-
PART BRD:	-	% RED. CHILDREN:	-	DINNER:	-

└ Adare 2km

Kathleen Glavin
CASTLEVIEW HOUSE
Clonshire, Adare, Co Limerick

Adare

OPEN:	All Year
NO. ROOMS:	4
ENSUITE:	3

(V)

TEL: **061 396394**   FAX: **061 396394**

"O'Sullivans B&B Guide" Recommended. Beautiful warm restful country home. Award winning gardens. Tea/Coffee. Excellent Breakfasts including Pancakes. Electric blankets. Hairdryers.

B&B PPS:	**£15.50/£17.50**	SNGL OCC. DBLE/TPL:	**£22/£24**	SNGL RM:	-
PART BRD:	**£185**	% RED. CHILDREN:	**50%**	DINNER:	**£13**

In Adare

Mrs Anna Harrington
AVONA
Kildimo Rd., Adare, Co Limerick

Adare

OPEN:	March-October
NO. ROOMS:	4
ENSUITE:	4

TEL: **061 396323**   FAX: **061 396323**

AA QQQ. Adjacent to Church, Hotels, Restaurants, Heritage Centre. TV, radio, hairdryers, tea/coffee facilities in guest lounge, breakfast menu.

B&B PPS:	£17/£17.50	SNGL OCC. DBLE/TPL:	£25	SNGL RM:	-
PART BRD:	-	% RED. CHILDREN:	25%	DINNER:	-

In Adare

Oliver and May Haskett
ABBEY VILLA
Kildimo Road, Adare, Co Limerick

Adare

OPEN:	All Year except Christmas
NO. ROOMS:	6
ENSUITE:	6

TEL: **061 396113**   FAX: **061 396969**

Warm (Temp 70 min) Electric Blankets, Tea/Coffee facilities, Hairdryers, Satelite TV's, Laundry. Ground floor bedrooms adjacent Dungarvan Arms, Pubs, Restaurants.

B&B PPS:	£20	SNGL OCC. DBLE/TPL:	£35	SNGL RM:	£25
PART BRD:	-	% RED. CHILDREN:	-	DINNER:	-

Adare Village 1km

Mrs Pauline Hedderman
ELM HOUSE
Mondellihy, Adare, Co Limerick

Adare

OPEN:	All Year except Christmas
NO. ROOMS:	3
ENSUITE:	1

TEL: **061 396306**   FAX: -

Elegant Restored 1892 Georgian Home with character. Welcoming Tea, Coffee on arrival. Shannon Airport 30 mins. Adare 4 mins drive.

B&B PPS:	£15/£17	SNGL OCC. DBLE/TPL:	£21.50	SNGL RM:	-
PART BRD:	-	% RED. CHILDREN:	50%	DINNER:	-

Adare 1km

Betty Hickey
IVY HOUSE
Craigue, Adare, Co Limerick

Adare

OPEN:	1st April-31st October
NO. ROOMS:	4
ENSUITE:	3

TEL: **061 396270**   FAX: **061 396270**

Beautifully restored 18th century country home, surrounded by Gardens, Lawns, Shrubbery, furnished with Antiques and "objects D'Art". Homely atmosphere.

B&B PPS:	£15/£18	SNGL OCC. DBLE/TPL:	£25/£30	SNGL RM:	-
PART BRD:	-	% RED. CHILDREN:	20%	DINNER:	-

Adare Village 1.2km

Florence and Donal Hogan
COATESLAND HOUSE B&B
Tralee/Killarney Road, Adare N21, Co Limerick

Adare

OPEN:	1st January-23rd December
NO. ROOMS:	6
ENSUITE:	6

TEL: **061 396372**   FAX: **061 396833**

Modern warm home, AA 4Q award for 1994 - 1997 inc, friendly atmosphere. Many extras ie, filtered water.

B&B PPS:	£18	SNGL OCC. DBLE/TPL:	£28	SNGL RM:	£22
PART BRD:	-	% RED. CHILDREN:	20%	DINNER:	-

Mrs Mary Hogan
BEECH MOUNT
Ardshanballa, Adare, Co Limerick

 Adare

OPEN:	March-October
NO. ROOMS:	3
ENSUITE:	3

TEL: **061 396285**   FAX: -

Spacious Peaceful Family Home on quiet cul-de-sac. Magnificent views, large Garden. Friendly atmosphere, hairdryers, orthopaedic beds. Tea/coffee.

B&B PPS:	£18/£20	SNGL OCC. DBLE/TPL:	£25/£26.50	SNGL RM:	-
PART BRD:	-	% RED. CHILDREN:	25%	DINNER:	-

Adare 0.5km

Mrs Maura Linnane
CARRIGANE HOUSE
Reinroe, Adare, Co Limerick

Adare

OPEN:	All Year except Christmas
NO. ROOMS:	6
ENSUITE:	6

TEL: **061 396778**   FAX: -

Luxurious and spacious country home just off main road, morning guests welcome, tea/coffee and home baking. Near Woodlands Hotel.

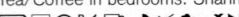

B&B PPS:	£17.50	SNGL OCC. DBLE/TPL:	£23.50/£25	SNGL RM:	-
PART BRD:	-	% RED. CHILDREN:	33.3%	DINNER:	-

Adare 2km

Mrs Margaret Liston
GLENELG
Mondellihy, Adare, Co Limerick

Adare

OPEN:	All Year except Christmas
NO. ROOMS:	3
ENSUITE:	3

TEL: **061 396077**   FAX: -

Luxurious superwarm home, retains Country Peacefulness, highly recommended. Tea/Coffee in bedrooms. Shannon airport 30 mins. Adare 4min drive. TV, hairdryers.

B&B PPS:	£17.50/£19	SNGL OCC. DBLE/TPL:	£24/£25.50	SNGL RM:	-
PART BRD:	-	% RED. CHILDREN:	50%	DINNER:	-

Adare 2km

O'Donnell Family
TUOGH-VILLA
Askeaton Road, Adare, Co Limerick

Adare

OPEN:	1st January-31st December
NO. ROOMS:	4
ENSUITE:	4

TEL: **061 396432**   FAX: **061 396432**

We welcome all our guests. Refreshments on arrival. Fishing, Golfing, Pitch & Putt, Horseriding, Shooting and Leisure and Heritage Centres nearby.

B&B PPS:	£17	SNGL OCC. DBLE/TPL:	£25	SNGL RM:	-
PART BRD:	-	% RED. CHILDREN:	25%	DINNER:	-

Adare Village 2km

Mrs Martha O'Riordan
EAGLE HOUSE
Smithfield, Croagh, Adare, Co Limerick

Adare

OPEN:	All Year
NO. ROOMS:	3
ENSUITE:	2

TEL: **069 64701/63303**   FAX: **069 63303**

Luxury Quality Georgian house located on family Farm, many recommendations. TV, Hairdryer, Bedrooms, Tea/Coffee, Golf, Horseriding. Shannon Airport 35 mins.

B&B PPS:	£15/£18	SNGL OCC. DBLE/TPL:	£25/£35	SNGL RM:	-
PART BRD:	£180	% RED. CHILDREN:	10%	DINNER:	£15

Adare 3km

Michael and Jennie Power
HILLCREST COUNTRY HOME
Clonshire, Croagh, Adare, Co Limerick

Adare

OPEN:	1st April-30th November
NO. ROOMS:	4
ENSUITE:	3

TEL: **061 396534**   FAX: **061 396534**   EMAIL: **hillcrest@webnet.ie.**

Hospitable, relaxed home. Amidst beautiful, tranquil pastures where nature abounds. Traditional farming. Forest and nature trails. Medieval ruins. Frommer recommended.

B&B PPS:	**£15.50/£17.50**	SNGL OCC. DBLE/TPL:	**£21.50/£23.50**	SNGL RM:	-
PART BRD:	-	% RED. CHILDREN:	-	DINNER:	**£14**

— Adare 5km

Mrs Bridie Riordan
CHURCHVIEW HOUSE
Kildimo Road, Adare, Co Limerick

Adare

OPEN:	All Year except Christmas
NO. ROOMS:	5
ENSUITE:	4

TEL: **061 396371**   FAX: -

Warm, friendly home in Ireland's prettiest village. Radio in bedrooms, tea facilities in lounge, sun lounge for guests. Airport 40 minutes.

B&B PPS:	**£15/£17**	SNGL OCC. DBLE/TPL:	**£21.50/£23.50**	SNGL RM:	**£21/£23.50**
PART BRD:	-	% RED. CHILDREN:	**25%**	DINNER:	-

— Adare

Nora M Rouine
OAKWOOD HOUSE
Graigue, Adare, Co Limerick

Adare

OPEN:	April-October
NO. ROOMS:	3
ENSUITE:	2

TEL: **061 396075**   FAX: -

Spacious family home in quiet wooded countryside off N21 Dingle/Killarney. Highly recommended. Golf, Equestrian Centre, Fishing nearby. Airport 30 mins.

B&B PPS:	**£15/£17**	SNGL OCC. DBLE/TPL:	**£21.50/£23.50**	SNGL RM:	-
PART BRD:	-	% RED. CHILDREN:	**25%**	DINNER:	-

— Adare 1km

Phil Clancy
DRUMINACLARA HOUSE
Pallaskenry, Co Limerick

Askeaton/Pallaskenry

OPEN:	All Year except Christmas
NO. ROOMS:	4
ENSUITE:	4

TEL: **061 393148**   FAX: -

2km from Kilcornan House off N69, scenic route, country setting, large attractive grounds, 3km Curragh Chase caravan park. Golf and fishing locally.

B&B PPS:	**£17**	SNGL OCC. DBLE/TPL:	**£23.50**	SNGL RM:	-
PART BRD:	**£180**	% RED. CHILDREN:	**25%**	DINNER:	**£12**

— Askeaton 6km

Mrs Maura Galvin
KILLEEN HOUSE
Askeaton Road, Limerick/Foynes Road, Kilcornan, Co Limerick

Askeaton

OPEN:	All Year except Christmas
NO. ROOMS:	6
ENSUITE:	3

TEL: **061 393023**   FAX: -

On N69 scenic route, Curraghchase Caravan Park, Golf, Fishing, Horseriding locally. Celtic Park gardens nearby. Shannon airport 40 mins.

B&B PPS:	**£15/£17**	SNGL OCC. DBLE/TPL:	**£21.50/£23.50**	SNGL RM:	**£17**
PART BRD:	**£180**	% RED. CHILDREN:	**50%**	DINNER:	**£12**

— Askeaton 5km

Ballyneety 2km

Mrs Mary Conway Ryan
FOUR SEASONS
Boherlode, Ballyneety, Co Limerick

Ballyneety

OPEN:	All Year except Christmas
NO. ROOMS:	5
ENSUITE:	5

 (V)

TEL: **061 351365**   FAX: -

Suberb residence, overlooking Golf Course, view from conservatory. T.V, hairdryers tea/coffee in rooms, orthopaedic beds. Shannon, Bunratty, Lough Gur nearby.

B&B PPS:	**£17**	SNGL OCC. DBLE/TPL:	**£23.50**	SNGL RM:	**£23.50**
PART BRD:	-	% RED. CHILDREN:	**50%**	DINNER:	**£13**

Limerick 7km

Mrs Margaret Ryan
GLENGROVE
Glen, Ballyneety, Co Limerick

Ballyneety

OPEN:	All Year except Christmas
NO. ROOMS:	4
ENSUITE:	2

(V)

TEL: **061 351399**   FAX: **061 351399**

Home overlooking Golf Course, tea/coffee and hairdryer in bedrooms. Ideal for Lough Gur, Shannon, Bunratty. Road R512, parallel with N7, N24.

B&B PPS:	**£15/£17**	SNGL OCC. DBLE/TPL:	**£21.50/£23.50**	SNGL RM:	-
PART BRD:	**£180**	% RED. CHILDREN:	**50%**	DINNER:	**£12**

Castleconnell 1km

Mrs Margaret Tyrrell
EDELWEISS
Stradbally, Castleconnell off N7, Co Limerick

Castleconnell

OPEN:	1st March-31st October
NO. ROOMS:	3
ENSUITE:	2

(V)

TEL: **061 377397**   FAX: -

Cosy family-run home, lovely view beside Castle Oaks House Hotel, River Shannon, Fishing, lovely Village, Restaurants, Limerick City 7 miles.

B&B PPS:	**£15/£17**	SNGL OCC. DBLE/TPL:	**£21.50/£23.50**	SNGL RM:	-
PART BRD:	-	% RED. CHILDREN:	**20%**	DINNER:	-

In Foynes

Jim & Teresa Counihan
RAHEEN HOUSE
Foynes, Co Limerick

Foynes

OPEN:	1st May-31st October
NO. ROOMS:	3
ENSUITE:	-

 (V)

TEL: **069 65236**   FAX: -

Bungalow on Shannon Estuary. Woodland Walks, Swimming Pool. Flying Boat Museum. Golf Tourist Office, Pubs, Restaurants nearby in village . N69.

B&B PPS:	**£15**	SNGL OCC. DBLE/TPL:	**£21.50**	SNGL RM:	-
PART BRD:	-	% RED. CHILDREN:	**20%**	DINNER:	-

Tarbert 4km

Mrs Catherine Sweeney
SCENIC VIEW HOUSE
Ballyculhane, Glin, Co Limerick

Glin

OPEN:	All Year
NO. ROOMS:	4
ENSUITE:	2

(V)

TEL: **068 34242/087 2313146**   FAX: -

Bungalow, 7 mins Tarbert Car Ferry. Panoramic view of Shannon Estuary. Enroute from Shannon to Ring of Kerry on N69.

B&B PPS:	**£15/£17**	SNGL OCC. DBLE/TPL:	**£21.50/£23.50**	SNGL RM:	-
PART BRD:	-	% RED. CHILDREN:	**20%**	DINNER:	**£12**

Kilmallock 9km

Kilfinane

Mrs Patricia Nunan
ST. ANDREW'S VILLA
Kilfinane, Kilmallock, Co Limerick

OPEN:	7th April-31st October
No. ROOMS:	4
ENSUITE:	-

TEL: **063 91008**   FAX: -

Spacious Georgian House in country setting, accessible via R517, N8, R512 or N20. Warm welcome assured.

B&B PPS:	**£15**	SNGL OCC. DBLE/TPL:	**£21.50**	SNGL RM:	**£15**
PART BRD:	-	% RED. CHILDREN:	**25%**	DINNER:	**£14**

In Kilmallock

Kilmallock

Mrs Anne O'Sullivan
DEEBERT HOUSE
Kilmallock, Co Limerick

OPEN:	1st February-30th November
No. ROOMS:	5
ENSUITE:	4

TEL: **063 98106**   FAX: **063 82002**

Splendid Georgian residence, award winning gardens. Ideal touring centre. Adjacent to Historic Sites, Golf, Hill Walking, Horseriding. On R515.

B&B PPS:	**£15/£17**	SNGL OCC. DBLE/TPL:	**£21.50/£23.50**	SNGL RM:	-
PART BRD:	**£180**	% RED. CHILDREN:	**25%**	DINNER:	**£13**

Limerick 5km

Limerick City/Castleroy

Lelia & Bernard Hanly
SANDVILLA
Monaleen Road, Castletroy, Co Limerick

OPEN:	All Year except Christmas
No. ROOMS:	4
ENSUITE:	2

TEL: **061 336484**   FAX: -

Luxurious bungalow off Dublin/Wexford roads. Award winning breakfast menu. Coffee, TV in rooms. Near Castletroy Kilmurry Hotels, University, Golf.

B&B PPS:	**£15/£17**	SNGL OCC. DBLE/TPL:	**£21.50/£23.50**	SNGL RM:	-
PART BRD:	**£180**	% RED. CHILDREN:	**25%**	DINNER:	**£12**

In Limerick City

Limerick City

Mrs Nora Coyne
MOUNT GERARD B&B
O'Connell Ave., Limerick City N21, Co Limerick

OPEN:	All Year
No. ROOMS:	3
ENSUITE:	2

TEL: **061 314981**   FAX: -

Beautiful family run Victorian home .5km to Rail/Bus Station, City Centre. T.V's, hairdryer, tea facilities. Warm welcome.

B&B PPS:	**£16/£20**	SNGL OCC. DBLE/TPL:	**£22/£28**	SNGL RM:	-
PART BRD:	-	% RED. CHILDREN:	**40%**	DINNER:	-

In Limerick City Centre

Limerick City

Mrs Jean N Daly
ROSMOY TOWNHOUSE
1 Alexandra Tce, O'Connell Ave., Limerick City N20-N21,Co Limerick

OPEN:	All Year except Christmas
No. ROOMS:	4
ENSUITE:	4

TEL: **061 314556**   FAX: -

Warm comfortable, Victorian town house. Distinct first class accommodation, convenient to Bus/Rail and Airport. T.V, tea/coffee facilities. N20/N21

B&B PPS:	**£17/£20**	SNGL OCC. DBLE/TPL:	**£25/£28**	SNGL RM:	**£22**
PART BRD:	-	% RED. CHILDREN:	**30%**	DINNER:	-

Limerick 6km

Michael & Therese Dvinskis
SHEMOND HOUSE
Ballyglass, Clonlara, Nr Limerick, Co Limerick

Limerick City

OPEN:	1st March-30th November	
NO. ROOMS:	6	
ENSUITE:	5	(V)

TEL: **061 343767/086 8117146**   FAX: -

Family run home, superb surroundings, Airport 25 minutes. Bunratty Castle, Fishing, Golfing, Horse Riding nearby. Complimentary Tea/Coffee. Hairdryers bedrooms.

B&B PPS:	**£15/£17**	SNGL OCC. DBLE/TPL:	**£21.50/£23.50**	SNGL RM:	-
PART BRD:	**£185**	% RED. CHILDREN:	**20%**	DINNER:	**£12**

Limerick 2km

Liam & Antoinette Fitzgibbon
WHITE HOUSE B & B
St Annes, Raheen, Co Limerick

Limerick City

OPEN:	All Year except Christmas	
NO. ROOMS:	3	
ENSUITE:	3	(V)

TEL: **061 301709**   FAX: -

On N20 direction Cork/Tralee. Beside Raheen roundabout. Restaurants etc walking distance. Bus stop to City (2 km) at front gate.

B&B PPS:	**£17/£19**	SNGL OCC. DBLE/TPL:	**£25/£28**	SNGL RM:	-
PART BRD:	-	% RED. CHILDREN:	**50%**	DINNER:	-

Limerick 3km

Mrs Elizabeth Gordon
AVONDALE
Cratloe Road, Limerick, Co Limerick

Limerick

OPEN:	All Year except Christmas	
NO. ROOMS:	3	
ENSUITE:	2	(V)

TEL: **061 451697**   FAX: -

Warm comfortable country family home. Peaceful surroundings, ensuite bedrooms. Choice Restaurants, leisure activities. Tea/Coffee available. Bunratty 3 miles. Airport 9 miles.

B&B PPS:	**£15/£17**	SNGL OCC. DBLE/TPL:	**£21.50/£23.50**	SNGL RM:	-
PART BRD:	-	% RED. CHILDREN:	**50%**	DINNER:	-

Limerick City 3km

Mrs Evelyn Moore
AVONDOYLE COUNTRY HOME
Dooradoyle Road, Co Limerick

Limerick City

OPEN:	All Year except Christmas	
NO. ROOMS:	4	
ENSUITE:	2	(V)

TEL: **061 301590/301501**   FAX: **061/301501**   EMAIL: **avondoyl@iol.ie**

Family run, 3km city, 2km off N20 at Crescent Shopping Centre roundabout. Hairdryer, tea facilities, Adare, Bunratty, Shannon Airport 20 minutes.

B&B PPS:	**£15/£18**	SNGL OCC. DBLE/TPL:	**£21.50/£24.50**	SNGL RM:	**£19**
PART BRD:	-	% RED. CHILDREN:	**40%**	DINNER:	-

Limerick City 2km

Mrs Carmel Beresford
ANNESVILLE
Ennis Road, Limerick, Co Limerick

Limerick City - Ennis Road

OPEN:	All Year except Christmas	
NO. ROOMS:	4	
ENSUITE:	3	(V)

TEL: **061 452703**   FAX: -

Very comfortable, well heated Town House, Sun Lounge overlooking small lawn with attractive flower borders. Frommer recommended. Rooms ensuite and i

B&B PPS:	**£15/£17**	SNGL OCC. DBLE/TPL:	-	SNGL RM:	-
PART BRD:	-	% RED. CHILDREN:	-	DINNER:	-

Limerick City 3km

Mrs Bergie Carroll
COONAGH LODGE
Coonagh, Off Ennis Rd., Limerick, Co Limerick
Tel: **061 327050**   Fax: -

Limerick City / Ennis Road

Open:	1st January-15th December
No. Rooms:	6
Ensuite:	6

(V)

Family run home, 10 minutes drive, Shannon, Bunratty. 5 minutes to City, off Ennis Road Roundabout at Elm Motors Garage.

B&B PPS:	£17	Sngl Occ. Dble/Tpl:	£23.50	Sngl Rm:	-
Part Brd:	-	% Red. Children:	50%	Dinner:	-

Limerick City 2km

Mrs Mary Collins
ST ANTHONY'S
8 Coolraine Terrace, Ennis Road, Limerick, Co Limerick
Tel: **061 452607**   Fax: -

Limerick City - Ennis Road

Open:	All Year except Christmas
No. Rooms:	3
Ensuite:	1

(V)

House adjacent to City Centre, beside Ryan Hotel on Shannon Airport/Bunratty Castle road. Recommended by Frommer, other travel guides.

B&B PPS:	£15.50/£17.50	Sngl Occ. Dble/Tpl:	£22/£24	Sngl Rm:	£15.50
Part Brd:	-	% Red. Children:	-	Dinner:	-

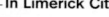

In Limerick City

Mary Cusack
CLONEEN HOUSE
Ennis Road, Limerick, Co Limerick
Tel: **061 454461**   Fax: **061 455545**

Limerick City - Ennis Road

Open:	7th January-22nd December
No. Rooms:	6
Ensuite:	6

Elegant Edwardian House, 10 mins walk City Centre. Perfect base for Golfing, Fishing, Horseriding, Shopping, touring the Historic and beautiful Mid-West.

B&B PPS:	£18/£22	Sngl Occ. Dble/Tpl:	£22/£28	Sngl Rm:	£22/£28
Part Brd:	-	% Red. Children:	25%	Dinner:	-

Limerick 2km

Des & Pauline Daly
ARMADA LODGE (TICKINCOR)
1 Elm Drive, Caherdavin Lawn, Ennis Road, Limerick, Co Limerick
Tel: **061 326993**   Fax: -

Limerick City - Ennis Road

Open:	All Year except Christmas
No. Rooms:	5
Ensuite:	2

 (V)

Modern Town house convenient to Shannon Airport, City Centre, Bunratty and King Johns Castle, opposite Greenhills Hotel, Private Car Parking.

B&B PPS:	£15/£17	Sngl Occ. Dble/Tpl:	£21.50/£23.50	Sngl Rm:	-
Part Brd:	-	% Red. Children:	50%	Dinner:	-

In Limerick City

Mrs Catherine A Gavin
SHANNONVILLE
Ennis Road, (Adjacent Limerick Ryan Hotel), Limerick, Co Limerick
Tel: **061 453690**   Fax: -

Limerick City / Ennis Road

Open:	May-September
No. Rooms:	3
Ensuite:	-

 (V)

Comfortable home. Quiet area Just off main road (N18). Adjacent Limerick Ryan Hotel and Shannon Bus. Walking distance City Centre.

B&B PPS:	£15	Sngl Occ. Dble/Tpl:	£21.50	Sngl Rm:	-
Part Brd:	-	% Red. Children:	-	Dinner:	-

Limerick 3km

Patricia Keane
SANTOLINA
Coonagh, Ennis Road, Limerick, Co Limerick

Limerick City / Ennis Road

OPEN:	All Year except Christmas
No. ROOMS:	6
ENSUITE:	6

TEL: **061 451590**   FAX: -

Spacious country home. Ground floor accommodation. Coonagh is off N18 at roundabout near Elm Motor Garage. Convenient City, Bunratty Castle, Shannon.

B&B PPS:	£16/£17	SNGL OCC. DBLE/TPL:	£18/£20	SNGL RM:	-
PART BRD:	-	% RED. CHILDREN:	50%	DINNER:	-

In Limerick

Mrs Joan McSweeney
TREBOR
Ennis Road, Limerick City, Co Limerick

Limerick City / Ennis Road

OPEN:	1st April-1st November
No. ROOMS:	4
ENSUITE:	4

TEL: **061 454632**   FAX: **061 454632**

Old fashioned Town House, short walk City Centre on Bunratty Castle/Shannon Airport road. Tea/coffee.

B&B PPS:	£17/£18	SNGL OCC. DBLE/TPL:	£23.50/£24.50	SNGL RM:	-
PART BRD:	£180	% RED. CHILDREN:	20%	DINNER:	-

Limerick 3km

John and Betty O'Shea
LISHEEN
Coonagh, Ennis Road, Limerick, Co Limerick

Limerick City - Ennis Road

OPEN:	1st March-31st October
No. ROOMS:	4
ENSUITE:	-

TEL: **061 455393**   FAX: -

Quiet Rural Setting, off Ennis road roundabout. Convenient to Shannon Airport, Bunratty and the West. Le Guide Du Routard recommended.

B&B PPS:	£15	SNGL OCC. DBLE/TPL:	£21.50	SNGL RM:	-
PART BRD:	-	% RED. CHILDREN:	25%	DINNER:	-

In Limerick City

Carole O'Toole
GLEN EAGLES
12 Vereker Gardens, Ennis Road, Limerick, Co Limerick

Limerick City - Ennis Road

OPEN:	1st.March-5th November
No. ROOMS:	4
ENSUITE:	4

TEL: **061 455521**   FAX: **061 455521**

Quiet cul-de-sac. Nearest B&B to the City Centre, Train/Bus/Tourist Office. Off N18 beside Jurys Hotel. Frommer recommended. Hairdryers.

B&B PPS:	£17/£18	SNGL OCC. DBLE/TPL:	£23.50/£24.50	SNGL RM:	£20/£22
PART BRD:	-	% RED. CHILDREN:	10%	DINNER:	£12

Limerick City 2km

John O'Toole
ENNIS HOUSE
2 Inagh Drive, Caherdavin, Ennis Road, Limerick, Co Limerick

Limerick City - Ennis Road

OPEN:	1st April-31st October
No. ROOMS:	4
ENSUITE:	4

TEL: **061 326257**   FAX: **061 326257**

Comfortable House on Shannon/Bunratty Castle Road, beside Greenhills Hotel. Shannon Bus Stop 20yds. Early morning arrivals welcome. TV rooms.

B&B PPS:	£17	SNGL OCC. DBLE/TPL:	£23.50	SNGL RM:	£18.50
PART BRD:	-	% RED. CHILDREN:	10%	DINNER:	-

Mary Power
CURRAGHGOWER HOUSE
Ennis Road, Limerick City, Co Limerick

OPEN:	All Year	
No. ROOMS:	3	
ENSUITE:	2	

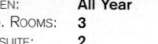

TEL: **061 454716**   FAX: -

Comfortable 3 bedroom home, walking distance of City Centre on Shannon, Bunratty Castle Airport Road. Frommer guide recommended.

B&B PPS:	£15/£18	SNGL OCC. DBLE/TPL:	£21.50	SNGL RM:	-
PART BRD:	-	% RED. CHILDREN:	-	DINNER:	-

Limerick City 1km

Noreen O'Farrell
DOONEEN LODGE
Caher Road, Mungret, Co Limerick

OPEN:	All Year except Christmas	
No. ROOMS:	3	
ENSUITE:	2	

TEL: **061 301332**   FAX: -

0.5 km off N20/21 between Limerick, Patrickswell, Sign-posted, Tea, Coffee facilities. All rooms TV. Convenient Adare, Bunratty, Shannon. Limerick 5 km.

B&B PPS:	£15/£17	SNGL OCC. DBLE/TPL:	£21.50/£23.50	SNGL RM:	-
PART BRD:	-	% RED. CHILDREN:	40%	DINNER:	-

Limerick 5km

Mrs Mary Walsh-Seaver
RINNAKNOCK
Glenstal, Murroe, Co Limerick

OPEN:	1st April-31st October	
No. ROOMS:	4	
ENSUITE:	3	

TEL: **061 386189**   FAX: -

Spacious bungalow beside Glenstal Abbey. Off N7 and N24. On Slieve Felim Cycling and Walking Trails.

B&B PPS:	£15/£17	SNGL OCC. DBLE/TPL:	£21.50/£23.50	SNGL RM:	-
PART BRD:	£177	% RED. CHILDREN:	25%	DINNER:	£12

Limerick

Ms Ita Devine
TUDOR LODGE
Killoughteen, Newcastle West, Co Limerick

OPEN:	All Year	
No. ROOMS:	3	
ENSUITE:	3	

TEL: **069 62642**   FAX: -

Dormer bungalow with conservatory and patio in beautiful secluded area Surrounded by lovely lawns, shrubs and beautiful Rose Garden.

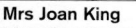

B&B PPS:	£17	SNGL OCC. DBLE/TPL:	£23.50	SNGL RM:	-
PART BRD:	-	% RED. CHILDREN:	50%	DINNER:	-

Newcastle West 3km

Mrs Joan King
RANCH HOUSE
Cork Road, Newcastle West, Co Limerick

OPEN:	1st January-20th December	
No. ROOMS:	5	
ENSUITE:	5	

TEL: **069 62313**   FAX: -

Luxurious home on large landscape gardens, quiet peaceful setting halfway between Shannon/Killarney/Tralee, adjacent to 18 hole Golf Course.

B&B PPS:	£17	SNGL OCC. DBLE/TPL:	£23.50	SNGL RM:	-
PART BRD:	£180	% RED. CHILDREN:	25%	DINNER:	£12

Newcastle West 1km

Newcastle West 1km

Mrs Eileen Murphy
THE ORCHARD
**Limerick Road, Newcastle West,
Co Limerick**

Newcastle West

Tel: **069 61029** Fax: -

Open:	1st January-31st December
No. Rooms:	5
Ensuite:	4

(V)

Century old home with spacious rooms, on secluded grounds. Own farm produce, breakfast chioce. Tea/coffee facilities in lounge.

| B&B PPS: | £15/£17 | Sngl Occ. Dble/Tpl: | £21.50/£23.50 | Sngl Rm: | - |
| Part Brd: | - | % Red. Children: | 50% | Dinner: | £14 |

Newcastle West 2km

Mrs Carmel O'Brien
BALLINGOWAN HOUSE
**Limerick Road, Newcastle West,
Co Limerick**

Newcastle West

Tel: **069 62341** Fax: -

Open:	1st January-31st December
No. Rooms:	5
Ensuite:	5

(V)

Luxurious pink Georgian house with distinctive features, attractive gardens, N21. Halfway stop between Shannon/Killarney. 18 hole Golf Course nearby.

| B&B PPS: | £17 | Sngl Occ. Dble/Tpl: | £23.50 | Sngl Rm: | - |
| Part Brd: | £180 | % Red. Children: | 25% | Dinner: | £12 |

Patrickswell 2km

Eilish Buckley
LAUREL LODGE
**Adare Road, Newboro, Patrickswell,
Co Limerick**

Patrickswell

Tel: **061 355059** Fax: **061 355059**

Open:	1st April-31st October
No. Rooms:	4
Ensuite:	3

(V)

-

Luxurious country home, award winning gardens. Frommer recommended. Between Limerick & Adare, 1.5 KM off N21 after Patrickswell. Shannon Airport 25 minutes.

| B&B PPS: | £15/£17 | Sngl Occ. Dble/Tpl: | £21.50/£23.50 | Sngl Rm: | £20 |
| Part Brd: | - | % Red. Children: | 50% | Dinner: | - |

Limerick 5km

The Geary Family
CARNLEA HOUSE
**Caher Road, Cloughkeating,
Patrickswell, Co Limerick**

Patrickswell

Tel: **061 302902/087 2386094** Fax: -

Open:	1st February-31st October
No. Rooms:	4
Ensuite:	2

(V)

Spacious bungalow situated midway between Limerick City and Patrickswell (N20). Ideal stopover, Cork/Kerry/Bunratty/Shannon. Friendly atmosphere. Highly recommended

| B&B PPS: | £15/£17 | Sngl Occ. Dble/Tpl: | £21.50/£23.50 | Sngl Rm: | £18/£20 |
| Part Brd: | - | % Red. Children: | 40% | Dinner: | - |

In Patrickswell

Mrs Margaret Kearney
BEECH GROVE
Barnakyle, Patrickswell, Co Limerick

Patrickswell

Tel: **061 355493** Fax: -

Open:	1st May-31st September
No. Rooms:	4
Ensuite:	1

(V)

Bungalow on N20/N21, between Limerick & Adare. Walking distance from Patrickswell village. Airport 20 mins. Golf, Fishing, Greyhound Track Racing. Visa accepted.

| B&B PPS: | £15/£17 | Sngl Occ. Dble/Tpl: | £21.50/£23.50 | Sngl Rm: | £19 |
| Part Brd: | - | % Red. Children: | 33% | Dinner: | - |

Limerick 2km

Mrs. Deirdre O'Grady
IROKO
Caher Road, Cloughkeating,
Patrickswell, Co Limerick

TEL: **061 227861**   FAX: -

OPEN:	All Year except Christmas
No. ROOMS:	5
ENSUITE:	5

First class accommodation, 2nd house off N20/21, all rooms T.V, tea facilities, hairdryers. Convenient to Golf, Adare, Bunratty, Shannon.

| B&B PPS: | **£17** | SNGL OCC. DBLE/TPL: | - | SNGL RM: | - |
| PART BRD: | - | % RED. CHILDREN: | **20%** | DINNER: | - |

Patrickswell 0.5km

Mrs Lily Woulfe
LURRIGA LODGE
Patrickswell, Co Limerick
061 355411

TEL: **061 355411**   FAX: **061 355411**

OPEN:	1st April-30thSeptember
No. ROOMS:	4
ENSUITE:	3

Luxurious country home set in landscape Gardens. Warm welcome with complimentary tea/coffee. Shannon Airport 20 minutes, Adare 6 minutes drive.

| B&B PPS: | **£17** | SNGL OCC. DBLE/TPL: | **£23.50** | SNGL RM: | **£20** |
| PART BRD: | - | % RED. CHILDREN: | **25%** | DINNER: | - |

In Rathkeale

Theresa Fitzgerald
THE WILLOWS
Castlematrix, Rathkeale, Co Limerick

TEL: **069 63157**   FAX: **069 63157**

OPEN:	All Year
No. ROOMS:	4
ENSUITE:	4

Luxurious very spacious home. Beautiful antique furniture, conservatory. Beautiful spacious gardens, patio. Ideal touring base Cork/Kerry/Clare. N21 route.

| B&B PPS: | **£22.50/£25** | SNGL OCC. DBLE/TPL: | **£29/£31.50** | SNGL RM: | - |
| PART BRD: | **£180** | % RED. CHILDREN: | **50%** | DINNER: | **£12** |

BOOKINGS

We recommend your first and last night is pre-booked. Your hosts will make a booking for you at your next selected home for the cost of the phone call. When travelling in high season (June, July, August), it is essential to pre-book your accommodation – preferably the evening before, or the following morning to avoid disappointment.

SOME HOMES ARE CLOSED DURING THE WINTER.
WHEN TRAVELLING OFF-SEASON IT IS ADVISABLE TO CALL
AHEAD AND GIVE A TIME OF ARRIVAL TO ENSURE YOUR HOSTS
ARE AT HOME TO GREET YOU.

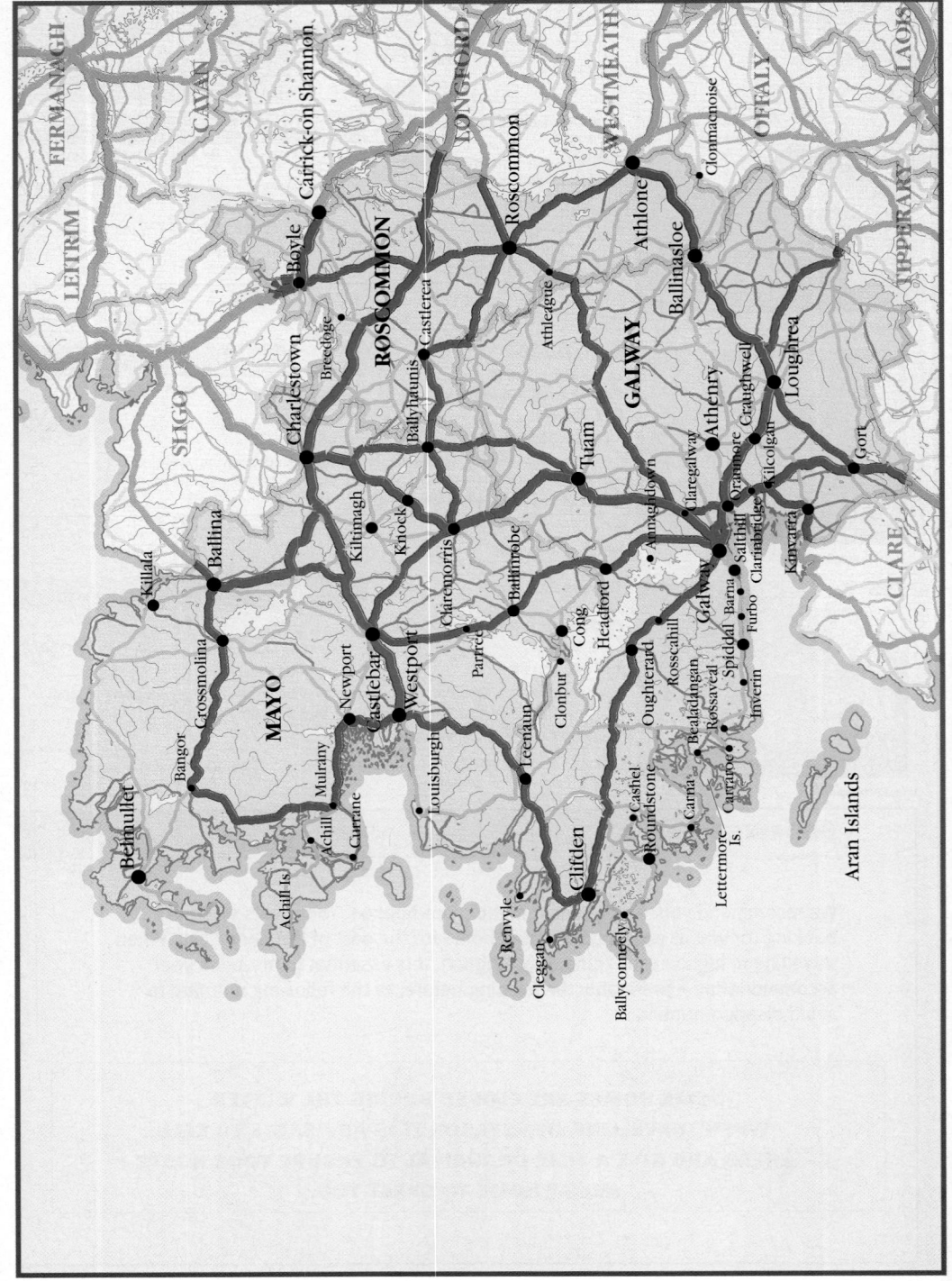

© ERA-Maptec

There is a special quality about these three beautiful Counties in the West of Ireland that is unique in Europe. The welcome is heartwarming, the quality of life, people and landscape is all there for our visitor to share.

The spectacularly beautiful countryside, the coast that has been etched by the Atlantic, rambling hills and mountains and the lovely lakes and bays that mirror that special light from the clear skies over the countryside. Each County has it's own special attractions and rich in all that is best in Irish folklore, music and song. There is something for here for everyone, you will not be disappointed.

Area Representatives

GALWAY
Mrs. Patricia Greaney, High Tide, 9 Grattan Park, Coast Road, Galway City.
Tel: 091-584324. Fax: 091-584324 (manual).

Mrs. Mary Noone, Ashbrook House, Dublin Road, Oranmore, Co. Galway.
Tel: 091-794196. Fax: 091-794196 (manual).

MAYO
Mrs. Carol O'Gorman, Ashfort, Galway/Knock Road, Charlestown,
Co. Mayo. Tel: 09454706.

Mr. Robert Kilkelly, St. Anthony's, Distillery Road, Westport, Co. Mayo.
Tel: 098-25172. Fax: 098-26121.

Mrs. Eileen Pierce, Four Winds, Maryland, Breaffy Road, Castlebar,
Co. Mayo. Tel: 094-21767.

ROSCOMMON
Mr. Martin Mitchell, Abbey House, Boyle, Co. Roscommon.
Tel: 079-62385.

Tourist Information Offices

Galway City
Eyre Square
Tel: (091) 563081

Oughterard
Tel: (091) 552808

Westport
The Mall
Tel: (098) 25711

Galway City 9km

Mrs Veronica Marley
SILVER BIRCH
Clonboo, Annaghdown, Co Galway

Annaghdown

OPEN:	1st March-31st October	
NO. ROOMS:	4	
ENSUITE:	3	(V)

TEL: **091 791036**   FAX: -

Friendly home. Main route Cong/Connemara on N84. Walking distance Pub/Restaurant - Clonboo Riding School, Galway City 9km, Lough Corrib 4km.

B&B PPS:	£17	SNGL OCC. DBLE/TPL:	£23.50	SNGL RM:	£19
PART BRD:	-	% RED. CHILDREN:	20%	DINNER:	--

Kilronan 4.5km

Mrs Bridie Conneely
BEACH VIEW HOUSE
**Oatquarter, Kilronan, Inis Mor,
Aran Islands, Co Galway**

Aran Islands (Inismore)

OPEN:	1st May-30th September	
NO. ROOMS:	6	
ENSUITE:	-	(V)

TEL: **099 61141**   FAX: **099 61141**

Family run home, 2 mins to safe sandy beach. Close to famous Fort Dun Aengus, Pub & Restaurant.

B&B PPS:	£15	SNGL OCC. DBLE/TPL:	£21.50	SNGL RM:	-
PART BRD:	-	% RED. CHILDREN:	-	DINNER:	-

Kilronan 6km

Mrs Margaret Conneely
CREGMOUNT HOUSE
**Creig-An-Cheirin, Kilronan, Inis Mor,
Aran Islands, Co Galway**

Aran Islands (Inismore)

OPEN:	April-31st October	
NO. ROOMS:	3	
ENSUITE:	1	(V)

TEL: **099 61139**   FAX: -

Spectacular sea panorama from house. Set in unspoilt location. Historic monuments easily accessible. Qualified cook/London City and Guilds.

B&B PPS:	£16/£17	SNGL OCC. DBLE/TPL:	£24.50/£25	SNGL RM:	£19/£20
PART BRD:	£180	% RED. CHILDREN:	25%	DINNER:	£12

In Kilronan

Bridie and Patrick McDonagh
AN CRUGAN
**Kilronan, Inis Mor, Aran Islands,
Co Galway**

Aran Islands (Inismore)

OPEN:	March-November	
NO. ROOMS:	6	
ENSUITE:	5	(V)

TEL: **099 61150**   FAX: **099 61468**

Situated in Kilronan Village, 10 mins walk from Harbour, convenient to Restaurants, Pubs, Beaches. Visa accepted.

B&B PPS:	£15/£17	SNGL OCC. DBLE/TPL:	£22/£25	SNGL RM:	-
PART BRD:	-	% RED. CHILDREN:	50%	DINNER:	-

Kilronan 6.5km

Joe & Maura Wolfe
MAN OF ARAN COTTAGES
**Kilmurvey, Inish Mor, Aran Islands,
Co Galway**

Aran Islands

OPEN:	17th March-October	
NO. ROOMS:	2	
ENSUITE:	1	(V)

TEL: **099 61301**   FAX: -

Built for the making of the film "The Man of Aran" on an acre of organic vegetable and herb gardens.

B&B PPS:	£16/£21	SNGL OCC. DBLE/TPL:	£22.50/£27.50	SNGL RM:	-
PART BRD:	-	% RED. CHILDREN:	-	DINNER:	£14.50

Angela Lyons
NEPHIN
Ballinasloe

Ballinasloe 3km

Portumna Road, Kellygrove, Ballinasloe, Co Galway

TEL: **0905 42685**   FAX: -

OPEN:	1st April-31st October	
No. Rooms:	3	
Ensuite:	2	

(V)

Spacious home on large landscaped gardens overlooking Golf Course, Le Guide du Routard recommended.

B&B PPS:	**£15/£17**	SNGL OCC. DBLE/TPL:	**£21.50/£23.50**	SNGL RM:	-
PART BRD:	-	% RED. CHILDREN:	**20%**	DINNER:	

Ms Elaine Forbes & Ella Casey
BRANDYBURN COTTAGE
Ballyconneely Connemara Area

Clifden

Ballyconneely, Clifden, Co Galway

TEL: **095 23591/087 401162**   FAX: -

OPEN:	15th June-15th September	
No. Rooms:	5	
Ensuite:	4	

(V)

Well appointed cottage style residence. Interesting gardens, guest lounges, peaceful surroundings. Close to Beaches, Golf Course, Fishing. Light meals available.

B&B PPS:	**£16/£18**	SNGL OCC. DBLE/TPL:	**£22.50/£24.50**	SNGL RM:	-
PART BRD:	-	% RED. CHILDREN:	**50%**	DINNER:	-

Bernie O'Neill
MANNIN LODGE
Ballyconneely Connemara Area

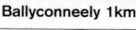
Ballyconneely 1km

Mannin Road, Ballyconneely, Co Galway

TEL: **095 23586**   FAX: -

OPEN:	1st April-31st October	
No. Rooms:	4	
Ensuite:	4	

(V)

Family run home, warm welcome. Convenient to Beaches, Golf Club, Pony Trekking. All with T.V and Hairdryers. Clifden 10 minutes drive.

B&B PPS:	**£17**	SNGL OCC. DBLE/TPL:	**£23.50**	SNGL RM:	-
PART BRD:	**£200**	% RED. CHILDREN:	**25%**	DINNER:	**£13**

Padraic & Angela O'Conghaile
TEACH ANACH MHEAIN
Beal A Daingin-Connemara Area

Lettermore 3km

Anach Mheain, Beal a Daingin, Connemara, Co Galway

TEL: **091 572348 /572212**   FAX: **091 572214**

OPEN:	May-September	
No. Rooms:	4	
Ensuite:	4	

(V)

Modern family house. All bedrooms with sea and mountain view. Convenient to Aran Islands Ferry, Golf, Fishing ,Walks.

B&B PPS:	**£17**	SNGL OCC. DBLE/TPL:	**£23.50**	SNGL RM:	-
PART BRD:	-	% RED. CHILDREN:	-	DINNER:	-

Mrs Irene Carr
VILLA DE PORRES
Barna

Galway 8km

Barna,Galway, Co Galway

TEL: **091 592239**   FAX: -

OPEN:	17th March-31st October	
No. Rooms:	5	
Ensuite:	4	

(V)

Off Coast Road. TV, Hairdryers, Electric Blankets. Close to good Restaurants, Beaches, Fishing, Barna Golf Club, Pony Trekking. Private Car Park.

B&B PPS:	**£16/£20**	SNGL OCC. DBLE/TPL:	-	SNGL RM:	-
PART BRD:	-	% RED. CHILDREN:	**25%**	DINNER:	-

Mrs Joan Codyre
FREEPORT HOUSE
Barna, Co Galway

Barna

OPEN:	March-November
NO. ROOMS:	6
ENSUITE:	5

TEL: 091 592199   FAX: -

Coast road overlooking Galway Bay. TV, hairdryers, electric blankets. Village Restaurants, Golf, Fishing, Tennis, Beaches. Trips to Aran Islands.

B&B PPS:	£16/£20	SNGL OCC. DBLE/TPL:	-	SNGL RM:	-
PART BRD:	-	% RED. CHILDREN:	25%	DINNER:	-

Galway City 8km

Mrs Geraldine Folan
AN FAOILEAN
Freeport, Barna Village, Co Galway

Barna

OPEN:	7th April-30th September
NO. ROOMS:	4
ENSUITE:	4

TEL: 091 592498   FAX: 091 592498   EMAIL: efolan@iol.ie

50m from seashore, central to Connemara, Aran, Galway/Salthill. Modern comforts, traditional welcome. 5 minutes to Restaurants, Pubs. Access/Visa Accepted.

B&B PPS:	£17/£20	SNGL OCC. DBLE/TPL:	£23.50/£26.50	SNGL RM:	-
PART BRD:	-	% RED. CHILDREN:	50%	DINNER:	-

Galway 6km

Marie Nee
SEA MIST
Muighros, Carna, Connemara,
Co Galway

Carna/Connemara

OPEN:	1st May-1st October
NO. ROOMS:	4
ENSUITE:	3

TEL: 095 32590   FAX: -

See the Atlantic Ocean, Twelve Bens, Maam Turks, Roundstone. Beautiful quiet beaches. Home Cooking. Vegetable garden,. Spacious ensuites. Relaxed atmosphere.

B&B PPS:	£15/£19	SNGL OCC. DBLE/TPL:	£21.50/£25.50	SNGL RM:	-
PART BRD:	£190	% RED. CHILDREN:	20%	DINNER:	£14

Carna 3km

Mrs Tina Donoghue
DONOGHUE'S
Carraroe,Connemara, Co Galway

Carraroe

OPEN:	All Year
NO. ROOMS:	4
ENSUITE:	2

TEL: 091 595174   FAX: -

Comfortable family home on spacious grounds. Beaches and Country Walks; daily trips to Aran Islands nearby. Credit Cards accepted.

B&B PPS:	£15/£17.50	SNGL OCC. DBLE/TPL:	£21.50/£24.50	SNGL RM:	-
PART BRD:	-	% RED. CHILDREN:	25%	DINNER:	-

Carraroe 1km

Mrs Mary Lydon
CARRAROE HOUSE
Carraroe, Connemara, Co Galway

Carraroe/Connemara

OPEN:	All Year except Christmas
NO. ROOMS:	5
ENSUITE:	4

TEL: 091 595188   FAX: -

Modern family home on outskirts of village. Ideal for touring Connemara, visiting Aran Islands, Fishing, Golfing, Beaches including Coral Beach.

B&B PPS:	£15/£17	SNGL OCC. DBLE/TPL:	£21.50	SNGL RM:	-
PART BRD:	-	% RED. CHILDREN:	50%	DINNER:	-

Galway 40km

Clifden 18km

Mrs Margaret McDonagh
GLEN-VIEW
Cashel Bay, Connemara, Co Galway

Cashel Bay/Connemara Area

OPEN:	1st January-22nd December
NO. ROOMS:	3
ENSUITE:	-

TEL: **095 31054**   FAX: -

Comfortable bungalow, Peat fires in scenic tranquil surroundings. Beaches, Pony Treking, Fishing. Tea/Coffee on arrival. Home from home.

B&B PPS:	£15	SNGL OCC. DBLE/TPL:	£21.50	SNGL RM:	-
PART BRD:	-	% RED. CHILDREN:	50%	DINNER:	£13

Galway 7km

Maura Campbell
AVONDALE
Cregboy, Claregalway, Co Galway

Claregalway

OPEN:	May-October
NO. ROOMS:	4
ENSUITE:	2

TEL: **091 798349**   FAX: -

Modern family home in country area. Ideal for touring Connemara/Clare etc, Fishing & Horseriding nearby.

B&B PPS:	£15/£17	SNGL OCC. DBLE/TPL:	£21.50/£23.50	SNGL RM:	-
PART BRD:	-	% RED. CHILDREN:	50%	DINNER:	-

Galway City 10 km

Mrs Mary McNulty
CREG LODGE
Cregboy, Claregalway, Co Galway

Claregalway

OPEN:	All Year except Christmas
NO. ROOMS:	3
ENSUITE:	3

TEL: **091 798862**   FAX: -

Luxury family home, on N17, Galway/Sligo Road, 10 minute drive Galway City and 5 minutes Airport. Restaurants/Pubs nearby.

B&B PPS:	£17	SNGL OCC. DBLE/TPL:	£23.50	SNGL RM:	£23.50
PART BRD:	-	% RED. CHILDREN:	25%	DINNER:	-

Galway 12km

Mr Niall Stewart
FARMISCH
Loughgeorge, Claregalway, Co Galway

Claregalway

OPEN:	All Year
NO. ROOMS:	4
ENSUITE:	4

TEL: **091 798606**   FAX: -

Luxury dormer bungalow on N17. Adjacent to Central Tavern Bar and Restaurant. Convenient for Fishing, Golfing and Touring. Galway Airport 6KM.

B&B PPS:	£17	SNGL OCC. DBLE/TPL:	£23.50	SNGL RM:	-
PART BRD:	-	% RED. CHILDREN:	33%	DINNER:	-

Clarinbridge 0.5 km

Mrs Dympna Callinan
CLAREVILLE
Stradbally North, Clarinbridge, Co Galway

Clarinbridge

OPEN:	March-November
NO. ROOMS:	3
ENSUITE:	3

TEL: **091 796248**   FAX: -

Luxurious spacious dormer home situated in the heart of oyster country. 0.5km off N18, within walking distance of village, Sea.

B&B PPS:	£17	SNGL OCC. DBLE/TPL:	£23.50	SNGL RM:	-
PART BRD:	-	% RED. CHILDREN:	25%	DINNER:	-

Mrs Bernie Diskin
ROCK LODGE
**Stradbally Nth., Clarinbridge,
Co Galway**

Clarinbridge

OPEN:	1st April-31st October
No. ROOMS:	3
ENSUITE:	2

(V)

TEL: 091 796071   FAX: -

Home in quiet location, private walkway to seashore. Tea/Coffee facilities. TV's, Breakfast choice. Near Burren/Connemara. Guide du Routard recommended.

Clairnbridge 1km

B&B PPS:	£15/£17	SNGL OCC. DBLE/TPL:	£21.50/£23.50	SNGL RM:	-
PART BRD:	£185	% RED. CHILDREN:	33%	DINNER:	£12

Martina Kinane
HARKIN HOUSE
**Stradbally North, Clarinbridge,
Co Galway**

Clarinbridge

OPEN:	May-October
No. ROOMS:	3
ENSUITE:	2

(V)

TEL: 091 796619   FAX: -

Superior Tudor designed home. 1KM off N18. Central to Connemara, Burren, Shannon Airport. Beside Sea & Restaurants. Peaceful setting. Clarinbridge 1KM.

Clarinbridge

B&B PPS:	£16/£17	SNGL OCC. DBLE/TPL:	£23.50	SNGL RM:	-
PART BRD:	-	% RED. CHILDREN:	25%	DINNER:	-

Mrs Maura McNamara
SPRINGLAWN
Stradbally, Clarinbridge, Co Galway

Clarinbridge

OPEN:	March-November
No. ROOMS:	3
ENSUITE:	3

(V)

TEL: 091 796045   FAX: -

Dillard Causin Guide recommended. Superbly located near sea. Ideal for touring Connemara, Burren, Aran islands. Breakfast menu. Credit cards accepted.

Clairnbridge 1km

B&B PPS:	£17	SNGL OCC. DBLE/TPL:	£23.50	SNGL RM:	-
PART BRD:	£190	% RED. CHILDREN:	25%	DINNER:	£13

Mrs Teresa O'Dea
KARAUN HOUSE
Stradbally, Clarinbridge, Co Galway

Clarinbridge

OPEN:	1st March-31st October
No. ROOMS:	3
ENSUITE:	2

(V)

TEL: 091 796182   FAX: -

Irish Times recommended. Near Sea, Burren, Connemara, Islands. Tea/Coffee facilities. Electric Blankets. Orthopaedic Beds. A.A. listed. Credit cards accepted.

Clarinbridge 1km

B&B PPS:	£15/£17	SNGL OCC. DBLE/TPL:	£23.50	SNGL RM:	-
PART BRD:	£185	% RED. CHILDREN:	33.3%	DINNER:	£13

Mary Rodgers
OYSTER CATCHER
**Weir Rd., Clarinbridge, Kilcolgan PO,
Co. Galway**

Clarinbridge

OPEN:	January-November
No. ROOMS:	4
ENSUITE:	4

(V)

TEL: 091 796744   FAX: -

Country home 1.5Km from Clarinbridge central to Burren, Connemara and Galway city. Superb restaurants and countryside locally. Breakfast menu available.

Clarinbridge 1.5km

B&B PPS:	£17	SNGL OCC. DBLE/TPL:	£23.50	SNGL RM:	-
PART BRD:	-	% RED. CHILDREN:	33.3%	DINNER:	-

Cleggan 1km

William & Bernie Hughes
COIS NA MARA
Cleggan, Clifden, Co Galway

Cleggan/Connemara Area

OPEN:	1st May-30th September
NO. ROOMS:	6
ENSUITE:	3

(V)

TEL: **095 44647**   FAX: -

Family home in scenic area, "Frommer" recommended. Daily boat trips to Inishbofin, safe, sandy Beaches within walking distance. Access/visa accepted.

B&B PPS:	**£15/£17**	SNGL OCC. DBLE/TPL:	**£21.50**	SNGL RM:	-
PART BRD:	-	% RED. CHILDREN:	25%	DINNER:	-

Clifden 10km

Mrs Mary King
CNOC BREAC
Cleggan, Co Galway

Cleggan/Connemara Area

OPEN:	1st May-30th September
NO. ROOMS:	4
ENSUITE:	4

(V)

TEL: **095 44688**   FAX: -

Family home. Peaceful, scenic area. Beside Sandy Beach. Fishing, Pony Riding. Bay Cruises arranged. Convenient for Inishbofin Ferry. Village 1 km.

B&B PPS:	**£17**	SNGL OCC. DBLE/TPL:	**£23.50**	SNGL RM:	-
PART BRD:	-	% RED. CHILDREN:	25%	DINNER:	-

Clifden 9km

Mrs Loretta O'Malley
HARBOUR HOUSE
Cleggan, Co Galway

Cleggan/Connemara Area

OPEN:	1st March-30th October
NO. ROOMS:	4
ENSUITE:	4

(V)

TEL: **095 44702**   FAX: -

Spacious family run home situated in pretty fishing village of Cleggan from which to explore the wonderful Land and Seascapes.

B&B PPS:	**£17**	SNGL OCC. DBLE/TPL:	**£23.50**	SNGL RM:	-
PART BRD:	-	% RED. CHILDREN:	25%	DINNER:	-

Clifden 7 km

Mrs Noreen Conneely
BEN BREEN HOUSE
Tooreen, Moyard, Clifden, Co Galway

Clifden/Connemara Area

OPEN:	1st April-31st October
NO. ROOMS:	6
ENSUITE:	6

(V)

TEL: **095 41171**   FAX: -

Comfortable well heated home. Peat fires. Magnificent view sea/mountain. Peaceful and tranquil location. Convenient to Connemara National Park.

B&B PPS:	**£17/£18**	SNGL OCC. DBLE/TPL:	**£23.50/£24.50**	SNGL RM:	-
PART BRD:	**£225**	% RED. CHILDREN:	25%	DINNER:	£15

Clifden 5km

Mrs Anne Conroy
ROCKMOUNT HOUSE
Bayleek, Sky Road, Clifden, Co Galway

Clifden/Connemara Area

OPEN:	15th April-30th September
NO. ROOMS:	4
ENSUITE:	2

(V)

TEL: **095 21763**   FAX: -

Beautiful modern bungalow, situated on scenic Sky Road, in peaceful settings. Convenient to Sandy Beaches, Fishing, Mountain Walks and Golf.

B&B PPS:	**£15/£17**	SNGL OCC. DBLE/TPL:	**£21.50/£23.50**	SNGL RM:	-
PART BRD:	-	% RED. CHILDREN:	25%	DINNER:	£12.50

Clifden 2km

John & Joan Coyne
SEA VIEW (Formerly Croagh View)
Westport Road, Clifden, Co Galway

Clifden/Connemara Area

Open:	April-1st October
No. Rooms:	5
Ensuite:	4

Tel: **095 21394**   Fax: -

Modern bungalow in peaceful surroundings. Panoramic view of Streamstown Bay and Sky Road. Ideal touring centre for Connemara. (N59).

cc P ⅌ ✄ ☕

B&B PPS:	**£15/£17**	Sngl Occ. Dble/Tpl:	-	Sngl Rm:	-
Part Brd:	-	% Red. Children:	25%	Dinner:	-

Clifden 1.5km

Michael & Jane Delapp
HEATHER LODGE
Westport Road, Clifden, Co Galway

Clifden/Connemara Area

Open:	All Year except Christmas
No. Rooms:	6
Ensuite:	5

Tel: **095 21331**   Fax: **095 22041**   Email: **231@tinet.ie**

Delightful family home, warm atmosphere, home baking, breakfast menu. Splendid views lakes/ mountains, peaceful surroundings, great base for touring Connemara

cc ♨ P ⅌ ✄ ☕ ➜ ♪ ☂ S

B&B PPS:	**£17/£19**	Sngl Occ. Dble/Tpl:	**£23.50/£25.50**	Sngl Rm:	**£18/£20**
Part Brd:	-	% Red. Children:	25%	Dinner:	£15

Clifden 3km

Mrs Breege Feneran
LOUGH FADDA HOUSE
Ballyconneely Road, Clifden, Co Galway

Clifden/Connemara Area

Open:	April-October
No. Rooms:	6
Ensuite:	5

Tel: **095 21165**   Fax: -

Spacious, well heated country home. Lovely quiet country walks in scenic area. Peat fires, Fishing & Pony Riding arranged. Credit Cards accepted.

cc P ☕ ☘ ♪ ☂

B&B PPS:	**£16/£17**	Sngl Occ. Dble/Tpl:	**£23.50**	Sngl Rm:	-
Part Brd:	-	% Red. Children:	20%	Dinner:	-

Mrs Carmel Gaughan
ARD AOIBHINN
Ardbeaar, Ballyconneely Road, Clifden, Co Galway

Clifden/Connemara Area

Open:	1st April-31st October
No. Rooms:	3
Ensuite:	2

Tel: **095 21339**   Fax: -

Modern bungalow in scenic surroundings on Clifden - Ballyconneely Road convenient to safe beaches and Golf Links. Excellent touring base.

P ☘ ☂

B&B PPS:	**£15/£17**	Sngl Occ. Dble/Tpl:	-	Sngl Rm:	-
Part Brd:	-	% Red. Children:	-	Dinner:	-

Clifden 1 km

Clifden 1km

Mrs Maureen Geoghegan
ROSSFIELD HOUSE
Westport Road, Clifden, Co Galway

Clifden/Connemara Area

Open:	1st April-1st November
No. Rooms:	4
Ensuite:	2

Tel: **095 21392**   Fax: -

Family run home. Warm welcome. Convenient to safe beaches & Golf Links. Excellent touring base. Orthopaedic beds and peaceful location.

P ⅌ ☘ ♪ ☂

B&B PPS:	**£15/£17**	Sngl Occ. Dble/Tpl:	-	Sngl Rm:	-
Part Brd:	-	% Red. Children:	25%	Dinner:	£12

Mrs Kathleen Hardman
MALLMORE HOUSE
**Ballyconneely Road, Clifden,
Co Galway**

TEL: **095 21460**   FAX: -

Clifden/Connemara Area

OPEN:	**1st March-1st November**
NO. ROOMS:	**6**
ENSUITE:	**6**

Lovingly restored Georgian home. 35 acre woodland grounds, spacious rooms, superb views, open fires and award-winning breakfasts. AA QQQQ.

B&B PPS:	£18/£20	SNGL OCC. DBLE/TPL:	-	SNGL RM:	-
PART BRD:	-	% RED. CHILDREN:	20%	DINNER:	-

— Clifden 2km —

Mrs Mary Hickey
TIRGNEEVES HOUSE
**Westport Road, Clifden,
Co Galway**

TEL: **095 21158**   FAX: -

Clifden/Connemara Area

OPEN:	**May-October**
NO. ROOMS:	**4**
ENSUITE:	**2**

Modern bungalow set in scenic and tranquil surroundings. Panoramic view, golf, fishing, beaches nearby. Ideal touring base. (N59).

B&B PPS:	£15/£17	SNGL OCC. DBLE/TPL:	-	SNGL RM:	-
PART BRD:	-	% RED. CHILDREN:	25%	DINNER:	-

— Clifden 1km —

Mrs Bridie Hyland
HYLANDS BAY VIEW
Westport Road, Clifden, Co Galway

TEL: **095 21286**   FAX: -

Clifden/Connemara Area

OPEN:	**7th March-12th November**
NO. ROOMS:	**4**
ENSUITE:	**3**

"Frommer Guide" recommended. Overlooking Streamstown Bay, Orthopaedic beds, electric blankets (N.59) View described 'most spectacular' in Ireland. Tea/coffee facilities.

B&B PPS:	£15/£17	SNGL OCC. DBLE/TPL:	-	SNGL RM:	-
PART BRD:	-	% RED. CHILDREN:	50%	DINNER:	-

— Clifden 2.5km —

Mrs Margaret Kelly
WINNOWING HILL
**Ballyconneely Road, Clifden,
Co Galway**

TEL: **095 21281**   FAX: -

Clifden/Connemara Area

OPEN:	**13th March-1st November**
NO. ROOMS:	**3**
ENSUITE:	**-**

Well appointed dormer bungalow with panoramic views. Tranquil surroundings. "Le Guide du Routard" recommended.

B&B PPS:	£15	SNGL OCC. DBLE/TPL:	-	SNGL RM:	-
PART BRD:	-	% RED. CHILDREN:	25%	DINNER:	-

— Clifden 1km —

Mrs Maureen Kelly
FAILTE
**Ardbear off Ballyconneely Road,
Clifden, Co Galway**

TEL: **095 21159**   FAX: -

Clifden/Connemara Area

OPEN:	**April-September**
NO. ROOMS:	**5**
ENSUITE:	**2**

Modern home overlooking town and Bay.Breakfast award winner. AA QQQs. "Frommer Guide" and "Le Guide du Routard" reccomended.

B&B PPS:	£15/£17	SNGL OCC. DBLE/TPL:	£21.50/£23.50	SNGL RM:	£15
PART BRD:	-	% RED. CHILDREN:	50%	DINNER:	-

— Clifden 2 km —

In Clifden

Mrs Vera Kilkenny
WEST COAST HOUSE
**Westport Road, Clifden,
Co Galway**
Tel: **095 21261**   Fax: -

Clifden/Connemara Area

Open:	**1st April-31st October**
No. Rooms:	3
Ensuite:	3

Modern family home, good view. Spacious en-suite bedrooms. Ideal touring base. Convenient Beaches, Golf, Fishing, Horse riding, sports centre.

B&B PPS:	**£17**	Sngl Occ. Dble/Tpl:	**£23.50**	Sngl Rm:	-
Part Brd:	-	% Red. Children:	**25%**	Dinner:	-

Clifden

Mrs Mary King
KINGSTOWN HOUSE
Bridge Street, Clifden, Co Galway
Tel: **095 21470**   Fax: **095 21530**

Clifden/Connemara Area

Open:	**1st January-23rd December**
No. Rooms:	8
Ensuite:	6

Long established family home in town. Convenient to Beaches, Golf, Riding, Fishing and Sports Centre. 2 mins walk to bus.

B&B PPS:	**£15/£18**	Sngl Occ. Dble/Tpl:	**£21.50/£24.50**	Sngl Rm:	-
Part Brd:	-	% Red. Children:	**25%**	Dinner:	-

Clifden 3km

Martin & Mary Kirby
LAKESIDE B&B
**Goulane, Galway Road, Clifden,
Co Galway**
Tel: **095 21168**   Fax: -

Clifden/Connemara Area

Open:	**April-October**
No. Rooms:	4
Ensuite:	3

Modern bungalow on spacious grounds in scenic surroundings, lake in front. Situated on Galway/Clifden Road (N59).

B&B PPS:	**£15/£17**	Sngl Occ. Dble/Tpl:	**£21.50/£23.50**	Sngl Rm:	-
Part Brd:	-	% Red. Children:	-	Dinner:	-

Clifden 3km

Miss Catherine Lowry
AVE MARIA
Ballinaboy, Clifden, Co Galway
Tel: **095 21368**   Fax: -

Clifden/Connemara

Open:	**1st April-31st October**
No. Rooms:	5
Ensuite:	1

Spacious 2 storey house on Coast road, scenic, tranquil location. Panoramic view. Close to local amenities, Beaches, Horse riding, Golf, Fishing.

B&B PPS:	**£15/£17**	Sngl Occ. Dble/Tpl:	**£21.50/£23.50**	Sngl Rm:	**£15**
Part Brd:	-	% Red. Children:	**33%**	Dinner:	-

In Clifden

The Lydon Family
BENBAUN HOUSE
**Westport Road, Clifden,
Co Galway**
Tel: **095 21462**   Fax: **095 21462**

Clifden/Connemara Area

Open:	**1st April-31st October**
No. Rooms:	6
Ensuite:	5

Modern family bungalow with lovely view of mountains. Convenient to beaches, golf and fishing. Electric blankets, tea and coffee, hairdryers.

B&B PPS:	**£15/£17**	Sngl Occ. Dble/Tpl:	**£24**	Sngl Rm:	-
Part Brd:	-	% Red. Children:	**10%**	Dinner:	-

Clifden 7.5km

Tina McDonagh
DOOAHILL LODGE
Aillebrack, Ballyconneely, Clifden, Co Galway

Clifden

OPEN:	1st April-31st October
NO. ROOMS:	3
ENSUITE:	3

TEL: **095 23726**   FAX: -

 (V)

Warm comfortable home, situated 0.5 km from Connemara Golf Club. Walking distance to Beaches and Pony Trekking. Clifden 7.5 km Ballyconneely 2 km.

B&B PPS:	£17	SNGL OCC. DBLE/TPL:	£23.50	SNGL RM:	-
PART BRD:	£200	% RED. CHILDREN:	25%	DINNER:	£13

Clifden 5km

Nora Mullen
SKY ROAD VIEW
Lower Sky Road, Fahy, Clifden, Co Galway

Clifden/Connemara Area

OPEN:	All Year
NO. ROOMS:	3
ENSUITE:	3

TEL: **095 21889**   FAX: -

(V)

Modern comfortable family home in quiet scenic location. Sea and mountain views. Ideal base for touring/fishing/walking/sailing/golf.

B&B PPS:	£17	SNGL OCC. DBLE/TPL:	£23.50	SNGL RM:	-
PART BRD:	£180	% RED. CHILDREN:	25%	DINNER:	£12

Clifden

The McEvaddy Family
BAYMOUNT HOUSE
Seaview, Clifden, Co Galway

Clifden/Connemara Area

OPEN:	March-October
NO. ROOMS:	10
ENSUITE:	10

TEL: **095 21459**   FAX: **095 21639**

(V)

Spacious family home overlooking Clifden Bay. Magnificent Sea Views. Peaceful location. Hairdryers, Tea/coffee making facilities and TV in bedrooms.

B&B PPS:	£15/£17	SNGL OCC. DBLE/TPL:	-	SNGL RM:	-
PART BRD:	-	% RED. CHILDREN:	33%	DINNER:	-

Clifden 2km

Mrs Mary O'Donnell
CREGG HOUSE
Galway Road, Clifden, Co Galway

Clifden/Connemara

OPEN:	Easter/November
NO. ROOMS:	6
ENSUITE:	5

TEL: **095 21326**   FAX: -

 (V)

On N59 landscaped garden, spacious rooms, breakfast menu, Owenglen River nearby. Ideal touring base. Recommended Elsie Dillard best B&B's Ireland.

B&B PPS:	£15/£17	SNGL OCC. DBLE/TPL:	£21.50/£23.50	SNGL RM:	-
PART BRD:	-	% RED. CHILDREN:	20%	DINNER:	-

Clifden 1.5km

Mrs Maureen O'Malley
HILLSIDE LODGE
Sky Road, Clifden, Co Galway

Clifden/Connemara Area

OPEN:	March-November
NO. ROOMS:	6
ENSUITE:	6

TEL: **095 21463**   FAX: -

 (V)

Modern family home located on scenic Sky Road. Beside Clifden Castle entrance. "Le Guide du Routard" recommended. Tea/coffee facilities.

B&B PPS:	£17	SNGL OCC. DBLE/TPL:	£23.50	SNGL RM:	-
PART BRD:	-	% RED. CHILDREN:	33.3%	DINNER:	-

Mrs Pauline O'Neill — Clifden/Connemara
CROFDEN HOUSE
Westport Road, Clifden, Co Galway

Open:	April-October
No. Rooms:	3
Ensuite:	2

TEL: **095 21444**   FAX: -

Modern family home on elevated site in peaceful location. Convenient to beaches, golf, and fishing. Ideal touring base for Connemara.

Clifden 0.2km

B&B PPS:	£14.50/£16	SNGL OCC. DBLE/TPL:	£20/£22	SNGL RM:	-
PART BRD:	-	% RED. CHILDREN:	20%	DINNER:	-

Mrs. Margaret Pryce — Clifden/Connemara Area
LETTERNOOSH HOUSE
Westport Road, Clifden, Co Galway

Open:	All Year
No. Rooms:	4
Ensuite:	-

TEL: **095 21291**   FAX: -

Modern bungalow in peaceful surroundings, overlooking Streamstown Bay, convenient to local amenities. Peat fires, ideal touring centre. 2 km from Clifden.

Clifden 2km

B&B PPS:	£15	SNGL OCC. DBLE/TPL:	-	SNGL RM:	£15
PART BRD:	-	% RED. CHILDREN:	25%	DINNER:	£12

Mrs Mary Ryan — Clifden/Connemara Area
DUN AENGUS HOUSE
Sky Road, Clifden, Connemara, Co Galway

Open:	All Year
No. Rooms:	6
Ensuite:	6

TEL: **095 21069**   FAX: **095 21069**

Superb location, spacious bedrooms. 5 mins walk to Town Centre. View from house described "Best in Ireland". Breakfast menu.

In Clifden

B&B PPS:	£16/£17.50	SNGL OCC. DBLE/TPL:	£21/£22.50	SNGL RM:	-
PART BRD:	£185	% RED. CHILDREN:	12%	DINNER:	£12.50

Mrs Kathleen Wallace — Clifden/Connemara Area
RIVERCREST HOUSE
off Galway Road, Clifden, Co Galway

Open:	1st May-30th September
No. Rooms:	3
Ensuite:	3

TEL: **095 21236**   FAX: -

Scenic, tranquil overlooking Owenglin river. Short walk to town. Guide du Routard recommended. Bedrooms, Tea/coffee/hairdryers. French spoken.

In Clifden

B&B PPS:	£17	SNGL OCC. DBLE/TPL:	£23.50	SNGL RM:	-
PART BRD:	-	% RED. CHILDREN:	25%	DINNER:	-

Mrs. Mary G. Morrin — Clonbur/Cong/Connemara Area
ISLAND VIEW HOUSE
Dooroy, Clonbur, Cong, Co Galway

Open:	May-October
No. Rooms:	3
Ensuite:	2

TEL: **092 46302**   FAX: -

Scenic setting overlooking Lough Corrib. Touring base for Connemara, West Mayo. Central to Restaurants, Angling, Mountain Climbing. Boat/engines for hire.

Clonbur 1km

B&B PPS:	£13/£16	SNGL OCC. DBLE/TPL:	£18/£21	SNGL RM:	-
PART BRD:	-	% RED. CHILDREN:	25%	DINNER:	-

Cornamona 3 km

Mrs Sorcha Peirce
GRASSHOPPER COTTAGE
Dooras, Cornamona, Co Galway

Cornamona/Connemara Area

OPEN:	13th March-27th October
NO. ROOMS:	4
ENSUITE:	3

(V)

TEL: **092 48165**   FAX: **092 48165**

Lodge on shore of Lough Corrib. Superb scenery. Angling centre (boat and tackle hire). Ideal for walking, touring Connemara.

B&B PPS:	**£15/£17**	SNGL OCC. DBLE/TPL:	**£22/£24**	SNGL RM:	-
PART BRD:	**£200**	% RED. CHILDREN:	**25%**	DINNER:	**£15**

In Craughwell

Mrs. Aine Flanagan SRN SCM
TEMPLEMARTIN THATCHED HSE
Craughwell, Co Galway

Craughwell

OPEN:	1st April-30th October
NO. ROOMS:	5
ENSUITE:	5

(V)

TEL: **091 846145**   FAX: -

Thatched house off N6 near Restaurants, Burren, Connemara, Aran Islands, Galway City. Arrangements for Vegetarians, Touring, Horse-Riding, Walking, Golf.

B&B PPS:	**£17**	SNGL OCC. DBLE/TPL:	-	SNGL RM:	**£17/£21**
PART BRD:	**£180**	% RED. CHILDREN:	**50%**	DINNER:	**£14**

In Craughwell

Mrs Peggy Gilligan
AHAVEEN HOUSE
Cappanraheen, Craughwell, Co Galway

Craughwell

OPEN:	1st January-31st December
NO. ROOMS:	5
ENSUITE:	4

(V)

TEL: **091 846147**   FAX: -

Comfortable home on spacious grounds, just off N6 Galway - Dublin road. Excellent Restaurants, Hunting, Golf. Ideal touring base, Burren, Connemara.

B&B PPS:	**£15/£17**	SNGL OCC. DBLE/TPL:	**£21.50/£23.50**	SNGL RM:	**£21.50**
PART BRD:	**£180**	% RED. CHILDREN:	**50%**	DINNER:	**£12**

Craughwell 1.5km

Mrs Marian Murphy
ASHFORD HOUSE
Ballynagran, Craughwell, Co Galway

Craughwell

OPEN:	1st May-30th October
NO. ROOMS:	3
ENSUITE:	2

(V)

TEL: **091 846112**   FAX: -

Enjoy Irish hospitality in this peaceful setting, 1.5 km off N6. Ideal base for touring. Excellent Restaurants. Golf, Bird watching locally.

B&B PPS:	**£15/£17**	SNGL OCC. DBLE/TPL:	**£21.50/£23.50**	SNGL RM:	**£18**
PART BRD:	**£180**	% RED. CHILDREN:	**50%**	DINNER:	**£12**

Galway City 9km

Brian Clancy
SUAN NA MARA
Stripe, Furbo, Spiddal, Co Galway

Furbo/Spiddal

OPEN:	All Year
NO. ROOMS:	4
ENSUITE:	3

(V)

TEL: **091 591512**   FAX: **091 524168**

Spacious well appointed rooms, chef owned. Evening meals. Fishing, Golfing, Beach nearby. Coast Road. Suitable for touring Aran Islands, Connemara.

B&B PPS:	**£15/£20**	SNGL OCC. DBLE/TPL:	**£21.50/£26.50**	SNGL RM:	-
PART BRD:	**£180**	% RED. CHILDREN:	**25%**	DINNER:	**£12**

Caroline Friel Gallagher
AN ROS OIR
Knocknavaddy, Furbo, Co Galway

Furbo

OPEN:	All Year except Christmas
NO. ROOMS:	3
ENSUITE:	3

TEL: **091 590522** FAX: **091 590642**

Coast Road overlooking the Aran Islands. TV, hairdryers, tea and coffee making facilities. Hotel, restaurant, golf, fishing, beach, horse riding nearby.

B&B PPS:	£17/£17.50	SNGL OCC. DBLE/TPL:	£23.50/£24	SNGL RM:	-
PART BRD:	-	% RED. CHILDREN:	50%	DINNER:	-

Galway 11km

Mrs Bridie Leonard
THE GABLES
Castlegar, Galway, Co Galway

Galway City/Castlegar Area

OPEN:	1st January-20th December
NO. ROOMS:	3
ENSUITE:	3

TEL: **091 755375** FAX: -

Attractive peaceful home on 1 acre on N17. Personally run. Golf, tennis, beaches nearby. Electric blankets.

B&B PPS:	£17/£18	SNGL OCC. DBLE/TPL:	£23.50/£25	SNGL RM:	-
PART BRD:	-	% RED. CHILDREN:	25%	DINNER:	-

Galway 3km

Mrs Louise O'Brien
LISAVA
Ballintemple, Monivea Rd (R339),
Galway, Co Galway

Galway City/Castlegar Area

OPEN:	1st April-30th September
NO. ROOMS:	3
ENSUITE:	2

TEL: **091 753730** FAX: -

Modern bungalow on edge of city. Close to the N6, 1.5km from Airport, on R339. Tea/coffee on arrival.

B&B PPS:	£17	SNGL OCC. DBLE/TPL:	£23.50	SNGL RM:	£19
PART BRD:	-	% RED. CHILDREN:	33%	DINNER:	-

Galway 4km

Mrs Bridie Carrick
SANTA MARIA
5 Glenina Heights, Dublin Rd., Galway,
Co Galway

Galway City

OPEN:	17th March-31st October
NO. ROOMS:	4
ENSUITE:	2

TEL: **091 755363** FAX: -

Warm, comfortable home on bus route(N6). 5 minutes drive from city centre. Near Corrib Great Southern Hotel. Tea/coffee on arrival.

B&B PPS:	£15/£18	SNGL OCC. DBLE/TPL:	£21.50/£24.50	SNGL RM:	£16/£18
PART BRD:	-	% RED. CHILDREN:	-	DINNER:	-

Galway 1km

Pauline Caulfield
CORRIB HOUSE
6 Sylvan Road, Fairlands Park,
Newcastle, Galway City, Co Galway

Galway City

OPEN:	All Year except Christmas
NO. ROOMS:	4
ENSUITE:	1

TEL: **091 521318** FAX: -

2km to city centre. Bus/train station, University Hospital. Private parking, i Local taxi service. Adjacent to Connemara/Clifden road (N59).

B&B PPS:	£15/£18	SNGL OCC. DBLE/TPL:	£21.50/£24.50	SNGL RM:	£17/£19
PART BRD:	-	% RED. CHILDREN:	25%	DINNER:	£12

Galway City 2km

Galway City 3km

Mrs Colette Cawley
DUNGUAIRE
8 Lurgan Park, Murrough, Dublin Road, Galway City (East), Co. Galway

Galway City

OPEN:	All Year
NO. ROOMS:	4
ENSUITE:	2

(V)

TEL: **091 757043**   FAX: -

Warm, friendly home. On bus route. Follow signs for Galway city east. House opposite Corrib Great Southern Hotel, RTC, (N6).

B&B PPS:	£15/£18.50	SNGL OCC. DBLE/TPL:	£21.50/£25	SNGL RM:	£18
PART BRD:	-	% RED. CHILDREN:	50%	DINNER:	£12

Galway City 1km

Mrs Noreen Collins
ST. ANTHONYS
Terryland Cross, Headford Road, Galway, Co Galway

Galway City

OPEN:	1st January-20th December
NO. ROOMS:	4
ENSUITE:	4

(V)

TEL: **091 766477**   FAX: -

Family run home. Warm welcome. Beside Shopping Centre. Cinema & Restaurants. Tea/Coffee facilities. Rooms ensuite. Private Car Park.

B&B PPS:	£17	SNGL OCC. DBLE/TPL:	£23.50	SNGL RM:	-
PART BRD:	-	% RED. CHILDREN:	-	DINNER:	-

In Galway City

Cathriona & Peter Connolly
ACHILL HOUSE
9 Whitestrand Road, Galway, Co Galway

Galway City

OPEN:	1st March-1st October
NO. ROOMS:	4
ENSUITE:	4

(V)

TEL: **091 589149**   FAX: -

Family run B&B 5 mins walk to City Centre & beach. Ensuite rooms, cable TV, private car park. Complementary tea/coffee.

B&B PPS:	£17/£17.50	SNGL OCC. DBLE/TPL:	£26/£31	SNGL RM:	-
PART BRD:	-	% RED. CHILDREN:	-	DINNER:	-

Galway City

Mrs Mary Corless
COOLAVALLA
22 Newcastle Road, Galway, Co Galway

Galway City

OPEN:	1st February-30th November
NO. ROOMS:	3
ENSUITE:	1

(V)

TEL: **091 522415**   FAX: -

Modern family house beside hospital and university, opposite Presentation school. 5 mins walk City Centre, 15 mins Salthill. Front, rear car park.

B&B PPS:	£15/£19	SNGL OCC. DBLE/TPL:	£21.50/£25.50	SNGL RM:	-
PART BRD:	-	% RED. CHILDREN:	-	DINNER:	-

Helen Kathleen Hanlon
CLOCHARD
4 Spires Gardens, Shantalla Road, Galway, Co Galway

Galway City

OPEN:	All Year except Christmas
NO. ROOMS:	3
ENSUITE:	3

(V)

TEL: **091 521533**   FAX: -

Situated in a quiet Historic Site within walking distance of City Centre and Beach. Close to University and Shopping.

B&B PPS:	£17.50/£20	SNGL OCC. DBLE/TPL:	£25/£26.50	SNGL RM:	£21
PART BRD:	-	% RED. CHILDREN:	-	DINNER:	-

In Galway

Mrs Elizabeth Hassell
IVERNIA
41 Maunsells Park, Taylors Hill, Galway, Co Galway

TEL: **091 523307**   FAX: -

Galway City

OPEN:	March-October
No. ROOMS:	3
ENSUITE:	1

(V)

Family home in quiet residential area. Convenient City Centre, University, Hospital, Salthill. Bus No 2. Car Parking. 1 Single room.

BUS No: **2**

B&B PPS:	£15/£19	SNGL OCC. DBLE/TPL:	£21.50/£25.50	SNGL RM:	£17/£20
PART BRD:	-	% RED. CHILDREN:	25%	DINNER:	

Galway 2km

Cyril & Kitty Joyce
HAZEL VILLA
20 Hazel Park, Newcastle, Galway, Co Galway

TEL: **091 523326**   FAX: -

Galway City

OPEN:	1st April-30th October
No. ROOMS:	4
ENSUITE:	-

(V)

Situated on Clifden/Connemara road, convenient to City Centre, University & Hospital. On City Bus route.

B&B PPS:	£16/£18	SNGL OCC. DBLE/TPL:	£22.50/£24.50	SNGL RM:	-
PART BRD:	-	% RED. CHILDREN:	-	DINNER:	-

Galway

Mrs Maureen McCallion
VILLA NOVA
40 Newcastle Road, Galway, Co Galway

TEL: **091 524849**   FAX: -

Galway City

OPEN:	1st January-16th December
No. ROOMS:	4
ENSUITE:	3

(V)

Quiet bungalow off the main road. Beside Hospital & University & convenient to city centre. Private car park.

B&B PPS:	£16/£20	SNGL OCC. DBLE/TPL:	£22.50/£28	SNGL RM:	-
PART BRD:	-	% RED. CHILDREN:	-	DINNER:	-

Galway 2km

Miss Bridget Phil McCarthy
PETRA
201 Laurel Park, Newcastle, Galway City, Co Galway

TEL: **091 521844**   FAX: -

Galway City

OPEN:	All Year except Christmas
No. ROOMS:	5
ENSUITE:	3

(V)

Convenient to city centre, bus/train station, Aran Ferry, University, Hospital, seaside, golf arranged. Adjacent to Clifden/Connemara road (N59).

BUS No: **4, 5**

B&B PPS:	£15/£18	SNGL OCC. DBLE/TPL:	£21.50/£25	SNGL RM:	£15/£18
PART BRD:	£180	% RED. CHILDREN:	-	DINNER:	£12

Galway 1km

Caitriona Mannion
THE GABLES
Terryland Cross, Headford Rd, Galway, Co Galway

TEL: **091 760448**   FAX: -

Galway City

OPEN:	All Year except Christmas
No. ROOMS:	4
ENSUITE:	4

(V)

Attractive comfortable home, within walking distance city centre, shopping centre, cinema, restaurants. Private car park, cable TV, tea/coffee facilities.

B&B PPS:	£17/£20	SNGL OCC. DBLE/TPL:	£23.50/£26.50	SNGL RM:	-
PART BRD:	-	% RED. CHILDREN:	50%	DINNER:	-

In Galway City

Mrs Corinne Mannion
ASHFORD MANOR
7 College Rd., Galway, Co Galway

Galway City

OPEN:	All Year except Christmas
No. ROOMS:	4
ENSUITE:	4

TEL: **091 563941**   FAX: **091 563941**

Luxurious home, city centre 3 mins. Bedrooms ensuite, telephone/fax, tea/coffee making. Breakfast menu. Car park. Credit Cards.

B&B PPS:	£18/£28	SNGL OCC. DBLE/TPL:	£20/£36	SNGL RM:	-
PART BRD:	-	% RED. CHILDREN:	-	DINNER:	-

Galway 1km

Mrs Marcella Mitchell
LIMA
Glenanail, Tuam Road, Galway, Co Galway

Galway City

OPEN:	1st March-31st October
No. ROOMS:	3
ENSUITE:	2

TEL: **091 757986**   FAX: -

Detached bungalow adjacent to city centre, N17 close to all amenities of a vibrant city. Private parking, TV all rooms.

BUS NO: **3**

B&B PPS:	£17/£18	SNGL OCC. DBLE/TPL:	-	SNGL RM:	£18
PART BRD:	-	% RED. CHILDREN:	50%	DINNER:	-

Galway 1km

Mrs Maureen Moran
LA RETRAITE
7 Cedarwood Close, Highfield Park, Galway, Co Galway

Galway City

OPEN:	All Year except Christmas
No. ROOMS:	4
ENSUITE:	3

TEL: **091 521450**   FAX: -

Modern home in quiet cul-de-sac. Between city and seaside. 3 bedrooms ensuite. Golf, horse riding nearby. Private car park.

B&B PPS:	£15/£17.50	SNGL OCC. DBLE/TPL:	£22/£24	SNGL RM:	£17
PART BRD:	-	% RED. CHILDREN:	-	DINNER:	-

Galway

Mrs Marguerite Mulcahy
BREAFFY
65 Shantalla Road, Galway, Co Galway

Galway City

OPEN:	All Year except Christmas
No. ROOMS:	5
ENSUITE:	4

TEL: **091 522536**   FAX: -

Convenient to University Hospital and bridge centre on city bus route No. 2.

B&B PPS:	£17.50	SNGL OCC. DBLE/TPL:	£24	SNGL RM:	£17
PART BRD:	-	% RED. CHILDREN:	-	DINNER:	-

Galway

Margaret & Dermot Walsh
DE SOTA
54 Newcastle Road, Galway, Co Galway

Galway City

OPEN:	All Year
No. ROOMS:	6
ENSUITE:	4

TEL: **091 585064/626900**   FAX: -

Warm comfortable home. Convenient to bus, train, Aran Ferry, University and city centre. Lock up car park.

B&B PPS:	£18/£20	SNGL OCC. DBLE/TPL:	£25/£26.50	SNGL RM:	£18
PART BRD:	-	% RED. CHILDREN:	-	DINNER:	-

Galway 3km

Mrs Phil Concannon
WINACRE LODGE
Bushy Park, Galway, Co Galway

Galway City/Dangan

OPEN:	All Year
NO. ROOMS:	3
ENSUITE:	3

(V)

TEL: **091 523459**   FAX: -

Modern friendly home overlooking River Corrib. On N59 main route to Connemara. Near Glenlo Abbey. Golf. Tea, coffee on arrival.

B&B PPS:	£17/£19	SNGL OCC. DBLE/TPL:	£23.50/£25.50	SNGL RM:	-
PART BRD:	£180	% RED. CHILDREN:	50%	DINNER:	£12

Galway 4km

Mrs Brenda Kelehan
LAKELAND HOUSE
Bushy Park, Galway, Co Galway

Galway City/Dangan Area

OPEN:	All Year
NO. ROOMS:	3
ENSUITE:	2

(V)

TEL: **091 524964**   FAX: -

Spectacular views of river Corrib/Glenlo Abbey, golf club. Adjacent to excellent restaurants and bars. On main route to Connemara.

B&B PPS:	£16/£18	SNGL OCC. DBLE/TPL:	£25	SNGL RM:	£21.50/£25
PART BRD:	£180	% RED. CHILDREN:	50%	DINNER:	£12

Galway 4km

Mrs Bernie McTigue
ABBEY VIEW
Bushy Park, Galway, Co Galway

Galway City/Dangan Area

OPEN:	All Year
NO. ROOMS:	4
ENSUITE:	3

(V)

TEL: **091 524488**   FAX: -

A warm welcome awaits you. View overlooks Glenlo Abbey Golf Course. Adjacent to Restaurants. Ideal for touring Connemara.

B&B PPS:	£16/£18	SNGL OCC. DBLE/TPL:	£25	SNGL RM:	£21.50
PART BRD:	£180	% RED. CHILDREN:	50%	DINNER:	£12

Galway 4km

Mrs Annette O'Grady
KILBREE
Circular Road, Dangan Upper, Galway, Co Galway

Galway City/Dangan Area

OPEN:	All Year
NO. ROOMS:	6
ENSUITE:	6

(V)

TEL: **091 527177**   FAX: **091 520404**   EMAIL: **kilbree@tinet.ie**

Luxurious home enroute to Connemara (N59), overlooking River Corrib, convenient City, University, Glenlo Abbey, beach. Tea/Coffee, TV's in rooms.

B&B PPS:	£18/£23	SNGL OCC. DBLE/TPL:	£25/£30	SNGL RM:	-
PART BRD:	-	% RED. CHILDREN:	20%	DINNER:	£14

Galway 6 km

Mrs Bridie Ward
THE ARCHES
Woodstock, Bushy Park, Galway, Co Galway

Galway City/Dangan Area

OPEN:	All Year except Christmas
NO. ROOMS:	5
ENSUITE:	3

(V)

TEL: **091 527815**   FAX: -

In scenic woodland setting. Lovely walks. On N59 en route to Connemara. 3 km from Glenlo Abbey Golf Course. Ideal touring base.

B&B PPS:	£15/£17	SNGL OCC. DBLE/TPL:	£21.50/£23.50	SNGL RM:	£21
PART BRD:	-	% RED. CHILDREN:	50%	DINNER:	-

Mrs. Kathleen Burke — Galway City/Grattan Park Area

Galway City 1km

LISCARNA
22 Grattan Park, Coast Road, Galway,
Co Galway

TEL: 091 585086   FAX: -

OPEN:	All Year except Christmas
NO. ROOMS:	5
ENSUITE:	5

Modern detached home beside beach on Coast Road, walking distance of City Centre and Leisureland. All rooms with shower/toilet, TV.

| B&B PPS: | £17 | SNGL OCC. DBLE/TPL: | £23.50 | SNGL RM: | - |
| PART BRD: | - | % RED. CHILDREN: | 25% | DINNER: | - |

Mary Connolly White — Galway City/Grattan Park

Galway City 1km

ATLANTIC HOUSE
32 Grattan Park, Galway City,
Co Galway

TEL: 091 589064   FAX: -

OPEN:	1st March-30th November
NO. ROOMS:	3
ENSUITE:	3

Luxurious detached home, walking distance city centre, Salthill. Adjacent to beach. All rooms ensuite, TV, golf, tennis, fishing nearby.

| B&B PPS: | £17/£18 | SNGL OCC. DBLE/TPL: | £23.50/£25 | SNGL RM: | £20/£25 |
| PART BRD: | - | % RED. CHILDREN: | 25% | DINNER: | - |

Mrs Freda Cunningham — Galway City/Grattan Park Area

Galway 1km

KYLE NA SHEE
37 Grattan Park, Salthill, Galway,
Co Galway

TEL: 091 583505   FAX: -

OPEN:	1st March-1st November
NO. ROOMS:	4
ENSUITE:	3

Modern, detached home beside beach on coast road. Quiet & close to all amenities. Tea/coffee facilities, cable T.V. all rooms.

| B&B PPS: | £17 | SNGL OCC. DBLE/TPL: | £23.50 | SNGL RM: | £20/£25 |
| PART BRD: | - | % RED. CHILDREN: | 25% | DINNER: | - |

Mrs. Mary B. Curran — Galway City/Grattan Park Area

Galway City 1km

CILL CUANA
16 Grattan Park, Via Coast Road,
Galway, Co Galway

TEL: 091 585979   FAX: -

OPEN:	1st January-31st December
NO. ROOMS:	5
ENSUITE:	5

Off coast road to Salthill. Beside beach, walking distance to all amenities. All rooms en-suite TV, hairdryers, tea/coffee facilities.

| B&B PPS: | £17 | SNGL OCC. DBLE/TPL: | £23.50 | SNGL RM: | - |
| PART BRD: | - | % RED. CHILDREN: | 25% | DINNER: | £12 |

Mrs Margaret Daly — Galway City/Grattan Park Area

Galway 1km

LINDALE
3 Grattan Park, Coast Road, Salthill,
Galway, Co Galway

TEL: 091 583048   FAX: -

OPEN:	17th March-17th October
NO. ROOMS:	3
ENSUITE:	1

On sea front overlooking Galway Bay. Close to golf, tennis, Leisureland, University, and Aran Island Ferry. Balcony, unsuitable for children.

| B&B PPS: | £15/£20 | SNGL OCC. DBLE/TPL: | - | SNGL RM: | - |
| PART BRD: | - | % RED. CHILDREN: | - | DINNER: | - |

Bernadette Donoghue
KILTEVNA
24 Grattan Park, Coast Road, Galway, Co Galway

	Galway City/Grattan Park Area	
OPEN:	All Year except Christmas	
No. ROOMS:	5	
ENSUITE:	5	V

TEL: **091 588477/581173**   FAX: -

Modern detached home beside beach, off coast road, within walking distance city, Leisureland. All rooms with bathrooms, TV, hairdryers.

B&B PPS:	**£17**	SNGL OCC. DBLE/TPL:	**£23.50**	SNGL RM:	-
PART BRD:	-	% RED. CHILDREN:	**25%**	DINNER:	-

— Galway City 1km

Mrs Pat Greaney
HIGH TIDE
9 Grattan Park, Coast Road, Galway, Co Galway

	Galway City/Grattan Park Area	
OPEN:	1st February-30th November	
No. ROOMS:	4	
ENSUITE:	4	V

TEL: **091 584324/589470**   FAX: **091 584324 (man)**

Panoramic views of Galway Bay and Clare Hills. Beside beach. Within walking distance city centre, Leisureland etc. Frommer/Inside Ireland recommended.

B&B PPS:	**£17**	SNGL OCC. DBLE/TPL:	-	SNGL RM:	-
PART BRD:	-	% RED. CHILDREN:	**25%**	DINNER:	-

— Galway City 1km

Mrs Rita Hoade
ANNAGH
28 Grattan Park, Coast Road, Galway, Co Galway

	Galway City/Grattan Park Area	
OPEN:	1st April-30th September	
No. ROOMS:	3	
ENSUITE:	1	V

TEL: **091 584884**   FAX: -

Georgian Home, situated off coast road, within walking distance of City, Aran Ferry and Leisureland. Beach 100 yds. Safe parking.

B&B PPS:	**£15/£17**	SNGL OCC. DBLE/TPL:	-	SNGL RM:	-
PART BRD:	-	% RED. CHILDREN:	**25%**	DINNER:	-

— Galway 1km

Mrs Maureen Loughnane
DUNKELLIN HOUSE
4 Grattan Park, Coast Road, Galway, Co Galway

	Galway City/Grattan Park Area	
OPEN:	All Year except Christmas	
No. ROOMS:	4	
ENSUITE:	3	V

TEL: **091 589037**   FAX: -

Panoramic views of Galway Bay. Walking distance to City Salthill & Aran Ferry. Safe parking in quiet area. Beside Beach.

B&B PPS:	**£15/£17**	SNGL OCC. DBLE/TPL:	**£21.50/£23.50**	SNGL RM:	-
PART BRD:	-	% RED. CHILDREN:	**25%**	DINNER:	-

— Galway City 1km

Mary Molloy
ORLANDO
58 Grattan Park, Coast Road, Galway City, Co Galway

	Galway City/Grattan Park Area	
OPEN:	1st March-1st November	
No. ROOMS:	4	
ENSUITE:	3	V

TEL: **091 582904**   FAX: -

Modern home in quiet cul-de-sac, convenient to all amenities, angling, beach, golf. Within walking distance of City and Salthill.

B&B PPS:	**£17**	SNGL OCC. DBLE/TPL:	**£23.50**	SNGL RM:	**£20**
PART BRD:	-	% RED. CHILDREN:	**25%**	DINNER:	-

— Galway City 1km

Galway 1km

Mrs Bridie Moore
COIS NA TRA
21 Grattan Park, Coast Road, Salthill, Galway, Co Galway
TEL: **091 583258**   FAX: -

Galway City/Grattan Park

OPEN:	**1st March-31stOctober**
NO. ROOMS:	5
ENSUITE:	3

New modern home. Walking distance City Centre and Salthill, Leisureland, off Coast Rd. & Grattan Road & all amenities.

B&B PPS:	**£16/£17**	SNGL OCC. DBLE/TPL:	-	SNGL RM:	-
PART BRD:	-	% RED. CHILDREN:	25%	DINNER:	-

Galway City 1km

Mrs Mary Murphy
WATERDALE
40 Grattan Park, Coast Road, Galway, Co Galway
TEL: **091 586501**   FAX: -

Galway City/Grattan Park Area

OPEN:	**1st March-1st November**
NO. ROOMS:	4
ENSUITE:	2

Detached home on coast road to Salthill. Convenient to all amenities, angling, beach, golf. Walking distance of City & Salthill.

B&B PPS:	**£15/£17**	SNGL OCC. DBLE/TPL:	**£21.50/£23.50**	SNGL RM:	**£20**
PART BRD:	-	% RED. CHILDREN:	25%	DINNER:	-

Galway City 3.5km

Mrs. Evelyn Collins
AVONDALE HOUSE
Roscam, Coast Road, Galway, Co. Galway
TEL: **091 753091**   FAX: -

Galway City/Merlin Park Area

OPEN:	**1st May-31st October**
NO. ROOMS:	3
ENSUITE:	2

Spilt level bungalow, Coast Rd. East Galway City near Galway Heritage Centre, Corrib Great Southern Hotel. Personally run. Golf, Tennis

B&B PPS:	**£15/£17**	SNGL OCC. DBLE/TPL:	**£21.50/£23.50**	SNGL RM:	-
PART BRD:	-	% RED. CHILDREN:	5%	DINNER:	-

Galway City 5 km

Mrs Olive Connolly
SEACREST
Coast Road, Roscam, Merlin Park, Galway, Co Galway
TEL: **091 757975**   FAX: **091 756531**

Galway City/Merlin Park Area

OPEN:	**20th February-5th November**
NO. ROOMS:	6
ENSUITE:	5

Overlooking Galway Bay, Golf Club, Indoor Pool. Tea/coffee facilities, hair dryers, New York Times, Boston Globe, Le Guide du Routard recommended.

B&B PPS:	**£15/£17.50**	SNGL OCC. DBLE/TPL:	**£21.50/£25**	SNGL RM:	-
PART BRD:	-	% RED. CHILDREN:	-	DINNER:	-

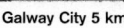

Galway 3km

Mrs. Phil Fahy
LARCHILL
14 Woodhaven, Merlin Park, Galway, Co Galway
TEL: **091 770915**   FAX: -

Galway City /Merlin Park Area

OPEN:	**1st March-31st December**
NO. ROOMS:	4
ENSUITE:	4

Modern spacious residence in quiet residential area near Corrib Great Southern Hotel. Rooms en-suite with TV.

B&B PPS:	**£17/£22**	SNGL OCC. DBLE/TPL:	**£23.50/£28.50**	SNGL RM:	-
PART BRD:	-	% RED. CHILDREN:	20%	DINNER:	-

Galway 5km

Mrs. Millie Forde
BAYSIDE
Coast Road, Curragreen, Merlin Park, Galway, Co Galway
TEL: **091 794310**   FAX: -

Modern bungalow on Galway/Oranmore Coast road, 5 km from Galway. km from Galway Crystal, overlooking the Bay. No smoking.

Ⓟ⊗ℝ⊁✈♪⌂

Galway City/Merlin Park		
OPEN:	1st May-30th September	
NO. ROOMS:	5	
ENSUITE:	4	Ⓥ

B&B PPS:	**£15/£20**	SNGL OCC. DBLE/TPL:	**£22/£26.50**	SNGL RM:	-
PART BRD:	-	% RED. CHILDREN:	**10%**	DINNER:	-

Galway City 4km

Mrs Ann McDonagh
AMBERVILLE
Coast Road, Roscam, Merlin Park, Galway, Co Galway
TEL: **091 757135**   FAX: -

Modern home overlooking Galway Bay & championship golf course. 1km from Galway Crystal factory shop. Off coast road, N6. No smoking.

⬆Ⓟ⊗ℝ⊁✈♪⌂Ⓢ

Galway City/Merlin Park Area		
OPEN:	April-October	
NO. ROOMS:	4	
ENSUITE:	2	Ⓥ

B&B PPS:	**£16/£20**	SNGL OCC. DBLE/TPL:	**£22.50/£26.50**	SNGL RM:	**£16**
PART BRD:	-	% RED. CHILDREN:	**25%**	DINNER:	-

Galway City 4km

Mrs Una McNulty
BEAUPRE
Coast Road (Oranmore), Roscam, Galway, Co Galway
TEL: **091 753858**   FAX: -   -

Overlooking Galway Bay, Burren Golf Course. Coast Rd N6. 1 km Galway Crystal. Heritage Centre, electric blankets, hairdryers, reduction low season.

Ⓟ⊗♪⌂

Galway City/Merlin Park Area		
OPEN:	Easter-November	
NO. ROOMS:	4	
ENSUITE:	4	Ⓥ

B&B PPS:	**£17**	SNGL OCC. DBLE/TPL:	**£23.50**	SNGL RM:	-
PART BRD:	-	% RED. CHILDREN:	-	DINNER:	-

Galway City 2km

Liam & Yvonne O'Reilly
CORRIB VIEW B&B
12 Woodhaven, Merlin Park, Galway, Co. Galway
TEL: **091 755667**   FAX: -

Luxurious residence, quiet Cul-de-Sac. Bus route. Recommended "Best B B in the West". km City Centre. Adjacent Corrib Great Southern Hotel.

ⒸⒸ⬆Ⓟ⊁▭➤♪⌂♣

Galway City/Merlin Park Area		
OPEN:	1st January-22nd December	
NO. ROOMS:	3	
ENSUITE:	3	Ⓥ

B&B PPS:	**£17.50/£18.50**	SNGL OCC. DBLE/TPL:	**£24/£25**	SNGL RM:	-
PART BRD:	-	% RED. CHILDREN:	-	DINNER:	-

Galway 1km

Mrs. Teresa Burke
LYNBURGH
Whitestrand Road, Lower Salthill, Galway, Co. Galway
TEL: **091 581555**   FAX: -

Spacious residence overlooking Galway Bay. Beach 100 yds. Walking distance to City Centre, Leisureland, University & Aran Ferry. TV, Hairdryers.

Ⓟ▭⌣♪⌂♣

Lower Salthill		
OPEN:	All Year	
NO. ROOMS:	6	
ENSUITE:	6	Ⓥ

B&B PPS:	**£17/£20**	SNGL OCC. DBLE/TPL:	-	SNGL RM:	-
PART BRD:	-	% RED. CHILDREN:	**20%**	DINNER:	-

Galway City 1km

Mrs. Esther Daly
GLENCAR
6 Beach Court Off Grattan Road, Lower Salthill, Galway, Co. Galway

Lower Salthill

OPEN:	1st February-1st December	
NO. ROOMS:	4	
ENSUITE:	4	(V)

TEL: 091 581431   FAX: -

Modern Georgian home overlooking Galway Bay. TV & Hair Dryers in bedrooms. Beside Beach. Walking distance City Centre. Tea-facilities.

B&B PPS:	£17	SNGL OCC. DBLE/TPL:	£23.50/£28	SNGL RM:	-
PART BRD:	-	% RED. CHILDREN:	25%	DINNER:	-

Galway 1km

Mrs Sara Davy
ROSS HOUSE
14 Whitestrand Avenue, Lower Salthill, Galway, Co. Galway

Lower Salthill

OPEN:	All Year except Christmas	
NO. ROOMS:	4	
ENSUITE:	4	(V)

TEL: 091 587431   FAX: -

Beside Galway Bay. All rooms with private facilities, TV, hairdryer, tea/coffee. Ten minutes walking to city centre, Aran Ferry.

B&B PPS:	£17	SNGL OCC. DBLE/TPL:	-	SNGL RM:	-
PART BRD:	-	% RED. CHILDREN:	-	DINNER:	-

Galway 1km

Mrs. Stella Faherty
CONSILIO
4 Whitestrand Avenue, Lower Salthill, Galway, Co Galway

Lower Salthill

OPEN:	All Year except Christmas	
NO. ROOMS:	4	
ENSUITE:	4	(V)

TEL: 091 586450   FAX: -

Comfortable home in quiet area between Galway and Salthill. Beside Beach and convenient to all City entertainment.

B&B PPS:	£17/£18	SNGL OCC. DBLE/TPL:	£23.50/£24.50	SNGL RM:	£20/£21
PART BRD:	-	% RED. CHILDREN:	25%	DINNER:	-

Galway 1km

Kathleen Fahy
ABHOG
28 Grattan Court, Fr. Griffin Road, Galway, Co. Galway

Lower Salthill

OPEN:	January-December	
NO. ROOMS:	3	
ENSUITE:	3	(V)

TEL: 091 589528   FAX: -

Newly refurbished home centrally located in quiet residential area. Ensuite, TV, tea/coffee, hairdryers in all rooms. Warm friendly atmosphere.

B&B PPS:	£17/£20	SNGL OCC. DBLE/TPL:	£23.50/£26.50	SNGL RM:	-
PART BRD:	-	% RED. CHILDREN:	25%	DINNER:	-

In Galway City

Susan & David Hogan
LE CHALET
60 Lower Salthill, Galway, Co Galway

Lower Salthill

OPEN:	All Year except Christmas	
NO. ROOMS:	4	
ENSUITE:	4	(V)

TEL: 091 5258801 / 526767   FAX: -

Beautiful old comfortable & cosy cottage. All en-suite with TV all rooms. Family run. Near city centre.

B&B PPS:	£17/£20	SNGL OCC. DBLE/TPL:	£23.50/£26.50	SNGL RM:	-
PART BRD:	-	% RED. CHILDREN:	25%	DINNER:	-

Galway 1km

Mrs Berna Kelly
DEVONDELL
47 Devon Park, Lower Salthill, Co Galway

TEL: **091 528306**   FAX: -

	Lower Salthill
OPEN:	1st March-31st October
NO. ROOMS:	4
ENSUITE:	4

Tastefully refurbished home with period furnishings,brass beds. Relaxed friendly atmosphere. Extensive breakfast Menu. Quiet cul-de-sac. Lonely Planet recommended.

BUS NO: **1**

B&B PPS:	£17.50/£20	SNGL OCC. DBLE/TPL:	£24/£26.50	SNGL RM:	£20
PART BRD:	-	% RED. CHILDREN:	-	DINNER:	-

Galway 1km

Ita Johnstone
ST. JUDES
110 Lower Salthill, Galway, Co. Galway

TEL: **091 521619**   FAX: -

	Lower Salthill
OPEN:	1st March-31st October
NO. ROOMS:	3
ENSUITE:	3

Distinguished family residence, private parking on City bus route, short walk to beach and all amenities, Galway City 10 minutes.

B&B PPS:	£18/£20	SNGL OCC. DBLE/TPL:	£25/£30	SNGL RM:	-
PART BRD:	-	% RED. CHILDREN:	-	DINNER:	-

Galway 1km

Mrs Eileen Mahon
WOODFORD
45 Beach Court off Grattan Road, Lower Salthill, Galway, Co. Galway

TEL: **091 581413**   FAX: -

	Lower Salthill
OPEN:	All Year except Christmas
NO. ROOMS:	4
ENSUITE:	4

Modern home in quiet residential area, beside Beach and City. Private parking. 1 room ground level. All with TV.

B&B PPS:	£17	SNGL OCC. DBLE/TPL:	£23.50	SNGL RM:	£20
PART BRD:	-	% RED. CHILDREN:	50%	DINNER:	-

Galway City 1km

Kathleen Melvin
LISKEA
16 Whitestrand Avenue, Lower Salthill, Galway, Co Galway

TEL: **091 584318**   FAX: -

	Lower Salthill
OPEN:	All Year except Christmas
NO. ROOMS:	4
ENSUITE:	4

Beside Galway Bay. Beach 100 yds. Short walk to City Centre. All rooms ensuite. Television, hairdryer, tea/coffee.

B&B PPS:	£17	SNGL OCC. DBLE/TPL:	-	SNGL RM:	-
PART BRD:	-	% RED. CHILDREN:	25%	DINNER:	£12

Galway City 1km

Mrs Maureen Nolan
GLENCREE
20 Whitestrand Avenue, Lr. Salthill, Galway City, Co. Galway

TEL: **091 581061**   FAX: -

	Lower Salthill
OPEN:	1st January-23rd December
NO. ROOMS:	4
ENSUITE:	4

Beside Galway Bay. All rooms shower & toilet, TV, hairdryers. Short walking distance city centre, university, Aran Ferry etc., beach 100 yds.

B&B PPS:	£17	SNGL OCC. DBLE/TPL:	-	SNGL RM:	-
PART BRD:	-	% RED. CHILDREN:	20%	DINNER:	-

Mrs. Colette O'Donnell
SEA BREEZE
Lower Salthill

13 Whitestrand Ave., Lr. Salthill, Galway,
Co Galway

OPEN:	Easter-30th September
NO. ROOMS:	4
ENSUITE:	2

TEL: **091 581530**   FAX: -

Warm comfortable home in quiet cul-de-sac off main Galway/Salthill Road. 10 minutes walk to Galway & Salthill.

B&B PPS:	£15/£17	SNGL. OCC. DBLE/TPL:	£21.50/£23.50	SNGL. RM:	£15
PART BRD:	-	% RED. CHILDREN:	50%	DINNER:	

Galway 1km

Tim and Carmel O'Halloran
RONCALLI HOUSE
Lower Salthill

24 Whitestrand Avenue
Lower Salthill, Co Galway

OPEN:	All Year
NO. ROOMS:	6
ENSUITE:	6

TEL: **091 584159/589013**   FAX: **091 584159**

Comfortable home beside Galway Bay. Frommer/Birnbaum recommended. Walking distance City Centre. All rooms shower/toilet, television, hairdryer, Tea/Coffee Facilities.

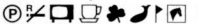

B&B PPS:	£17	SNGL. OCC. DBLE/TPL:	-	SNGL. RM:	-
PART BRD:	-	% RED. CHILDREN:	20%	DINNER:	-

Galway 1km

Mrs Anne O'Malley
DUHALLOW
Lower Salthill

12 Whitestrand Road, Lower Salthill,
Galway, Co Galway

OPEN:	10th April-28th October
NO. ROOMS:	6
ENSUITE:	6

TEL: **091 582383**   FAX: -

Large two storey house, 5 mins to town and beach. Quiet, large parking area. All rooms ensuite, electric blankets, hairdryers.

B&B PPS:	£17	SNGL. OCC. DBLE/TPL:	-	SNGL. RM:	-
PART BRD:	-	% RED. CHILDREN:	-	DINNER:	-

Mrs Christina Ruane
25 Grattan Court,
Lower Salthill

Fr Griffin Road, Lower Salthill, Co.
Galway

OPEN:	All Year except Christmas
NO. ROOMS:	5
ENSUITE:	4

TEL: **091 586513**   FAX: -

Modern detached house, quiet residential area. 10 mins walk Salthill, 5 mins beach, golf club, 10 mins Hospital & University.

B&B PPS:	£15/£20	SNGL. OCC. DBLE/TPL:	£22/£26.50	SNGL. RM:	-
PART BRD:	-	% RED. CHILDREN:	25%	DINNER:	-

Galway City

Kay Scarry
CILLMARA HOUSE
Lower Salthill

40 Beach Court
Grattan Road, Salthill, Co. Galway

OPEN:	1st March-31st October
NO. ROOMS:	4
ENSUITE:	4

TEL: **091 526037**   FAX: -

Modern detached home. Walking distance to City Centre/Salthill/Leisureland. Beach 100 yrds. Tea/coffee facilities available in lounge.

B&B PPS:	£17/£20	SNGL. OCC. DBLE/TPL:	£23.50/£26.50	SNGL. RM:	-
PART BRD:	-	% RED. CHILDREN:	25%	DINNER:	£12

Galway 1km

Mrs Marie Silke
SEAGROVE
21 Beach Court, Grattan Road, Lower Salthill, Galway, Co. Galway

Lower Salthill

OPEN:	1st April-October
NO. ROOMS:	3
ENSUITE:	1

(V)

TEL: **091 588740**   FAX: -

Situated in quiet cul-de-sac off Main Galway/Salthill road. Close to beaches, promenade and Leisureland.

B&B PPS:	**£15/£18**	SNGL OCC. DBLE/TPL:	**£21.50/£24.50**	SNGL RM:	-
PART BRD:	-	% RED. CHILDREN:	**20%**	DINNER:	-

— Galway 1km —

Ms. Maureen Tarpey
THE DORMERS
Whitestrand Road, Lr. Salthill, Galway, Co. Galway

Lower Salthill

OPEN:	All Year
NO. ROOMS:	6
ENSUITE:	6

(V)

TEL: **091 585034**   FAX: -

Bungalow, conveniently situated within walking distance to city & beach. All rooms with shower/toilet & TV. Some rooms on ground floor.

B&B PPS:	**£17/£20**	SNGL OCC. DBLE/TPL:	-	SNGL RM:	-
PART BRD:	-	% RED. CHILDREN:	**20%**	DINNER:	-

— Galway 1km —

Mrs. Bridie Thomson
ROCK LODGE
Whitestrand Road, Galway, Co Galway

Lower Salthill

OPEN:	All Year
NO. ROOMS:	6
ENSUITE:	6

(V)

TEL: **091 583789**   FAX: **091 583789**

Spacious residence beside Galway Bay. Walking distance city centre. TV and hairdryers in all rooms. Private parking. Beach 100 yds.

B&B PPS:	**£17/£18**	SNGL OCC. DBLE/TPL:	-	SNGL RM:	-
PART BRD:	-	% RED. CHILDREN:	**20%**	DINNER:	-

— In Galway —

Mrs. Frances Tiernan
VILLA MARUEA
94 Fr. Griffin Rd., Lower Salthill, Galway, Co Galway

Lower Salthill

OPEN:	All Year except Christmas
NO. ROOMS:	3
ENSUITE:	3

(V)

TEL: **091 589033**   FAX: -

Modern home. Frommer Guide recommended. Walking distance from beach, city centre and Leisureland. TV, Tea/Coffee all rooms. Private Parking.

B&B PPS:	**£17/£18**	SNGL OCC. DBLE/TPL:	-	SNGL RM:	-
PART BRD:	-	% RED. CHILDREN:	-	DINNER:	-

— Galway 1km —

Mrs. Margaret Walsh
LAWNDALE
5 Beach Court off Grattan Road, Lower Salthill, Galway, Co. Galway

Lower Salthill

OPEN:	All Year
NO. ROOMS:	5
ENSUITE:	5

(V)

TEL: **091 586676**   FAX: -

Warm, quiet hospitable home. Walking distance to city. Overlooking Galway Bay. Frommer, Best Guides recommended. TV.

B&B PPS:	**£17**	SNGL OCC. DBLE/TPL:	**£23.50/£28**	SNGL RM:	-
PART BRD:	-	% RED. CHILDREN:	-	DINNER:	-

— Galway 1km —

In Salthill

Mrs. Mary Barry
TRIESTE — Salthill
12 Forster Park off Dalysfort Road, Salthill, Co Galway

OPEN: March-October
NO. ROOMS: 5
ENSUITE: 3

(V)

TEL: **091 521014** FAX: -

Modern bungalow in quiet cul-de-sac. Near beach, golf, tennis Club & Leisureland. Tea/coffee facilities. Salthill bus route, single room.

B&B PPS:	**£15/£19**	SNGL OCC. DBLE/TPL:	**£21.50/£25.50**	SNGL RM:	**£17/£20**
PART BRD:	-	% RED. CHILDREN:	**25%**	DINNER:	-

Mrs Ann Brady
CARRICKVALE — Salthill
20 Dr Mannix Road, Salthill, Co Galway

OPEN: All Year except Christmas
NO. ROOMS: 6
ENSUITE: 4

(V)

TEL: **091 522317** FAX: -

Modern home convenient to beach and Leisureland, on bus route to City Centre. Private car park.

B&B PPS:	**£17/£18**	SNGL OCC. DBLE/TPL:	**£23.50/£24.50**	SNGL RM:	**£17**
PART BRD:	-	% RED. CHILDREN:	**25%**	DINNER:	-

Galway 3km

Mrs Brenda Brennan
OCEAN VILLA — Salthill
7 Cashelmara, Knocknacarra Cross, Salthill, Galway, Co. Galway

OPEN: All Year except Christmas
NO. ROOMS: 4
ENSUITE: 4

(V)

TEL: **091 529549** FAX: -

New luxury B & B overlooking Galway Bay. Cable TV's. Convenient golf, horse riding, surfing, Leisureland, Tennis. Ideal touring base. Credit Cards accepted.

B&B PPS:	**£17/£22**	SNGL OCC. DBLE/TPL:	**£23.50/£28.50**	SNGL RM:	-
PART BRD:	-	% RED. CHILDREN:	**25%**	DINNER:	-

Galway 2km

Mrs Margaret Brennan
GLENARIFF — Salthill
4 Rockhill Ave., Salthill, Galway, Co. Galway

OPEN: Easter-October
NO. ROOMS: 4
ENSUITE: 4

(V)

TEL: **091 522521** FAX: -

Long established recommended home. Adjacent to Prom and all amenities. TV in rooms. Smoke free home. Friendly service our priority.

B&B PPS:	**£17/£18**	SNGL OCC. DBLE/TPL:	**£23.50/£24.50**	SNGL RM:	-
PART BRD:	-	% RED. CHILDREN:	-	DINNER:	-

Galway 2km

Mrs. Catherine Carey
THE GREENWAYS — Salthill
9 Glenard Crescent off Dr. Mannix Road, Salthill, Galway, Co. Galway

OPEN: March-October
NO. ROOMS: 4
ENSUITE: 4

(V)

TEL: **091 522308** FAX: -

Comfortable warm home. View of Galway Bay. Private parking. Close to Leisureland, golf, tennis & beach.

B&B PPS:	**£17/£20**	SNGL OCC. DBLE/TPL:	**£23.50/£26.50**	SNGL RM:	-
PART BRD:	-	% RED. CHILDREN:	**20%**	DINNER:	-

Mrs. Christina Connolly
CLARE VILLA
38 Threadneedle Road, Salthill, Co. Galway

Salthill

OPEN:	**1st January-31st October**
NO. ROOMS:	**6**
ENSUITE:	**6**

(V)

TEL: **091 522520**   FAX: -

Spacious family residence adjacent to Tennis Club. 5 mins walk from beach, Leisureland and golf. On bus route. Private parking.

B&B PPS:	**£17.50/£18.50**	SNGL. OCC. DBLE/TPL:	**£24/£25**	SNGL RM:	-
PART BRD:	-	% RED. CHILDREN:	**25%**	DINNER:	-

Galway 2km

Noreen Cosgrove
MAPLE HOUSE
Dr. Mannix Road, Salthill, Co Galway

Salthill

OPEN:	**All Year except Christmas**
NO. ROOMS:	**4**
ENSUITE:	**4**

(V)

TEL: **091 526136**   FAX: -

New luxurious home adjacent beach, golf, tennis, riding, Leisureland, private parking, tea/coffee, TV bedrooms, Bus route. Open all year.

B&B PPS:	**£18/£22**	SNGL. OCC. DBLE/TPL:	**£24.50**	SNGL RM:	-
PART BRD:	-	% RED. CHILDREN:	**25%**	DINNER:	-

In Salthill

Mrs. Marian Coyne
COOLIN HOUSE
11 Seamount, Threadneedle Road, Salthill, Co Galway

Salthill

OPEN:	**1st April-31st October**
NO. ROOMS:	**3**
ENSUITE:	**3**

(V)

TEL: **091 523411**   FAX: -

Modern Georgian-style home, beside beach, tennis club, golf course, Leisureland. On bus route. Private parking.

B&B PPS:	**£17.50/£18**	SNGL. OCC. DBLE/TPL:	**£22.50/£25**	SNGL RM:	-
PART BRD:	-	% RED. CHILDREN:	**10%**	DINNER:	-

Galway City 2km

Phil Flannery
FLANNERY'S
54 Dalysfort Road, Salthill, Galway, Co Galway

Salthill

OPEN:	**All Year except Christmas**
NO. ROOMS:	**4**
ENSUITE:	**3**

(V)

TEL: **091 522048**   FAX: **091 522048**   EMAIL: **phil.flannery@storm.ie**

AA 3Q Quality Award House, quiet area off seafront, near Leisureland, Golf, Tennis. Private parking, German spoken. City bus route.

BUS No: **1**

B&B PPS:	**£15/£18**	SNGL. OCC. DBLE/TPL:	**£21.50/£24.50**	SNGL RM:	-
PART BRD:	-	% RED. CHILDREN:	-	DINNER:	-

Galway 2km

Johnny & Helen Geraghty
CILL DARA HOUSE
23 Rockhill Avenue, Oaklands, Salthill, Galway, Co Galway

Salthill

OPEN:	**Easter-October**
NO. ROOMS:	**5**
ENSUITE:	**4**

(V)

TEL: **091 522401**   FAX: -

Highly recommended home in quiet Cul-de-sac. Orthopaedic beds, electric blankets, TV in bedrooms, smoke-free home. Beach, Leisureland 250 metres.

B&B PPS:	**£15/£18**	SNGL. OCC. DBLE/TPL:	**£21.50/£24.50**	SNGL RM:	-
PART BRD:	-	% RED. CHILDREN:	-	DINNER:	-

Galway 2km

Mrs. Mary Geraghty
MARLESS HOUSE
Threadneedle Road, Salthill, Galway, Co Galway

Salthill

OPEN:	All Year except Christmas
NO. ROOMS:	6
ENSUITE:	6

(V)

TEL: **091 523931**   FAX: **091 529810**

Luxurious georgian residence, beach - 100 metres. Frommer recommended. Leisureland, golf closeby. TV, electric blankets, tea/coffee facilities in all rooms.

Galway 2km

| B&B PPS: | £17.50/£18.50 | SNGL OCC. DBLE/TPL: | £25 | SNGL RM: | - |
| PART BRD: | - | % RED. CHILDREN: | 25% | DINNER: | - |

Mrs. Nora Hanniffy
ANNA REE HOUSE
49 Oaklands, Salthill, Galway, Co Galway

Salthill

OPEN:	All Year except Christmas
NO. ROOMS:	6
ENSUITE:	4

(V)

TEL: **091 522583**   FAX: -

Modern home. Private parking. Rear of Church by Sacre Coeur Hotel. 5 mins walk beach, Leisureland and bus route. Electric blankets.

| B&B PPS: | £17/£18 | SNGL OCC. DBLE/TPL: | £23.50/£24.50 | SNGL RM: | £17 |
| PART BRD: | - | % RED. CHILDREN: | 25% | DINNER: | - |

Mrs. Anne Lally
BAYVIEW
20 Seamount off Threadneedle Road, Salthill, Galway, Co. Galway

Salthill

OPEN:	March-October
NO. ROOMS:	3
ENSUITE:	3

(V)

TEL: **091 526008**   FAX: -

Situated in quiet Cul-de-sac off promenade, beside tennis, golf, Leisureland. On bus route. Tea/Coffee facilities. TV in all rooms.

Galway 2km

| B&B PPS: | £17.50/£18 | SNGL OCC. DBLE/TPL: | £24/£25 | SNGL RM: | - |
| PART BRD: | - | % RED. CHILDREN: | 10% | DINNER: | - |

Mrs. Catherine Lydon
CARRAIG BEAG
1 Burren View Heights, Knocknacarra Road, Salthill, Galway, Co. Galway

Salthill

OPEN:	All Year except Christmas
NO. ROOMS:	4
ENSUITE:	4

(V)

TEL: **091 521696**   FAX: -

Luxurious brick residence. Convenient to beaches, golf, tennis. Recommended Dillard/Causin guide. Fran Sullivan Irish B&B Book. Ideal touring base.

BUS NO: **2**

Galway 2km

| B&B PPS: | £17/£19 | SNGL OCC. DBLE/TPL: | £25/£32 | SNGL RM: | - |
| PART BRD: | - | % RED. CHILDREN: | 33.3% | DINNER: | - |

Mrs. Rena McDonagh
CYRENE
10 Emerson Ave., Salthill, Galway, Co. Galway

Salthill

OPEN:	May-October
NO. ROOMS:	4
ENSUITE:	3

(V)

TEL: **091 522861**   FAX: -

Luxury accommodation off main Salthill Road by Sacre Couer Hotel. Close to all amenities. Smoke free home.

Galway 2km

| B&B PPS: | £15/£17 | SNGL OCC. DBLE/TPL: | £23.50 | SNGL RM: | - |
| PART BRD: | - | % RED. CHILDREN: | - | DINNER: | - |

Galway 2km

Mrs. Mairead McGuire
WESTPOINT
87 Threadneedle Road, Salthill, Galway, Co. Galway

Salthill

OPEN:	**All Year except Christmas**
No. ROOMS:	6
ENSUITE:	6

 (V)

TEL: **091 521026**   FAX: **091 582152**

Comfortable warm home, views of Bay. AA listed. Bus route, Leisureland, beach, tennis & golf close by. Multi recommendations. Private parking.

[cc] [P] [symbols] [S]

B&B PPS:	£17.50/£20	SNGL OCC. DBLE/TPL:	£24/£26.50	SNGL RM:	-
PART BRD:	-	% RED. CHILDREN:	25%	DINNER:	£12.50

Galway 2km

Mrs. Mary McLoughlin
ARDEEN HOUSE
Rockbarton North, Salthill, Galway, Co Galway

Salthill

OPEN:	**All Year except Christmas**
No. ROOMS:	6
ENSUITE:	6

(V)

TEL: **091 524295**   FAX: -

Spacious family residence in secluded area. Beside Leisureland, beach, tennis, golf. On bus route. Private car park. Official Bureau de Change.

[P] [symbols]   BUS NO: **1**

B&B PPS:	£17	SNGL OCC. DBLE/TPL:	£23.50	SNGL RM:	£23.50
PART BRD:	-	% RED. CHILDREN:	20%	DINNER:	-

Galway 2km

Marian Mitchel
CHESTNUT LODGE
35 Rockbarton Road, Salthill, Co. Galway

Salthill

OPEN:	**March-November**
No. ROOMS:	3
ENSUITE:	3

(V)

TEL: **091 524726**   FAX: -

Luxurious home beside Sea and Salthill Promenade. Golf, tennis, horse riding and beach closeby. On bus route. Private Parking.

[symbols] [S]

B&B PPS:	£17/£20	SNGL OCC. DBLE/TPL:	£23.50/£26.50	SNGL RM:	-
PART BRD:	-	% RED. CHILDREN:	20%	DINNER:	£15

In Salthill

Mrs Nora O'Malley
ST. KIERANS
33 Rockbarton Road, Salthill, Galway, Co Galway

Salthill

OPEN:	**1st February-1st December**
No. ROOMS:	4
ENSUITE:	3

(V)

TEL: **091 523333**   FAX: -

Modern family run home beside Leisureland. Home cooking. Close to bus stop and tennis club.

[P] [symbols]

B&B PPS:	£15/£17	SNGL OCC. DBLE/TPL:	£21.50/£23.50	SNGL RM:	-
PART BRD:	-	% RED. CHILDREN:	-	DINNER:	-

Galway 2km

Mrs. Ann O'Toole
TOWER HOUSE
16 Threadneedle Rd. Salthill, Galway, Co Galway

Salthill

OPEN:	**All Year**
No. ROOMS:	6
ENSUITE:	5

(V)

TEL: **091 526213**   FAX: **091 526213**

Family run, Gaelic speakers, rooms have TV, tea/coffee. Off promenade, close to tennis, golf, beach & Leisureland nearby, sauna. On bus route.

[cc] [symbols] [S]

B&B PPS:	£17/£18.00	SNGL OCC. DBLE/TPL:	£23.50/£25	SNGL RM:	£17/£22
PART BRD:	-	% RED. CHILDREN:	25%	DINNER:	-

Galway City 2km

Mrs. Nora Patten
LOCKERBIE
3 Rockbarton Green off Rockbarton Road, Salthill, Galway, Co. Galway
TEL: **091 521434**   FAX: -

Salthill

OPEN:	March-October
NO. ROOMS:	4
ENSUITE:	4

(V)

Warm comfortable home in quiet area, beside Galway Bay, Leisureland, golf, tennis clubs, beach and bus stop. Tea/coffee facilities.

B&B PPS:	£17/£20	SNGL. OCC. DBLE/TPL:	£23.50/£26.50	SNGL RM:	£17/£20
PART BRD:	-	% RED. CHILDREN:	20%	DINNER:	-

Galway 2km

Mrs. Catherine Quinlan
CAPPA VEAGH
76 Dalysfort Rd., Salthill, Galway, Co. Galway
TEL: **091 526518**   FAX: **091 526518**

Salthill

OPEN:	1st February-30th November
NO. ROOMS:	4
ENSUITE:	3

(V)

Comfortable warm home, beside beach, Leisureland, golf and tennis clubs. On bus route. Tea/coffee on arrival. Ideal touring base.

B&B PPS:	£15/£17	SNGL. OCC. DBLE/TPL:	£21.50/£25	SNGL RM:	-
PART BRD:	-	% RED. CHILDREN:	25%	DINNER:	-

Galway City 2km

Mrs. Ethna Regan
LISCARRA HOUSE
6 Seamount on Threadneedle Rd., Salthill, Galway, Co. Galway
TEL: **091 521299**   FAX: -

Salthill

OPEN:	1st March-30th November
NO. ROOMS:	5
ENSUITE:	4

(V)

Luxurious home overlooking Galway Bay, beside beach, tennis, golf, Leisureland. On bus route. Tea/coffee facilities, TV, electric blankets all rooms.

B&B PPS:	£16/£18.50	SNGL. OCC. DBLE/TPL:	£22.50/£25	SNGL RM:	-
PART BRD:	-	% RED. CHILDREN:	25%	DINNER:	-

Mrs Joan Staunton
PADUA
75 Threadneedle Road, Salthill, Co Galway
TEL: **091 529252/087 433630**   FAX: -

Salthill

OPEN:	1st January-23rd December
NO. ROOMS:	4
ENSUITE:	3

(V)

Modern comfortable residence, 5 minutes walk from beach. Near Leisureland, Tennis, Golf. Private parking. TV all rooms. On Bus route.

B&B PPS:	£15/£18	SNGL. OCC. DBLE/TPL:	£21.50/£24.50	SNGL RM:	-
PART BRD:	-	% RED. CHILDREN:	50%	DINNER:	-

Galway City 2km

Galway City 3km

Mrs. Phil Waldron
CLUAIN ARD
86 Threadneedle Rd., Salthill, Galway City, Co Galway
TEL: **091 525333**   FAX: -

Salthill

OPEN:	1st January-31st December
NO. ROOMS:	4
ENSUITE:	4

(V)

Comfortable home in peaceful surroundings within walking distance of Salthill beach, golf club, tennis club and Leisureland.

B&B PPS:	£17/£18	SNGL. OCC. DBLE/TPL:	£23.50/£24.50	SNGL RM:	-
PART BRD:	-	% RED. CHILDREN:	25%	DINNER:	-

Galway 1km

Mrs. Evelyn Wrynn
FENAGH HOUSE
11 Rockbarton Green off Rockbarton Road, Salthill, Galway, Co. Galway

Salthill

TEL: **091 522835** FAX: -

OPEN:	March-October
NO. ROOMS:	4
ENSUITE:	3

 (V)

House in scenic area beside Galway Bay. Safe parking. Near all amenities. All rooms with private bathrooms. Turn off Leisureland.

B&B PPS:	£15/£20	SNGL OCC. DBLE/TPL:	£23.50/£26.50	SNGL RM:	-
PART BRD:	-	% RED. CHILDREN:	20%	DINNER:	-

In Salthill

Mrs Georgianna Darby
MANDALAY BY THE SEA
10 Gentian/Blakes Hill, Galway, Co. Galway

Upper Salthill/Gentian Hill Area

TEL: **091 524177/529952** FAX: **091 524177**

OPEN:	All Year
NO. ROOMS:	6
ENSUITE:	5

(V)

Luxurious balconied residence panoramic view of Galway Bay. Recommended " Best B&B's in Ireland", Lonely Planet and Hidden Places of Ireland.

B&B PPS:	£15/£20	SNGL OCC. DBLE/TPL:	£22.50/£26.50	SNGL RM:	-
PART BRD:	-	% RED. CHILDREN:	20%	DINNER:	-

Salthill 2km

Mrs. Mary Duggan
KNOCKMOY HOUSE
7 Westbrook, Barna Road, Galway, Co Galway

Upper Salthill

TEL: **091 590674** FAX: -

OPEN:	15th March-31st October
NO. ROOMS:	4
ENSUITE:	4

(V)

Neo Georgian house overlooking Galway Bay. TV Lounge. Only 10 mins drive from Salthill, golf, tennis, Leisureland and horse riding.

BUS NO: **2**

B&B PPS:	£17/£19	SNGL OCC. DBLE/TPL:	£23.50/£25.50	SNGL RM:	-
PART BRD:	-	% RED. CHILDREN:	20%	DINNER:	-

Salthill 1km

Michael & Celine Glynn
DRUMLIN VIEW
6 Cashelmara, Upper Salthill, Galway, Co Galway

Upper Salthill

TEL: **091 529513** FAX: **091 529513** EMAIL: **Cglynn@iol.ie**

OPEN:	All Year except Christmas
NO. ROOMS:	6
ENSUITE:	6

(V)

Luxurious home, overlooking Galway Bay. Near Promenade, Beach. Home Baking. One of the finest Breakfasts in Ireland - Brooklyn Spectator , September 1996.

B&B PPS:	£17/£22	SNGL OCC. DBLE/TPL:	£23.50/£28.50	SNGL RM:	-
PART BRD:	-	% RED. CHILDREN:	10%	DINNER:	-

Salthill 2km

Guilfoyle Family
BAY VIEW HOUSE
Gentian Hill, Salthill, Galway, Co Galway

Upper Salthill-Gentian Hill Area

TEL: **091 522116** FAX: -

OPEN:	17th March-1st November
NO. ROOMS:	6
ENSUITE:	6

(V)

Warm luxurious "smoke free home", TV, Telephone & Electric blankets in all rooms. Tea/Coffee facilities. Close to all amenities.

B&B PPS:	£17	SNGL OCC. DBLE/TPL:	£23.50	SNGL RM:	£19
PART BRD:	£207	% RED. CHILDREN:	-	DINNER:	£15.50

Mrs Barbara Joyce
ROSSLYN
4 Woodfield, Barna Road, Galway, Co Galway

Upper Salthill

OPEN:	31stMarch-1stNovember
NO. ROOMS:	4
ENSUITE:	4

TEL: **091 590032**   FAX: -

Home on Coast Road, overlooking Galway Bay. Ideal touring base for Connemara and the Aran Islands. Good Restaurants, Golf, Fishing, Horse riding.

B&B PPS:	£17/£18	SNGL OCC. DBLE/TPL:	£23 .50/£24.50	SNGL RM:	-
PART BRD:	-	% RED. CHILDREN:	20%	DINNER:	-

Galway 4km

Mrs Colette Keaveney
THE CONNAUGHT
Barna Road, Salthill, Galway, Co Galway

Upper Salthill

OPEN:	March-October
NO. ROOMS:	6
ENSUITE:	5

TEL: **091 525865**   FAX: **091 525865**

Overlooking Galway Bay, TV, Hairdryers, Electric Blankets. Leisureland, Beaches closeby. Recommended 'Best B&Bs in Ireland'/'Guide du Routard'. Chef owner.

BUS NO: **2**

B&B PPS:	£15/£20	SNGL OCC. DBLE/TPL:	£21.50	SNGL RM:	-
PART BRD:	-	% RED. CHILDREN:	20%	DINNER:	-

Salthill 2km

Mrs Caroline Larkin
KILBRACK HOUSE
2 Woodfield, Barna Road, Galway, Co Galway

Upper Salthill

OPEN:	April-November
NO. ROOMS:	3
ENSUITE:	3

TEL: **091 590802**   FAX: -

Luxurious home overlooking Galway Bay. Golf, Fishing, Horseriding, Leisureland, Tennis and good restaurants nearby. Breakfast menu available. Home baking.

B&B PPS:	£17/£19	SNGL OCC. DBLE/TPL:	£23.50/£25.50	SNGL RM:	-
PART BRD:	-	% RED. CHILDREN:	50%	DINNER:	-

Salthill 2km

David & Rita Lenihan
ARCH VILLA
Coast Road, Gentian Hill, Upper Salthill, Galway, Co Galway

Upper Salthill / Gentian Hill Area

OPEN:	All Year except Christmas
NO. ROOMS:	5
ENSUITE:	5

TEL: **091 521425**   FAX: -

Luxurious comfortable home in scenic peaceful surroundings overlooking Galway Bay and bird sanctuary. Close to Golf, Fishing, Beach and Leisureland.

B&B PPS:	£17/£20	SNGL OCC. DBLE/TPL:	£36.50	SNGL RM:	-
PART BRD:	-	% RED. CHILDREN:	25%	DINNER:	-

Salthill 2km

Mrs Teresa McDonagh
ARD MHUIRE
Knocknacarra Road
Upper Salthill, Galway, Co Galway

Upper Salthill

OPEN:	All Year except Christmas
NO. ROOMS:	6
ENSUITE:	6

TEL: **091 522344**   FAX: **091 529629**

Attractive, comfortable home within walking distance of the Seaside. Close to Golfing, Tennis, Fishing, Swimming & All Amenities.

B&B PPS:	£17.50/£20	SNGL OCC. DBLE/TPL:	£25/£26.50	SNGL RM:	-
PART BRD:	-	% RED. CHILDREN:	25%	DINNER:	-

Galway 2km

Mrs Mary McLoughlin
SAILIN
Gentian Hill, Upper Salthill, Galway
Co Galway

Upper Salthill - Gentian Hill Area

OPEN:	1st May-30th September
NO. ROOMS:	3
ENSUITE:	3

TEL: **091 521676**   FAX: **091 521676**

Located in Bird Sanctuary, beside Championship Golf Course, overlooking bay. All rooms with bathrooms. Frommer recommended. Non Smoking. Secure parking.

BUS NO: **2**

B&B PPS:	**£17**	SNGL. OCC. DBLE/TPL:	**£23.50**	SNGL RM:	-
PART BRD:	-	% RED. CHILDREN:	**20%**	DINNER:	-

— Salthill 1km

Mrs Christina Maloney
LOCH-LURGAN HOUSE
Knocknacarra, Barna Road, Galway,
Co Galway

Upper Salthill

OPEN:	15th March-31st October
NO. ROOMS:	4
ENSUITE:	3

TEL: **091 522450**   FAX: -

Caring, Comfortable hospitality. Beautiful Galway Bay View. Conveniently on Coast road. Excellent touring base. Golf, Tennis Riding nearby. Frommer recommended.

BUS NO: **2**

B&B PPS:	**£15/£18**	SNGL. OCC. DBLE/TPL:	**£21.50/£24.50**	SNGL RM:	-
PART BRD:	-	% RED. CHILDREN:	**20%**	DINNER:	-

— Salthill 2km

Mrs Mary Meehan
SUMMERVILLE
4 Westbrook, Barna Rd., Galway,
Co Galway

Upper Salthill

OPEN:	1st March-1st December
NO. ROOMS:	4
ENSUITE:	4

TEL: **091 590424**   FAX: **091 590424**

Luxurious residence with balcony overlooking Galway Bay. Cable TV, Hairdryers, tea/coffee all rooms.Near Leisureland, Beach, Horse-riding, Golf. Recommended

B&B PPS:	**£17/£19**	SNGL. OCC. DBLE/TPL:	**£23.50/£25.50**	SNGL RM:	-
PART BRD:	-	% RED. CHILDREN:	**50%**	DINNER:	-

— Galway 3km

Mrs Alice Murphy
CLOGHEEN
31 Oldfield, Kingston, Galway,
Co Galway

Upper Salthill

OPEN:	13th March-31st October
NO. ROOMS:	3
ENSUITE:	2

TEL: **091 523441**   FAX: -

Peaceful, comfortable home. TV in bedrooms. On No 2 bus route, near Golf, Tennis, Beach, Leisureland.

BUS NO: **2**

B&B PPS:	**£15/£18**	SNGL. OCC. DBLE/TPL:	**£21.50/£24.50**	SNGL RM:	-
PART BRD:	-	% RED. CHILDREN:	**25%**	DINNER:	-

— Galway 2km

Bridie & Mike Murray
DUN ROSS
Kingston, Upper Salthill, Galway,
Co Galway

Upper Salthill

OPEN:	March-September
NO. ROOMS:	3
ENSUITE:	2

TEL: **091 523404**   FAX: -

Residence on own spacious grounds including car park. Close to Beaches, Golf, Tennis, City buses. Families welcome.

B&B PPS:	**£15/£17**	SNGL. OCC. DBLE/TPL:	**£21.50/£23.50**	SNGL RM:	-
PART BRD:	-	% RED. CHILDREN:	**50%**	DINNER:	-

— Salthill 1km

Padraig and Maureen O'Donnell
SHAMROCK LODGE
4 Carragh Drive, Knocknacarra Road, Upper Salthill, Galway, Co Galway

Upper Salthill

OPEN:	1st March-31st October
NO. ROOMS:	4
ENSUITE:	4

(V)

TEL: **091 521429**   FAX: **091 521429**

Overlooking bay, Beach, Golf, Tennis, Leisureland, TV, Electric blankets. Follow promenade, Golf course, right at Spinnaker, 3rd left, 4th on right.

BUS NO: **2**

Galway 2 km

B&B PPS:	**£17/£20**	SNGL OCC. DBLE/TPL:	**£23.50/£26.50**	SNGL RM:	-
PART BRD:	-	% RED. CHILDREN:	25%	DINNER:	-

Bernie Power
FOUR WINDS LODGE
Gentian Hill, Salthill, Co Galway

Upper Salthill

OPEN:	1st January-20th December
NO. ROOMS:	4
ENSUITE:	4

(V)

TEL: **091 526026**   FAX: -

Old world home, scenic peaceful surroundings overlooking Galway Bay. Private Gardens. Private Car Park. Beside Leisureland, Prominade, Tennis, Horseriding, Fishing, Golf.

Salthill 1.5km

B&B PPS:	**£17/£25**	SNGL OCC. DBLE/TPL:	**£23.50/£31.50**	SNGL RM:	-
PART BRD:	-	% RED. CHILDREN:	50%	DINNER:	-

Mrs Betty Reidy
CHATEAU
1 Woodfield, Barna Road, Galway, Co Galway

Upper Salthill

OPEN:	1st April-31st October
NO. ROOMS:	3
ENSUITE:	2

(V)

TEL: **091 590732**   FAX: -

Detached home on Coast Road overlooking Galway Bay. Ajacent to Golf, Tennis, fishing, Pony Trekking & excellent Restaurants. Convenient for touring. Non Smoking.

Galway City 4km

B&B PPS:	**£15/£19**	SNGL OCC. DBLE/TPL:	**£21.50/£25.50**	SNGL RM:	-
PART BRD:	-	% RED. CHILDREN:	20%	DINNER:	-

Mrs Patty Wheeler
WOODVILLE
Barna Rd, Salthill, Galway, Co Galway

Upper Salthill

OPEN:	1st March-31st October
NO. ROOMS:	4
ENSUITE:	4

(V)

TEL: **091 524260**   FAX: -

On Coast Road overlooking Galway Bay. Ideal touring base. Close to beaches, Leisureland, Golf, Tennis, Horseriding, Windsurfing, Canoeing.

Salthill 2km

B&B PPS:	**£16/£17**	SNGL OCC. DBLE/TPL:	**£22.50/£23.50**	SNGL RM:	-
PART BRD:	-	% RED. CHILDREN:	50%	DINNER:	-

Mrs Kathleen O'Connor
THE ASHTREE
Glenbrack, Galway Road, Gort, Co Galway

Gort

OPEN:	1st April-31st October
NO. ROOMS:	3
ENSUITE:	3

TEL: **091 631380**   FAX:

On N18. Galway & Ennis 30 mins. The Burren, Yeats Tower, Coole Park, Golf nearby. Shannon Airport 1 hr. Pitch & Putt 200 mtrs.

In Gort

B&B PPS:	**£17**	SNGL OCC. DBLE/TPL:	**£23.50**	SNGL RM:	-
PART BRD:	-	% RED. CHILDREN:	25%	DINNER:	-

Kinvarra 4km

Mrs Maureen Fawle
HOLLYOAK
Kinvara Road, Ballinderreen, Kilcolgan, Co Galway

TEL: **091 637165**   FAX: -

Kinvarra

OPEN:	**1st April-1st November**
NO. ROOMS:	4
ENSUITE:	2

Spacious, warm, country home, situated on N67 between Kinvarra - Kilcolgan. Central Burren, Cliffs of Moher, Connemara. Banquets in Dunguire Castle.

B&B PPS:	**£15/£17**	SNGL OCC. DBLE/TPL:	**£21.50/£23.50**	SNGL RM:	**£16/£17**
PART BRD:	-	% RED. CHILDREN:	**25%**	DINNER:	-

Kilcolgan 1km

Mrs Anne Kerins
CASTLE VIEW
Weir Road, Kilcolgan, Galway, Co Galway

TEL: **091 796172**   FAX: -

Kilcolgan / Clarenbridge

OPEN:	**All Year**
NO. ROOMS:	4
ENSUITE:	2

"O'Sullivan B&B Guide" recommended. Tranquil, scenic surroundings. Galway 15km. Ideal touring base - Connemare & Burren. Excellent restaurants - walking distance.

B&B PPS:	**£15/£17**	SNGL OCC. DBLE/TPL:	**£21.50/£23.50**	SNGL RM:	-
PART BRD:	**£180**	% RED. CHILDREN:	-	DINNER:	**£12**

Clifden 32km

Mrs Sally Roberts
SANCTA MARIA
Leenane, Connemara, Co Galway

TEL: **095 42250**   FAX: -

Leenane - Connemara Area

OPEN:	**Easter - October**
NO. ROOMS:	4
ENSUITE:	-

Comfortable family run home on own grounds, ideal centre for touring Connemara, car park, personal super-vision.

B&B PPS:	**£15**	SNGL OCC. DBLE/TPL:	-	SNGL RM:	-
PART BRD:	-	% RED. CHILDREN:	-	DINNER:	-

In Leenane

Mrs Margaret Wallace
AVONDALE HOUSE
Leenane, Co Galway

TEL: **095 42262**   FAX: -

Leenane - Connemara Area

OPEN:	**All Year except Christmas**
NO. ROOMS:	4
ENSUITE:	3

Bungalow in scenic area, beside village, adventure centres, Pony trekking, Fishing, Hill walking and Restaurants closeby.

B&B PPS:	**£15/£17**	SNGL OCC. DBLE/TPL:	-	SNGL RM:	-
PART BRD:	-	% RED. CHILDREN:	**10%**	DINNER:	-

Carraroe

Mr & Mrs John & Barbara O'Malley
THE LODGE
Bealadangan, Connemara, Co Galway

TEL: **091 572434**   FAX: **091 572434**

Lettermore

OPEN:	**1st May-1st October**
NO. ROOMS:	5
ENSUITE:	1

Beautifully renovated 19th century home by the sea. Spacious grounds with stables and manege base for Horse riding, Golf, Aran Islands.

B&B PPS:	**£15/£17**	SNGL OCC. DBLE/TPL:	**£21.50/£23.50**	SNGL RM:	-
PART BRD:	-	% RED. CHILDREN:	**30%**	DINNER:	-

Mrs Rose Plower
LA RIASC
Clostoken, Loughrea, Co Galway

Loughrea

OPEN:	All Year except Christmas
NO. ROOMS:	4
ENSUITE:	3

(V)

TEL: 091 841069   FAX: -

Comfortable modern home, just off Dublin - Galway Road (N6). Adjacent to award winning restaurant "Meadow Court". Ideal touring base.

B&B PPS:	£15/£17	SNGL OCC. DBLE/TPL:	£21.50/£23.50	SNGL RM:	-
PART BRD:	-	% RED. CHILDREN:	25%	DINNER:	

Loughrea 4km

Mary Carney
ARDFINNAN HOUSE
Maree Road, Oranmore, Co Galway

Oranmore

OPEN:	All Year
NO. ROOMS:	3
ENSUITE:	3

(V)

TEL: 091 790749   FAX: -

Comfortable accommodation, orthopaedic beds, home baking, 5 Mins from Galway city. Close to resteraunts, beaches, golf, parks, sailing. Heritage facilities

B&B PPS:	£17/£20	SNGL OCC. DBLE/TPL:	£23.50/£26.50	SNGL RM:	-
PART BRD:	£190	% RED. CHILDREN:	50%	DINNER:	£12.50

In Oranmore

Mrs Patricia Collins
CASTLE VIEW HOUSE
Galway Coast Road, Oranmore, Co Galway

Oranmore

OPEN:	All Year
NO. ROOMS:	4
ENSUITE:	4

(V)

TEL: 091 794648   FAX: -

Quiet country home, spacious bedrooms. Overlooking Galway bay, Burren mountains. Golf course and horse riding nearby. Galway 7 Mins drive.

B&B PPS:	£17	SNGL OCC. DBLE/TPL:	-	SNGL RM:	-
PART BRD:	-	% RED. CHILDREN:	20%	DINNER:	-

In Oranmore

Evelyn Corless
ARD MHARA LODGE
Maree Road, Oranmore, Co Galway

Oranmore

OPEN:	All Year
NO. ROOMS:	4
ENSUITE:	4

(V)

TEL: 091 790295/087 440014   FAX: -

Charming traditional-style family home. Enjoy old world hospitality in luxurious surroundings, with views of Galway bay. Excellent facilities/amenities nearby.

B&B PPS:	£17	SNGL OCC. DBLE/TPL:	£25	SNGL RM:	-
PART BRD:	-	% RED. CHILDREN:	25%	DINNER:	-

In Oranmore

Mrs Ann Costello
RINN VIEW
Dublin Road, Oranmore, Co Galway

Oranmore

OPEN:	1st April-30th October
NO. ROOMS:	4
ENSUITE:	3

(V)

TEL: 091 794918   FAX: -

Spacious residence located old Galway/Dublin road. 400 yards from Oranmore. Golf, Sailing, Surfing nearby. TV lounge, Ideal touring Burren etc.

B&B PPS:	£15/£18	SNGL OCC. DBLE/TPL:	£21.50/£25	SNGL RM:	-
PART BRD:	-	% RED. CHILDREN:	25%	DINNER:	-

In Oranmore

Mrs Mary Curran
BIRCHGROVE
Oranbeg, Oranmore, Co Galway

Oranmore

OPEN:	All Year
NO. ROOMS:	3
ENSUITE:	3

TEL: **091 790238**   FAX: -

Comfortable modern bungalow just off N6 Friendly relaxed atmosphere. Spacious grounds. Quality restaurants / pubs nearby. Ideal touring base. Quiet location.

B&B PPS:	**£17**	SNGL OCC. DBLE/TPL:	**£23.50**	SNGL RM:	-
PART BRD:	**£180**	% RED. CHILDREN:	**33.3%**	DINNER:	**£12**

Oranmore 1km

Teresa Dundon
MILLBROOK
**Dublin Road, Oranmore
Co Galway**

Oranmore

OPEN:	April-October
NO. ROOMS:	4
ENSUITE:	3

TEL: **091 794404**   FAX: -

Dormer Bungalow on Dublin Road, 5 mins walk from Oranmore Village. Sailing, Windsurfing, Golf nearby. Ideal touring base for Connemara, Burren.

B&B PPS:	**£15/£18**	SNGL OCC. DBLE/TPL:	**£21.50/£24.50**	SNGL RM:	-
PART BRD:	-	% RED. CHILDREN:	**25%**	DINNER:	-

In Oranmore

Geraldine & Seamus Grady
SHANLIN HOUSE
Maree Road, Oranmore, Co Galway

Oranmore

OPEN:	All Year
NO. ROOMS:	3
ENSUITE:	3

TEL: **091 790381/088 2798529**   FAX: **091 790381**   EMAIL: **ggrady@indigo.ie**

Friendly Georgian home. Quiet location. Golf, Horseriding, Leisure Park, Sailing nearby. Centrally located to tour Connemara/Burren/Aran Islands.

B&B PPS:	**£17/£20**	SNGL OCC. DBLE/TPL:	**£23.50/£26.50**	SNGL RM:	-
PART BRD:	-	% RED. CHILDREN:	**25%**	DINNER:	**£14**

In Oranmore

Bridgie Hanley
FAIRWAYS LODGE
Renville, Oranmore, Co Galway

Oranmore

OPEN:	All Year except Christmas
NO. ROOMS:	4
ENSUITE:	4

TEL: **091 790393**   FAX: **091 790393**

Charming residence at entrance to Galway Bay Golf Club, Sailing Club, Renville Park. Centrally located, Connemara, Aran Islands & The Burren.

B&B PPS:	**£20/£25**	SNGL OCC. DBLE/TPL:	**£26.50/£31.50**	SNGL RM:	-
PART BRD:	-	% RED. CHILDREN:	**20%**	DINNER:	-

Oranmore 1km

Mrs Triona Higgins
SEA BREEZE
**Carrowmoneash, Oranmore
Co Galway**

Oranmore

OPEN:	All Year
NO. ROOMS:	4
ENSUITE:	4

TEL: **091 794884**   FAX: -

Modern Home. Spacious Gardens. Galway 6kms. Ideal for touring Connemara & Burren. Sailing, Golf 4 kms.

B&B PPS:	**£17/£20**	SNGL OCC. DBLE/TPL:	**£23.50/£26.50**	SNGL RM:	-
PART BRD:	-	% RED. CHILDREN:	**25%**	DINNER:	-

Oranmore 0.5km

Mrs Maureen Kelly
COOLIBAH HOUSE
Dublin Road, Oranmore, Co Galway

Oranmore

OPEN:	All Year
No. Rooms:	3
Ensuite:	3

TEL: **091 794996**   FAX: -

Modern bungalow on N6, 100 mts N18 & N6 roundabout. Galway 5 mins drive. Golf, Pitch & Putt, Rinville Park nearby.

B&B PPS:	**£17**	SNGL OCC. DBLE/TPL:	**£23.50**	SNGL RM:	-
PART BRD:	**£180**	% RED. CHILDREN:	**50%**	DINNER:	**£12**

Oranmore 1km

Mrs Mary Killoran
BELMONT
Creganna, Oranmore, Co Galway

Oranmore

OPEN:	All Year
No. Rooms:	4
Ensuite:	4

TEL: **091 790289**   FAX: -

Comfortable home off the Oranmore/Clarenbridge Road (N18), bedrooms with TV/radio/Tea making/hairdryers. City 10 mins. Ideal touring base.

B&B PPS:	**£17**	SNGL OCC. DBLE/TPL:	**£23.50**	SNGL RM:	-
PART BRD:	**£180**	% RED. CHILDREN:	**25%**	DINNER:	**£12**

Oranmore 2km

Mrs Moira Kilroe
GLEN CURRAGH
Limerick Road, Moneymore West, Oranmore, Co Galway

Oranmore

OPEN:	1st April-30th November
No. Rooms:	3
Ensuite:	3

TEL: **091 794637**   FAX: -

Spacious Georgian home on N18. Ideal touring Burren and Connemara. Golf, Sailing, Horse riding nearby. Residents TV lounge.

B&B PPS:	**£17/£20**	SNGL OCC. DBLE/TPL:	**£23.50/£26.50**	SNGL RM:	-
PART BRD:	-	% RED. CHILDREN:	**20%**	DINNER:	-

Oranmore 2km

Mrs Kathleen McCarthy-Leyne
SON AMAR
**Coast Road
Oranmore, Galway, Co Galway**

Oranmore

OPEN:	All Year
No. Rooms:	6
Ensuite:	4

TEL: **091 794176**   FAX: -

Georgian home, overlooking Galway Bay & Burren Mountains. Golf, Surfing & Horse-riding close by. Residents TV lounge. Smoke free home.

B&B PPS:	**£17/£20**	SNGL OCC. DBLE/TPL:	**£25/£26.50**	SNGL RM:	**£18/£19**
PART BRD:	-	% RED. CHILDREN:	**10%**	DINNER:	-

Oranmore 1km

Mrs Eucharia McDonagh
ROCKFIELD HOUSE
Creganna, Oranmore, Galway, Co Galway

Oranmore

OPEN:	15th April-1st October
No. Rooms:	4
Ensuite:	1

TEL: **091 794157**   FAX: -

Modern bungalow in a very quiet area. Close to Golf, Sailing, Park. Ideal touring base. 1km off Clarinbridge/Oranmore road.

B&B PPS:	**£15/£18**	SNGL OCC. DBLE/TPL:	**£21.50/£24.50**	SNGL RM:	-
PART BRD:	**£180**	% RED. CHILDREN:	**25%**	DINNER:	**£12**

Oranmore 5km

Oranmore 1km

Maureen Murphy
HILLVIEW
Moneymore, Oranmore, Co Galway

Oranmore

OPEN:	1st April-31st October
NO. ROOMS:	3
ENSUITE:	2

(V)

TEL: **091 794341**   FAX: -

Dormer bungalow, view of Clare hills, on N18. Ideal touring Burren & Connemara. Golf, Sailing, Surfing, Pitch & Putt nearby.

B&B PPS:	**£17/£20**	SNGL OCC. DBLE/TPL:	**£25/£26.50**	SNGL RM:	-
PART BRD:	-	% RED. CHILDREN:	**25%**	DINNER:	-

Oranmore 2km

Mrs Noeleen Murren
AVONDALE
Renville West, Oranmore, Co Galway

Oranmore

OPEN:	1st April-1st December
NO. ROOMS:	3
ENSUITE:	3

(V)

TEL: **091 790527**   FAX: -

Spacious warm Georgian House. Large ensuite bedrooms. Quiet location. Golf, Sailing & Leisure Park 1Km. Galway City & Airport 10 mins drive.

B&B PPS:	**£17/£18**	SNGL OCC. DBLE/TPL:	**£23.50/£24.50**	SNGL RM:	-
PART BRD:	-	% RED. CHILDREN:	**50%**	DINNER:	**£13**

Oranmore 1km

Mrs Mary Noone
ASHBROOK HOUSE
Dublin Road, Oranmore, Co Galway

Oranmore

OPEN:	All Year except Christmas
NO. ROOMS:	4
ENSUITE:	4

(V)

TEL: **091 794196**   FAX: **091 794196**

Purpose built, spacious grounds. Opposite Water Tower N6. Tea/coffee TV all rooms. Smoke free home. Golf/sailing nearby. AA QQQ.

B&B PPS:	**£17/£20**	SNGL OCC. DBLE/TPL:	**£23.50/£26.50**	SNGL RM:	-
PART BRD:	-	% RED. CHILDREN:	**20%**	DINNER:	-

In Oranmore

Margaret & Anthony O'Neill
CEO NA MARA
Oranbeg (Old Dublin Road), Oranmore, Co Galway

Oranmore

OPEN:	April-October
NO. ROOMS:	4
ENSUITE:	3

(V)

TEL: **091 794960**   FAX: -

Modern dormer style home within walking distance of Oranmore village. 10 mins drive to Galway. Golf, Sailing, Horse riding nearby.

B&B PPS:	**£15/£17**	SNGL OCC. DBLE/TPL:	**£21.50/£23.50**	SNGL RM:	-
PART BRD:	-	% RED. CHILDREN:	**25%**	DINNER:	-

Oughterard 2km

Mrs Nora Angland
WHITETHORN HOUSE
Portacarron, Oughterard, Co Galway

Oughterard / Connemara Area

OPEN:	1st April-30th September
NO. ROOMS:	3
ENSUITE:	3

(V)

TEL: **091 552586**   FAX: **091 552586**

Modern bungalow quiet countryside. Oughterard 2km. Fishing, Boats arranged. Golfing, Horseriding locally. Ideal touring Connemara, Aran Islands, Galway off N59.

B&B PPS:	**£17**	SNGL OCC. DBLE/TPL:	**£23.50**	SNGL RM:	-
PART BRD:	**£189**	% RED. CHILDREN:	**50%**	DINNER:	**£12**

Mrs Teresa Butler
CROSSRIVER
Glann Road, Oughterard, Co Galway

Oughterard / Connemara

OPEN:	1st March-31st November
NO. ROOMS:	6
ENSUITE:	3

TEL: **091 552676** FAX: -

Purpose built B & B Golf course 2 km. Angling Lough Corrib, Boats arranged. Base for touring Connemara, Galway, Aran Islands.

B&B PPS:	£15/£17	SNGL OCC. DBLE/TPL:	£21.50/£23.50	SNGL RM:	-
PART BRD:	-	% RED. CHILDREN:	-	DINNER:	-

— In Oughterard —

Kathleen Dolly
WATERFALL LODGE
Oughterard, Co Galway

Oughterard - Connemara Area

OPEN:	All Year except Christmas
NO. ROOMS:	6
ENSUITE:	6

TEL: **091 552168** FAX: -

Elegant period residence. Antique furnishings. Picturesque gardens. AA 4Q's Quality award. Private Game Fishing. All bedrooms ensuite with colour TV.

B&B PPS:	£18/£20	SNGL OCC. DBLE/TPL:	£25/£26.50	SNGL RM:	-
PART BRD:	-	% RED. CHILDREN:	50%	DINNER:	-

— In Oughterard —

Cathy & Michael English
LOUGH CORRIB HOUSE
Ardvarna,
Oughterard, Co Galway

Oughterard / Connemara Area

OPEN:	1st May-31st October
NO. ROOMS:	6
ENSUITE:	5

TEL: **091 552177** FAX: **091 552177**

Family home, ideal for touring Connemara, Frommer guide & Inside Ireland recommended. TV, Hairdryers, Electric blankets, Tea facilities, Golfing, Fishing.

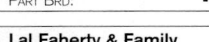

B&B PPS:	£15/£17	SNGL OCC. DBLE/TPL:	£21.50/£23.50	SNGL RM:	-
PART BRD:	-	% RED. CHILDREN:	-	DINNER:	£13

— In Oughterard —

Lal Faherty & Family
LAKELAND COUNTRY HOUSE
Portacarron,
Oughterard, Co Galway

Oughterard / Connemara Area

OPEN:	All Year except Christmas
NO. ROOMS:	9
ENSUITE:	8

TEL: **091 552121/552146** FAX: **091 552146**

Lakeside home; turf fires; electric blankets. Private gardens to lake. Fishing/Boating centre. Golf. Breakfast choice. Recommended Frommer, AA. Off N59.

B&B PPS:	£15/£17	SNGL OCC. DBLE/TPL:	£21.50/£23.50	SNGL RM:	-
PART BRD:	£200	% RED. CHILDREN:	-	DINNER:	£14

— Oughterard 2km —

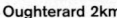

Mrs Mary C Faherty
ASHLAWN HOUSE
Ardvarna, Oughterard, Co Galway

Oughterard - Connemara Area

OPEN:	1st April-31st October
NO. ROOMS:	3
ENSUITE:	1

TEL: **091 552349** FAX: -

Modern home near Lake, route N59. Beautiful gardens, bright spacious rooms on ground floor. Turf fires. Excellent home cooking.

B&B PPS:	£15/£17	SNGL OCC. DBLE/TPL:	£21.50/£23.50	SNGL RM:	-
PART BRD:	-	% RED. CHILDREN:	20%	DINNER:	-

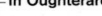
— In Oughterard —

In Oughterard

Ms Deirdre Forde
CAMILLAUN
Eighterard, Oughterard, Co Galway

Oughterard - Connemara Area

OPEN:	1st May-30th September
NO. ROOMS:	3
ENSUITE:	2

TEL: **091 552678**   FAX: **091 552678**

Located on bank of Owenriff River in Sylvan setting. A short walk from Town Centre. Lakeboats moored in the garden.

| B&B PPS: | **£15/£18** | SNGL OCC. DBLE/TPL: | **£21.50/£24.50** | SNGL RM: | - |
| PART BRD: | - | % RED. CHILDREN: | **20%** | DINNER: | - |

Oughterard 4km

Mrs Brenda Joyce
THE SUNSET
Killola, Rosscahill, Oughterard, Co Galway

Oughterard / Connemara

OPEN:	February-November
NO. ROOMS:	4
ENSUITE:	3

TEL: **091 550146**   FAX: -

Modern country home in route N59. Ideal base for touring Connemara. Golfing, Fishing, Horse riding available locally. Excellent home cooking.

| B&B PPS: | **£15/£17** | SNGL OCC. DBLE/TPL: | **£21.50/£23.50** | SNGL RM: | - |
| PART BRD: | **£190** | % RED. CHILDREN: | **25%** | DINNER: | **£14** |

Oughterard 6km

Mrs Phil Kavanagh
FOREST HAVEN
Rosscahill, Oughterard, Co Galway

Oughterard / Connemara Area

OPEN:	All Year except Christmas
NO. ROOMS:	4
ENSUITE:	4

TEL: **091 550387**   FAX: -

Peaceful, 12 miles Galway city. .25miles off N 59 at Kinneveys bar. Restaurants, fishing, golf, walks. Enjoy Connanamara, Aran islands.

| B&B PPS: | **£17** | SNGL OCC. DBLE/TPL: | **£23.50/£25** | SNGL RM: | - |
| PART BRD: | - | % RED. CHILDREN: | **50%** | DINNER: | **£12** |

Oughterard 1km

Mrs Brid Kelly
AVONDALE HOUSE
Portacarron, Oughterard, Co Galway

Oughterard / Connemara Area

OPEN:	Easter-November
NO. ROOMS:	4
ENSUITE:	4

TEL: **091 552398**   FAX: -

Comfortable home near Lough Corrib and Golf course. Ideal for touring Connemara. Fishing/Boating available - boatmen arranged. French spoken.

| B&B PPS: | **£17** | SNGL OCC. DBLE/TPL: | **£23.50** | SNGL RM: | **£21** |
| PART BRD: | - | % RED. CHILDREN: | **25%** | DINNER: | - |

In Oughterard

Mrs Kathleen Kenny
RIVER WALK HOUSE
Riverside, Oughterard, Co Galway

Oughterard - Connemara Area

OPEN:	1st April-1st November
NO. ROOMS:	3
ENSUITE:	3

TEL: **091 552788**   FAX: -

Family home located in quiet rural setting, adjacent to Owen Riff River. Three minutes walk Oughterard. Ideal base to tour Connemara.

| B&B PPS: | **£18** | SNGL OCC. DBLE/TPL: | **£24.50** | SNGL RM: | - |
| PART BRD: | - | % RED. CHILDREN: | **25%** | DINNER: | - |

Oughterard 6km

Mrs Patricia Lee
WOODLAWN HOUSE
Doon, Rosscahill, Oughterard, Co Galway

Oughterard - Connemara Area

TEL: **091 550198/087 2303638**   FAX: -

OPEN:	1st April-1st October	
NO. ROOMS:	3	
ENSUITE:	2	(V)

Situated on 1 acre mature gardens, 10 mls from Galway City. Near Ross Lake, Excellent walking area. Caters for anglers.

B&B PPS:	£15/£17	SNGL OCC. DBLE/TPL:	£21.50/£23.50	SNGL RM:	-
PART BRD:	£185	% RED. CHILDREN:	25%	DINNER:	£12

Oughterard 4km

Mrs Dolores Leonard
FOREST HILL
Glann Road, Oughterard, Co Galway

Oughterard - Connemara Area

TEL: **091 552549**   FAX: -

OPEN:	5th April-7th October	
NO. ROOMS:	5	
ENSUITE:	3	(V)

Country home. Quiet and peaceful, surrounded by spectacular Connemara scenery. 5 mins walk to panoramic Lough Corrib. Gillies arranged.

B&B PPS:	£15/£17	SNGL OCC. DBLE/TPL:	£21.50/£23.50	SNGL RM:	-
PART BRD:	-	% RED. CHILDREN:	50%	DINNER:	£12

Oughterard 8km

Mrs Mary Maloney
PINE GROVE
Glann, Hill of Doon Road, Oughterard, Co Galway

Oughterard / Connemara Area

TEL: **091 552101**   FAX: -

OPEN:	17th March-31st October	
NO. ROOMS:	4	
ENSUITE:	3	(V)

Quiet Family home on"Western Way". Overlooking Lough Corrib. Turf fires, Fishing, Golfing, Horseriding & Hill Walks nearby.

B&B PPS:	£15/£17	SNGL OCC. DBLE/TPL:	£21.50/£23.50	SNGL RM:	-
PART BRD:	-	% RED. CHILDREN:	-	DINNER:	£14

Oughterard 6km

Mrs Dympna Noone
WESTERN STAR HOUSE
Rosscahill, Oughterard, Connemara, Co Galway

Oughterard - Connemara Area

TEL: **091 550162**   FAX: -

OPEN:	1st April-31st October	
NO. ROOMS:	6	
ENSUITE:	2	(V)

Imposing country house peaceful surroundings luxury accommodation . Ideal base for touring Connemara and Aran Islands, Golfing, Fishing, Horse-riding.

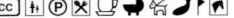

B&B PPS:	£15/£17	SNGL OCC. DBLE/TPL:	£21.50/£23.50	SNGL RM:	-
PART BRD:	£180	% RED. CHILDREN:	50%	DINNER:	£13

Oughterard 7km

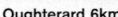

Mrs Mary O'Halloran
LAKESIDE
Ardnasilla, Oughterard, Co Galway

Oughterard - Connemara Area

TEL: **091 552846**   FAX: -

OPEN:	1st March-30th November	
NO. ROOMS:	4	
ENSUITE:	4	(V)

Superbly situated on the shores of Lough Corrib. Fishing, golfing, horse-riding, Aughnanure Castle and choice of first-class restaurants locally.

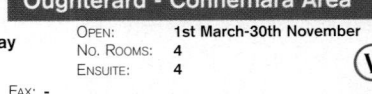

B&B PPS:	£17	SNGL OCC. DBLE/TPL:	£23.50	SNGL RM:	-
PART BRD:	-	% RED. CHILDREN:	25%	DINNER:	-

Oughterard 6km

Mark & Christine Roche
DOON LODGE
Rosscahill, Oughterard, Co Galway

Oughterard / Connemara

OPEN:	1st June-1st October
NO. ROOMS:	4
ENSUITE:	-

(V)

TEL: **091 550238**   FAX: **091 550238**

A home of genuine welcome. Surrounded by splendid Fishing waters, Golf Courses, Restaurants, Galway City. Breathtaking walks & Connemara splendour.

B&B PPS:	£15	SNGL OCC. DBLE/TPL:	£21.50	SNGL RM:	-
PART BRD:	-	% RED. CHILDREN:	25%	DINNER:	-

In Oughterard

Tina Small
WESTERN WAY
Camp Street, Oughterard, Co Galway

Oughterard

OPEN:	1st March-1st November
NO. ROOMS:	3
ENSUITE:	2

(V)

TEL: **091 552475**   FAX: -

Old style spacious two storey town home in quaint Village of Oughterard. Top class Restaurants and lively Traditional Pubs nearby.

B&B PPS:	£15/£17	SNGL OCC. DBLE/TPL:	£21.50/£23.50	SNGL RM:	-
PART BRD:	-	% RED. CHILDREN:	50%	DINNER:	-

Oughterard 1.5km

Miss Brid Tierney
GORTREVAGH HOUSE
Portacarron, Oughterard, Co Galway

Oughterard / Connemara

OPEN:	All Year
NO. ROOMS:	5
ENSUITE:	2

(V)

TEL: **091 552129**   FAX: -

Old style charm, beside Golf course, 10 mins from Lough Corrib. Tennis and Horse riding nearby. Traditional cooking, speciality vegetarian.

B&B PPS:	£15/£17	SNGL OCC. DBLE/TPL:	£21.50/£23.50	SNGL RM:	-
PART BRD:	£180	% RED. CHILDREN:	25%	DINNER:	£12

Oughterard 4km

Mary & Tom Walsh
THE WATERFRONT
Corrib View, Oughterard, Co Galway

Oughterard

OPEN:	All Year except Christmas
NO. ROOMS:	6
ENSUITE:	6

(V)

TEL: **091 552797**   FAX: **091 552730**

Taking Oughterard Road from Galway and 2 km before Oughterard, at the Golf Course, turn right and then take a left.

B&B PPS:	£17/£19	SNGL OCC. DBLE/TPL:	£23.50/£25.50	SNGL RM:	-
PART BRD:	-	% RED. CHILDREN:	50%	DINNER:	-

Oughterard 5km

Sally Walsh
WOODSIDE LODGE
Killola, Rosscahill, Co Galway

Oughterard - Connemara Area

OPEN:	1st May-15th September
NO. ROOMS:	4
ENSUITE:	4

(V)

TEL: **091 550123**   FAX: -

Warm friendly family home. Peaceful mountain and lake surroundings. Ideal walking/touring base. Charming Oughterard Village, Fishing, Golf within 5 Km.

B&B PPS:	£17	SNGL OCC. DBLE/TPL:	£23.50	SNGL RM:	-
PART BRD:	-	% RED. CHILDREN:	50%	DINNER:	£12

In Portumna

Michael & Bridie Dolan
SHANNON VILLA
Bridge Road, Portumna, Galway

Portumna

OPEN:	1st January-31st December	
NO. ROOMS:	5	
ENSUITE:	4	(V)

TEL: **0509 41269**   FAX: -

Delightful family home, warm atmosphere. Ideal leisure activity, angling, boating, golf, walks, equestrian. Central for touring Clonmacnois, Clonfert, Birr Castle.

B&B PPS:	£16/£17	SNGL OCC. DBLE/TPL:	£22.50/£23.50	SNGL RM:	£20
PART BRD:	£200	% RED. CHILDREN:	25%	DINNER:	£16

In Portumna

Mrs Elizabeth Ryan
AUVERGNE LODGE
Dominic Street, Portumna, Co Galway

Portumna

OPEN:	All Year	
NO. ROOMS:	4	
ENSUITE:	4	(V)

TEL: **0509 41138**   FAX: **0509 41138**

Enjoy Irish hospitality long established family home, Quiet area, Golf, Fishing, Horse riding, Tea/Coffee, Credit cards. Taxi on premises.

B&B PPS:	£17	SNGL OCC. DBLE/TPL:	£23.50	SNGL RM:	-
PART BRD:	-	% RED. CHILDREN:	50%	DINNER:	-

Clifden 19km

Conneely Family
SUNNYMEADE
Tullymore, Renvyle, Co Galway

Renvyle / Connemara

OPEN:	1st January-20th December	
NO. ROOMS:	4	
ENSUITE:	4	(V)

TEL: **095 43491**   FAX: **095 43491**

Panoramic setting. Convenient , Beaches, Connemara National Park, Kylemore Abbey, restaurants. Pony trekking, Renvyle House Hotel, Walks, Scuba Dive West nearby.

B&B PPS:	£17/£22	SNGL OCC. DBLE/TPL:	£23.50/£28.50	SNGL RM:	-
PART BRD:	-	% RED. CHILDREN:	25%	DINNER:	-

Clifden 19km

Mrs Noreen Conneely
SEA BREEZE
Gurteen, Renvyle, Co Galway

Renvyle / Connemara

OPEN:	All Year except Christmas	
NO. ROOMS:	4	
ENSUITE:	3	(V)

TEL: **095 43489**   FAX: **095 43489**

Scenic Location, spacious bedrooms overlooking Sea, Mountains, convenient Kylemore Abbey, Connemara National Park, Golf, Fishing, Scuba Dive West, Guest Conservatory.

B&B PPS:	£15/£18	SNGL OCC. DBLE/TPL:	£21.50/£24.50	SNGL RM:	-
PART BRD:	-	% RED. CHILDREN:	50%	DINNER:	-

Clifden 20km

Davin Family
OLDE CASTLE HOUSE
Curragh, Renvyle, Connemara, Co Galway

Renvyle / Connemara

OPEN:	16th March-31st December	
NO. ROOMS:	5	
ENSUITE:	4	

TEL: **095 43460**   FAX: -

Traditional Irish House, Beautiful landscape,jutting out into Atlantic Ocean, beside Renvyle Castle. House features in famous film Purple Taxi.

B&B PPS:	£15/£17	SNGL OCC. DBLE/TPL:	£21.50/£23.50	SNGL RM:	-
PART BRD:	£175	% RED. CHILDREN:	-	DINNER:	£12

Mrs Monica Lydon
OCEAN LODGE
Renvyle, Co Galway

Renvyle - Connemara

OPEN:	All Year except Christmas
NO. ROOMS:	5
ENSUITE:	5

TEL: **095 43481**   FAX: **095 43481**

Quiet accommodation, signposted at Letterfrack & Tullycross villages. Ocean views, close to Connemara National Park, Kylemore Abbey and Scuba Dive West.

B&B PPS:	**£17/£18**	SNGL OCC. DBLE/TPL:	**£24.50**	SNGL RM:	-
PART BRD:	-	% RED. CHILDREN:	**25%**	DINNER:	-

Tullycross 1.5km

Mrs Dee Walsh
FUCHSIA HOUSE
Curragh, Renvyle, Co Galway

Renvyle / Connemara

OPEN:	Easter-November
NO. ROOMS:	3
ENSUITE:	3

TEL: **095 43502**   FAX: -   -

Country house, nestled between the mountains and Atlantic. Spectacular sunsets. Turf fires. Old world atmosphere. Lovely walks and beautiful Beaches.

B&B PPS:	**£17**	SNGL OCC. DBLE/TPL:	**£23.50**	SNGL RM:	-
PART BRD:	-	% RED. CHILDREN:	**33%**	DINNER:	**£12**

Tully 5km

Miss Sile Mullin
DERRYKYLE COUNTRY HOUSE
Casla/Costello P.O., Co Galway

Rossaveal

OPEN:	1st May-1st October
NO. ROOMS:	4
ENSUITE:	2

TEL: **091 572412**   FAX: -

Wonderful Mountain & Sea views. Ideal for Angling, Swimming, Walking, touring Connemara. Spacious bedrooms, Restaurant/Ferry/Plane to Aran nearby.

B&B PPS:	**£15/£17**	SNGL OCC. DBLE/TPL:	**£21.50/£23.50**	SNGL RM:	-
PART BRD:	-	% RED. CHILDREN:	**10%**	DINNER:	-

Spiddal 14km

Mrs Bernadette Conneely
THE FISHERY LODGE
Toombeola, Roundstone, Co Galway

Roundstone / Connemara

OPEN:	1st March-31st October
NO. ROOMS:	4
ENSUITE:	4

TEL: **095 31116**   FAX: -

Newly refurbished house, idealistic settings overlooking Ballinahinch River. Close to amenities; Golf, Beaches, Pony Trekking, Fishing, Bike Hire on Premises.

B&B PPS:	**£17/£18**	SNGL OCC. DBLE/TPL:	**£25/£28**	SNGL RM:	-
PART BRD:	-	% RED. CHILDREN:	**25%**	DINNER:	**£14**

Clifden 15km

Mrs Patricia Keane
HEATHERGLEN HOUSE
Roundstone, Co Galway

Roundstone / Connemara Area

OPEN:	All Year except Christmas
NO. ROOMS:	4
ENSUITE:	4

TEL: **095 35837**   FAX: **095 35793**   EMAIL: **spkeane@tinet.ie**

Overlooking Roundstone Bay. Panoramic views, convenient to Beaches, Pony Trekking, Tennis courts, Golf, Angling and Hill Walking.

B&B PPS:	**£17/£20**	SNGL OCC. DBLE/TPL:	**£23.50/£30**	SNGL RM:	-
PART BRD:	-	% RED. CHILDREN:	**25%**	DINNER:	-

Clifden 15km

Clifden 18km

Christina Lowry
ST. JOSEPH'S
Roundstone,
Connemara, Co Galway
TEL: **095 35865/35930**   FAX: -

Roundstone - Connemara

OPEN:	1st January-20th December
No. ROOMS:	6
ENSUITE:	6

(V)

Spacious 19th century house overlooking Roundstone Harbour. Family-run B&B for 30 years. Ideal touring location, hill walking and cycling.

B&B PPS:	£17	SNGL OCC. DBLE/TPL:	£23.50/£25	SNGL RM:	-
PART BRD:	£180	% RED. CHILDREN:	25%	DINNER:	£12

Roundstone 0.25km

Linda Nee
RUSH LAKE HOUSE
Roundstone, Co Galway
TEL: **095 35915**   FAX: **095 35915**

Roundstone - Connemara Area

OPEN:	All Year except Christmas
No. ROOMS:	4
ENSUITE:	4

(V)

Peaceful setting overlooking sea and mountains, walking distance from village. Friendly and relaxed atmosphere in a family run home.

B&B PPS:	£17	SNGL OCC. DBLE/TPL:	£25	SNGL RM:	-
PART BRD:	£187	% RED. CHILDREN:	30%	DINNER:	£12

In Spiddal

Mrs Margaret Burke
COIS NA TRA
Spiddal, Co Galway
TEL: **091 553717**   FAX: -

Spiddal / Connemara

OPEN:	March-October
No. ROOMS:	4
ENSUITE:	4

(V)

Spacious seaside purpose-built home, panoramic views, 3 mins walk Beach. Ideal touring base-Connemara.

B&B PPS:	£17/£19	SNGL OCC. DBLE/TPL:	-	SNGL RM:	-
PART BRD:	-	% RED. CHILDREN:	25%	DINNER:	-

Spiddal 5.5km

Ann Canavan
BUN-AN-CROIC
Cor-Na-Ron, Inverin, Co Galway
TEL: **091 593022**   FAX: -

Spiddal - Connemara Area

OPEN:	All Year except Christmas
No. ROOMS:	6
ENSUITE:	4

(V)

House refurbished to excellent standard. Superb sun lounge for relaxation and comfort. Hill walks, fishing, ferries/airport close by.

B&B PPS:	£15/£17	SNGL OCC. DBLE/TPL:	£21.50/£23.50	SNGL RM:	£19
PART BRD:	£177	% RED. CHILDREN:	50%	DINNER:	£12

Spiddal 3km

Mrs Alice Concannon
DUN LIOS
Park West, Spiddal, Co Galway
TEL: **091 553165**   FAX: -

Spiddal - Connemara Area

OPEN:	1st May-31st October
No. ROOMS:	4
ENSUITE:	4

(V)

Modern country home overlooking Galway Bay. Gateway to Connemara/ Aran Islands. Seafood Restaurants/traditional entertainment nearby. Home baking.

B&B PPS:	£17	SNGL OCC. DBLE/TPL:	£23.50	SNGL RM:	-
PART BRD:	-	% RED. CHILDREN:	25%	DINNER:	-

Spiddal 5km

Mrs Maura Conneely (Ni Chonghaile)

Spiddal / Connemara	

CALADH GEARR THATCH COTTAGE,
Knock, Spiddal, Co Galway

TEL: **091 593124** FAX: -

OPEN:	1st March-1st November
NO. ROOMS:	3
ENSUITE:	3

 V

Thatched cottage (Circa 1890) with 1990's standards, overlooking Galway Bay. Bogwalks, Angling, Aran Ferries, Inverin Airport. Ideal base touring Connemara.

B&B PPS:	£17	SNGL OCC. DBLE/TPL:	£25/£27	SNGL RM:	-
PART BRD:	-	% RED. CHILDREN:	10%	DINNER:	-

Spiddal 4km

Mrs Phil Conneely

Spiddal / Connemara	

CLUAIN BARRA
Knock, Inverin, Co Galway

TEL: **091 593140** FAX: -

OPEN:	1st June-31st October
NO. ROOMS:	3
ENSUITE:	2

V

Overlooking Clare Hills, Galway Bay, Aran Islands. Sandy beaches, Aran ferries and Inverin Airport nearby. Ideal for touring Connemara.

B&B PPS:	£15/£17	SNGL OCC. DBLE/TPL:	£21.50/£23.50	SNGL RM:	-
PART BRD:	-	% RED. CHILDREN:	30%	DINNER:	-

Spiddal 3km

Mrs Frances Cummins (Ui Chuimin)

Spiddal - Connemara Area	

Briseadh na Carraige Pairc
Spiddal, Co Galway

TEL: **091 553212** FAX: -

OPEN:	March-November
NO. ROOMS:	4
ENSUITE:	4

V

Overlooking Galway Bay, Aran Islands, Burren, Beaches. Fishing, scenic walks, golf, Restaurants, Horse riding. Central touring location to Connemara, Aran.

B&B PPS:	£17	SNGL OCC. DBLE/TPL:	-	SNGL RM:	-
PART BRD:	-	% RED. CHILDREN:	25%	DINNER:	-

In Spiddal

Mrs Barbara O'Malley-Curran

Spiddal - Connemara Area	

ARD AOIBHINN
Spiddal
Connemara, Co Galway

TEL: **091 553179** FAX: **091 553179**

OPEN:	All Year
NO. ROOMS:	6
ENSUITE:	5

V

0.5 km west village.Multi Guidebook recommendations.Convenient Aran Ferries, Seafood Restaurants, Pubs, Bog, Seashore walks. Laundry service. AA QQQ award

B&B PPS:	£17	SNGL OCC. DBLE/TPL:	£21.50/£23.50	SNGL RM:	£15/£17
PART BRD:	-	% RED. CHILDREN:	50%	DINNER:	£12.50

Spiddal 1.5km

Mrs Sarah Curran

Spiddal / Connemara	

SLIABH RUA HOUSE
Salahoona, Spiddal, Galway, Co Galway

TEL: **091 553243** FAX: -

OPEN:	10th April-26th October
NO. ROOMS:	4
ENSUITE:	4

V

Dormer, seaside, spacious bungalow on relaxing, peaceful scenic coastal route. Overlooking Galway Bay, Cliffs of Moher, beside Beaches, Walks, Aran Ferries.

B&B PPS:	£17/£18	SNGL OCC. DBLE/TPL:	£25/£27	SNGL RM:	-
PART BRD:	-	% RED. CHILDREN:	-	DINNER:	-

Eamonn & Siobhan Feeney
TUAR BEAG
Spiddal, Co Galway

Spiddal / Connemara Area

OPEN:	All Year except Christmas
NO. ROOMS:	6
ENSUITE:	6

TEL: **091 553422/087 483581**   FAX: **091 553010**

Unique home, purpose built around 19th century thatched cottage, overlooking Galway Bay. Extensive breakfast menu. AA QQQ award. West of village.

B&B PPS:	£17/£20	SNGL OCC. DBLE/TPL:	-	SNGL RM:	-
PART BRD:	-	% RED. CHILDREN:	50%	DINNER:	-

Spiddal 1km

Mrs Moya Feeney
CALA 'N UISCE
Greenhill, Spiddal, Co Galway

Spiddal - Connemara Area

OPEN:	March-November
NO. ROOMS:	6
ENSUITE:	6

TEL: **091 553324**   FAX: -

Dillard Causin Guide recommended. Overlooking Atlantic Ocean & Aran Islands. On Sea side of Coast Road R335. Cead Mile Failte

B&B PPS:	£17/£17.50	SNGL OCC. DBLE/TPL:	£23.50/£25	SNGL RM:	-
PART BRD:	-	% RED. CHILDREN:	25%	DINNER:	-

Spiddal 1km

Mrs Rita Feeney
ARD MHUIRBHI
AilleInverin, Spiddal, Co Galway

Spiddal - Connemara Area

OPEN:	All Year except Christmas
NO. ROOMS:	5
ENSUITE:	4

TEL: **091 593215**   FAX: -

Spacious seaside accommodation, overlooking Galway Bay, Aran Islands. Mature gardens, Tranquil Walks & Angling locally. Family suites, electric blankets.

B&B PPS:	£15/£17	SNGL OCC. DBLE/TPL:	£21.50/£23.50	SNGL RM:	-
PART BRD:	-	% RED. CHILDREN:	33.3%	DINNER:	-

Spiddal 5km

Vera Feeney
ARDMOR COUNTRY HOUSE
Greenhill, Spiddal, Co Galway

Spiddal / Connemara Area

OPEN:	March-December
NO. ROOMS:	7
ENSUITE:	7

TEL: **091 553145**   FAX: **091 553596**

Superb location overlooking Bay. AA 4Q selected. Recommended Frommer/Sullivan Guides. Breakfast Awards. Spacious Rooms, Lounge with extensive Library, Video.

B&B PPS:	£18/£20	SNGL OCC. DBLE/TPL:	£24.50/£26.50	SNGL RM:	-
PART BRD:	-	% RED. CHILDREN:	25%	DINNER:	-

In Spiddal

Mrs Sarah Flaherty
COIS CAOLAIRE
Ballintleva, Spiddal, Co Galway

Spiddal - Connemara Area

OPEN:	June-September
NO. ROOMS:	6
ENSUITE:	3

TEL: **091 553176**   FAX: **091 53624**

"Cead Mile Failte to Cois Caolaire" on the coast road to Connemara Gaeltacht area, overlooking Galway Bay and Aran Islands.

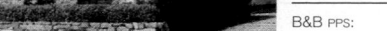

B&B PPS:	£15/£17	SNGL OCC. DBLE/TPL:	£21.50/£23.50	SNGL RM:	-
PART BRD:	-	% RED. CHILDREN:	25%	DINNER:	-

Spiddal 2km

Spiddal 6km

Mrs Mary Anne Flavin
TIGH NA MARA
Teach Mor, Inverin, Co Galway

Spiddal - Connemara Area

OPEN:	1st May-30th September
NO. ROOMS:	3
ENSUITE:	2

(V)

TEL: **091 593064** FAX: -

Dormer bungalow, overlooking Galway Bay. Ideal for touring Connemara and Burren areas. Aran Ferries/Airport nearby. Peaceful location. Spiddal village 6 km.

B&B PPS:	**£15/£17**	SNGL OCC. DBLE/TPL:	**£23.50**	SNGL RM:	**£21.50**
PART BRD:	-	% RED. CHILDREN:	10%	DINNER:	-

Spiddal 1.5km

Mrs Maureen Keady
(Ni Cheidigh)
COL-MAR HOUSE
Salahoona, Spiddal, Co Galway

Spiddal / Connemara

OPEN:	April-October
NO. ROOMS:	5
ENSUITE:	5

(V)

TEL: **091 553247** FAX: **091 553247**

Warm hospitality, secluded country home. Mature gardens. "Le Guide du Routard" "Lonely Planet" recommended. Spacious 1.5km West of Spiddal.

B&B PPS:	**£17**	SNGL OCC. DBLE/TPL:	**£23.50**	SNGL RM:	-
PART BRD:	-	% RED. CHILDREN:	-	DINNER:	-

Spiddal 2km

Mrs Patsy McCarthy
(MacCarthaigh)
SAILIN
Coill Rua, Spiddal, Co Galway

Spiddal / Connemara

OPEN:	1st April-31st October
NO. ROOMS:	4
ENSUITE:	3

(V)

TEL: **091 553308** FAX: -

Bungalow overlooking Galway Bay & Cliffs of Moher. 5 mins sandy beach. Ideal for touring Connemara & Aran Islands. Canoeing, Angling & Horse-riding.

B&B PPS:	**£15/£17**	SNGL OCC. DBLE/TPL:	**£21.50/£25**	SNGL RM:	-
PART BRD:	-	% RED. CHILDREN:	25%	DINNER:	-

Spiddal 1.5km

Mrs. Peg O'Connor
RADHARC AN CHLAIR
Kellough, Spiddal, Co Galway

Spiddal - Connemara Area

OPEN:	12th May-1st October
NO. ROOMS:	4
ENSUITE:	2

TEL: **091 553267** FAX: -

Bungalow tastefully decorated. Spacious rooms , mature gardens overlooking Galway Bay & Aran Islands. Canoeing, Angling, Horse riding, Walks, Seafood Restaurants.

B&B PPS:	**£15/£17.50**	SNGL OCC. DBLE/TPL:	**£21.50**	SNGL RM:	-
PART BRD:	-	% RED. CHILDREN:	10%	DINNER:	-

Spiddal 2km

Mrs Mary O'Dowd
RADHARC NA FARRAIGE
Moycullen Road, Spiddal, Co Galway

Spiddal / Connemara Area

OPEN:	Easter-31st October
NO. ROOMS:	4
ENSUITE:	3

TEL: **091 553434** FAX: -

Rural location, magnificent views. Angling, Golf, Horseriding & Canoeing available. From Galway, turn right in Village and travel 2 km.

B&B PPS:	**£15/£17**	SNGL OCC. DBLE/TPL:	**£21.50/£25**	SNGL RM:	-
PART BRD:	-	% RED. CHILDREN:	25%	DINNER:	-

Spiddal 8km

Mrs. Mairead O'Flaherty — Spiddal/Connemara Area
DUN-CHAOIN HOUSE
Cor-na Ron East, Inverin, Co Galway

OPEN:	1st June-30th September
NO. ROOMS:	3
ENSUITE:	2

TEL: **091 593302**   FAX: -

Experience real comfort in a friendly, rural home, overlooking Galway Bay. Home-cooking, tranquil bog walks, beaches. Aran ferries, Airport nearby.

(V)

B&B PPS:	£15/£17	SNGL OCC. DBLE/TPL:	£21.50/£23.50	SNGL RM:	-
PART BRD:	£180	% RED. CHILDREN:	25%	DINNER:	£12

Tuam 2km

Mrs. Gabrielle Hurst — Tuam
FOUR SEASONS
Carrowmoneen, Dublin Road, Tuam, Co Galway

OPEN:	All Year except Christmas
NO. ROOMS:	3
ENSUITE:	3

TEL: **093 25934**   FAX: **093 25934**   EMAIL: **thp@gpo.iol.ie**

Spacious family residence in scenic, rural setting. Convenient for touring Galway Connemara and Cong. Golf, fishing and horse riding.

(V)

B&B PPS:	£17	SNGL OCC. DBLE/TPL:	£23.50	SNGL RM:	-
PART BRD:	-	% RED. CHILDREN:	20%	DINNER:	-

Tuam 8km

Mrs. Kathleen Mullins — Tuam
THE ROADSIDE
Anbally, Cummer, Tuam, Co Galway

OPEN:	1st March-30th November
NO. ROOMS:	3
ENSUITE:	2

TEL: **093 41334**   FAX: -

Spacious comfortable warm home on main Galway/Tuam road, N17. Convenient for touring Connemara, Knock & Cong. Golf, Fishing & Horse riding locally.

(V)

B&B PPS:	£15/£17	SNGL OCC. DBLE/TPL:	£21.50/£23.50	SNGL RM:	-
PART BRD:	£180	% RED. CHILDREN:	50%	DINNER:	£12

Tuam 1km

Mrs. Josephine O'Connor — Tuam
KILMORE HOUSE
Galway Road, Tuam, Co. Galway

OPEN:	All Year
NO. ROOMS:	7
ENSUITE:	7

TEL: **093 28118**   FAX: **093 28118**

Spacious modern residence on farm. Warm Hospitality. Frommer reccommmennded. All rooms TV Fastext. Knock, Galway, Connemara convenient. Safe car parks.

(V)

B&B PPS:	£17	SNGL OCC. DBLE/TPL:	£23.50	SNGL RM:	£19
PART BRD:	£180	% RED. CHILDREN:	20%	DINNER:	£12

Tuam 7km

John & Cecilia O'Grady — Tuam
GLENWORTH HOUSE
Rusheens, Tuam, Co. Galway

OPEN:	All Year
NO. ROOMS:	4
ENSUITE:	4

TEL: **093 55722**   FAX: -

Superb residence on N17 Galway/Tuam Road. Convenient for touring Galway, Connemara, Cong, The Burren. Golf, fishing, horse riding nearby.

(V)

B&B PPS:	£17	SNGL OCC. DBLE/TPL:	£23.50	SNGL RM:	-
PART BRD:	£180	% RED. CHILDREN:	40%	DINNER:	£12

Mrs. Margo Cannon
TEACH MWEEWILLIN
Currane, Achill, Co Mayo

Achill Island

OPEN:	1st April-30th September
NO. ROOMS:	4
ENSUITE:	3

TEL: **098 45134**   FAX: **098 45225**

Ⓥ

Hilltop house overlooking Achill Island. Mountain climbing, Sailing. Frommer Guide Recommended. Community centre. Area has geological, historical and botanical interests.

B&B PPS:	£15/£17	SNGL OCC. DBLE/TPL:	£23.50	SNGL RM:	£22
PART BRD:	-	% RED. CHILDREN:	40%	DINNER:	£14

Achill Sound 7km

Mrs. Teresa McNamara
WEST COAST HOUSE
School Road, Dooagh, Achill Island, Co Mayo

Achill Island

OPEN:	March-November
NO. ROOMS:	5
ENSUITE:	4 -

TEL: **098 43317**   FAX: **098 43317**

Ⓥ

New bungalow, picturesque surroundings. Orthopaedic beds, hairdryers, electric blankets, payphone. Philadelphia Inquirer, Frommer recommended, AA QQQ. Walkers paradise, superior room.

B&B PPS:	£15/£17	SNGL OCC. DBLE/TPL:	£21.50/£23.50	SNGL RM:	-
PART BRD:	£180	% RED. CHILDREN:	-	DINNER:	£12

Keel 1km

Mrs. Frances Masterson
ROCKMOUNT
Achill Sound, Achill Island, Co Mayo

Achill Island

OPEN:	All Year except Christmas
NO. ROOMS:	6
ENSUITE:	4

TEL: **098 45272**   FAX: -

Ⓥ

Frommer Guide recommended. Scenic surroundings, adjacent to bus stop, House of Prayer, village, sea, mountains, electric blankets. Tea/making facilities.

B&B PPS:	15/£17	SNGL OCC. DBLE/TPL:	£21.50/£23.50	SNGL RM:	-
PART BRD:	-	% RED. CHILDREN:	25%	DINNER:	-

In Achill Sound

Mrs. T Moran
WOODVIEW HOUSE
Springvale, Achill Sound, Co Mayo

Achill Island

OPEN:	All Year except Christmas
NO. ROOMS:	4
ENSUITE:	3

TEL: **098 45261**   FAX: -

Ⓥ

Modern bungalow in quiet scenic surroundings with panoramic view of sea and mountains, 1km from House of Prayer.

B&B PPS:	£15/£17	SNGL OCC. DBLE/TPL:	£21.50/£23.50	SNGL RM:	-
PART BRD:	£180	% RED. CHILDREN:	25%	DINNER:	£12

Achill Sound 1km

Mrs. Noelle Curry
EVERGREEN
Foxford Road, Ballina, Co. Mayo

Ballina

OPEN:	All Year except Christmas
NO. ROOMS:	3
ENSUITE:	3

TEL: **096 71343**   FAX: -

Ⓥ

Warm comfortable bungalow in peaceful location walking distance of town. Rooms ensuite with TV, tea/coffee, hairdryers & electric blankets.

B&B PPS:	£17	SNGL OCC. DBLE/TPL:	£23.50	SNGL RM:	-
PART BRD:	-	% RED. CHILDREN:	33.3%	DINNER:	-

Ballina 1km

Mrs. Marie Dempsey
WHITESTREAM HOUSE
Foxford Rd (N26), Ballina, Co. Mayo

Ballina

In Ballina

OPEN:	All Year
NO. ROOMS:	6
ENSUITE:	5

TEL: **096 21582** FAX: -

Highly recommended, spacious residence, extensive Gardens within walking distance from town. Rooms ensuite with Cable TV, tea/coffee facilities, hairdryers.

| B&B PPS: | £15/£20 | SNGL OCC. DBLE/TPL: | £21.50/£26.50 | SNGL RM: | - |
| PART BRD: | - | % RED. CHILDREN: | 25% | DINNER: | £14 |

Mrs. Mary Harman
Quay Road,
Ballina, Co Mayo

Ballina

Ballina 3km

OPEN:	1st April-15th October
NO. ROOMS:	3
ENSUITE:	3

TEL: **096 21226** FAX: -

Our home overlooks River Moy. Excellent fishing, golfing in the locality. Convenient to Enniscrone beach. Private car park.

| B&B PPS: | £17 | SNGL OCC. DBLE/TPL: | £23.50 | SNGL RM: | - |
| PART BRD: | - | % RED. CHILDREN: | 25% | DINNER: | - |

Ms. Dolores Jordan
RED RIVER LODGE
Iceford, Quay Rd., Ballina, Co Mayo

Ballina

Ballina 6km

OPEN:	March-October
NO. ROOMS:	4
ENSUITE:	4

TEL: **096 22841** FAX: -

Luxurious country family home on 1 acre of landscaped gardens overlooking the Moy Estuary on the coast road to Enniscrone.

| B&B PPS: | £17 | SNGL OCC. DBLE/TPL: | £23.50 | SNGL RM: | - |
| PART BRD: | - | % RED. CHILDREN: | 20% | DINNER: | - |

Ms. Margie Lennon
WOODLANDS
Sligo Rd., Ballina, Co Mayo

Ballina

In Ballina

OPEN:	17th March-31st October
NO. ROOMS:	6
ENSUITE:	6

TEL: **096 22956** FAX: -   -

Modern two storey townhouse, situated in select residential area, overlooking River Moy and Town Park. Five minutes from town centre.

| B&B PPS: | £17/£20 | SNGL OCC. DBLE/TPL: | £23.50/£26.50 | SNGL RM: | - |
| PART BRD: | £180 | % RED. CHILDREN: | 25% | DINNER: | £12 |

Agnes and Brendan McElvanna
CLADDAGH HOUSE
Sligo Rd., Ballina, Co Mayo

Ballina

Ballina 3.5km

OPEN:	1st March-31st October
NO. ROOMS:	6
ENSUITE:	6

TEL: **096 71670/087 2333236** FAX: -

Modern country home, excellent views surrounding countryside. Comfortable spacious accommodation. Guest TV lounge, complimentary tea/coffee. Full fire safety certificate.

| B&B PPS: | £17 | SNGL OCC. DBLE/TPL: | £23.50 | SNGL RM: | - |
| PART BRD: | - | % RED. CHILDREN: | 40% | DINNER: | - |

Ballina

Mrs. Mary Mongan
CORRAN MHUIRE
Belleek Castle Road, Ballina, Co. Mayo

Ballina

OPEN: **1st April-30th September**
NO. ROOMS: **4**
ENSUITE: **1**

(V)

TEL: **096 21074**   FAX: -

Comfortable relaxing home, within walking distance of town, peaceful location, near Dunnes Stores, Belleek Castle, overlooking River Moy, private parking.

B&B PPS:	£15/£17	SNGL OCC. DBLE/TPL:	£21.50/£23.50	SNGL RM:	-
PART BRD:	-	% RED. CHILDREN:	33%	DINNER:	-

Ballina 1km

Mrs. Carmel Murray
ASHLEY HOUSE
Ardoughan, Ballina, Co. Mayo

Ballina

OPEN: **1st March-31st October**
NO. ROOMS: **4**
ENSUITE: **4**

(V)

TEL: **096 22799**   FAX: -

Weclome to "Ashley House" peaceful surroundings off main road N59. Highly recommended. Ground floor bedrooms. Landscaped gardens. Near Belleek Castle.

B&B PPS:	£17	SNGL OCC. DBLE/TPL:	£23..50	SNGL RM:	-
PART BRD:	-	% RED. CHILDREN:	33%	DINNER:	-

Ballina 5km

Mrs. Mary O'Dowd
CNOC BREADAIN
Quay Road, Ballina, Co. Mayo

Ballina

OPEN: **1st May-30th September**
NO. ROOMS: **4**
ENSUITE: **4**

(V)

TEL: **096 22145**   FAX: -

Country home overlooking Moy Estuary. Noted for hospitality, good food. Many International Guide recommendations. 2km past Quay Village towards Enniscrone.

B&B PPS:	£17	SNGL OCC. DBLE/TPL:	£23.50	SNGL RM:	-
PART BRD:	-	% RED. CHILDREN:	-	DINNER:	-

Ballina 3km

Mrs. Annette O'Toole
MOY CALL
Creggs Road, The Quay, Ballina, Co. Mayo

Ballina

OPEN: **1st May-30th September**
NO. ROOMS: **4**
ENSUITE: **3**

(V)

TEL: **096 22440/087 418417**   FAX: -

Modern home, beside River Moy. River/Deep Sea/Lake Fishing. Beaches, Golf, Ceide fields. Tea/coffee facilities, fire system installed.

B&B PPS:	£15/£22	SNGL OCC. DBLE/TPL:	£21.50/£28.50	SNGL RM:	-
PART BRD:	-	% RED. CHILDREN:	25%	DINNER:	£12.50

Ballina 3km

Mrs. Breege Padden
QUIGNALEGAN HOUSE
Quignalegan, Sligo Road, Ballina, Co Mayo

Ballina

OPEN: **1st March-31st October**
NO. ROOMS: **5**
ENSUITE: **5**

(V)

TEL: **096 71644**   FAX: -

Warm welcoming country home pleasantly located. Convenient to golf, beach, fishing, horse riding, country walks. Electric blankets. Complementary refreshments. Private parking.

B&B PPS:	£17	SNGL OCC. DBLE/TPL:	£23.50	SNGL RM:	-
PART BRD:	-	% RED. CHILDREN:	33%	DINNER:	-

In Ballina

Mrs. Mary Reilly
BELVEDERE HOUSE
Foxford Rd., Ballina, Co Mayo

Ballina

OPEN:	January-20th December
No. ROOMS:	4
ENSUITE:	4

(V)

TEL: **096 22004** FAX: -

Georgian style home, 10mins walk from town, bus and train. Ideal for fishing, golfing, walking. Recommended "300 Best B/B".

B&B PPS:	**£17/£20**	SNGL OCC. DBLE/TPL:	**£23.50/£26.50**	SNGL RM:	-
PART BRD:	-	% RED. CHILDREN:	**25%**	DINNER:	-

Ballina 4km

Mrs. Helen Smyth
ASHLEAM HOUSE
Mount Falcon, Foxford Rd., Ballina, Co Mayo

Ballina

OPEN:	March-September
No. ROOMS:	6
ENSUITE:	4

(V)

TEL: **096 22406** FAX: -

Country home, half way between Ballina and Foxford N26. Beside River Moy. Noted for hospitality. Ideal as base for touring.

B&B PPS:	**£15/£17**	SNGL OCC. DBLE/TPL:	**£21.50/£23.50**	SNGL RM:	-
PART BRD:	-	% RED. CHILDREN:	**25%**	DINNER:	-

In Ballina

Mrs. Breda Walsh
SUNCROFT
3 Cathedral Close, Ballina, Co Mayo

Ballina

OPEN:	All Year except Christmas
No. ROOMS:	5
ENSUITE:	4

(V)

TEL: **096 21573** FAX: **096 21573** -

Town house in quiet location behind Cathedral, town centre and River Moy, Ridge Pool 300 mtrs. Le Guide De Routard recommended.

B&B PPS:	**£15/£18**	SNGL OCC. DBLE/TPL:	**£21.50/£24.50**	SNGL RM:	-
PART BRD:	-	% RED. CHILDREN:	**50%**	DINNER:	**£12**

In Ballinrobe

Martin & Breege Kavanagh
FRIARSQUARTER HOUSE
Convent Road, Ballinrobe, Co. Mayo

Ballinrobe

OPEN:	All Year except Christmas
No. ROOMS:	4
ENSUITE:	3

(V)

TEL: **092 41154** FAX: -

Elegent house, period furnishings, off N84. Ideal touring base for Connemara, Knock, Ashford Castle, Ballintubber, 18 hole Golf Course.

B&B PPS:	**£15/£17**	SNGL OCC. DBLE/TPL:	**£21.50/£23.50**	SNGL RM:	**£21**
PART BRD:	-	% RED. CHILDREN:	-	DINNER:	-

In Ballinrobe

Jerry & Beatrice Keane
HAZELWOOD HOUSE
Golf Course Rd., Ballinrobe, Co. Mayo

Ballinrobe

OPEN:	1st January-20th December
No. ROOMS:	4
ENSUITE:	4

(V)

TEL: **092 41372** FAX: -

Comfortable family run home, tranquil location 0.5 km from Ballinrobe, 0.5 km from new 18 hole golf course. Close Mask, Corrib and Carra.

B&B PPS:	**£17**	SNGL OCC. DBLE/TPL:	**£23.50**	SNGL RM:	**£18**
PART BRD:	-	% RED. CHILDREN:	**25%**	DINNER:	-

In Ballinrobe

Ballinrobe

Anne Mahon
RIVERSIDE HOUSE
Cornmarket, Ballinrobe, Co. Mayo

Ballinrobe

OPEN:	**All Year**
NO. ROOMS:	4
ENSUITE:	3

 (V)

TEL: **092 41674** FAX: - EMAIL: **annmahon@iol.ie**

Modern home in Lake District. Championship golf course, scenic walks. Easy driving distance Ashford Castle, Westport, Knock Shrine, Galway.

B&B PPS:	£15/£17	SNGL. OCC. DBLE/TPL:	£21.50/£23.50	SNGL RM:	£18
PART BRD:	-	% RED. CHILDREN:	25%	DINNER:	-

Ballycastle 10km

Mrs. Carmel Murphy
THE HAWTHORNS
Belderrig, Ballina, Co Mayo

Ballycastle

OPEN:	**All Year**
NO. ROOMS:	3
ENSUITE:	2

(V)

TEL: **096 43148** FAX: -

Enjoy warm friendly hospitality in the picturesque village of Belderrig. Beside sea fishing port. Hill/cliff walking. Ceide Fields nearby.

B&B PPS:	£15/£17	SNGL. OCC. DBLE/TPL:	£21.50/£23.50	SNGL RM:	-
PART BRD:	£180	% RED. CHILDREN:	25%	DINNER:	£12

Ballyhaunis 8km

Annette Fleming
EASCAI
Lavallyroe, Clonfad, Ballyhaunis, Co Mayo

Ballyhaunis

OPEN:	**All Year**
NO. ROOMS:	4
ENSUITE:	4

(V)

TEL: **0907 46040** FAX: -

Ideally situated on N83 for touring Galway, Westport, Sligo, Roscommon, all 1 hr drive.18km from Knock, 25 km from Knock Airport.

B&B PPS:	£17	SNGL. OCC. DBLE/TPL:	£23.50	SNGL RM:	£18
PART BRD:	£180	% RED. CHILDREN:	40%	DINNER:	£12

Belmullet

Mrs. Evelyn Cosgrove
HILLCREST HOUSE
Main Street, Bangor Erris, Ballina, Co. Mayo

Bangor Erris

OPEN:	**All Year**
NO. ROOMS:	4
ENSUITE:	2

(V)

TEL: **097 83494** FAX: -

Visit Ceide Fields. 18 hole golf course 24km. Recommended B&B Guide to Ireland. Ideal for fishing. Afternoon tea on arrival.

B&B PPS:	£15/£17	SNGL. OCC. DBLE/TPL:	£21.50/£23.50	SNGL RM:	-
PART BRD:	£180	% RED. CHILDREN:	50%	DINNER:	£12

Belmullet 13km

Josephine Geraghty
BRU CHIANN LIR
Tirrane, Clogher, Belmullet, Ballina, Co. Mayo

Belmullet Peninsula

OPEN:	**1st April-30th September**
NO. ROOMS:	4
ENSUITE:	4

(V)

TEL: **097 85741** FAX: **097 85741**

Visit this unspoilt Peninsula location. Surrounded by Blacksod Bay/Atlantic. Island tours/angling arranged. Guide du Routard/home cooking recommended.

B&B PPS:	£17	SNGL. OCC. DBLE/TPL:	£23.50	SNGL RM:	-
PART BRD:	-	% RED. CHILDREN:	33.3%	DINNER:	£12

In Belmullet

Ms. Mairin Maguire-Murphy
DROM CAOIN
Belmullet, Co. Mayo

Belmullet

OPEN:	All Year except Christmas
NO. ROOMS:	4
ENSUITE:	4

 V

TEL: **097 81195**   FAX: **097 81195**

Panoramic view of Blacksod Bay. Cycle storage and fishing tackle room. Deep sea angling, Carn links golf course. Sculpture trail nearby.

| B&B PPS: | £17/£20 | SNGL OCC. DBLE/TPL: | £23.50/£26.50 | SNGL RM: | - |
| PART BRD: | £186 | % RED. CHILDREN: | - | DINNER: | £12 |

In Belmullet

Mrs Anne Reilly
HIGHDRIFT
Haven View, Ballina Road, Belmullet, Co. Mayo

Belmullet

OPEN:	1st April-3rd October
NO. ROOMS:	4
ENSUITE:	3

V

TEL: **097 81260**   FAX: -

Quiet scenic surroundings overlooking Broadhaven Bay, 5 mins walk to town. Turf fires, warm welcome. Visit Mullet Peninsula & Ceide Fields.

| B&B PPS: | £15/£17 | SNGL OCC. DBLE/TPL: | £21.50/£23.50 | SNGL RM: | - |
| PART BRD: | - | % RED. CHILDREN: | 25% | DINNER: | - |

Castlebar 2km

Mrs. Bernie Collins
DRUMSHINNAGH HOUSE
Rahins, Newport Road, Castlebar, Co Mayo

Castlebar

OPEN:	All Year
NO. ROOMS:	4
ENSUITE:	4

V

TEL: **094 24211**   FAX:

On Newport/Mulranny/Achill Road (R311). 300mt off main road. Ideal for touring, fishing, golfing. Boat & wet room available.

| B&B PPS: | £17/£18 | SNGL OCC. DBLE/TPL: | £23.50/£24.50 | SNGL RM: | £17/£20 |
| PART BRD: | - | % RED. CHILDREN: | 50% | DINNER: | £12 |

Castlebar 4km

Mrs. Maureen Daly
WOODVIEW LODGE
Breaffy (Breaghwy), Castlebar, Co Mayo

Castlebar

OPEN:	1st January-20th December
NO. ROOMS:	4
ENSUITE:	4

V

TEL: **094 23985 / 087 2383695**   FAX: **094 23985**

Luxurious country home, quiet peaceful location, N60 on Claremorris Rd opposite Breaffy House Hotel. Rooms ensuite tea/coffee, TV, hairdryers.

| B&B PPS: | £17 | SNGL OCC. DBLE/TPL: | £23.50 | SNGL RM: | - |
| PART BRD: | - | % RED. CHILDREN: | 25% | DINNER: | - |

Castlebar 1km

Mrs. Breeda Flannelly
FORT-VILLA HOUSE
Moneen, Castlebar, Co Mayo

Castlebar

OPEN:	All Year except Christmas
NO. ROOMS:	5
ENSUITE:	5

V

TEL: **094 21002**   FAX: **094 24395**

Old Georgian House, walking distance town centre. Touring centre, outdoor activities, fishing, golf. Beside N5 roundabout. Rooms TV, teasmaid. Friendly welcome.

| B&B PPS: | £17 | SNGL OCC. DBLE/TPL: | £23.50/£25 | SNGL RM: | - |
| PART BRD: | - | % RED. CHILDREN: | 20% | DINNER: | - |

Castlebar 2km

Mrs Nora Hoban
ALL SEASONS
Breaffy Road, Castlebar, Co Mayo

Castlebar

OPEN:	15th January-15th December	
NO. ROOMS:	6	
ENSUITE:	3	

TEL: **094 22817**   FAX: -

Detached spacious residence. Landscaped gardens N60 Claremorris/Galway Rd. Golf, horse riding, fishing. Visit Knock Shrine, Breaffy House Hotel, Ballintubber Abbey.

B&B PPS:	**£15/£17**	SNGL OCC. DBLE/TPL:	**£21.50/£23.50**	SNGL RM:	-
PART BRD:	-	% RED. CHILDREN:	-	DINNER:	-

In Castlebar

Mrs. Evelyn Kenny
TREES
Turlough/Swinford Road, Castlebar, Co. Mayo

Castlebar

OPEN:	1st April-30th November	
NO. ROOMS:	3	
ENSUITE:	3	

TEL: **094 22074**   FAX: -

Bungalow on two acres of grounds. Golf, fishing, horse riding nearby. Walking distance to town, convenient to Welcome Inn Hotel. Guests TV lounge.

B&B PPS:	**£17**	SNGL OCC. DBLE/TPL:	**£23.50**	SNGL RM:	-
PART BRD:	-	% RED. CHILDREN:	**50%**	DINNER:	**£13**

Castlebar 4km

Mrs Ann Lavelle
HILLCREST
Westport Rd., Castlebar, Co Mayo

Castlebar

OPEN:	All Year	
NO. ROOMS:	3	
ENSUITE:	2	

TEL: **094 21554**   FAX: -

Highly recommended family home, 4km from Castlebar, 12km from Westport. Ideal location for touring - Achill Island, Connemara, Clifden etc.

B&B PPS:	**£15/£17**	SNGL OCC. DBLE/TPL:	**£21.50/£23.50**	SNGL RM:	-
PART BRD:	**£180**	% RED. CHILDREN:	**25%**	DINNER:	**£12**

Castlebar 1km

Mrs. Noreen McGinley
ASHLEIGH
Westport Rd. N60, Castlebar, Co Mayo

Castlebar

OPEN:	All Year except Christmas	
NO. ROOMS:	4	
ENSUITE:	3	

TEL: **094 24714**   FAX: -   EMAIL: **ashleigh@iol.ie**

Cosy, welcoming home, TV, Electric blankets, Hairdryers all bedrooms. Guest lounge. Tea/coffee facilities. Breakfast menu. Superb touring base - highly recommended.

B&B PPS:	**£15/£17**	SNGL OCC. DBLE/TPL:	**£21.50/£23.50**	SNGL RM:	**£17.50**
PART BRD:	-	% RED. CHILDREN:	**33%**	DINNER:	-

Castlebar 6km

Mrs. Kay McGrath
WINDERMERE HOUSE
Westport Road, Islandeady, Castlebar, Co Mayo

Castlebar

OPEN:	1st January-31st December	
NO. ROOMS:	4	
ENSUITE:	3	

TEL: **094 23329**   FAX: -

Spacious home Between Castlebar/Westport. Bilberry Lake 1KM. Hairdryers, trouser press, breakfast menu. Brittany Ferries selected. Home away from home. Teasmaid.

B&B PPS:	**£15/£17**	SNGL OCC. DBLE/TPL:	**£21.50/£23.50**	SNGL RM:	-
PART BRD:	**£180**	% RED. CHILDREN:	**33%**	DINNER:	**£12**

Castlebar 4km

Mrs Mary Moran
LAKEVIEW HOUSE
Westport Road, Castlebar, Co. Mayo

Castlebar	
OPEN:	All Year except Christmas
No. ROOMS:	4
ENSUITE:	4

TEL: **094 22374**   FAX: -

Bungalow on spacious grounds. Guest TV lounge. Peat fire. tea/coffee on arrival. Frommer Guide Recommended. Route N5. Hairdryers.

B&B PPS:	£17	SNGL OCC. DBLE/TPL:	£23.50	SNGL RM:	-
PART BRD:	-	% RED. CHILDREN:	50%	DINNER:	-

In Castlebar

Mrs Sheila Murphy
IVY HOUSE
Castle St., Castlebar, Co Mayo

Castlebar	
OPEN:	All Year except Christmas
No. ROOMS:	5
ENSUITE:	4

TEL: **094 21527**   FAX: -

18th Century house in town centre. Completely refurbished. Guaranteed comfort hospitality and all the comforts of a modern home.

B&B PPS:	£15/£17	SNGL OCC. DBLE/TPL:	£21.50/£23.50	SNGL RM:	£16/£20
PART BRD:	-	% RED. CHILDREN:	50%	DINNER:	-

In Castlebar

Mrs. Eileen Pierce
FOUR WINDS
Maryland, Breaffy Road, Castlebar, Co. Mayo

Castlebar	
OPEN:	1st April-30th November
No. ROOMS:	5
ENSUITE:	5

TEL: **094 21767**   FAX: -

Spacious house walking distance town. Convenient to Breaffy House Hotel, railway station. Electric blankets. Visit Knock Shrine, Ballintubber/Abbey.

B&B PPS:	£17	SNGL OCC. DBLE/TPL:	£17/£23.50	SNGL RM:	-
PART BRD:	-	% RED. CHILDREN:	50%	DINNER:	£12

In Castlebar

Mrs. Teresa Quinn
NEPHIN HOUSE
Westport Road, Castlebar, Co. Mayo

Castlebar	
OPEN:	May-October
No. ROOMS:	4
ENSUITE:	4

TEL: **094 23840**   FAX: -

Comfortable home. Beside Westport Rd. Roundabout. Hairdryers, TV in rooms, tea/coffee making facilities in lounge. Close Travellers Friend Hotel, Hospital.

B&B PPS:	£17	SNGL OCC. DBLE/TPL:	£23.50	SNGL RM:	-
PART BRD:	-	% RED. CHILDREN:	50%	DINNER:	-

Castlebar 4km

Mrs. Breege Scahill
MILLHILL HOUSE
Westport Road, Castlebar, Co Mayo

Castlebar	
OPEN:	May-October
No. ROOMS:	3
ENSUITE:	2

TEL: **094 24279**   FAX: -

Ideal location, off main road. Convenient to Castlebar and Westport. TV, tea/coffee facilities in lounge, home baking, breakfast menu.

B&B PPS:	£15/£17	SNGL OCC. DBLE/TPL:	£21.50/£23.50	SNGL RM:	-
PART BRD:	-	% RED. CHILDREN:	50%	DINNER:	-

Castlebar 1km

Mrs Nora Ward
DEVARD
Westport Road, Castlebar, Co. Mayo

Castlebar

OPEN:	**March/November**
NO. ROOMS:	5
ENSUITE:	4

TEL: **094 23462**   FAX: **094 23462**

Bungalow on Westport Rd, 2 doors from Spar Foodstore. TV, tea/coffee, hairdryers, electric blankets in bed rooms. Ideal touring base.

B&B PPS:	**£15/£17**	SNGL OCC. DBLE/TPL:	**£21.50/£23.50**	SNGL RM:	-
PART BRD:	-	% RED. CHILDREN:	**50%**	DINNER:	

In Charlestown

Mrs. Josephine Keane
HAWTHORN HOUSE
Charlestown, Co. Mayo

Charlestown

OPEN:	**1st May/30th September**
NO. ROOMS:	4
ENSUITE:	-

TEL: **094 54237**   FAX: -

Gracious period home on N5. Enclosed car park. Knock Airport 4 miles. Shrine 15 miles. Ideal touring base.

B&B PPS:	**£15**	SNGL OCC. DBLE/TPL:	**£21.50**	SNGL RM:	-
PART BRD:	-	% RED. CHILDREN:	-	DINNER:	-

Charlestown

Anthony & Anne Kelly
RIVERSIDE
Church St., Charlestown, Co. Mayo

Charlestown

OPEN:	**All Year except Christmas**
NO. ROOMS:	6
ENSUITE:	6

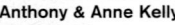

TEL: **094 54200**   FAX: **094 54207**

Olde world friendly home celebrating 30 years in family business. Award winning chef-owner and highly recommended restaurant. Frommer recommended.

B&B PPS:	**£17**	SNGL OCC. DBLE/TPL:	**£23.50**	SNGL RM:	-
PART BRD:	-	% RED. CHILDREN:	**20%**	DINNER:	**£15**

Charlestown 1km

Philip & Carol O'Gorman
ASHFORT
Galway/Knock Road, Charlestown, Co Mayo

Charlestown

OPEN:	**16th March/31st October**
NO. ROOMS:	5
ENSUITE:	5

TEL: **094 54706**   FAX: -

Frommer recommended spacious home N17. Suitable base to tour North/West Mayo, Connemara, Sligo. Knock Airport 5min. Knock Shrine 20 mins.

B&B PPS:	**£17**	SNGL OCC. DBLE/TPL:	**£23.50**	SNGL RM:	-
PART BRD:	-	% RED. CHILDREN:	**20%**	DINNER:	-

In Claremorris

Mrs Rita Cleary
CASA MIA
Ballyhaunis Road, Claremorris, Co Mayo

Claremorris

OPEN:	**15th March-30th November**
NO. ROOMS:	4
ENSUITE:	2

TEL: **094 71405**   FAX: -

Situated Claremorris/Ballyhaunis Road N60. Convenient Knock Shrine, Airport, Ballintubber Abbey riding school. Golf course.

B&B PPS:	**£15/£17**	SNGL OCC. DBLE/TPL:	**£21.50/£23.50**	SNGL RM:	**£17**
PART BRD:	-	% RED. CHILDREN:	**25%**	DINNER:	-

Cong 1km

Mrs Ann Coakley
HAZEL GROVE
Drumshiel, Cong, Co Mayo

Cong

OPEN:	1st February/30th November
No. ROOMS:	5
ENSUITE:	4

TEL: **092 46060**   FAX: -

Warm friendly home, peaceful location between lakes Corrib/Mask. Panoramic view of Mountains, Old Castle. Ideal base for touring Connemara.

B&B PPS:	**£15/£17**	SNGL OCC. DBLE/TPL:	**£21.50/£23.50**	SNGL RM:	-
PART BRD:	-	% RED. CHILDREN:	40%	DINNER:	-

Cong 3km

Mrs Ann Holian
VILLA PIO
Gortacurra, Cross, Cong, Co Mayo

Cong

OPEN:	All Year
No. ROOMS:	3
ENSUITE:	2

TEL: **092 46403/087 2386820**   FAX: **092 46403**

Situated near Quiet Man Film locations, Cong Abbey, 5 mins walk Lough Corrib, Boats/Fishing. Galway, Knock Airports 40KM. Bus & Taxi Service.

B&B PPS:	**£15/£17**	SNGL OCC. DBLE/TPL:	**£21.50/£23.50**	SNGL RM:	-
PART BRD:	-	% RED. CHILDREN:	25%	DINNER:	-

Cong 0.5 km

Dermot & Kathy O'Connor
DOLMEN HOUSE
Drumsheel, Cong, Co Mayo

Cong

OPEN:	1st January-31st December
No. ROOMS:	5
ENSUITE:	5

TEL: **092 46466**   FAX: **092 46466**

Luxurious new house overlooking Connemara Mountains. Excellent touring base. Paradise for Anglers, Walkers, Golfers. Sauna available.

B&B PPS:	**£17/£18**	SNGL OCC. DBLE/TPL:	**£23.50/£24.50**	SNGL RM:	-
PART BRD:	-	% RED. CHILDREN:	25%	DINNER:	-

In Crossmolina

Mrs Ann Gallagher
LAKE VIEW HOUSE
Ballina Road, Crossmolina, Co Mayo

Crossmolina

OPEN:	1st March-31stOctober
No. ROOMS:	6
ENSUITE:	6

TEL: **096 31296**   FAX: -

Country home Lough Conn Family Research/Archaeological Centres and Ceide Fields closeby. Boat/Ghillie hire. Fishing arranged. Tea/Coffee facilities.

B&B PPS:	**£17**	SNGL OCC. DBLE/TPL:	-	SNGL RM:	£17
PART BRD:	-	% RED. CHILDREN:	33.3%	DINNER:	-

Crossmolina 3km

Mrs Nora Naughton
WOODVIEW HOUSE
Enniscoe, Castlehill, Crossmolina, Co Mayo

Crossmolina

OPEN:	April-October
No. ROOMS:	6
ENSUITE:	4

TEL: **096 31125**   FAX: -

Country house, beside Lough Conn. Family Research Centre - 1996 Award. Tea/coffee bedrooms. Fishing arranged. Boats/Engines - Hire. Pontoon - 20 mins.

B&B PPS:	**£15/£17**	SNGL OCC. DBLE/TPL:	-	SNGL RM:	£15/£17
PART BRD:	-	% RED. CHILDREN:	50%	DINNER:	-

Killala 3km

Mrs Mary O'Hara
BEACH VIEW HOUSE
Ross, Killala, Co Mayo

Killala

Open:	**All Year**
No. Rooms:	4
Ensuite:	3

(V)

Tel: **096 32023**   Fax: -

Bungalow on peninsula. 200 metres, to glorious Beaches. Fishing, Historical interests. On route to Ceide Fields. R314 Northbound of Killala.

B&B PPS:	**£15/£17**	Sngl Occ. Dble/Tpl:	**£21.50/£23.50**	Sngl Rm:	-
Part Brd:	**£180**	% Red. Children:	-	Dinner:	-

In Kiltimagh

Mrs Mary Carney
HILLCREST
Kilkelly Rd, Kiltimagh, Co Mayo

Kiltimagh

Open:	**All Year except Christmas**
No. Rooms:	6
Ensuite:	6

(V)

Tel: **094 81112**   Fax: -

Spacious landscaped grounds, 5 mins drive Knock Shrine, Connaught Regional Airport, Fishing, Golf. Ideal touring base for West of Ireland.

B&B PPS:	**£17**	Sngl Occ. Dble/Tpl:	**£23.50**	Sngl Rm:	-
Part Brd:	-	% Red. Children:	**20%**	Dinner:	-

Kiltimagh 8km

Maureen Carney and Family
BURREN
Kiltimagh Road, Knock, Co Mayo

Knock

Open:	**May-September**
No. Rooms:	5
Ensuite:	4

(V)

Tel: **094 88362**   Fax: -

Bungalow on R323 West off N17. 1 kilometer from roundabout. All Ground floor rooms. Named in "The Real Guide - Ireland".

B&B PPS:	**£15/£17**	Sngl Occ. Dble/Tpl:	**£21.50/£23.50**	Sngl Rm:	-
Part Brd:	-	% Red. Children:	**33.3%**	Dinner:	-

In Knock

Mrs Kathleen Carty
CARRAMORE HOUSE
Airport Road, Knock, Co Mayo

Knock

Open:	**17th March-31st October**
No. Rooms:	6
Ensuite:	6

(V)

Tel: **094 88149**   Fax: -

Family home 400 metres from Shrine (N17). Tea/Coffee on arrival. Breakfast menu. Convenient to bus stop, Guidance on Genealogy Tracing.

B&B PPS:	**£17**	Sngl Occ. Dble/Tpl:	**£23.50**	Sngl Rm:	-
Part Brd:	-	% Red. Children:	**33.3%**	Dinner:	**£14**

Claremorris 10km

Mrs Marion Casby
ST THOMAS
Claremorris Road, Knock, Co Mayo

Knock

Open:	**1st April-31stOctober**
No. Rooms:	6
Ensuite:	4

(V)

Tel: **094 88188**   Fax: -

Family home on N17, in quiet location, on own landscaped ground. Ground floor accommodation. Private parking.

B&B PPS:	**£15/£17**	Sngl Occ. Dble/Tpl:	−	Sngl Rm:	-
Part Brd:	-	% Red. Children:	**50%**	Dinner:	-

Knock 1.6km

Mrs Brid McGrath
BRIDGE HOUSE
Airport Rd., Knock, Co Mayo

Knock

OPEN:	**1st April-1st November**
NO. ROOMS:	**3**
ENSUITE:	**3**

TEL: **094 88205**   FAX: -

Family run accommodation in country setting on N17. All rooms on ground floor. Fifteen mins. walk to Shrine. Convenient to Airport.

B&B PPS:	**£17**	SNGL OCC. DBLE/TPL:	**£23.50**	SNGL RM:	-
PART BRD:	-	% RED. CHILDREN:	**66.6%**	DINNER:	-

Knock 0.5km

Henry Taaffe
ESKERVILLE
Claremorris Rd, Knock, Co Mayo

Knock

OPEN:	**All Year except Christmas**
NO. ROOMS:	**5**
ENSUITE:	**2**

TEL: **094 88413**   FAX: -

Beige Dormer Bungalow situated on N17 - Claremorris, Galway Road - In Knock. Private Car Park and Mature Gardens to the front.

B&B PPS:	**£15/£18**	SNGL OCC. DBLE/TPL:	**£21.50/£25**	SNGL RM:	**£16/£20**
PART BRD:	-	% RED. CHILDREN:	**30%**	DINNER:	-

Louisburgh 12km

Mrs Catherine Conneely-Heneghan
SILVER STRAND HOUSE
Thallabawn, Killadoon, Louisburgh, Co Mayo

Louisburgh

OPEN:	**All Year except Christmas**
NO. ROOMS:	**6**
ENSUITE:	**5**

TEL: **098 68730**   FAX: **098 68730**

Overlooking one Europes finest Beaches. Magnificent views. Safe Beaches. Unique location - "Away from it all". Credit Cards. Tea/Coffee in bedrooms.

B&B PPS:	**£15/£17**	SNGL OCC. DBLE/TPL:	**£21.50/£23.50**	SNGL RM:	-
PART BRD:	**£180**	% RED. CHILDREN:	**25%**	DINNER:	**£12**

In Louisburgh

Mrs Claire Kenny
SPRINGFIELD HOUSE
Westport Rd., Louisburgh, Co Mayo

Louisburgh

OPEN:	**May-September**
NO. ROOMS:	**4**
ENSUITE:	**3**

TEL: **098 66289**   FAX: -

On main Westport/Louisburgh road (R335). Sandy safe Beaches, Sea & River Fishing. Ideal area for Walking, Mountain Climbing & Cycling.

B&B PPS:	**£15/£17**	SNGL OCC. DBLE/TPL:	**£21.50/£23.50**	SNGL RM:	-
PART BRD:	**£180**	% RED. CHILDREN:	**50%**	DINNER:	**£12**

In Louisburgh

Mrs Ann McNamara
WHITETHORNS
Bunowen Road, Louisburgh, Co Mayo

Louisburgh

OPEN:	**April-September**
NO. ROOMS:	**4**
ENSUITE:	**4**

TEL: **098 66062**   FAX: -

Bungalow in scenic location off R335 opposite Roman Catholic Church, 5 minutes walk Louisburgh. Excellent Sandy Beaches, Walking, Cycling, Fishing.

B&B PPS:	**£17**	SNGL OCC. DBLE/TPL:	**£23.50**	SNGL RM:	-
PART BRD:	-	% RED. CHILDREN:	**50%**	DINNER:	-

In Louisburgh

Betty McSweeney
CAHIR HOUSE
Louisburgh, Co Mayo

Louisburgh

OPEN:	10th March-31st October
NO. ROOMS:	4
ENSUITE:	4

(V)

TEL: **098 66278**   FAX: -

On Leenane Road. 5 minutes walk from centre of Louisburgh.15 Minutes walk to Blue Flag Beach.

B&B PPS:	**£17**	SNGL OCC. DBLE/TPL:	**£23.50**	SNGL RM:	-
PART BRD:	-	% RED. CHILDREN:	-	DINNER:	-

Louisburgh 3km

Mrs Mary Sammin
THE THREE ARCHES
Askelane, Louisburgh, Co Mayo

Louisburgh

OPEN:	1st May-30th September
NO. ROOMS:	4
ENSUITE:	2

(V)

TEL: **098 66484**   FAX: -

Modern bungalow with panoramic view. Ideal touring centre for Clare Island. Croagh Patrick. Safe Sandy Beaches. Scenic Walks. Home Cooking.

B&B PPS:	**£15/£17**	SNGL OCC. DBLE/TPL:	**£21.50/£23.50**	SNGL RM:	-
PART BRD:	**£190**	% RED. CHILDREN:	**50%**	DINNER:	**£14**

Mulranny 1km

Mrs Catherine Reilly
BREEZEMOUNT B&B
Mulranny, Co Mayo

Mulranny

OPEN:	All Year except Christmas
NO. ROOMS:	4
ENSUITE:	4

(V)

TEL: **098 36145**   FAX: -

Modern bungalow with panoramic view, opposite Croagh Patrick on Clew Bay, adjoining Golf Links. Ideal location for touring Achill Island.

B&B PPS:	**£17**	SNGL OCC. DBLE/TPL:	**£23.50**	SNGL RM:	**£23.50**
PART BRD:	**£180**	% RED. CHILDREN:	**10%**	DINNER:	**£12**

In Newport

Mrs Phil Chambers
DEBILLE HOUSE
Main Street, Newport, Co Mayo

Newport

OPEN:	1st June-30th September
NO. ROOMS:	4
ENSUITE:	4

(V)

TEL: **098 41145**   FAX: **098 41777**

Beautifully restored historical Georgian house near Clew Bay, Furnace Lakes/ Letterkeen Forest/ 6km. Paradise for Angler's, Walkers, Golfers. Home cooking.

B&B PPS:	**£18**	SNGL OCC. DBLE/TPL:	**£24.50**	SNGL RM:	**£21.50/£23.50**
PART BRD:	-	% RED. CHILDREN:	**50%**	DINNER:	**£14**

In Newport

Mrs Maureen McGovern
ANCHOR HOUSE
Quay Rd, Newport, Co Mayo

Newport

OPEN:	March-October
NO. ROOMS:	5
ENSUITE:	3

(V)

TEL: **098 41178**   FAX: **094 24903**

Quiet residential area overlooking harbour. Convenient to Town, Restaurants, Pubs. Excellent base for Touring, Golf, Fishing, Walking or simply relaxing.

B&B PPS:	**£15/£18**	SNGL OCC. DBLE/TPL:	**£22**	SNGL RM:	-
PART BRD:	-	% RED. CHILDREN:	-	DINNER:	-

Evelyn Byrne
LOUGH CARRA HOUSE
Partry, Co Mayo

Partry

OPEN:	All Year except Christmas
NO. ROOMS:	3
ENSUITE:	3

(V)

TEL: **092 43121**   FAX: **094 24252**

On Deer Farm with Lake and Mountains views. Snooker room, Angling facilities. On N84. Ideal Touring Base for Ireland West.

B&B PPS:	£17	SNGL OCC. DBLE/TPL:	£23.50	SNGL RM:	-
PART BRD:	-	% RED. CHILDREN:	20%	DINNER:	-

— Ballinrobe 10km

Paul & Liz Bree
SUNNYSIDE
Deerpark East, Westport, Co. Mayo

Westport

OPEN:	17th March-31st October
NO. ROOMS:	4
ENSUITE:	3

(V)

TEL: **098 26883**   FAX: **098 27122**   EMAIL: **paulbree@iol.ie**

Ours is a comfortable, well appointed home, convenient to golf and other leisure facilities, with splendid views and private parking.

B&B PPS:	£15/£17	SNGL OCC. DBLE/TPL:	£21.50/£23.50	SNGL RM:	-
PART BRD:	-	% RED. CHILDREN:	50%	DINNER:	-

— In Westport

Mrs Noreen Broderick
ANNAGH HOUSE
Leenane Road, Westport, Co Mayo

Westport

OPEN:	1st May-31st October
NO. ROOMS:	3
ENSUITE:	3

 (V)

TEL: **098 25557**   FAX: -

Newly constructed Dormer Home on Leenane Road, route N59. 1km from town centre. Ideal for touring Connemara, Clifden, Achill.

B&B PPS:	£17	SNGL OCC. DBLE/TPL:	£23.50	SNGL RM:	-
PART BRD:	-	% RED. CHILDREN:	50%	DINNER:	-

— Westport 1km

Mrs Mary Cafferkey
HAZELBROOK
Deer Park East, Newport Road, Westport, Co Mayo

Westport

OPEN:	1st January-31st December
NO. ROOMS:	6
ENSUITE:	6

(V)

TEL: **098 26865 / 088 639043**   FAX: -

Home in residential area. Bedrooms with TV, Tea facilities. 4 mins walk to town. Ideally situated for touring West coast.

B&B PPS:	£17	SNGL OCC. DBLE/TPL:	£25	SNGL RM:	-
PART BRD:	-	% RED. CHILDREN:	10%	DINNER:	-

— In Westport

Mrs Sandra Corcoran
PLOUGASTEL HOUSE
Distillery Rd, Westport, Co Mayo

Westport

OPEN:	All Year except Christmas
NO. ROOMS:	6
ENSUITE:	6

(V)

TEL: **098 25198**   FAX: -

Modern new town house. Located in town centre with private car park. TV's in all bedrooms. Tea/coffee facilities.

B&B PPS:	£17/£20	SNGL OCC. DBLE/TPL:	-	SNGL RM:	-
PART BRD:	-	% RED. CHILDREN:	-	DINNER:	-

— In Westport

297

L Westport 1km

Mary Doherty
LUI-NA-GREINE
Castlebar Road, Westport, Co Mayo

Westport

OPEN:	1st April-31st October
No. ROOMS:	6
ENSUITE:	4

TEL: **098 25536**   FAX: -

Bungalow on N5 scenic area within walking distance of town. Spacious gardens. Car park.Recommended "Guide to Ireland", "En Irlande"

B&B PPS:	**£15/£17**	SNGL OCC. DBLE/TPL:	**£21.50/£23.50**	SNGL RM:	-
PART BRD:	-	% RED. CHILDREN:	**50%**	DINNER:	-

L Westport 1km

Mrs Vera English
HILLSIDE LODGE
Castlebar Road, Westport, Co Mayo

Westport

OPEN:	March-October
No. ROOMS:	3
ENSUITE:	2

TEL: **098 25668**   FAX: -

Warm friendly home. Take N5(N60) from Westport for 1mile. Look for sign on left past Reek View Garage.

B&B PPS:	**£15/£17**	SNGL OCC. DBLE/TPL:	**£21.50/£23.50**	SNGL RM:	-
PART BRD:	-	% RED. CHILDREN:	-	DINNER:	-

Maureen & Peter Flynn
CEDAR LODGE
Kings Hill, Newport Rd N59, Westport, Co Mayo

Westport

OPEN:	All Year except Christmas
No. ROOMS:	4
ENSUITE:	3

TEL: **098 25417**   FAX: **098 25417**

Bungalow. 1997 award winning mature gardens, 5 mins town centre, Golf, Tennis, Pedestrian Walk to sea front. Recommended "Best B & B Guide", Frommer.

B&B PPS:	**£15.50/£17.50**	SNGL OCC. DBLE/TPL:	**£22/£25.50**	SNGL RM:	-
PART BRD:	-	% RED. CHILDREN:	**20%**	DINNER:	-

L In Westport

Mr Paddy Gallagher
SUNSET
Belclare, Westport, Co Mayo

Westport

OPEN:	1st June-31 August
No. ROOMS:	4
ENSUITE:	-

TEL: **098 25638**   FAX: -

Modern, well heated family home. TV lounge, turf fires. On the coast road to Louisburgh. Central to Achill and Connemara.

B&B PPS:	**£15**	SNGL OCC. DBLE/TPL:	**£21.50**	SNGL RM:	**£16**
PART BRD:	-	% RED. CHILDREN:	**50%**	DINNER:	-

L Westport 5km

L Westport 1km

Mrs Angela Gavin
CARRABAUN HOUSE
Carrabaun, Leenane Road, Westport, Co Mayo

Westport

OPEN:	1st March-10th December
No. ROOMS:	6
ENSUITE:	6

TEL: **098 26196**   FAX: -

New spacious period house, Elevated 1 acre site, Panoramic views. Hairdryers bedrooms, Breakfast menu, Near Fishing, Golfing, Traditional Pubs, Restaurants, N59.

B&B PPS:	**£17**	SNGL OCC. DBLE/TPL:	**£24**	SNGL RM:	-
PART BRD:	-	% RED. CHILDREN:	**25%**	DINNER:	-

Westport 8km

Mrs Mary Churchill Gavin
HIGHGROVE
Murrisk, Westport, Co Mayo

Westport

OPEN:	1st May-30th September
NO. ROOMS:	4
ENSUITE:	2

TEL: **098 64819/087 2314839**   FAX: **098 64819**

Spacious bungalow on Route R335. Tranquil surroundings, Foothill's of Croagh Patrick. Ideal for Climbing, Walking. Restaurants, Beaches, nearby.

| B&B PPS: | **£15/£17** | SNGL OCC. DBLE/TPL: | **£21.50/£23.50** | SNGL RM: | - |
| PART BRD: | - | % RED. CHILDREN: | 25% | DINNER: | - |

In Westport

Mrs Bridget Gibbons
BROADLANDS
Quay Road, Westport, Co Mayo

Westport

OPEN:	January-December
NO. ROOMS:	4
ENSUITE:	4

TEL: **098 27377**   FAX: -

Large bungalow, situated on the coast road to Louisburgh. Close to Town Centre, Pubs & Restaurants.

| B&B PPS: | **£17/£18** | SNGL OCC. DBLE/TPL: | **£23.50/£30** | SNGL RM: | - |
| PART BRD: | - | % RED. CHILDREN: | 20% | DINNER: | - |

Westport 12km

Mrs Beatrice Gill
SEA BREEZE
Kilsallagh, Westport, Co Mayo

Westport

OPEN:	March-3rd November
NO. ROOMS:	3
ENSUITE:	3

TEL: **098 66548**   FAX: -

Comfortable, friendly home, breathtaking views. Gateway to Connemara, Knock. From Westport take R335 to avail of hospitality and delicious food.

| B&B PPS: | **£17** | SNGL OCC. DBLE/TPL: | **£23.50/£25** | SNGL RM: | - |
| PART BRD: | **£180** | % RED. CHILDREN: | 25% | DINNER: | **£12.50** |

Westport

Tom & Kathleen Keane
THE WESTERLY
Newport Road, Westport, Co Mayo

Westport

OPEN:	1st May-1st October
NO. ROOMS:	3
ENSUITE:	3

TEL: **098 26117**   FAX: -

Residence set in its own Gardens with private Carpark. Convenient to Golf, Tennis, Sailing Centre. 3 minutes walk to Town Centre.

| B&B PPS: | **£17** | SNGL OCC. DBLE/TPL: | **£25** | SNGL RM: | - |
| PART BRD: | - | % RED. CHILDREN: | 25% | DINNER: | - |

In Westport

David and Sara Kelly
QUAY WEST
Quay Road, Westport, Co Mayo

Westport

OPEN:	All Year
NO. ROOMS:	6
ENSUITE:	6

TEL: **098 27863**   FAX: -

Purpose built house on T39/R335. Rooms Ensuite, Power Showers, Orthopaedic Beds. TV Lounge, Walking distance Town, Pubs, Restaurants.

| B&B PPS: | **£17/£20** | SNGL OCC. DBLE/TPL: | **£25/£30** | SNGL RM: | - |
| PART BRD: | - | % RED. CHILDREN: | 25% | DINNER: | - |

Mary Kelly
BIRCHSIDE
Streamstown, Westport, Co Mayo

Westport	
OPEN:	May-30th September
NO. ROOMS:	3
ENSUITE:	2

TEL: **098 25406/087 2346740** FAX: -

New spacious house on T39/R335 Coast Road, close to Beaches, Pubs, Restaurants. Panoramic views Croagh Patrick, Clew Bay. 2 km Quay.

B&B PPS:	**£15/£17**	SNGL OCC. DBLE/TPL:	**£22/£25**	SNGL RM:	-
PART BRD:	-	% RED. CHILDREN:	**30%**	DINNER:	-

Westport 4km

Robert & Sheila Kilkelly
ST ANTHONY'S
Distillery Rd, Westport, Co Mayo

Westport	
OPEN:	All Year except Christmas
NO. ROOMS:	5
ENSUITE:	5

TEL: **098 25172** FAX: **098 26121**

1820 house in town, on quiet street with private car park in one acre of grounds. All rooms with TV.

B&B PPS:	**£17/£20**	SNGL OCC. DBLE/TPL:	-	SNGL RM:	-
PART BRD:	-	% RED. CHILDREN:	-	DINNER:	-

In Westport

Mrs Martha Loughrey
BAYVILLE
Leenane Rd, Westport, Co Mayo

Westport	
OPEN:	1st May-30th September
NO. ROOMS:	4
ENSUITE:	3

TEL: **098 25569** FAX: -

House on Westport Leenane Road N59, overlooking Clew Bay. Scenic Views of Islands. 7 minutes walk from town.

B&B PPS:	**£16/£17**	SNGL OCC. DBLE/TPL:	**£22.50/£23.50**	SNGL RM:	-
PART BRD:	-	% RED. CHILDREN:	**25%**	DINNER:	-

In Westport

Mrs Angela McDonagh
DOVEDALE
Rampart Wood, Golf Course Rd, Westport, Co Mayo

Westport	
OPEN:	1st April-30th September
NO. ROOMS:	4
ENSUITE:	4

TEL: **098 25154** FAX: **098 25154**

Modern home set in woodland surroundings. Landscaped Gardens, Private Parking, within walking distance of Town Centre. Tennis, Golf, Sailing, nearby.

B&B PPS:	**£17**	SNGL OCC. DBLE/TPL:	**£23.50/£25**	SNGL RM:	-
PART BRD:	-	% RED. CHILDREN:	-	DINNER:	-

Westport 1km

Mrs Josephine McGreal
CEOL NA MARA
Lower Quay, Westport, Co Mayo

Westport	
OPEN:	1st April-31st October
NO. ROOMS:	3
ENSUITE:	3

TEL: **098 26969** FAX: -

Newly constructed two storey house, walking distance to town. Close to Pubs, Restaurants and Harbour. Private car park available.

B&B PPS:	**£17**	SNGL OCC. DBLE/TPL:	**£23.50/£25**	SNGL RM:	-
PART BRD:	-	% RED. CHILDREN:	**50%**	DINNER:	-

Westport 2km

In Westport

Mrs Margaret Madigan
ADARE HOUSE
Quay Road, Westport, Co Mayo

OPEN:	All Year except Christmas
NO. ROOMS:	6
ENSUITE:	4

TEL: **098 26102** FAX: -

New house on T39/R335, Coast Road. Walking distance Town, Pubs, Restaurants. Panoramic view Croagh Patrick. Orthopaedic beds. Parking front/rear.

B&B PPS:	£15/£17	SNGL OCC. DBLE/TPL:	£21.50/£23.50	SNGL RM:	-
PART BRD:	-	% RED. CHILDREN:	-	DINNER:	

Westport 1.5km

Mrs Mary Mitchell
CILLCOMAN LODGE
Rosbeg, Westport, Co Mayo

OPEN:	13th March-26th October
NO. ROOMS:	4
ENSUITE:	4

TEL: **098 26379** FAX: -

Situated on Coast Road. Quiet location with parking facilities and garden. Guest TV lounge. Adjacent to Harbour, Pubs & Restaurants.

B&B PPS:	£17	SNGL OCC. DBLE/TPL:	£23.50	SNGL RM:	-
PART BRD:	-	% RED. CHILDREN:	-	DINNER:	-

Westport 0.5km

Mrs Bridie Moran
GLENSIDE
Deerpark East, Newport Rd, Westport, Co Mayo

OPEN:	14th March-1st November
NO. ROOMS:	4
ENSUITE:	4

TEL: **098 25806** FAX: -

Two storey house, quiet residential area. 5 minutes walk from Town, Tennis, Golf, Scenic, Walks, private car park.

B&B PPS:	£17	SNGL OCC. DBLE/TPL:	£25/£26	SNGL RM:	-
PART BRD:	-	% RED. CHILDREN:	10%	DINNER:	-

Mrs Ann O'Flaherty
GLENDERAN
Rosbeg, Westport, Co Mayo

OPEN:	1st March-31st October
NO. ROOMS:	6
ENSUITE:	4

TEL: **098 26585/087 464045** FAX: -

New house, quiet location, T39/R335, beside Harbour, walking distance Pubs/Restaurants. Satellite, TV, Coffee, Hairdryers in bedrooms. Car Park.

B&B PPS:	£15/£17	SNGL OCC. DBLE/TPL:	£22.50/£24	SNGL RM:	-
PART BRD:	-	% RED. CHILDREN:	50%	DINNER:	-

Westport 1.5km

Kay O'Halloran
WATERSIDE
1 The Harbour, Westport, Co Mayo

OPEN:	March-October
NO. ROOMS:	4
ENSUITE:	4

TEL: **098 27357** FAX: -

Waterside offer accommodation coupled with panoramic views of Clew Bay and Croagh Patrick, with a stronge emphasis on the customer.

B&B PPS:	£17	SNGL OCC. DBLE/TPL:	£23.50/£25	SNGL RM:	-
PART BRD:	-	% RED. CHILDREN:	-	DINNER:	-

Westport 1km

Mrs Marie O'Keeffe
LAKESIDE HOUSE
Leenane Rd, Westport, Co Mayo

Westport

OPEN:	**1st June-1st September**
NO. ROOMS:	3
ENSUITE:	2

TEL: **098 25670**   FAX: -

5 minutes drive from Westport. Free fishing from nearby jetties. On Westport - Clifden Road Route N59. Spacious bedrooms. Gateway to Connemara.

B&B PPS:	**£15/£17**	SNGL OCC. DBLE/TPL:	**£21.50/£23.50**	SNGL RM:	-
PART BRD:	-	% RED. CHILDREN:	**50%**	DINNER:	

Westport 2km

Mrs Kay O'Malley
RIVERBANK HOUSE
Rosbeg, Westport Harbour, Co Mayo

Westport

OPEN:	**1st April-31st October**
NO. ROOMS:	8
ENSUITE:	6

TEL: **098 25719**   FAX: -

Peaceful Country home, car park, Home Baking, walking distance to Pubs, Restaurants on T39/R335. Recommended "300 Best B & B's Ireland".

B&B PPS:	**£15/£17**	SNGL OCC. DBLE/TPL:	**£21.50/£23.50**	SNGL RM:	-
PART BRD:	-	% RED. CHILDREN:	**33.3%**	DINNER:	-

Westport 2km

Mrs Marian O'Malley
MOHER HOUSE
Liscarney, Westport, Co Mayo

Westport

OPEN:	**14th March-31st October**
NO. ROOMS:	4
ENSUITE:	3

TEL: **098 21360**   FAX: -

Westport, Clifden Rd (N59). Breakfast, Dinner, Vegetarian menu. Walkers - off Western Way. Recommended Best B&B Guide. Frommer. Afternoon tea on arrival.

B&B PPS:	**£15/£17**	SNGL OCC. DBLE/TPL:	**£21.50/£23.50**	SNGL RM:	-
PART BRD:	**£180**	% RED. CHILDREN:	**50%**	DINNER:	**£12**

Westport 8km

Mrs Mary O'Malley
ARD CAOIN
The Quay, Westport, Co Mayo

Westport

OPEN:	**May-October**
NO. ROOMS:	4
ENSUITE:	4

TEL: **098 25492**   FAX: -   EMAIL: **malley@cbn.ie**

House beside entrance to Westport House, within walking distance of Westports Best Restaurants & Pubs. Private Car Park. Tea/coffee facilities.

B&B PPS:	**£17/£18**	SNGL OCC. DBLE/TPL:	**£23.50/£24.50**	SNGL RM:	-
PART BRD:	-	% RED. CHILDREN:	**25%**	DINNER:	

Westport 1.5km

Vincent & Catherine O'Reilly
EMANIA
Castlebar Road, Sheeaune, Westport, Co Mayo

Westport

OPEN:	**1st June-30th September**
NO. ROOMS:	4
ENSUITE:	2

TEL: **098 26459/21460**   FAX: -

Country dwelling , own grounds. Private parking located on N60 road between Westport &Castlebar. Friendly, hospitable atmosphere. Free Tea/Coffee on arrival.

B&B PPS:	**£15/£17**	SNGL OCC. DBLE/TPL:	**£21.50/£23.50**	SNGL RM:	-
PART BRD:	-	% RED. CHILDREN:	**50%**	DINNER:	

Westport 1.75km

Westport 1km

Mrs Noreen Reddington
BROOKLODGE
Deerpark East, Newport Rd, Westport, Co Mayo

Westport

TEL: **098 26654**   FAX: -

OPEN:	1st March-31st October
NO. ROOMS:	4
ENSUITE:	2

Modern home in quiet residential area. 5 minutes walk from town. A warm welcome awaits you with Tea/coffee on arrival.

B&B PPS:	£15/£17	SNGL OCC. DBLE/TPL:	£21.50/£23.50	SNGL RM:	-
PART BRD:	-	% RED. CHILDREN:	50%	DINNER:	

In Westport

Julie & Aiden Redmond
HARMONY HEIGHTS
Kings Hill, Newport Road, Westport, Co Mayo

Westport

TEL: **098 25491**   FAX: **094 22231**

OPEN:	All Year except Christmas
NO. ROOMS:	3
ENSUITE:	2

Elevated bungalow with verandah, surrounded by shrubs/flowers. Route 59. 5 mins walk town centre. Close to Golf, Fishing, Sailing, Tennis.

B&B PPS:	£15/£17	SNGL OCC. DBLE/TPL:	£21.50/£25	SNGL RM:	-
PART BRD:	-	% RED. CHILDREN:	50%	DINNER:	-

Westport 1km

Mrs Teresa Reidy
HARBOUR LODGE
Lower Quay, Westport, Co Mayo

Westport

TEL: **098 27224**   FAX: -

OPEN:	1st April-1st October
NO. ROOMS:	4
ENSUITE:	4

Modern house built in the Old Style, located in scenic Westport Harbour. Beside award winning Restaurants and entertaining Public Houses.

B&B PPS:	£17	SNGL OCC. DBLE/TPL:	£23.50	SNGL RM:	-
PART BRD:	-	% RED. CHILDREN:	-	DINNER:	-

Westport 1km

Mrs Marie Ruane
WOODVIEW HOUSE
Buckwaria
Castlebar Rd N5, Westport, Co Mayo

Westport

TEL: **098 27879**   FAX: -

OPEN:	All Year except Christmas
NO. ROOMS:	6
ENSUITE:	6

Hospitality/comfort awaits you in modern home, peaceful wooded area, .5 km off N5 walking distance Town Centre. All facilities.

B&B PPS:	£17	SNGL OCC. DBLE/TPL:	£23.50	SNGL RM:	£21
PART BRD:	-	% RED. CHILDREN:	30%	DINNER:	-

SYMBOLS

LOOK OUT FOR THESE SYMBOLS WHICH SHOULD BE DISPLAYED BY ALL MEMBERS OF TOWN & COUNTRY HOMES.

In Westport

Mrs Rita Sheridan	Westport		
ALTAMONT HOUSE			
Ballinrobe Road, Westport, Co Mayo	OPEN:	March-October	
	NO. ROOMS:	8	
	ENSUITE:	5	
TEL: **098 25226**	FAX: -		

Pre-famine (1848). Tastefully modernised home, 5 minutes walk from Town Centre, Quiet Area, Interesting Garden, Recommended "300 Best B&B's Ireland".

♣ ♪ ⌂

B&B PPS:	**£15/£17**	SNGL OCC. DBLE/TPL:	**£21.50/£23.50**	SNGL RM:	-
PART BRD:	-	% RED. CHILDREN:	-	DINNER:	-

Westport 5km

Aidan & Mary Walsh	Westport		
EAGLE BROOK			
Knockrooskey, Westport, Co Mayo	OPEN:	3rd May-13th September	
	NO. ROOMS:	3	
	ENSUITE:	2	
TEL: **098 35347**	FAX: -		

Modern country home. Main Galway/Westport Road (R330). Adjacent to Ballintubber Abbey, Ayle Caves. Warm welcome. Tea/Coffee on arrival.

⊞ Ⓟ ⅀ ✂ ♪ ⌂ ⑤

B&B PPS:	**£17**	SNGL OCC. DBLE/TPL:	**£23.50**	SNGL RM:	**£15**
PART BRD:	-	% RED. CHILDREN:	**50%**	DINNER:	-

WATCH OUT FOR THE SIGN THAT MARKS AN OFFICIAL IRISH TOURIST BOARD INFORMATION OFFICE.

Their Tourist Advisors are expert on the surrounding areas and on all aspects of Irish holidays. The friendly staff have an extensive range of language skills and they will be delighted to help you with:

- Accommodation - bookings to all Bord Fáilte registered and approved accommodation.
- Credit card bookings by telephone.
- Advice on routes/places to visit.
- National and local events.
- Maps, guides, literature on Ireland.
- Scenic coach tours.
- Boat trips – lakes/offshore islands.
- Flights to offshore islands.
- Holiday gift vouchers.
- Banquet and theatre bookings.
- Local crafts and gifts.
- Bureau de change facilities.

Athleague 2km

Mrs Maura Galvin
FORT VIEW HOUSE
Creggs Road, Athleague, Co Roscommon

Athleague

Tel: **0903 63342**   Fax: -

Open:	Easter-October	
No. Rooms:	3	
Ensuite:	-	(V)

Situated in beautiful countryside outside Athleague on scenic River Suck. Course Fishing, Trout, Laked, Walks, and Historical Monuments nearby.

B&B pps:	£15	Sngl Occ. Dble/Tpl:	£21.50	Sngl Rm:	-
Part Brd:	£180	% Red. Children:	25%	Dinner:	£12

Athlone 5 km

Ms Carmel Coyle
BAYVIEW
Hodson Bay, Athlone, Co Roscommon

Athlone

Tel: **0902 94019**   Fax: -

Open:	All Year except Christmas	
No. Rooms:	3	
Ensuite:	3	(V)

Lakeside bungalow, ensuite ground floor accomodation. Central for touring. Ideal for Leisure or Activity. Angling, Boating, Golfing, Shopping locally.

B&B pps:	£17.50/£18.50	Sngl Occ. Dble/Tpl:	£24/£25	Sngl Rm:	-
Part Brd:	-	% Red. Children:	50%	Dinner:	-

Athlone 6km

Mrs Noreen Fayne
FAIRWAYS
Hodson Bay, Athlone, Co Roscommon

Athlone

Tel: **0902 94492**   Fax: -

Open:	All Year except Christmas	
No. Rooms:	3	
Ensuite:	3	(V)

Dormer bungalow on N61 - 6 Km Athlone. 1 Km from Golf Club, Hodson Bay Hotel and Lough Ree - Mature Garden's - Extensive Parking.

B&B pps:	£17.50/£18.50	Sngl Occ. Dble/Tpl:	£24/£25	Sngl Rm:	-
Part Brd:	-	% Red. Children:	33.3%	Dinner:	-

Athlone 5km

Mrs. Catherine Harney
REESIDE
Barrymore, Athlone, Co Roscommon

Athlone

Tel: **0902 92051**   Fax: -

Open:	All Year except Christmas	
No. Rooms:	5	
Ensuite:	5	(V)

Country Home on two acres. Road N61, beside Lough Ree & Golf Club, Snooker room, boat, canoe available. Barbecue.

B&B pps:	£17	Sngl Occ. Dble/Tpl:	£23.50	Sngl Rm:	-
Part Brd:	-	% Red. Children:	50%	Dinner:	-

Athlone 7km

Mrs Teresa Hegarty
CASTLESIDE
Kiltoom, Athlone, Co Roscommon

Athlone

Tel: **0902 89195**   Fax: **0902 89195**

Open:	All Year except Christmas	
No. Rooms:	5	
Ensuite:	4	(V)

Quiet Country home on N61, adjacent Moyvannion Castle. Convenient to Lough Ree, Fishing, Boating, Water Sports, Golf, Hodson Bay Hotel.

B&B pps:	£17	Sngl Occ. Dble/Tpl:	£23.50	Sngl Rm:	£19
Part Brd:	£180	% Red. Children:	40%	Dinner:	£12

Gerald & Eleanor Kelly
LOUGHREE LODGE
Kiltoom, Athlone, Co Roscommon

Athlone

OPEN:	All Year except Christmas
NO. ROOMS:	4
ENSUITE:	4

Ⓥ

TEL: **0902 89214**   FAX: -

Detached house on large elevated site overlooking Lough Ree, situated on the Athlone/Roscommon Road. Close to Hodson Bay.

B&B PPS:	**£17**	SNGL OCC. DBLE/TPL:	**£23.50**	SNGL RM:	-
PART BRD:	-	% RED. CHILDREN:	**25%**	DINNER:	-

— Athlone 7km —

Mrs Marie O'Brien
CARNIVAN HOUSE
Hodson Bay, Athlone, Co Roscommon

Athlone

OPEN:	All Year except Christmas
NO. ROOMS:	4
ENSUITE:	4

Ⓥ

TEL: **0902 94486**   FAX: -

Modern bungalow off N61, 5 km from Athlone, 1km from Athlone Golf Club, Hodson Bay Hotel and Lough Ree.

B&B PPS:	**£18**	SNGL OCC. DBLE/TPL:	**£25**	SNGL RM:	**£22**
PART BRD:	-	% RED. CHILDREN:	**33.3%**	DINNER:	-

— Athlone 5km —

Nora Ward
CARRICK VIEW
Curraghboy, Athlone, Co Roscommon

Athlone

OPEN:	1st March-31st October
NO. ROOMS:	4
ENSUITE:	4

Ⓥ

TEL: **0902 88294**   FAX: -

Dormer bungalow in peaceful country surroundings 6Km off N61. TV Lounge, Private Parking, Golf/Fishing nearby. Guaranteed hospitality and comfort.

B&B PPS:	**£17**	SNGL OCC. DBLE/TPL:	**£23.50**	SNGL RM:	-
PART BRD:	-	% RED. CHILDREN:	**50%**	DINNER:	-

— Athlone 12km —

Carmel & Martin Dolan
AVONLEA
Carrick Road, Boyle, Co Roscommon

Boyle

OPEN:	All Year except Christmas
NO. ROOMS:	4
ENSUITE:	2

Ⓥ

TEL: **079 62538**   FAX: -

Modern house on the outskirts of Boyle. On N4 Dublin/Sligo, opposite Forest Park Hotel. Lough Key Forest Park 5 minutes.

B&B PPS:	**£15/£17**	SNGL OCC. DBLE/TPL:	**£21.50/£23.50**	SNGL RM:	-
PART BRD:	**£180**	% RED. CHILDREN:	**25 %**	DINNER:	-

— Boyle 1km —

Mrs Eileen Kelly
FOREST PARK HOUSE
Carrick Road, Boyle, Co Roscommon

Boyle

OPEN:	All Year
NO. ROOMS:	6
ENSUITE:	6

Ⓥ

TEL: **079 62227**   FAX: **079 62227**

Tea/coffee facilities, spacious, high standards, adjoining Forest Park, Lough Key. N4 5 mins drive Boyle. Electric blankets, large car park.

B&B PPS:	**£17**	SNGL OCC. DBLE/TPL:	**£23.50**	SNGL RM:	-
PART BRD:	-	% RED. CHILDREN:	**50%**	DINNER:	**£14**

— Boyle 4km —

In Boyle

Christina and Martin Mitchell
ABBEY HOUSE
Boyle, Co Roscommon

Boyle

OPEN:	**March-October**
No. ROOMS:	6
ENSUITE:	5

(V)

TEL: **079 62385**   FAX: -

Georgian House adjoining Boyle Abbey, Midway Dublin/Donegal, near Forest Park. Open fires. Recommended Frommer Guide, Ireland-The Rough Guide.

B&B PPS:	**£15/£17**	SNGL OCC. DBLE/TPL:	**£21.50/£23.50**	SNGL RM:	-
PART BRD:	-	% RED. CHILDREN:	**20%**	DINNER:	-

Boyle Town 7km

Seamus & Pauline Ryan
BORRIS HOUSE
Cootehall, Boyle, Co Roscommon

Boyle

OPEN:	**All Year except Christmas**
No. ROOMS:	3
ENSUITE:	2

(V)

TEL: **079 67096/087 2379292**   FAX: -

Tudor style residence, Peaceful Rural Setting,500 metres off N4, Carrick-on-Shannon 9kms,Boyle 7kms. Lough Key Forest Park,Lakes & Rivers nearby.

B&B PPS:	**£15/£17**	SNGL OCC. DBLE/TPL:	**£21.50/£23.50**	SNGL RM:	-
PART BRD:	**£180**	% RED. CHILDREN:	**33.3%**	DINNER:	**£12**

Boyle 6km

Mrs A Taylor
HILLSIDE HOUSE
Doon, Corrigeenroe, Boyle, Co Roscommon

Boyle

OPEN:	**All Year except Christmas**
No. ROOMS:	4
ENSUITE:	2

(V)

TEL: **079 66075**   FAX: -

Old style Residence overlooking Lough Key. Lough Arrow nearby. Situated in Woodland Area. Bricklieve Magalithic Cementery 10 miles. Recommended Frommer Guide.

B&B PPS:	**£15/£17**	SNGL OCC. DBLE/TPL:	**£21.50/£23.50**	SNGL RM:	-
PART BRD:	-	% RED. CHILDREN:	**25%**	DINNER:	-

Castlerea 1km

Mrs Rita Morgan
ARMCASHEL B & B
Knock Rd, Castlerea, Co Roscommon

Castlerea

OPEN:	**1st January-22nd December**
No. ROOMS:	4
ENSUITE:	3

(V)

TEL: **0907 20117**   FAX: -

Modern spacious dormer Bungalow on N60. Peaceful surroundings overlooking Clonalis Estate. Private parking. Ideal base touring, Golfing, Fishing. Knock 25 minutes.

B&B PPS:	**£16/£17**	SNGL OCC. DBLE/TPL:	**£23.50**	SNGL RM:	-
PART BRD:	-	% RED. CHILDREN:	**33%**	DINNER:	-

In Rooskey Village

Mrs Carmel Davis
AVONDALE HOUSE
Rooskey, Carrick-on-Shannon, Co Roscommon

Rooskey

OPEN:	**All Year except Christmas**
No. ROOMS:	4
ENSUITE:	4

(V)

TEL: **078 38095**   FAX: -

Highly recommended family home in quiet, peaceful surroundings, beside River Shannon. Ideal touring location. Midway Dublin/Donegal. Orthopaedic beds.

B&B PPS:	**£17**	SNGL OCC. DBLE/TPL:	**£23.50**	SNGL RM:	**£17**
PART BRD:	-	% RED. CHILDREN:	**50%**	DINNER:	**£12**

Roscommon 2km

Mrs Kathleen Carthy
HILLCREST HOUSE
**Racecourse Road, Roscommon,
Co Roscommon**

TEL: **0903 25201**   FAX: -

Roscommon	
OPEN:	**All Year**
NO. ROOMS:	4
ENSUITE:	3

 (V)

Warm hospitality in a modern country house in a peaceful location. Ideal base for touring West and Midlands.

B&B PPS:	**£15/£17**	SNGL OCC. DBLE/TPL:	**£21.50/£23.50**	SNGL RM:	-
PART BRD:	**£200**	% RED. CHILDREN:	**50%**	DINNER:	**£12**

In Roscommon

Noelle Hynes
RIVERSIDE HOUSE
**Riverside Avenue, Circular Road,
Roscommon Town, Co Roscommon**

TEL: **0903 26897**   FAX: -

Roscommon Town	
OPEN:	**All Year**
NO. ROOMS:	5
ENSUITE:	3

(V)

Modern dormer bungalow set in mature grounds in Roscommon Town within walking distance of golf course, castle and museum.

B&B PPS:	**£15/£17**	SNGL OCC. DBLE/TPL:	**£21.50/£23.50**	SNGL RM:	**£16/£18**
PART BRD:	-	% RED. CHILDREN:	**50%**	DINNER:	-

In Roscommon

Mrs. Paula McNamara
THE GARDENS
**The Walk, Roscommon,
Co Roscommon**

TEL: **0903 26828**   FAX: -

Roscommon	
OPEN:	**May-October**
NO. ROOMS:	6
ENSUITE:	3

(V)

Modern familly home, large gardens. Peaceful location, beside town.

B&B PPS:	**£15/£18**	SNGL OCC. DBLE/TPL:	**£21.50**	SNGL RM:	-
PART BRD:	-	% RED. CHILDREN:	**20%**	DINNER:	-

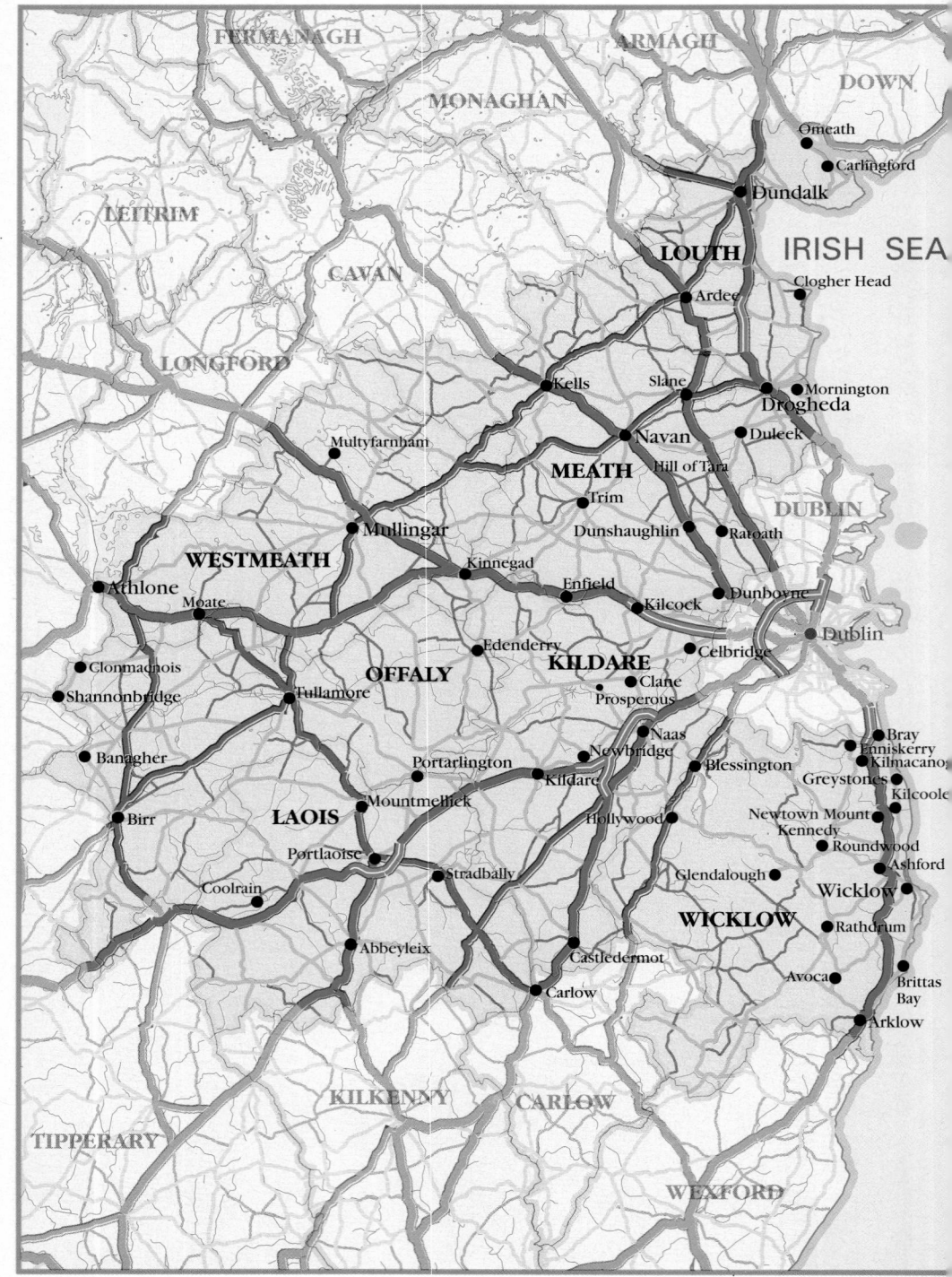

© ERA-Maptec

East Coast and Lakelands Region of Ireland offers relaxation, interest, excitement and good value.

There is something for everybody - activity holidays, short breaks, culture and heritage, entertainment, good food, interesting comfortable affordable accommodation, indoor and outdoor leisure facilities suitable for young and old alike and indeed, there is much more to discover.

There are many important heritage sites throughout the Region, some of these include Clonmacnoise, Glendalough and the Boyne Valley. Great Houses, Castles and Gardens are also important Visitor Attractions. The Region has excellent golfing, top-class equestrian facilities, and the horse-racing enthusiast is also well catered for.

Enjoy a cruising break on the Shannon or Grand Canal. Walking in the Region on any of the marked routes brings its own satisfaction.

Auto-tour scenic Wicklow, the Cooley Peninsula or the Slieve Blooms and if your fancy takes you, why not treat yourself or a friend and stay in one of the many delightful Town & Country Homes where you will find good food, company and a range of activities.

Area Representatives

KILDARE
Mrs. Mrs Maire McGinley, Cnoc an Ti, Pitchfordstown, Kilcock, Co. Kildare.
Tel: 01-628 7754.
LAOIS
Mrs. Lily Saunders, Rosedene, Limerick Road, Portlaoise, Co. Laois.
Tel: 0502-22345. Fax: 0502-22345 (manual).
LONGFORD
Mrs. Martha O'Kane, Sancian, Dublin Road, Longford, Co. Longford.
Tel: 043-46187.
LOUTH
Mrs. Evelyn Carolan, Lynolan, Mullaharlin Road, Heynestown, Dundalk,
Co. Louth. Tel: 042-36553.
MEATH
Mrs. Anne Finnegan, Crannmor, Dunderry Road, Trim, Co. Meath.
Tel: 046 31635. Fax: 046-31635 (manual).
OFFALY
Mrs. Celine Grennan, The Bungalow, River View, Shannonbridge,
Athlone, Co. Offaly. Tel: 0905-74180.
WESTMEATH
Mrs. Dympna Casey, Hilltop, Delvin Road, Rathconnell, Mullingar,
Co. Westmeath. Tel: 044-48958. Fax: 044-48013.

Mrs. Nancy Denby, Shelmalier House, Cartrontroy, Athlone, Co. Westmeath.
Tel: 0902-72245. Fax: 73190.
WICKLOW
Mrs. Maura Byrne, Escombe, Lockstown, Valleymount, Blessington,
Co. Wicklow. Tel: 045-867157. Fax: 045-867450.
Mrs. Jackie Burns, Ashdene, Knockanree Lr., Avoca, Co. Wicklow.
Tel: 0402-35327. Fax: 0402 35327 (manual).

ℹ️ Tourist Information Offices

Mullingar
Tel: (044) 48650

Trim
Tel: (046) 37111

Dundalk
Tel: (042) 35484

Wicklow
Tel: (0404) 69117

Longford Town
Tel: (043) 46566

Portlaoise
Tel: (0502) 21178

Castledermot 5km

Agnes Donoghue
WOODCOURTE HOUSE
Moone, Athy, Co Kildare

Castledermot

OPEN:	**All Year**
NO. ROOMS:	4
ENSUITE:	2

 (V)

TEL: **0507 24167**   FAX: **0507 24326**

Beautiful country home with Extensive gardens in woodland setting beside N9, 35 miles from Dublin. Hourly Bus service, Taxi available.

B&B PPS:	**£15/£20**	SNGL OCC. DBLE/TPL:	**£21.50/£26.50**	SNGL RM: **£21.50/£24.50**
PART BRD:	**£180**	% RED. CHILDREN:	**25%**	DINNER: **£12.50**

Celbridge 2km

Mrs Rose McCabe
GREEN ACRE
Dublin Rd, Celbridge, Co Kildare

Celbridge

OPEN:	**All Year except Christmas**
NO. ROOMS:	6
ENSUITE:	6

(V)

TEL: **01 6271163**   FAX: -

Bungalow on own grounds, Dublin 20 mins, 30 mins. Airport, Ferries, Bus Route, Car park. Castletown House 2km. Golf, fishing.

BUS NO. **67, 67A**

B&B PPS:	**£17**	SNGL OCC. DBLE/TPL:	**£23.50**	SNGL RM: -
PART BRD:	-	% RED. CHILDREN:	**50%**	DINNER: -

In Clane

Mrs Breda Byrne
CEDARWOOD
Prosperous Road, Clane, Co Kildare

Clane

OPEN:	**2nd January-1st December**
NO. ROOMS:	4
ENSUITE:	2

(V)

TEL: **045 868183**   FAX: -

Modern residence convenient to Dublin, Airport, Ferries, Curragh Race Course, Mondello Park. Golfing, Fishing locally. Dublin City 35 mins.

B&B PPS:	**£18/£21**	SNGL OCC. DBLE/TPL:	**£23**	SNGL RM: -
PART BRD:	-	% RED. CHILDREN:	**50%**	DINNER: **£13**

In Clane

Mrs Mary Lynch
THE LAURELS
Dublin Road, Clane, Co Kildare

Clane

OPEN:	**All Year except Christmas**
NO. ROOMS:	3
ENSUITE:	3

(V)

TEL: **045 868274**   FAX: -

Dublin 30 mins drive. Bus to and from City Centre. Convenient to Airport/Ferries. Maynooth, Kilcock, Naas 10 mins drive.

B&B PPS:	**£17**	SNGL OCC. DBLE/TPL:	**£23.50**	SNGL RM: **£17**
PART BRD:	-	% RED. CHILDREN:	**50%**	DINNER: **£12**

Kilcock 1km

Mrs Tess Barrett
LIOS CIUIN
Duncreevan, Kilcock, Co Kildare

Kilcock

OPEN:	**1st June-30th September**
NO. ROOMS:	3
ENSUITE:	1

(V)

TEL: **01 6287537**   FAX: -   EMAIL: **pbarrett@tinet.ie**

Pleasant dormer bungalow in secluded location. Convenient for Dublin Air & Sea Ports. Ideal for touring Kildare & Boyne Valley.

BUS NO. **66**

B&B PPS:	**£15/£17**	SNGL OCC. DBLE/TPL:	**£21.50/£23.50**	SNGL RM: -
PART BRD:	-	% RED. CHILDREN:	**25%**	DINNER: -

Kilcock 4km

Mrs Kathleen Farrell
BREEZY HEIGHTS
Cappagh, Kilcock, Co Kildare

Kilcock

OPEN:	31st March-30th November
NO. ROOMS:	3
ENSUITE:	2

(V)

TEL: **0405 41183**　　FAX: -

2 mins off Dublin/Galway N4 road. Dublin 30 mins. Convenient to Airport/Ferries. Quiet & peaceful. Golf, Fishing nearby.

B&B PPS:	£15/£17	SNGL OCC. DBLE/TPL:	£21.50/£23.50	SNGL RM:	-
PART BRD:	-	% RED. CHILDREN:	25%	DINNER:	-

Kilcock 2km

Mrs Maire McGinley
CNOC-AN-TI
Pitchfordstown, Kilcock, Co Kildare

Kilcock

OPEN:	May-October
NO. ROOMS:	3
ENSUITE:	1

(V)

TEL: **01 6287754**　　FAX: -

Select dormer bungalow on main Dublin/Galway N4 road. 500 metres west of M4 motorway. Airport 35 minutes via M50.

B&B PPS:	£15/£17	SNGL OCC. DBLE/TPL:	£21.50/£23.50	SNGL RM:	-
PART BRD:	-	% RED. CHILDREN:	25%	DINNER:	-

Kildare 1.5km

Mrs Eileen Corcoran
MOUNT RUADHAN
Old Road, Southgreen, Kildare, Co Kildare

Kildare

OPEN:	1st March-30th November
NO. ROOMS:	3
ENSUITE:	2

(V)

TEL: **045 521637**　　FAX: -

Modern bungalow. Convenient to Japanese Gardens, National Stud, Curragh Race Course. Fishing, Golfing, Cathedral. Airport, Ferries, signposted at traffic lights.

B&B PPS:	£16/£25	SNGL OCC. DBLE/TPL:	£23/£31.50	SNGL RM:	-
PART BRD:	-	% RED. CHILDREN:	20%	DINNER:	-

Mrs Margaret Doyle
WEST LODGE
Lucan Rd, Leixlip, Co Kildare

Leixlip

OPEN:	7th January-21st December
NO. ROOMS:	4
ENSUITE:	3

(V)

TEL: **01 6281192**　　FAX: -

Period house, convenient to Leixlip intersection on N4/M4. 5-6minutes west of Westlink. 20 minutes Dublin City Centre, Airport, Ferryport.

BUS NO. **66,66A,67,67A**

Dublin City 15km

B&B PPS:	£15/£17	SNGL OCC. DBLE/TPL:	£21.50/£23.50	SNGL RM:	-
PART BRD:	-	% RED. CHILDREN:	50%	DINNER:	-

Naas 4km

Mrs Bridie Doherty
TWO MILE HOUSE
Naas, Co Kildare

Naas

OPEN:	All Year except Christmas
NO. ROOMS:	5
ENSUITE:	5

(V)

TEL: **045 879824**　　FAX: -

Peaceful location - 200 yds off N 9 Dublin/Waterford road. Dublin 30 mins drive. Convenient to Airport and Ferries.

B&B PPS:	£17	SNGL OCC. DBLE/TPL:	£23.50	SNGL RM:	£23
PART BRD:	-	% RED. CHILDREN:	50%	DINNER:	-

Naas

Mrs Olive Hennessy
DUN AONGHUS
Beggars End, Naas, Co Kildare

OPEN:	All Year except Christmas
NO. ROOMS:	6
ENSUITE:	4

TEL: **045 875126**   FAX: -

Tranquil location, 4 mins N7. Walking distance Punchestown. Ideal for visiting Wicklow, Kildare, Dublin, Golf, Equestrian, Horseracing.

B&B PPS:	£16/£20	SNGL OCC. DBLE/TPL:	£22.50/£30	SNGL RM:	£20/£25
PART BRD:	-	% RED. CHILDREN:	33%	DINNER:	-

— Naas 2km

Naas

Mrs Sheila O'Brien
HILLVIEW HOUSE
Prosperous, Naas, Co Kildare

OPEN:	2nd January-15th December
NO. ROOMS:	10
ENSUITE:	8

TEL: **045 868252**   FAX: -

22 miles Dublin, 10 minutes off N7, N4, 45 mins Airport, Ferryport. Nearby Golfing, Fishing, Equestrian, Race Courses. Frommer recommended.

B&B PPS:	£16/£22	SNGL OCC. DBLE/TPL:	£22.50/£29	SNGL RM:	£20/£25
PART BRD:	£190	% RED. CHILDREN:	20%	DINNER:	£12

— Naas 11km

Newbridge

Mrs Kathleen Garrett
SEVEN SPRINGS
Hawkfield, Newbridge, Co Kildare

OPEN:	1st May-30th September
NO. ROOMS:	3
ENSUITE:	

TEL: **045 431677**   FAX: -

Bungalow, beside Newbridge and N7. Convenient to National Stud, Japanese Gardens, Curragh, Naas. Punchestown Race Course, Boat, Airport, Dog-racing & Mondello nearby.

B&B PPS:	£16/£20	SNGL OCC. DBLE/TPL:	£22.50/£26.50	SNGL RM:	£20/£25
PART BRD:	£180	% RED. CHILDREN:	50%	DINNER:	£12

— Newbridge 3km

Newbridge

Mrs Breda Kelly
BELLA VISTA
105 Moorefield Park, Newbridge, Co Kildare

OPEN:	All Year
NO. ROOMS:	4
ENSUITE:	4

TEL: **045 431047**   FAX: -

Long established Residence in quiet Residential Area. Convenient to Curragh, Punchestown, Japanese Gardens. Rooms en-suite, TV, Video, hairdryers, tea- making facilities.

B&B PPS:	£18/£25	SNGL OCC. DBLE/TPL:	£24.50/£31.50	SNGL RM:	£18/£25
PART BRD:	-	% RED. CHILDREN:	25%	DINNER:	£12

— In Newbridge

Newbridge

Mary O'Shea
KERRYHILL
Morristown Biller, Newbridge, Co Kildare

OPEN:	1st March-30th November
NO. ROOMS:	3
ENSUITE:	2

TEL: **045 432433**   FAX: -

Spacious bungalow, Private Car Park, Easy Access, Japanese Gardens, National Stud, Airport, Ferries, Horse, Dog, Motor Racing.

B&B PPS:	£16/£25	SNGL OCC. DBLE/TPL:	£22.50/£31.50	SNGL RM:	-
PART BRD:	-	% RED. CHILDREN:	25%	DINNER:	-

— Newbridge 1km

Naas 12km

Mrs Mary Cassidy
CORNAMONA
Prosperous, Naas, Co Kildare

Prosperous

OPEN:	**March-October**
NO. ROOMS:	4
ENSUITE:	2

(V)

TEL: **045 868173**   FAX: -

Bungalow in quiet area en route to Air & Ferry Ports. Enjoy Golf, Motor Racing, Fishing & Canal Walks locally.

B&B PPS: **£17/£21**	SNGL OCC. DBLE/TPL: **£23.50/£27.50**	SNGL RM: **£23.50/£25.50**
PART BRD: -	% RED. CHILDREN: **25%**	DINNER: -

Naas 12km

Mrs M Duffe
LISSADEL
Prosperous, Naas, Co Kildare

Prosperous

OPEN:	**1st April-30th September**
NO. ROOMS:	4
ENSUITE:	2

(V)

TEL: **045 868314**   FAX: -

Ideal out-of-Dublin stopover (35km) on R403 between N4 and N7. Airport and Ferry Ports 35km. Fishing, Golfing, Touring.

B&B PPS: **£18/£21**	SNGL OCC. DBLE/TPL: **£24.50/£27.50**	SNGL RM: -
PART BRD: -	% RED. CHILDREN: **10%**	DINNER: -

Abbeyleix 1km

Maureen Lalor
COIS NA TINE

Portlaoise Road, Abbeyleix, Co Laois

OPEN:	All Year except Christmas
NO. ROOMS:	3
ENSUITE:	3

TEL: **0502 31976**   FAX: -

Charming bungalow. On main Dublin Cork route, 1 km from Abbeyleix Heritage Town. Adjacent to Golf, Pony/Riding, Fishing Pubs/Restaurants.

Ⓟ 🖥 ☕ 🎣 🏠

B&B PPS:	£17	SNGL OCC. DBLE/TPL:	£23.50	SNGL RM:	-
PART BRD:	-	% RED. CHILDREN:	50%	DINNER:	-

Abbeyleix 1.5km

Mrs Brigid Lawlor
NOREFIELD HOUSE

The Old Town, Abbeyleix, Co Laois

OPEN:	1st March-31st October
NO. ROOMS:	4
ENSUITE:	3

TEL: **0502 31059**   FAX: -

Secluded 18th Century period residence. 1.5km from heritage town of Abbeyleix (N8). 3 Double rooms ensuite. Golfing, Tennis, Fishing nearby.

Ⓟ ✂ 🖥 ☕ 🎣 🏠 Ⓢ

B&B PPS:	£17.50/£25	SNGL OCC. DBLE/TPL:	£24/£31.50	SNGL RM:	£20/£25
PART BRD:	-	% RED. CHILDREN:	25%	DINNER:	-

Portlaoise 2km

Mrs Audrey J Canavan
CHEZ NOUS

Kilminchy, Portlaoise, Co Laois

OPEN:	3rd January-20th December
NO. ROOMS:	4
ENSUITE:	4

TEL: **0502 21251**   FAX: -

Pamper yourself in one of 100 best. Tastefully decorated in interior design and antiquity. Excellent cuisine. Frommer, R.A.C. highly acclaimed.

Ⓟ ⊗ ✂ ♣ 🎣 🏠 Ⓢ

B&B PPS:	£18.50/£20	SNGL OCC. DBLE/TPL:	-	SNGL RM:	£25
PART BRD:	-	% RED. CHILDREN:	-	DINNER:	£12.50

Portlaoise 5km

Marion Clancy
AUGHNAHILLA HOUSE B&B

Rock of Dunamase, Portlaoise, Co Laois

OPEN:	All Year except Christmas
NO. ROOMS:	3
ENSUITE:	3

TEL: **0502 25589**   FAX: **0502 25589**

Excellent hospitality in country home on 6 acres. Adjacent to historic Rock of Dunamase. Families welcome. One hour Dublin Airport.

🛏 Ⓗ Ⓟ ⊗ ✂ ✖ ☕ ✈ 🍴 🎣 🏠 Ⓢ

B&B PPS:	£17	SNGL OCC. DBLE/TPL:	£23.50	SNGL RM:	£20
PART BRD:	£190	% RED. CHILDREN:	20%	DINNER:	£13

Portlaoise

Mrs Carrie Crean
CREAN'S VICARSTOWN INN

Vicarstown, Co Laois

OPEN:	1st March-1st November
NO. ROOMS:	6
ENSUITE:	2

TEL: **0502 25189**   FAX: **0502 25652**

Long established Inn beside canal, ideal for tourists crossing country. Off N7/N80. Many recommendations, fully licensed. Fishing, Golf, Horseriding.

ⒸⒸ 🍷 Ⓟ ✂ ✖ ✈ ♣ 🎣 🏠

B&B PPS:	£16.50/£18.50	SNGL OCC. DBLE/TPL:	£23/£25	SNGL RM:	-
PART BRD:	-	% RED. CHILDREN:	-	DINNER:	-

Portlaoise 2.2km

Mrs Janet Dooley
LANLEY B&B

Mountsalem, Coolrain, Portlaoise, Co Laois

TEL: 0502 35013   FAX: -

Portlaoise / Coolrain

OPEN:	All Year
NO. ROOMS:	3
ENSUITE:	2

(V)

6 bedroom detached bungalow facing the Slieve Bloom mountains. 4 PVC windows and patio door facing road.

B&B PPS:	£15/£18	SNGL OCC. DBLE/TPL:	£21.50/£24.50	SNGL RM:	-
PART BRD:	-	% RED. CHILDREN:	10%	DINNER:	-

Portlaoise 1km

Mrs Vera Hade
RENARD

Limerick Road, Portlaoise, Co Laois

TEL: 0502 21735   FAX: 0502 21735

Portlaoise

OPEN:	All Year except Christmas
NO. ROOMS:	3
ENSUITE:	1

(V)

Warm welcoming home on N7. Relaxed atmosphere. Tea/Scones on arrival. Secure Parking. Close to all amenities. 1hour to Dublin.

B&B PPS:	£15/£17	SNGL OCC. DBLE/TPL:	£21.50/£23.50	SNGL RM:	-
PART BRD:	-	% RED. CHILDREN:	25%	DINNER:	-

Portlaoise 6km

Noreen & Joe Llewellyn
ASPEN

Rock of Dunamase, Portlaoise, Co Laois

TEL: 0502 25405   FAX: 0502 25442

Portlaoise

OPEN:	April-October
NO. ROOMS:	4
ENSUITE:	4

(V)

Breakfast award winning home beside Dunamase Castle. Frommer recommended. Extensive landscaped gardens. Tea/Coffee making facilities. One hour Dublin airport.

B&B PPS:	£18.50	SNGL OCC. DBLE/TPL:	£25	SNGL RM:	-
PART BRD:	-	% RED. CHILDREN:	20%	DINNER:	-

Portlaoise 1km

Mrs. Lily Saunders
ROSEDENE

Limerick Road, Portlaoise, Co Laois

TEL: 0502 22345   FAX: 0502 22345

Portlaoise

OPEN:	2nd January-24th December
NO. ROOMS:	3
ENSUITE:	2

Warm welcome complimentrary tea/coffee. Quiet location on N7. Just off motorway, Dublin 80km. Walking distance restaurants, pubs.

B&B PPS:	£15/£17	SNGL OCC. DBLE/TPL:	£21.50/£23.50	SNGL RM:	-
PART BRD:	-	% RED. CHILDREN:	25%	DINNER:	-

Mountmellick 1km

Abigail Mc Evoy
GAROON HOUSE

Birr Road, Mountmellick, Co Laois

TEL: 0502 24641   FAX: -

Mountmellick

OPEN:	1st April-31st October
NO. ROOMS:	4
ENSUITE:	4

Newly built accommodation situated on edge of Slieve Bloom mountains. Central location for touring any part of Ireland. Breakfast menu.

B&B PPS:	£18	SNGL OCC. DBLE/TPL:	£24.50	SNGL RM:	-
PART BRD:	-	% RED. CHILDREN:	50%	DINNER:	-

		Stradbally
Mrs Pauline McEvoy		
THE COURT		OPEN: **All Year except Christmas**
Main St, Stradbally, Portlaoise,		NO. ROOMS: 3
Co Laois		ENSUITE: 1
TEL: **0502 25519**	FAX: **0502 25494**	EMAIL: **jfmc@iol.ie**

(V)

Comfortable family home with spacious rooms in picturesque Village on N80. Golf, Fishing, Walks nearby. Portlaoise 10 km.

B&B PPS:	**£16/£17**	SNGL OCC. DBLE/TPL:	**£22.50/£23.50**	SNGL RM:	-
PART BRD:	-	% RED. CHILDREN:	-	DINNER:	-

RESERVATIONS

- Confirm phone bookings in writing without delay with agreed deposit.
- To avoid misunderstandings later, check rate on booking and clarify any additional changes which may apply to your booking.
- Give details of any special requirements.
- State clearly day, date of arrival and departure date.

WATCH OUT FOR THE SIGN THAT MARKS AN OFFICIAL IRISH TOURIST BOARD INFORMATION OFFICE.

Their Tourist Advisors are expert on the surrounding areas and on all aspects of Irish holidays. The friendly staff have an extensive range of language skills and they will be delighted to help you with:

- Accommodation - bookings to all Bord Fáilte registered and approved accommodation.
- Credit card bookings by telephone.
- Advice on routes/places to visit.
- National and local events.
- Maps, guides, literature on Ireland.
- Scenic coach tours.
- Boat trips – lakes/offshore islands.
- Flights to offshore islands.
- Holiday gift vouchers.
- Banquet and theatre bookings.
- Local crafts and gifts.
- Bureau de change facilities.

Longford Town 10km

Miss Bridie Kenny
ARDKEN
Ardagh, Co Longford

Ardagh

OPEN:	All Year
NO. ROOMS:	3
ENSUITE:	3

TEL: **043 75029/088 668401** FAX: **043 75029**

Beautiful house in unique Estate Village. Winner of National Tidy Towns award. Identified as Heritage Village just off N4, N55.

B&B PPS:	£17	SNGL OCC. DBLE/TPL:	£23.50	SNGL RM:	-
PART BRD:	£180	% RED. CHILDREN:	50%	DINNER:	£12

Drumlish 1.5km

Pascal and Joan Etienne
CHEZ-NOUS
Arva Road, Drumlish, Co Longford

Drumlish

OPEN:	All Year
NO. ROOMS:	5
ENSUITE:	5

TEL: **043 24368** FAX: **043 24368**

Delightful country house with attic bedrooms, Conservatory and Stable Yard. Self catering also available. We speak French and Italian.

B&B PPS:	£17	SNGL OCC. DBLE/TPL:	£23.50	SNGL RM:	-
PART BRD:	£180	% RED. CHILDREN:	10%	DINNER:	£12

In Lanesborough

Mrs. Eileen Watts
DUNAMASE
Rathcline Road, Lanesborough, Co Longford

Lanesborough

OPEN:	All Year
NO. ROOMS:	3
ENSUITE:	2

TEL: **043 21201** FAX: -

Bungalow beside River Shannon, excellent Fishing, Tennis Courts, Pitch and Putt Locally. Situated mid-way Dublin/Galway route N4, N63.

B&B PPS:	£15/£17	SNGL OCC. DBLE/TPL:	£21.50/£23.50	SNGL RM:	-
PART BRD:	-	% RED. CHILDREN:	50%	DINNER:	-

In Longford Town

Mrs M McDonagh
MAYFIELD
9 Midara Gardens, Dublin Road, Longford, Co Longford

Longford

OPEN:	1st May-30th September
NO. ROOMS:	5
ENSUITE:	2

TEL: **043 45801** FAX: -

Modern detached bungalow in quiet surroundings, Golf Lnks nearby, Private Car Park. Walking distance from Town 10 mins.

B&B PPS:	£15/£16	SNGL OCC. DBLE/TPL:	£21	SNGL RM:	-
PART BRD:	-	% RED. CHILDREN:	25%	DINNER:	-

In Longford

Pat & Breege O'Donnell
TIVOLI
Dublin Road, Longford, Co Longford

Longford

OPEN:	1st January-21st December
NO. ROOMS:	11
ENSUITE:	7

TEL: **043 46898/41569** FAX: -

Modern detached house, beside Golf Links. Frommer Recommended, Large Garden, Private Car Park.

B&B PPS:	£15/£17	SNGL OCC. DBLE/TPL:	£21.50/£23.50	SNGL RM:	£15/£17
PART BRD:	£185	% RED. CHILDREN:	50%	DINNER:	£15

In Longford

Mrs Martha O'Kane
SANCIAN
Dublin Road, Longford, Co Longford

Longford

OPEN:	**1st March-30th November**
NO. ROOMS:	**5**
ENSUITE:	**3**

(V)

TEL: **043 46187**   FAX: -

Situated on N4. Travelling from Dublin keep left at bypass. Travelling from West etc watch for N4 signs.

Ⓟ 🛏 ✕ 🖥 ⚓ 🐾 S

B&B PPS:	**£16/£17**	SNGL OCC. DBLE/TPL:	**£22.50/£23.50**	SNGL RM:	**£16**
PART BRD:	-	% RED. CHILDREN:	**50%**	DINNER:	-

Longford 4km

Mrs Eileen Prunty
EDEN HOUSE
Newtownforbes, Longford, Co Longford

Longford

OPEN:	**All Year except Christmas**
NO. ROOMS:	**5**
ENSUITE:	**4**

(V)

TEL: **043 41160**   FAX: -

Peaceful home in picturesque village off Newtownforbes on N4. All facilities closeby. Refreshments on arrival. Orthopaedic beds, electric blankets, TV.

Ⓟ ✂ 🛏 🚶

B&B PPS:	**£15/£16**	SNGL OCC. DBLE/TPL:	**£22**	SNGL RM:	-
PART BRD:	-	% RED. CHILDREN:	**25%**	DINNER:	-

Ardee 2km

Mrs Sheila Magennis
CARRAIG MOR
Blakestown, Ardee, Co Louth

Ardee

OPEN:	**All Year except Christmas**
NO. ROOMS:	5
ENSUITE:	4

TEL: **041 53513**   FAX: -

Spacious comfortable home N2 (Dublin/Derry) 2 km south Ardee. Restaurants, Golf, Fishing nearby. Central to Monasterboice, Mellifont, Newgrange. Dublin Airport 45mins.

B&B PPS:	**£15/£17**	SNGL. OCC. DBLE/TPL:	**£21.50/£23.50**	SNGL RM:	-
PART BRD:	-	% RED. CHILDREN:	50%	DINNER:	-

Carlingford 2km

Mrs Lyn Grills
MOURNEVIEW
Belmont, Carlingford, Co Louth

Carlingford

OPEN:	**All Year**
NO. ROOMS:	4
ENSUITE:	2

TEL: **042 73551**   FAX: -

Modern bungalow in scenic area. TV all rooms and tea-making facilities. Garden and patio for visitors use.

B&B PPS:	**£15/£17**	SNGL. OCC. DBLE/TPL:	**£21.50/£23.50**	SNGL RM:	-
PART BRD:	-	% RED. CHILDREN:	50%	DINNER:	-

Carlingford

Mrs Jackie Woods
SHALOM
Ghan Road, Carlingford, Co Louth

Carlingford

OPEN:	**All Year except Christmas**
NO. ROOMS:	5
ENSUITE:	5

TEL: **042 73151**   FAX: -

Situated in this medieval town on the Sea, overlooked by Cooley and Mourne Mountains. All rooms TV and tea making facilities.

B&B PPS:	**£17**	SNGL. OCC. DBLE/TPL:	**£23.50**	SNGL RM:	-
PART BRD:	-	% RED. CHILDREN:	50%	DINNER:	-

Drogheda 5km

Mrs Mary Dolores McEvoy
THE CROSS GARDEN
Ganderstown, Clogherhead, Co Louth

Clogherhead

OPEN:	**All Year**
NO. ROOMS:	3
ENSUITE:	2

TEL: **041 22675**   FAX: -

Modern dormer bungalow, elevated site, overlooking Irish Sea. One mile Clogherhead on Termonfeckin Road. All rooms private facilities.

B&B PPS:	**£16**	SNGL. OCC. DBLE/TPL:	**£22**	SNGL RM:	-
PART BRD:	-	% RED. CHILDREN:	30%	DINNER:	-

Drogheda 4km

Mrs Christine Dunne
LINKS VIEW
Golf Links Road, Bettystown, Drogheda, Co Louth

Drogheda

OPEN:	**January-December**
NO. ROOMS:	3
ENSUITE:	1

TEL: **041 27222**   FAX: -

Luxurious home in quiet residential area. Beside Golf Course and Beach. 30 mins Airport, 10km Newgrange. Tranquility assured.

B&B PPS:	**£18/£20**	SNGL. OCC. DBLE/TPL:	**£26.50**	SNGL RM:	£22
PART BRD:	-	% RED. CHILDREN:	-	DINNER:	-

Mrs Angela Kerrigan
KILLOWEN HOUSE
Woodgrange, Dublin Rd, Drogheda, Co Louth

Drogheda

OPEN:	1st January-20th December
NO. ROOMS:	4
ENSUITE:	3

TEL: **041 33547**   FAX: -

Spacious, luxurious home 50 m off N1 in quiet cul-de-sac, near hotels, Newgrange, golf, beach,Mosney. 35 minutes Airport, 45 mins Dublin city.

| B&B PPS: | £16/£19.50 | SNGL OCC. DBLE/TPL: | £22.50/£30 | SNGL RM: | £18 |
| PART BRD: | - | % RED. CHILDREN: | 20% | DINNER: | - |

— Drogheda 3km

Mrs Mary McCabe
SHERDARA
Beaulieu Cross, Termonfeckin Road, Drogheda, Co Louth

Drogheda

OPEN:	May-September
NO. ROOMS:	4
ENSUITE:	3

TEL: **041 36159**   FAX: -

A warm welcome awaits you at our family-run modern bungalow on Drogheda - Termonfeckin road. Convenient Newgrange, Golf & Airport.

| B&B PPS: | £15/£17 | SNGL OCC. DBLE/TPL: | £21.50/£23.50 | SNGL RM: | - |
| PART BRD: | - | % RED. CHILDREN: | 20% | DINNER: | - |

— Drogheda 5km

Cepta & Eobhain McDonnell
TULLYESKER COUNTRY HOUSE
Tullyesker, Monasterboice NI, Drogheda, Co Louth

Drogheda

OPEN:	1st March-31st October
NO. ROOMS:	5
ENSUITE:	5

TEL: **041 30430/32624**   FAX: **041 32624**

Award winning house. AA 4QQQQ, RAC 4 star Bestguide, Visaguide. 4 acre gardens, N1. Extensive menu. Orthapaedic beds, tea/coffee, satellite, hairdryers.

| B&B PPS: | £19 | SNGL OCC. DBLE/TPL: | £33 | SNGL RM: | - |
| PART BRD: | - | % RED. CHILDREN: | - | DINNER: | - |

— Drogheda 4km

Tara McDonnell
BOYNE HAVEN HOUSE
Opposite Rossnaree Hotel, Dublin Road, Drogheda, Co Louth

Drogheda

OPEN:	1st January-31st December
NO. ROOMS:	3
ENSUITE:	3

TEL: **041 36700**   FAX: -

Highly recommended. Award winning AA QQQQ. South of Drogheda on N1. Airport 25 minutes. Beautiful luxury rooms. TV, Hairdryer, Tea/coffee.

| B&B PPS: | £18/£22 | SNGL OCC. DBLE/TPL: | £30/£35 | SNGL RM: | - |
| PART BRD: | - | % RED. CHILDREN: | - | DINNER: | - |

— Drogheda 2km

Mrs Betty Nallen
ELEVENTH TEE HOUSE
Golf Links Road, Bettystown, Drogheda, Co Louth

Drogheda

OPEN:	All Year except Christmas
NO. ROOMS:	4
ENSUITE:	3

TEL: **041 27613**   FAX: **041 28150**

Situated in beautiful gardens adjoining Golf Course. Large Beach 0.5 km. Bettystown 1.5 km. Convenient Newgrange, Mosney. Airport 30 mins. 4 km off N1.

| B&B PPS: | £18/£20 | SNGL OCC. DBLE/TPL: | £25/£26.50 | SNGL RM: | £18/£23 |
| PART BRD: | - | % RED. CHILDREN: | 33% | DINNER: | - |

— Drogheda 5km

In Drogheda

Peter & Mary Phillips
ORLEY HOUSE

Bryanstown, Dublin Road, Drogheda, Co Louth

TEL: 041 36019   FAX: 041 36019

OPEN:	All Year except Christmas		
NO. ROOMS:	4		
ENSUITE:	4		

Luxurious Town home off N1. Conservatory Breakfast Room, Breakfast Menu. Convenient Newgrange/Boyne Valley, Bus/Rail, Airport/Ferries/Restaurants/Hotels.

cc ℗ ⚡ 🛏 ✗ 🖥

B&B PPS:	£18/£20	SNGL OCC. DBLE/TPL:	£25/£28	SNGL RM:	-
PART BRD:	£185	% RED. CHILDREN:	20%	DINNER:	£14

Dundalk 4km

Mrs Evelyn Carolan
LYNOLAN

Mullaharlin Road, Heynestown, Dundalk, Co Louth

TEL: 042 36553   FAX: -

OPEN:	1st January-15th December		
NO. ROOMS:	6		
ENSUITE:	5		

Modern Home, (off N1). Frommer recommended. Turn at Dundalk Garden Centre, South of Dundalk and Travel 1 mile.

B&B PPS:	£15/£17	SNGL OCC. DBLE/TPL:	£21.50/£23.50	SNGL RM:	-
PART BRD:	£180	% RED. CHILDREN:	50%	DINNER:	£12

Dundalk 5km

Mrs Aine Forde
KEERNAUN HOUSE

Greengates, Dublin Road, Dundalk, Co Louth

TEL: 042 21795   FAX: 042 21795

OPEN:	All Year except Christmas		
NO. ROOMS:	6		
ENSUITE:	6		

Luxurious home, N1. Convenient to Golf Course, Restaurants, Fairways Hotel. All rooms Colour TV, Tea/coffee, Hairdryer, Direct dial phones.

B&B PPS:	£17/£20	SNGL OCC. DBLE/TPL:	£23.50/£26.50	SNGL RM:	£20/£22
PART BRD:	-	% RED. CHILDREN:	-	DINNER:	-

Dundalk 2km

Anne McLoughlin
DERRYVEIGH

Upper Merches, Dublin Rd, Dundalk, Co Louth

TEL: 042 38466   FAX: -

OPEN:	All Year except Christmas		
NO. ROOMS:	4		
ENSUITE:	4		

Luxury home, peaceful locality, 200 m off N1. Large Private Car Park, TV room. Convenient to Fairways Hotel, Golf Courses.

B&B PPS:	£17	SNGL OCC. DBLE/TPL:	£23.50	SNGL RM:	£23.50
PART BRD:	-	% RED. CHILDREN:	50%	DINNER:	-

Mrs Maisie Meehan
ROSEMONT

Dublin Road, Dundalk, Co Louth

TEL: 042 35878   FAX: -

OPEN:	1st January-23rd December		
NO. ROOMS:	6		
ENSUITE:	5		

Luxury home on N1, convenient to Fairways Hotel and Golf Course. Dublin Airport 45 mins. Car Park, TV lounge.

B&B PPS:	£15/£17	SNGL OCC. DBLE/TPL:	£23.50	SNGL RM:	-
PART BRD:	-	% RED. CHILDREN:	50%	DINNER:	-

Mrs Patricia Murphy
PINEWOODS
Dublin Road, Dundalk, Co Louth

Dundalk

OPEN:	**All Year**	
NO. ROOMS:	**4**	
ENSUITE:	**4**	

(V)

TEL: **042 21295**   FAX: -

Traditional Irish Welcome in modern dormer bungalow on main Dublin/Belfast (N1) road. Beside Hotel, Beaches, Golf Course.

B&B PPS:	**£17/£18**	SNGL OCC. DBLE/TPL:	**£23.50/£24.50**	SNGL RM:	-
PART BRD:	-	% RED. CHILDREN:	**20%**	DINNER:	-

Dundalk 3km

Gerry & Brenda Rogers
BLACKROCK HOUSE
Main Street, Blackrock Village, Blackrock, Dundalk, Co Louth

Dundalk

OPEN:	**1st January-22nd December**	
NO. ROOMS:	**5**	
ENSUITE:	**5**	

(V)

TEL: **042 21829**   FAX: **042 21829**

Accommodation by shore. Panoramic view Dundalk Bay. Convenient Golf Club, Fairways Hotel, Bird Sanctuary, Bars, Restaurants. 50 minutes Dublin Airport/Belfast.

B&B PPS:	**£16**	SNGL OCC. DBLE/TPL:	**£25**	SNGL RM:	**£18**
PART BRD:	-	% RED. CHILDREN:	**25%**	DINNER:	-

Dundalk 5km

Mrs Marian Witherow
KRAKOW
190 Ard Easmuinn, Dundalk, Co Louth

Dundalk

OPEN:	**All Year**	
NO. ROOMS:	**5**	
ENSUITE:	**3**	

(V)

TEL: **042 37535**   FAX: -   EMAIL: **krakow@destination.ireland.com**

Modern detached bungalow, covenient Railway Station, Derryhale Hotel, first turn right after Railway Station, 2 directional signs Krakow B & B. Frommer recommended.

B&B PPS:	**£15/£17**	SNGL OCC. DBLE/TPL:	**£21.50/£23.50**	SNGL RM:	-
PART BRD:	**£180**	% RED. CHILDREN:	**20%**	DINNER:	**£12**

In Dundalk

Florence Shields
THE LODGE
Coney Hall, Mornington, Co Louth

Mornington - Near Drogheda

OPEN:	**All Year except Christmas**	
NO. ROOMS:	**3**	
ENSUITE:	**3**	

(V)

TEL: **041 27007**   FAX: **041 28594**   EMAIL: **mshields@iol.ie**

300 year old coach house, 2 minutes from Mornington Beach and Bettystown Golf Club. Convenient for Newgrange, Drogheda, Airport.

B&B PPS:	**£18/£21**	SNGL OCC. DBLE/TPL:	**£25/£30**	SNGL RM:	-
PART BRD:	-	% RED. CHILDREN:	**25%**	DINNER:	-

Drogheda 4km

Mrs Eileen McGeown
DELAMARE HOUSE
Ballyoonan, Omeath, Co Louth

Omeath

OPEN:	**15th March-15th November**	
NO. ROOMS:	**3**	
ENSUITE:	**2**	

(V)

TEL: **042 75101**   FAX: -

In peaceful rural area, overlooking Carlingford Lough and Mourne Mountains. On Carlingford/Omeath road opposite Calvary Shrine. Carlingford 3 miles.

B&B PPS:	**£15/£17**	SNGL OCC. DBLE/TPL:	**£21.50/£23.50**	SNGL RM:	-
PART BRD:	-	% RED. CHILDREN:	**40%**	DINNER:	-

Omeath 1km

Ashbourne 2Km

Mrs Kathleen Kelly
BALTRASNA LODGE — Ashbourne
Baltrasna, Ashbourne, Co Meath

OPEN:	All Year except Christmas
NO. ROOMS:	4
ENSUITE:	4

TEL: **01 8350446**   FAX: -

Dublin City Airport 20 minutes drive. Just off N2. Separate entrance for guests. Tea/coffee making facilities. Situated on 1 acre.

B&B PPS:	£18/£23	SNGL OCC. DBLE/TPL:	£20/£30	SNGL RM:	£20/£30
PART BRD:	-	% RED. CHILDREN:	33%	DINNER:	-

Duleek 1km

James & Patricia Harding
HILLBROOK HOUSE — Duleek
Newlanes, Duleek, Co Meath

OPEN:	All Year
NO. ROOMS:	4
ENSUITE:	4

TEL: **041 23894**   FAX: -   EMAIL: **hillbrook@destination-ireland.com**

Situated heart of country. Ideal base, touring Boyne Valley area. 30 min Dublin Airport. 10 min Drogheda, Slane. 5 mins Bru Na Boinne Visitors Centre.

B&B PPS:	£17	SNGL OCC. DBLE/TPL:	£23.50	SNGL RM:	£20
PART BRD:	-	% RED. CHILDREN:	50%	DINNER:	-

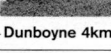
Dunboyne 4km

Mrs Anne Mannion
GORTKERRIN B&B — Dunboyne
Piercetown, Dunboyne, Co Meath

OPEN:	May-October
NO. ROOMS:	3
ENSUITE:	3

TEL: **01 8252096**   FAX: **01 8252096**

Luxury dormer bungalow situated 1km off the N3. Tattersalls and Fairyhouse 3km, Airport 15 minutes. 20 mins from City Centre.

BUS NO: **70**

B&B PPS:	£18/£20	SNGL OCC. DBLE/TPL:	£24.50/£26.50	SNGL RM:	-
PART BRD:	-	% RED. CHILDREN:	50%	DINNER:	-

In Dunshaughlin

Mrs Margaret Madden
ROSGRAERIN HOUSE — Dunshaughlin
Lagore Rd, Dunshaughlin, Co Meath

OPEN:	1st February-30th November
NO. ROOMS:	3
ENSUITE:	3

TEL: **01 8250392**   FAX: **01 8250640**   EMAIL: **rosgraer@ripi.ie**

Luxury accommodation on 4 acres. Spacious bedrooms, Breakfast menu, Guest Library. Historical well on grounds. Dublin Airport/City Centre 25 minutes.

B&B PPS:	£18/£20	SNGL OCC. DBLE/TPL:	£25/£30	SNGL RM:	-
PART BRD:	-	% RED. CHILDREN:	30%	DINNER:	-

Dunshaughlin 5km

Joe & Ita Morris
KILLEENTIERNA HOUSE — Dunshaughlin
Powderlough, Dunshaughlin, Co Meath

OPEN:	All Year except Christmas
NO. ROOMS:	4
ENSUITE:	4

TEL: **01 8259722**   FAX: **01 8250673**   EMAIL: **imorris@clubi.ie**

Modern residence Dublin/Navan road N3, 5km Dublin side of Dunshaughlin. Lounge bar/restaurant 5 mins walk. Airport 25km.

B&B PPS:	£18	SNGL OCC. DBLE/TPL:	£24.50	SNGL RM:	-
PART BRD:	-	% RED. CHILDREN:	33.3%	DINNER:	-

In Enfield

Teresa and Patrick Prendergast
WOODVILLE
Enfield, Co Meath

Enfield

Open:	**All Year**
No. Rooms:	4
Ensuite:	2

(V)

TEL: 0405 41113   Fax: -

Bungalow 400 metres off N4 road, Dublin 40 km, Fishing, Golf, Boating nearby. Convenient to Ferries and Airport. Frommer recommended.

B&B PPS:	**£15/£17**	SNGL OCC. DBLE/TPL:	**£30/£33**	SNGL RM:	**£18**
PART BRD:	-	% RED. CHILDREN:	**25%**	DINNER:	-

Kells 1.5km

Tom & Marie Clarke
BIRCHWOOD
Balrath, Kells, Co Meath

Kells

Open:	**All Year except Christmas**
No. Rooms:	3
Ensuite:	1

(V)

TEL: 046 40688   Fax: **046 40688**   EMAIL: **clarket@iol.ie**

Spacious modern country farmhouse. Kells 1km on N52 Kells-Mullingar. Airport 1 hr. Convenient Newgrange, Kells Crosses, Golf, Tennis and Fishing.

B&B PPS:	**£15/£18**	SNGL OCC. DBLE/TPL:	**£21.50/£24.50**	SNGL RM:	-
PART BRD:	-	% RED. CHILDREN:	**25%**	DINNER:	-

(photo: house) In Kells

Rosemary Murray
WOODVIEW
Athboy Road, Kells, Co Meath

Kells

Open:	**All Year except Christmas**
No. Rooms:	3
Ensuite:	1

(V)

TEL: 046 40200   Fax: -

Spacious house quiet area Kells Town. Within walking distance of all amenities. TV/Tea making facilities in all rooms.

B&B PPS:	**£15/£17**	SNGL OCC. DBLE/TPL:	**£21.50/£23.50**	SNGL RM:	-
PART BRD:	-	% RED. CHILDREN:	**50%**	DINNER:	-

(photo: house) Kells 3km

Peggy O'Reilly
TEACH CUAILGNE
Carlanstown, Kells, Co Meath

Kells

Open:	**All Year except Christmas**
No. Rooms:	3
Ensuite:	2

(V)

TEL: 046 46621   Fax: **046 46621**

Dormer bungalow N52. Beside Carlanstown Village. 3km from Kells and N3. Breakfast Menu. TV Lounge. Convenient : Newgrange, Historical Sites, Airport.

B&B PPS:	**£16/£18**	SNGL OCC. DBLE/TPL:	**£22.50/£24.50**	SNGL RM:	-
PART BRD:	-	% RED. CHILDREN:	**25%**	DINNER:	**£12**

Kells 1.5km

Mary Reilly
OWL'S REST
Navan Rd, Kells, Co Meath

Kells

Open:	**All Year**
No. Rooms:	4
Ensuite:	4

(V)

TEL: 046 49337   Fax: **046 49337**   EMAIL: **owlsrest@surfersparadise.com**

200 yr old Tudor Cottage N3 Kells beside Headfort Golf Club. 40 mins Dublin-Airport, Ferry. Central Meath's surrounding historical counties attractions.

B&B PPS:	**£18**	SNGL OCC. DBLE/TPL:	**£24.50**	SNGL RM:	-
PART BRD:	-	% RED. CHILDREN:	**50%**	DINNER:	**£12**

Mrs Pauline Boylan
ATHLUMNEY MANOR
**Athlumney, Duleek Road, Navan,
Co Meath**

Navan

OPEN:	All Year
NO. ROOMS:	4
ENSUITE:	4

(V)

TEL: **046 71388**   FAX: -

Luxury accommodation overlooking Athlumney Castle. Rooms en-suite with TV, Coffee/tea maker, phone. 10 minutes walk to Town Centre.

| B&B PPS: | **£17** | SNGL OCC. DBLE/TPL: | **£23.50** | SNGL RM: | - |
| PART BRD: | - | % RED. CHILDREN: | 25% | DINNER: | |

In Navan Town

Mrs Louie Burke
RAHEEN
Trim Road, Navan, Co Meath

Navan

OPEN:	All Year
NO. ROOMS:	4
ENSUITE:	2

(V)

TEL: **046 23791**   FAX: -

Luxury bungalow, mature gardens. Navan 2km, Dublin Airport 30km. Newgrange, Tara, Trim easily accessible. Golf, Fishing, Horse Riding locally.

| B&B PPS: | **£15/£17** | SNGL OCC. DBLE/TPL: | **£21.50/£23.50** | SNGL RM: | **£15** |
| PART BRD: | - | % RED. CHILDREN: | 33.3% | DINNER: | - |

Navan 2km

Mrs Mary Callanan
LIOS NA GREINE
**Athlumney, Duleek Road, Navan,
Co Meath**

Navan

OPEN:	All Year except Christmas
NO. ROOMS:	3
ENSUITE:	2

(V)

TEL: **046 28092**   FAX: -

Luxurious family home, 1km off N3 on Kentstown /Duleek/Ashbourne/Airport (R153) road. Close to Golfing, Fishing, Archaeological interests, Newgrange.

| B&B PPS: | **£15/£17** | SNGL OCC. DBLE/TPL: | **£21.50/£23.50** | SNGL RM: | - |
| PART BRD: | - | % RED. CHILDREN: | 20% | DINNER: | **£14** |

Navan 1km

Mrs Paula Casserly
BOYNE DALE
**Donaghmore, Slane Road, Navan,
Co Meath**

Navan

OPEN:	April-October
NO. ROOMS:	3
ENSUITE:	3

(V)

TEL: **046 28015**   FAX: -

Comfortable warm home on main Navan/Slane road (N51). Convenient for Touring Meath, Louth, Dublin area. Golf, Fishing etc, locally.

| B&B PPS: | **£17** | SNGL OCC. DBLE/TPL: | **£23.50** | SNGL RM: | - |
| PART BRD: | - | % RED. CHILDREN: | 20% | DINNER: | - |

Navan 2km

Margaret Dunne
DUNLAIR HOUSE
**Old Road, Athlumney, Navan,
Co Meath**

Navan

OPEN:	All Year
NO. ROOMS:	4
ENSUITE:	3

(V)

TEL: **046 72551**   FAX: -

Luxury home, large mature gardens, quiet location. 1 km Navan Town. Ensuite rooms with TV/Tea//Coffee facilities, convenient to Airport.

| B&B PPS: | **£15/£17** | SNGL OCC. DBLE/TPL: | **£21.50/£23.50** | SNGL RM: | - |
| PART BRD: | - | % RED. CHILDREN: | 25% | DINNER: | - |

Navan 1km

Mrs Nora Loughran
MEADOW VIEW
Slane Road, Navan, Co Meath

Navan

OPEN:	All Year except Christmas
NO. ROOMS:	3
ENSUITE:	2

TEL: **046 23994/73131**   FAX: **046 73131**

Luxurious house on Slane road (N51). Close to Newgrange and other historical sites. Fishing, Golf closeby. Convenient to Airport.

Navan 0.5km

B&B PPS:	£15/£17	SNGL OCC. DBLE/TPL:	£21.50/£23.50	SNGL RM:	-
PART BRD:	-	% RED. CHILDREN:	33%	DINNER:	

Antoinette Moynihan
BARNANE HOUSE
Oldtown, Johnstown, Navan, Co Meath

Navan

OPEN:	All Year except Christmas
NO. ROOMS:	3
ENSUITE:	2

TEL: **046 71261**   FAX: -

Luxurious modern country home. Centrally located in a peaceful rural setting. Adjacent to Tara, Newgrange, Trim Castle. Golf, Fishing nearby.

Navan 4km

B&B PPS:	£16/£18	SNGL OCC. DBLE/TPL:	£22.50/£24.50	SNGL RM:	£16/£18
PART BRD:	-	% RED. CHILDREN:	50%	DINNER:	-

Ann Marie Russell
RUSSELLS SYCAMORES
Dublin Road, Navan, Co Meath

Navan

OPEN:	All Year except Christmas
NO. ROOMS:	4
ENSUITE:	3

TEL: **046 23719**   FAX: -

Luxurious bungalow on River Boyne. Fine antique furnishings, pictures, books, silver. Breakfast menu, home made preserves. Beside Hotel, good Restaurants.

Navan 1km

B&B PPS:	£17	SNGL OCC. DBLE/TPL:	£23.50	SNGL RM:	-
PART BRD:	-	% RED. CHILDREN:	-	DINNER:	-

Mrs. Betty Gough
MATTOCK HOUSE
Newgrange, Slane, Co Meath

Newgrange

OPEN:	All Year
NO. ROOMS:	3
ENSUITE:	2

TEL: **041 24592**   FAX: **041 24592**

Luxury Bungalow situated 4km East of Slane, 1km from Newgrange, Knowth and Dowth. Convenient to Dublin Airport and Ferries.

Drogheda 7km

B&B PPS:	£15/£17	SNGL OCC. DBLE/TPL:	£21.50/£23.50	SNGL RM:	-
PART BRD:	-	% RED. CHILDREN:	50%	DINNER:	-

Mrs Anne Ryan
PINEHILL
Skryne Road, Ratoath, Co Meath

Ratoath

OPEN:	1st April-30th September
NO. ROOMS:	3
ENSUITE:	2

TEL: **01 8256296**   FAX: -

Bungalow 6km off N2-N3. Tattersalls/Fairyhouse 3kms. Dublin Airport- City Centre 30 mins. Local Restaurant, Golf, Hunting, Horseriding nearby.

In Ratoath

B&B PPS:	£17/£18	SNGL OCC. DBLE/TPL:	£23.50/£24.50	SNGL RM:	-
PART BRD:	-	% RED. CHILDREN:	25%	DINNER:	-

Mrs Lily Bagnall
HILLVIEW HOUSE
Gernonstown, Slane, Co Meath

Slane 2km

Slane

OPEN:	All Year except Christmas
NO. ROOMS:	5
ENSUITE:	3

(V)

TEL: **041 24327**   FAX: -

Luxurious family home, situated on own grounds beautiful landscaped Gardens. Convenient to historic Monuments and Towns. Tea and coffee facilities.

B&B PPS:	£15/£17	SNGL OCC. DBLE/TPL:	£21.50/£23.50	SNGL RM:	-
PART BRD:	-	% RED. CHILDREN:	20%	DINNER:	-

Roly Bond
BONDIQUE HOUSE
Cullen, Beauparc, Slane, Co Meath

Slane 4km

Slane

OPEN:	1st January-31st December
NO. ROOMS:	4
ENSUITE:	2

(V)

TEL: **041 24823**   FAX: -

Situated on N2, 4 km south of Slane. Bru na Boinne/Newgrange 8 km. Navan/Drogheda 10mins. Dublin Airport/ City 30 mins.

B&B PPS:	£15/£18	SNGL OCC. DBLE/TPL:	£21.50/£24.50	SNGL RM:	-
PART BRD:	-	% RED. CHILDREN:	50%	DINNER:	-

Mrs Ann Curtis
WOODVIEW
Flemington, Balrath, Co Meath

Slane 6km

Slane

OPEN:	1st March-15th October
NO. ROOMS:	3
ENSUITE:	3

(V)

TEL: **041 25694**   FAX: -

Luxury Country home 6 km South of Slane, 100 metres off N2 Dublin/Derry Rd. Convenient to Newgrange Interpretative Centre.

B&B PPS:	£17	SNGL OCC. DBLE/TPL:	£23.50	SNGL RM:	-
PART BRD:	-	% RED. CHILDREN:	25%	DINNER:	-

Mrs Mary Hevey
BOYNE VIEW
Slane, Co Meath

In Slane Village

Slane

OPEN:	6th-January-20th December
NO. ROOMS:	3
ENSUITE:	2

(V)

TEL: **041 24121**   FAX: -

Georgian period house overlooking scenic Boyne Vally, close to all historical Monuments. Dublin road Slane Village. Dublin Airport 45 minutes.

B&B PPS:	£15/£17	SNGL OCC. DBLE/TPL:	£21.50/£23.50	SNGL RM:	-
PART BRD:	-	% RED. CHILDREN:	25%	DINNER:	-

Olive Owens
SAN GIOVANNI HOUSE
Johnstown, Slane, Co Meath

Slane 2km

Slane

OPEN:	All Year except Christmas
NO. ROOMS:	3
ENSUITE:	3

(V)

TEL: **041 24147**   FAX: -

Large modern house on N2 in picturesque Boyne Valley, breathtaking view from house. 7 km from Newgrange. 30 mins from Airport (Dublin).

B&B PPS:	£17	SNGL OCC. DBLE/TPL:	£23.50	SNGL RM:	-
PART BRD:	-	% RED. CHILDREN:	50%	DINNER:	-

Navan 12km

Mrs Eilish Smith
CASTLE VIEW
Slane, Co Meath

Slane

OPEN:	**January-November**	
NO. ROOMS:	**5**	
ENSUITE:	**4**	(V)

TEL: **041 24510**   FAX: -

Dormer bungalow situated Slane village, close all Historical Interests. 45 minutes Dublin Airport. Tea making facilities in rooms. On N51 route.

B&B PPS:	**£15/£17**	SNGL OCC. DBLE/TPL:	**£21.50/£23.50**	SNGL RM:	-
PART BRD:	-	% RED. CHILDREN:	-	DINNER:	-

Navan 7km

Irene Meehan
ROYAL TARA
Castletown, Tara, Co Meath

Tara

OPEN:	**1st January-31st December**	
NO. ROOMS:	**3**	
ENSUITE:	**3**	(V)

TEL: **046 25920/086 8140073**   FAX: -   EMAIL: **royaltara@hotmail.com**

Modern peaceful accommodation on 1 acre, off N3 between Dunshaughlin - Navan. Beside Golf Club, Hill of Tara. Guest lounge. Airport convenient.

B&B PPS:	**£17**	SNGL OCC. DBLE/TPL:	**£23.50**	SNGL RM:	-
PART BRD:	-	% RED. CHILDREN:	**50%**	DINNER:	-

Trim .5 km

Colin & Anne Finnegan
CRANNMOR
Dunderry Road, Trim, Co Meath

Trim

OPEN:	**1st April-30th September**	
NO. ROOMS:	**4**	
ENSUITE:	**4**	(V)

TEL: **046 31635**   FAX: **046 31635**   EMAIL: **crannmorbandb@touristaccomm.iol.ie**

Old country house. Peaceful countryside. Breakfast menu. Gardens. Old farm equipment. Disabled guests welcome. Ideal base Boyne valley. Airport 35 minutes.

B&B PPS:	**£18**	SNGL OCC. DBLE/TPL:	**£21/£24.50**	SNGL RM:	-
PART BRD:	-	% RED. CHILDREN:	**25%**	DINNER:	-

Trim 1km

Lynda O'Brien
BRAMLEY
Friarspark, Dublin Rd, Trim, Co Meath

Trim

OPEN:	**April-September**	
NO. ROOMS:	**3**	
ENSUITE:	**2**	(V)

TEL: **046 31745/31316**   FAX: **046 31745**

Luxury dormer bungalow. Rooms ensuite. Spacious grounds. Close to King John's Castle, featured in award winning film "Braveheart". Airport 50 mins.

B&B PPS:	**£15/£17**	SNGL OCC. DBLE/TPL:	**£21.50/£23.50**	SNGL RM:	-
PART BRD:	-	% RED. CHILDREN:	**25%**	DINNER:	-

In Trim

Mrs Eliz (Libby) O'Loughlin
WHITE LODGE B & B
New Road (Navan Road), Trim, Co Meath

Trim

OPEN:	**1st March-31st October**	
NO. ROOMS:	**6**	
ENSUITE:	**5**	(V)

TEL: **046 36549/37697**   FAX: **046 36549**

Townhouse, Large Bedrooms, Country setting, Gardens. Tea/Coffee - TV Bedrooms. Restaurant closeby. Dublin Airport 30 mins. City 40 mins. Former Dumont Guide Recommended.

B&B PPS:	**£15/£18**	SNGL OCC. DBLE/TPL:	**£21.50/£25**	SNGL RM:	-
PART BRD:	-	% RED. CHILDREN:	-	DINNER:	-

Mrs Carmel Horan
LAKYLE

Shannon Harbour Cross, Banagher, Co Offaly

TEL: **0509 51566** FAX: -

OPEN:	May-October
No. ROOMS:	4
ENSUITE:	3

(V)

Georgian style house, 3km off N62, convenient Bog-Rail Tours, Bird Watching (Corncrake), Fishing, Golf, Horse-Riding, Boating, Canoeing, Pitch-Putt. Clonmacnois.

| B&B PPS: | £15/£17 | SNGL OCC. DBLE/TPL: | £21.50/£23.50 | SNGL RM: | - |
| PART BRD: | - | % RED. CHILDREN: | 20% | DINNER: | - |

Banagher 2km

Ann Marie Wall-Deery
THE GREEN HOUSE B & B

Emmet Street, Birr, Co Offaly

TEL: **0509 21214** FAX: -

OPEN:	1st January-31st December
No. ROOMS:	4
ENSUITE:	2

(V)

Centrally located Georgian town house with large walled green garden at rear. Interestingly furnished and decorated. Orthopaedic beds, Electric blankets.

| B&B PPS: | £15/£19 | SNGL OCC. DBLE/TPL: | £21.50/£25.50 | SNGL RM: | - |
| PART BRD: | - | % RED. CHILDREN: | 15% | DINNER: | - |

In Birr

Jerry & Ann O'Meara
ROSELAWN

Roscrea Road, Birr, Co Offaly

TEL: **0509 20468** FAX: -

OPEN:	All Year except Christmas
No. ROOMS:	3
ENSUITE:	-

(V)

Highly recommended friendly family home on N62. Private parking, Open fires, Orthopaedic beds, Electric blankets, Hairdryer. Complimentary refreshments on arrival.

| B&B PPS: | £15 | SNGL OCC. DBLE/TPL: | £21.50 | SNGL RM: | - |
| PART BRD: | - | % RED. CHILDREN: | - | DINNER: | - |

Birr 3km

Mrs Gertrude Spain
ARD NA GREINE

Hillside, Birr, Co Offaly

TEL: **0509 20256** FAX: -

OPEN:	All Year except Christmas
No. ROOMS:	3
ENSUITE:	-

(V)

House over 100 years old, very quiet. Within walking distance of Birr Town (off Roscrea Road).

| B&B PPS: | £15 | SNGL OCC. DBLE/TPL: | £21.50 | SNGL RM: | - |
| PART BRD: | - | % RED. CHILDREN: | 50% | DINNER: | - |

Birr 1km

Mrs Catherine Harte
KAJON HOUSE

Creevagh, Clonmacnoise, Co Offaly

TEL: **0905 74191** FAX: -

OPEN:	1st February-30th October
No. ROOMS:	4
ENSUITE:	3

(V)

Red brick bungalow on elevated site overlooking the River Shannon, with mature gardens back and front for guests use.

| B&B PPS: | £15/£17 | SNGL OCC. DBLE/TPL: | £21.50/£23.50 | SNGL RM: | - |
| PART BRD: | £185 | % RED. CHILDREN: | 20% | DINNER: | £12.50 |

Shannon Bridge 5km

In Edenderry

Catherine and Dermot Byrne
AUBURN LODGE
Colonel Perry Street, Edenderry, Co Offaly

Edenderry

OPEN:	All Year	
NO. ROOMS:	3	
ENSUITE:	2	(V)

TEL: **0405 31319/087 2313990**   FAX: -

Family run town house. Rooms ensuite, car park. Off N4 en route to airport and ferryport. Touring, Fishing, Golf.

B&B PPS:	£15/£17	SNGL OCC. DBLE/TPL:	£21.50/£23.50	SNGL RM:	-
PART BRD:	-	% RED. CHILDREN:	-	DINNER:	£12

Edenderry 5km

Kay & Eileen Delaney
CLONKEEN LODGE
Dublin Road, Edenderry, Co Offaly

Edenderry

OPEN:	All Year except Christmas	
NO. ROOMS:	6	
ENSUITE:	6	(V)

TEL: **0405 31058**   FAX: **0405 31058**

Georgian schoolhouse 1810. Golf. Hairdryers, Tea-making in rooms, great power showers, great beds. 15 mins Enfield N4, Dublin 57 km. Credit cards.

B&B PPS:	£17	SNGL OCC. DBLE/TPL:	£23.50	SNGL RM:	£17
PART BRD:	-	% RED. CHILDREN:	50%	DINNER:	-

Portarlington 4km

Liam & Marguerite Kirwan
TREASCON LODGE
Portarlington, Co Offaly

Portarlington

OPEN:	6th January-30th November	
NO. ROOMS:	4	
ENSUITE:	4	(V)

TEL: **0502 43183**   FAX: **0502 43183**   EMAIL: **treascon@indigo.ie**

Country home on two acres. Tennis Court, Playground in quiet setting. All rooms ensuite. Golf 5 mins. Wheelchair access.

B&B PPS:	£17.50/£19	SNGL OCC. DBLE/TPL:	£24/£25.50	SNGL RM:	-
PART BRD:	£195	% RED. CHILDREN:	50%	DINNER:	£15

Ballinasloe 10km

Mrs Patricia Corbett
RACHRA HOUSE (SHANNON VIEW)
Shannonbridge (via Athlone), Co Offaly

Shannonbridge

OPEN:	All Year except Christmas	
NO. ROOMS:	4	
ENSUITE:	2	(V)

TEL: **0905 74249**   FAX: -

Modern house in picturesque village overlooking rivers Shannon and Suck. Clonmacnoise 6 km. Bog Railtours 3 km. Fishing, Golf, Horse-Riding, Tennis.

B&B PPS:	£15/£17	SNGL OCC. DBLE/TPL:	£21.50/£23.50	SNGL RM:	-
PART BRD:	£180	% RED. CHILDREN:	25%	DINNER:	£12

In Shannonbridge Village

Mrs Celine Grennan
THE BUNGALOW
River View, Shannonbridge, Athlone, Co Offaly

Shannonbridge

OPEN:	February-November	
NO. ROOMS:	5	
ENSUITE:	3	(V)

TEL: **0905 74180**   FAX: -

In village with panoramic view of Shannon, Clonmacnoise 6 km, Clonfert 26 km. Bog tours, Pubs, Fishing, Golf, Swimming, Tennis, Horseriding.

B&B PPS:	£15/£17	SNGL OCC. DBLE/TPL:	£21.50/£23.50	SNGL RM:	-
PART BRD:	£180	% RED. CHILDREN:	5%	DINNER:	£13

Mrs Bridie Casey
PADRAIG VILLA
Glaskill, Screggan, Tullamore, Co Offaly

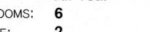
Tullamore

OPEN:	**All Year**
NO. ROOMS:	6
ENSUITE:	2

(V)

TEL: **0506 55962**   FAX: **0506 55962**

Frommer recommended. 1.5 KM off Tullamore/Birr Road. Panoramic view. Renowned for food excellence. Bicycle collection from 1880. Touring cycling complementary.

B&B PPS:	**£18/£22**	SNGL OCC. DBLE/TPL:	**£25/£29**	SNGL RM:	-
PART BRD:	-	% RED. CHILDREN:	**20%**	DINNER:	**£16**

— Tullamore 6km —

Mrs Bernadette Keyes
CANAL VIEW COUNTRY HOUSE
Killina, Rahan, Tullamore, Co Offaly

Tullamore

OPEN:	**All Year except Christmas**
NO. ROOMS:	4
ENSUITE:	3

(V)

TEL: **0506 55868**   FAX: **0506 55825**

3km off Tullamore/Birr Road, N52 overlooking canal. Rooms hairdryer. Recommended best 300 B&B's. Complimentary sauna, steamroom, jacuzzi, pedal/row boating.

B&B PPS:	**£15/£18**	SNGL OCC. DBLE/TPL:	**£21.50/£24.50**	SNGL RM:	**£21.50/£22**
PART BRD:	**£190**	% RED. CHILDREN:	**33%**	DINNER:	**£15**

— Tullamore 10km —

Mrs Claudia Krygel
PINE LODGE
Ross, Tullamore, Co Offaly

Tullamore

OPEN:	**15th February-15th December**
NO. ROOMS:	4
ENSUITE:	4

(V)

TEL: **0506 51927**   FAX: **0506 51927**

Award winning elegant country home, tranquil surroundings. Indoor pool, sauna, steamroom, gamesroom. Golf, 1 mile. Use of pool charged separately.

B&B PPS:	**£22**	SNGL OCC. DBLE/TPL:	**£27**	SNGL RM:	-
PART BRD:	**£250**	% RED. CHILDREN:	-	DINNER:	**£20**

— Tullamore 7km —

Eileen &
Johann MacSweeney -Thieme
SHEPHERDS WOOD
Screggan, Tullamore, Co Offaly

Tullamore

OPEN:	**1st April-30th September**
NO. ROOMS:	3
ENSUITE:	3

TEL: **0506 21499**   FAX: **0506 21499**   EMAIL: **jgott@iol.ie**

Michael Scott designed house with historical connections to "Irish Mist". In 50 acres own forest, a wildlife sanctuary. Swimming Pool.

B&B PPS:	**£22**	SNGL OCC. DBLE/TPL:	**£29**	SNGL RM:	**£29**
PART BRD:	-	% RED. CHILDREN:	-	DINNER:	**£23**

— Tullamore 6km —

Mrs Anne O'Brien
GORMAGH
Durrow, Tullamore, Co Offaly

Tullamore

OPEN:	**All Year except Christmas**
NO. ROOMS:	4
ENSUITE:	3

(V)

TEL: **0506 51468**   FAX: -

Country Home in rural setting with natural warm interior. 5 minutes from busy Town. Off N52. North of Tulllamore.

B&B PPS:	**£17**	SNGL OCC. DBLE/TPL:	**£23.50**	SNGL RM:	-
PART BRD:	-	% RED. CHILDREN:	-	DINNER:	**£14**

— Tullamore 4km —

Athlone 8km

Pat &Teresa Byrne
BENOWN HOUSE
Glasson, Athlone, Co Westmeath

Athlone

OPEN:	**All Year**
NO. ROOMS:	6
ENSUITE:	6

(V)

TEL: **0902 85406**   FAX: -   EMAIL: **patbyrne@indigo.ie**

Relaxing residence beside picturesque village, 100m off N55 towards Glasson Golf. Restaurant, Pubs, Fishing, Sailing nearby. Tea/coffee facilities.

B&B PPS:	**£17**	SNGL OCC. DBLE/TPL:	**£23.50**	SNGL RM:	**£20**
PART BRD:	-	% RED. CHILDREN:	**33.3%**	DINNER:	-

In Athlone

Mrs Joan Collins
DUN MHUIRE HOUSE
Bonavalley, Dublin Road, (Town Route), Athlone, Co Westmeath

Athlone

OPEN:	**All Year**
NO. ROOMS:	4
ENSUITE:	2

(V)

TEL: **0902 75360**   FAX: -

Close to Shops, Pubs. All rooms with TV, Tea & Coffee facilities.

B&B PPS:	**£15/£17**	SNGL OCC. DBLE/TPL:	**£21.50/£23.50**	SNGL RM:	-
PART BRD:	-	% RED. CHILDREN:	-	DINNER:	-

Athlone 1km

Sean & Carmel Corbett
RIVERVIEW HOUSE
Summerhill, Galway Road, (N6), Athlone, Co Westmeath

Athlone

OPEN:	**All Year except Christmas**
NO. ROOMS:	5
ENSUITE:	5

(V)

TEL: **0902 94532**   FAX: -

Two storey red brick. Rooms en-suite and TV's. Guest lounge, Evening meals, Tea/Coffee, Private Parking, Telephone, Landscaped lawns.

B&B PPS:	**£17**	SNGL OCC. DBLE/TPL:	**23.50**	SNGL RM:	**£20**
PART BRD:	**£195**	% RED. CHILDREN:	**25%**	DINNER:	**£13**

Athlone 4km

Mrs Assumpta Dempsey
LAKE BREEZE LODGE
Ballykeeran, Athlone, Co Westmeath

Athlone

OPEN:	**March-October**
NO. ROOMS:	4
ENSUITE:	4

(V)

TEL: **0902 85087**   FAX: -

In quiet scenic countryside, overlooking Lough Ree. 1Km off N55 in Ballykeeran village. Fishing, Golf, Restaurants nearby. Tea/Coffee facilities/T.V./Hairdryers.

B&B PPS:	**£17**	SNGL OCC. DBLE/TPL:	**£23.50**	SNGL RM:	-
PART BRD:	-	% RED. CHILDREN:	**50%**	DINNER:	-

Athlone 2km

Jim and Nancy Denby
SHELMALIER HOUSE
Cartrontroy, Athlone, Co Westmeath

Athlone

OPEN:	**All Year except Christmas**
NO. ROOMS:	7
ENSUITE:	7

(V)

TEL: **0902 72245/73190**   FAX: **0902 73190**   EMAIL: **shelmal@iol.ie**

Quiet accommodation signposted off N6 (town route). National Award winning breakfast and good food. Luxury rooms with radio, TV, Telephone.

B&B PPS:	**£17**	SNGL OCC. DBLE/TPL:	**£23.50**	SNGL RM:	-
PART BRD:	**£205**	% RED. CHILDREN:	**33%**	DINNER:	**£14**

334

Athlone 1km

Mrs Jean Dowd
AUBURN
Dublin Road, Athlone, Co Westmeath

Athlone

TEL: **0902 74323**   FAX: -

OPEN:	1st April-31st October
NO. ROOMS:	4
ENSUITE:	2

Large bungalow in spacious cul-de-sac off main Dublin Road, (N6) between Auburn House Hotel and Regional College. Tea and Coffee facilities.

| B&B PPS: | £15/£17 | SNGL OCC. DBLE/TPL: | £21.50/£23.50 | SNGL RM: | - |
| PART BRD: | - | % RED. CHILDREN: | 33.3% | DINNER: | - |

Athlone 0.5km

Mrs Brigid Duffy
DE VERE HOUSE
Retreat Road, Athlone, Co Westmeath

Athlone

TEL: **0902 75376**   FAX: -

OPEN:	1st Feburary-1st December
NO. ROOMS:	4
ENSUITE:	3

Modern residence on own grounds. Near Swimming Pool. Close to Town Centre. Rail and Bus Station. Private car park.

| B&B PPS: | £15/£17 | SNGL OCC. DBLE/TPL: | £21.50/£23.50 | SNGL RM: | - |
| PART BRD: | - | % RED. CHILDREN: | 50% | DINNER: | - |

Athlone 1km

Mrs Maura Duggan
VILLA ST JOHN
Roscommon Road
Athlone, Co Westmeath

Athlone

TEL: **0902 92490**   FAX: -

OPEN:	All Year except Christmas
NO. ROOMS:	8
ENSUITE:	5

On N61, 200 yds off N6. Convenient town, Lough Ree, Clonmacnoise. Walking distance Lounge Bars. "Guide to Ireland" recommended. Tours arranged.

| B&B PPS: | £15/£17 | SNGL OCC. DBLE/TPL: | £21.50/23.50 | SNGL RM: | £20 |
| PART BRD: | £180 | % RED. CHILDREN: | 50% | DINNER: | £12 |

In Athlone

Mark & Linda Egan
SHANNONSIDE HOUSE
West Lodge Road, Athlone,
Co Westmeath

Athlone

TEL: **0902 94773**   FAX: **0902 94773**

OPEN:	All Year except Christmas
NO. ROOMS:	5
ENSUITE:	5

Large detached family run town house. Convenient to all amenities. Rooms with tea, cofffee, multi channel TV. Secure Car Park.

| B&B PPS: | £17 | SNGL OCC. DBLE/TPL: | £23.50 | SNGL RM: | - |
| PART BRD: | £224 | % RED. CHILDREN: | 33.3% | DINNER: | £15 |

Athlone 2km

Mrs Catherine Fox
DE PORRES
Cornamaddy, Athlone, Co Westmeath

Athlone

TEL: **0902 75759**   FAX: -

OPEN:	1st April-31st October
NO. ROOMS:	4
ENSUITE:	3

100m off N55, signposted at Garage. Quiet, Beautiful gardens. Clonmacnoise, Lakes, Pubs, Restaurants Near. TV, Tea/Coffee, Hairdryers in rooms.

| B&B PPS: | £15/£17 | SNGL OCC. DBLE/TPL: | £21.50/£23.50 | SNGL RM: | - |
| PART BRD: | - | % RED. CHILDREN: | 33.3% | DINNER: | - |

Athlone 10km

Mrs Elizabeth Heavin
LACKAGH HOUSE
Doon, Ballinahown, Athlone, Co Westmeath

Athlone

TEL: **0902 30156**   FAX: -

OPEN:	All Year except Christmas	
NO. ROOMS:	4	
ENSUITE:	2	(V)

Country residence, Clonmacnoise 6km, Bog Tour 10 km. Pub walking distance, Golf, Fising, Rural Heritage Museum .5km. Sign posted off N62.

B&B PPS:	£15/£17	SNGL OCC. DBLE/TPL:	£21.50/£23.50	SNGL RM:	-
PART BRD:	-	% RED. CHILDREN:	-	DINNER:	

Athlone 5km

Mrs Bernadette Keegan
HARBOUR HOUSE
Ballykeeran, Athlone, Co Westmeath

Athlone

TEL: **0902 85063**   FAX: **0902 85063**   EMAIL: **pkeegan@tinet.ie**

OPEN:	March - October	
NO. ROOMS:	6	
ENSUITE:	6	(V)

Luxurious quiet home on Lough Ree. 1.5Km off N55 in Ballykeeran. Fishing, Golf, Restaurants locally. Tea/Coffee/TV, Hairdryers facilities.

B&B PPS:	£17	SNGL OCC. DBLE/TPL:	£23.50	SNGL RM:	-
PART BRD:	-	% RED. CHILDREN:	33.3%	DINNER:	-

Athlone 2km

Jim & Eucharia King
BUSHFIELD HOUSE
Cornamaddy, Blyry, Athlone, Co Westmeath

Athlone

TEL: **0902 75979/73702**   FAX: -

OPEN:	All Year except Christmas	
NO. ROOMS:	5	
ENSUITE:	5	(V)

Signposted off N6/ N55. Exit 5 Blyry off motorway. Rooms TV's, Telephones, Lounge bar nearby. Restaurants 2Km. Customer service award winner.

B&B PPS:	£17	SNGL OCC. DBLE/TPL:	£23.50	SNGL RM:	-
PART BRD:	-	% RED. CHILDREN:	50%	DINNER:	-

Athlone 2km

Mrs Mary Linnane
BURREN LODGE
Creggan, Dublin Road, Athlone, Co Westmeath

Athlone

TEL: **0902 75157**   FAX: -

OPEN:	All Year	
NO. ROOMS:	4	
ENSUITE:	3	(V)

Situated on N6, close to roundabout at Kilmartins Ford Garage. Convenient to Clonmacnoise. Rooms with TV, Tea/Coffee, Hairdryer, Electric Blanket..

B&B PPS:	£15/£17	SNGL OCC. DBLE/TPL:	£21.50/£23.50	SNGL RM:	-
PART BRD:	-	% RED. CHILDREN:	30%	DINNER:	-

Athlone 3km

Mrs Joanne Mulligan
MOUNT ALVERNA HOUSE
Monksland, Athlone, Co Westmeath

Athlone

TEL: **0902 94016**   FAX: -

OPEN:	April-October	
NO. ROOMS:	4	
ENSUITE:	4	(V)

Spacious bungalow. All rooms en-suite. Private grounds off N6 on R362. Near Clonmacnoise, Golf, Fishing, Open Farm.

B&B PPS:	£17	SNGL OCC. DBLE/TPL:	£23.50	SNGL RM:	-
PART BRD:	-	% RED. CHILDREN:	30%	DINNER:	-

Mrs Audrey O'Brien
BOGGANFIN HOUSE
**Roscommon Road, Athlone,
Co Westmeath**

Athlone

Open:	All Year except Christmas
No. Rooms:	6
Ensuite:	5

(V)

Tel: **0902 94255**   Fax: **0902 94255**

Tudor style residence, private parking, "Guide to Ireland" recommended. Off N6, on N61. Beside Town, Golf, Fishing. Rooms TV, coffee.

| B&B PPS: | **£15/£17** | Sngl Occ. Dble/Tpl: | **£21.50/£23.50** | Sngl Rm: | - |
| Part Brd: | - | % Red. Children: | **50%** | Dinner: | |

— Athlone 1.5km —

Des & Mary O'Neill
AVONREE HOUSE
Coosan, Athlone, Co Westmeath

Athlone

Open:	1st March-31st October
No. Rooms:	5
Ensuite:	5

(V)

Tel: **0902 75485**   Fax: -

House, Gardens. Close N6 (Exit Coosan No3 Junction) and N55. Italian spoken. Two Golf Clubs - 10mins. Non-smoking. Clonmacnoise 20 mins, Dublin 1 hr 20 mins.

| B&B PPS: | **£17/£18** | Sngl Occ. Dble/Tpl: | **£23.50/£24.50** | Sngl Rm: | - |
| Part Brd: | - | % Red. Children: | **30%** | Dinner: | - |

— Athlone 1km —

Mrs Kathleen Shaw
CLUAIN-INIS
**Summerhill, Galway Road, N6,
Athlone, Co Westmeath**

Athlone

Open:	1st April-31st October
No. Rooms:	3
Ensuite:	1

(V)

Tel: **0902 94202**   Fax: -

Recommended "Guide to Ireland"and "Dillard & Causin" guides. Situated N6, Clonmacnoise, Bog Tour nearby. Close to Golf and Fishing.

| B&B PPS: | **£15/£17** | Sngl Occ. Dble/Tpl: | **£21.50/£23.50** | Sngl Rm: | - |
| Part Brd: | - | % Red. Children: | **50%** | Dinner: | - |

— Athlone 3km —

Mrs Deirdre Walsh
ROCWAL
**The Beeches, Coosan, Athlone,
Co Westmeath**

Athlone

Open:	April-September
No. Rooms:	4
Ensuite:	3

(V)

Tel: **0902 75640**   Fax: **0902 75640**

Quiet area, convenient Bus/Rail Station. Tea making facilities. TV in rooms. Signposted off N6 at Coosan Junction. Access/Visa.

| B&B PPS: | **£15/£17** | Sngl Occ. Dble/Tpl: | **£21.50/£23.50** | Sngl Rm: | - |
| Part Brd: | - | % Red. Children: | - | Dinner: | |

— Athlone 1.5km —

Mrs Mary Walsh
CARRAUN VIEW
Glasson Village, Athlone, Co Westmeath

Athlone

Open:	All Year except Christmas
No. Rooms:	3
Ensuite:	3

(V)

Tel: **0902 85391**   Fax: -

Located on N55 in Glasson village. Private car park. Tea/coffee facilities, TV Lounge, Restaurants, Pubs, Golfing, Fishing, Horseriding nearby.

| B&B PPS: | **£17** | Sngl Occ. Dble/Tpl: | **£23.50** | Sngl Rm: | - |
| Part Brd: | **£177** | % Red. Children: | **50%** | Dinner: | **£12** |

— In Glasson Village —

Stephen & Mary O'Reilly
INNY SIDE LODGE
Finea Village, Co Westmeath

Finea

OPEN:	All Year except Christmas	
NO. ROOMS:	6	
ENSUITE:	3	

TEL: 043 81124   FAX: -

Home on banks of River. Beside Lough Sheelin, Lough Kinale, Jetty & Boats, Trout Fishing, Pike, Bream & Tench, Farm attached.

B&B PPS:	£15/£17	SNGL OCC. DBLE/TPL:	£21.50/£23.50	SNGL RM:	£16
PART BRD:	£180	% RED. CHILDREN:	50%	DINNER:	£12

— Finea

Jimmey and Eileen Whelehan
THE VILLAGE B&B
Killucan, Co Westmeath

Kinnegad

OPEN:	All Year	
NO. ROOMS:	3	
ENSUITE:	2	

TEL: 044 74760   FAX: -

Follow the B & B sign on route N4 West of Kinnegad. Royal Canal 2 km. Golf courses 14km en route Trim, Newgrange, Boyne Valley.

B&B PPS:	£15/£17	SNGL OCC. DBLE/TPL:	£21.50/£23.50	SNGL RM:	-
PART BRD:	-	% RED. CHILDREN:	20%	DINNER:	-

— In Village

Mrs May Glynn
RAILWAY LODGE
Cartronkeel, Ballymore Rd, Moate, Co Westmeath

Moate

OPEN:	All Year	
NO. ROOMS:	3	
ENSUITE:	2	

TEL: 0902 81596   FAX: -

Bungalow situated in peaceful area with landscaped Gardens, private car parking, home cooking, rooms ensuite. Knowledge of German and French.

B&B PPS:	£15/£18	SNGL OCC. DBLE/TPL:	£21.50/£24.50	SNGL RM:	£15
PART BRD:	-	% RED. CHILDREN:	-	DINNER:	

— In Moate

Mrs Ethna Kelly
COOLEEN COUNTRY HOME
Ballymore Rd, Moate, Co Westmeath

Moate

OPEN:	All Year except Christmas	
NO. ROOMS:	3	
ENSUITE:	3	

TEL: 0902 81044   FAX: -

Picturesque bungalow set in private gardens, 2 km off Dublin/Galway Rd. Close to Golf, Pitch and Putt, Clonmacnoise, Heritage Centre.

B&B PPS:	£17	SNGL OCC. DBLE/TPL:	£23.50	SNGL RM:	-
PART BRD:	-	% RED. CHILDREN:	30%	DINNER:	

— Moate 2km

Louise and Colm Quinn
BEECHFIELD HOUSE
Athlone Road, Moate, Co Westmeath

Moate

OPEN:	All Year except Christmas	
NO. ROOMS:	4	
ENSUITE:	4	

TEL: 0902 82030   FAX: -

Secluded country residence, extensive grounds. Excellent accommodation and good food. All rooms en-suite with TV and Tea/Coffee making facilities.

B&B PPS:	£18.50	SNGL OCC. DBLE/TPL:	£25	SNGL RM:	-
PART BRD:	-	% RED. CHILDREN:	25%	DINNER:	

— In Moate

Pat and Elizabeth Birmingham — Mullingar
Marlinstown Court, Dublin Road, Mullingar, Co Westmeath

OPEN:	All Year except Christmas
NO. ROOMS:	5
ENSUITE:	5

TEL: **044 40053**   FAX: **044 43158**

Situated on a beautiful setting. Experience real comfort and quality. Bedrooms completed with television, choice of Breakfast menus. Secluded Parking.

B&B PPS:	£17	SNGL OCC. DBLE/TPL:	£23.50	SNGL RM:	-
PART BRD:	-	% RED. CHILDREN:	-	DINNER:	

— Mullingar 2km —

Sean and Dympna Casey — Mullingar
HILLTOP
Delvin Road, (N52 off N4), Rathconnell, Mullingar, Co Westmeath

OPEN:	All Year except Christmas
NO. ROOMS:	5
ENSUITE:	5

TEL: **044 48958**   FAX: **044 48013**

Unique modern Country home, Award winning garden, breakfast. One hour from Dublin. AA selected QQQQ Recommended Frommer, Dillard/Cousin, Sullivan guides.

B&B PPS:	£18	SNGL OCC. DBLE/TPL:	£24.50	SNGL RM:	-
PART BRD:	-	% RED. CHILDREN:	-	DINNER:	

— Mullingar 3km —

Margaret and Jack Daly — Mullingar
LAKEVIEW
Navan/Delvin Rd (N52), Rathconnell, Mullingar, Co Westmeath

OPEN:	All Year except Christmas
NO. ROOMS:	5
ENSUITE:	3

TEL: **044 48995**   FAX: -

Family residence situated in Lakeland district. Ideal location for Fishing, Golf, House overlooking Lough Sheever and Lough Drin. Good Restaurants.

B&B PPS:	£15/£17	SNGL OCC. DBLE/TPL:	£21.50/£23.50	SNGL RM:	£21
PART BRD:	£177	% RED. CHILDREN:	20%	DINNER:	-

— Mullingar 3km —

Rita Fahey — Mullingar
BALLINAFIDLAKE HOUSE
Ballinafid, Longford Road, Mullingar, Co Westmeath

OPEN:	1st March-31st October
NO. ROOMS:	4
ENSUITE:	4

TEL: **044 71162**   FAX: -   EMAIL: **fahey@iol.ie**

Spacious bungalow 8 km. From Mullingar on the N4 beside the Covert Pub opposite Ballinafid Lake. Guest sitting room, laundry facilities.

B&B PPS:	£17	SNGL OCC. DBLE/TPL:	£23.50	SNGL RM:	-
PART BRD:	-	% RED. CHILDREN:	33%	DINNER:	-

— Mullingar 8km —

Mrs Regina Healy — Mullingar
GLENMORE HOUSE
Dublin Road, Mullingar, Co Westmeath

OPEN:	All Year except Christmas
NO. ROOMS:	4
ENSUITE:	2

TEL: **044 48905**   FAX: -

Georgian house on N4, set in four acres of secluded woodlands with Croquet Lawn and extensive Putting Green.

B&B PPS:	£17/£19	SNGL OCC. DBLE/TPL:	£23.50/£25.50	SNGL RM:	-
PART BRD:	-	% RED. CHILDREN:	25%	DINNER:	-

— Mullingar —

Mullingar 2.5km

Mrs May McCarthy
MOORLAND
Marlinstown, Curraghmore (Off N4) Mullingar, Co Westmeath

Mullingar

OPEN:	All Year
NO. ROOMS:	6
ENSUITE:	6

TEL: 044 40905   FAX: -

House off main Dublin Road. Six rooms with private facilities. Turf Fires, Electric Blankets. Warm welcome.

| B&B PPS: | £18 | SNGL OCC. DBLE/TPL: | £24.50 | SNGL RM: | - |
| PART BRD: | - | % RED. CHILDREN: | 20% | DINNER: | £14 |

Mullingar 2km

Mrs. Margaret McCormack
McCORMACKS BED & BREAKFAST
Old Dublin Rd., Mullingar, Co Westmeath

Mullingar

OPEN:	All Year
NO. ROOMS:	4
ENSUITE:	2

TEL: 044 41483   FAX: -

On Old Dublin Road, 100 metres from Mullingar Bypass, adjacent to Roundabout. Old farm machinery display. Tennis court on grounds.

| B&B PPS: | £15/£17 | SNGL OCC. DBLE/TPL: | £21.50/£23.50 | SNGL RM: | - |
| PART BRD: | £180 | % RED. CHILDREN: | 33% | DINNER: | £12 |

Mullingar 2km

Frank & Teresa Mullen
ROSSLARE HOUSE
Dublin Road, Mullingar, Co Westmeath

Mullingar

OPEN:	All Year
NO. ROOMS:	3
ENSUITE:	3

TEL: 044 48574   FAX: -

Situated on own grounds 1 mile from Town Centre, all rooms ensuite with TV. Private Parking. Convenient to Fishing, Golf, Swimming.

| B&B PPS: | £17 | SNGL OCC. DBLE/TPL: | £23.50 | SNGL RM: | £19 |
| PART BRD: | - | % RED. CHILDREN: | 25% | DINNER: | - |

Mullingar 8km

John & Goretti Plunkett
ARDNAGROSS
Kilmaglish, Knockdrin, Mullingar, Co Westmeath

Mullingar

OPEN:	1st May-1st October
NO. ROOMS:	3
ENSUITE:	2

TEL: 044 72122   FAX: -

Family home set in Lakeland district of Ireland with tranquil surroundings, beautiful scenery and guaranteed warm Irish welcome on arrival.

| B&B PPS: | £15/£17 | SNGL OCC. DBLE/TPL: | £21.50/£23.50 | SNGL RM: | - |
| PART BRD: | - | % RED. CHILDREN: | 50% | DINNER: | - |

Mullingar 2km

Mrs Anne Quinn,
GLENCAR HOUSE
Tullamore Rd/Lynn Rd, Mullingar, Co Westmeath

Mullingar

OPEN:	All Year except Christmas
NO. ROOMS:	3
ENSUITE:	3

TEL: 044 48545   FAX: -

Family residence on N52, convenient to Lakes, Golf, Sporting Amenities, Horseriding School nearby. Warm welcome.

| B&B PPS: | £17 | SNGL OCC. DBLE/TPL: | £23.50 | SNGL RM: | - |
| PART BRD: | - | % RED. CHILDREN: | 25% | DINNER: | - |

Mullingar 15km

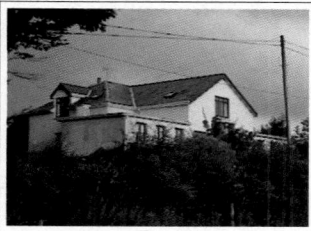

Marian Gillespie
THE SCHOOL HOUSE
Leney, Multyfarnham, Co Westmeath

Multyfarnham

OPEN: **All Year except Christmas**
NO. ROOMS: **3**
ENSUITE: **3**

TEL: **044 71153** FAX: **-**

Tastefully converted old National School set in peaceful surroundings just off the N4, 15 km Mullingar. Close to Village of Multyfarnham.

B&B PPS:	£17	SNGL OCC. DBLE/TPL:	£23.50	SNGL RM:	-
PART BRD:	£180	% RED. CHILDREN:	50%	DINNER:	£12

TELEPHONE

- Operator assisted calls within Ireland Dial 10
- International telephone operator Dial 114
- Directory Enquiries Dial 1190

FOR TROUBLE-FREE TELEPHONE CALLS FROM PUBLIC PAY PHONES IT IS ADVISABLE TO PURCHASE A TELEPHONE CALLCARD AVAILABLE IN POST OFFICES AND WHEREVER YOU SEE A CALLCARD SIGN.

TO DIAL IRELAND FROM ABROAD: Country Access Code + 353 + Area Code (omit first zero) + Local Number

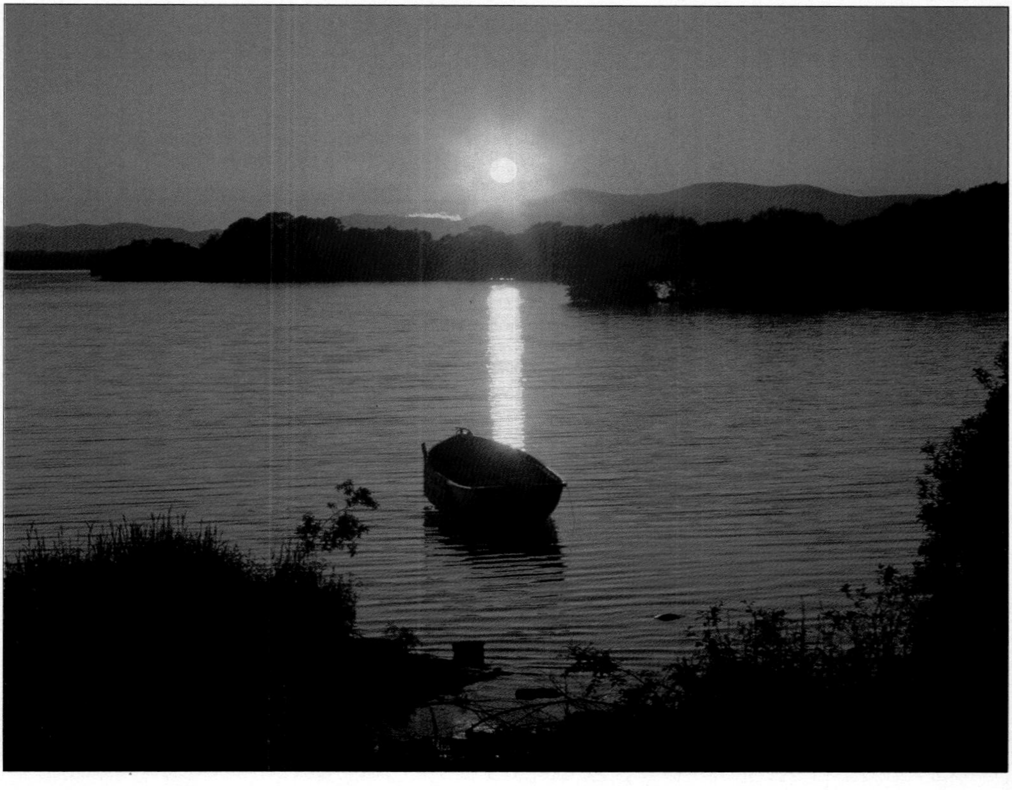

In Arklow

Deirdre Bishop-Power
VALENTIA
Coolgreany Rd, Arklow, Co Wicklow   Arklow

OPEN:	1st March-15th November
NO. ROOMS:	4
ENSUITE:	4

TEL: **0402 39200/32750**   FAX: **0402 39200**

Luxurious bungalow situated quiet road, 5 mins Town Centre close Beach, Golf & Tennis, Horse-riding, Fishing. All of which we can arrange.

| B&B PPS: | **£17/£19** | SNGL OCC. DBLE/TPL: | **£23.50/£25.50** | SNGL RM: | - |
| PART BRD: | - | % RED. CHILDREN: | **50%** | DINNER: | - |

Arklow 1km

Mrs Margaret Connors
GLENDALE HOUSE
Wexford Road, Arklow, Co Wicklow   Arklow

OPEN:	All Year
NO. ROOMS:	3
ENSUITE:	1

TEL: **0402 32816**   FAX: -

Comfortable friendly accommodation in picturesque landscaped gardens N11. All amenities closeby. TV/Coffee/Tea facilities. Credit Cards accepted.

| B&B PPS: | **£15/£17.50** | SNGL OCC. DBLE/TPL: | **£21.50/£24** | SNGL RM: | **£21.50/£23.50** |
| PART BRD: | - | % RED. CHILDREN: | **50%** | DINNER: | - |

Arklow 1km

Mrs Lourdes Crotty
VALE VIEW
Coolgreaney Rd, Arklow, Co Wicklow   Arklow

OPEN:	1st March-30th November
NO. ROOMS:	6
ENSUITE:	4

TEL: **0402 32622**   FAX: **0402 32622**

Edwardian house with period furnishings on landscaped gardens. Panoramic views. Conservatory, Sun Lounge, Tea/Coffee. 5 mins walk town centre.

| B&B PPS: | **£15.50/£18.50** | SNGL OCC. DBLE/TPL: | **£22/£26** | SNGL RM: | - |
| PART BRD: | - | % RED. CHILDREN: | **25%** | DINNER: | - |

Arklow 1km

Roy & Marie Dempsey
NAOMH GERARD
Monument Lane, Dublin Rd, Arklow, Co Wicklow   Arklow

OPEN:	1st March-1st November
NO. ROOMS:	3
ENSUITE:	3

TEL: **0402 39319**   FAX: -

Family home, spacious gardens, off N11, panoramic view. 10 mins walk to Arklow Town, Sea, Golf, Restaurants and Leisure Facilities.

| B&B PPS: | **£17** | SNGL OCC. DBLE/TPL: | **£23.50** | SNGL RM: | - |
| PART BRD: | - | % RED. CHILDREN: | - | DINNER: | - |

In Arklow

Dennehy Family
LAKEVILLA
Seaview Avenue, Ferrybank, Arklow, Co Wicklow   Arklow

OPEN:	1st April-30th September
NO. ROOMS:	4
ENSUITE:	-

TEL: **0402 32734**   FAX: -

Quiet location, Beside Beach, Resort, Town & Amenities. Tea/Coffee facilities. 3 Shower rooms. Guest TV Lounge, Recommended Dillard 300 Best B&Bs.

| B&B PPS: | **£15** | SNGL OCC. DBLE/TPL: | **£21.50** | SNGL RM: | - |
| PART BRD: | - | % RED. CHILDREN: | **33.3%** | DINNER: | - |

In Arklow

Mrs Dolores Fennell
DUNGUAIRE
Coolgreany Road, Arklow, Co Wicklow

OPEN:	1st May-14th September
No. ROOMS:	3
ENSUITE:	1

TEL: **0402 32774**   FAX: -

Spacious split level family home in Arklow on N11 route. Extensive garden, patio with panoramic views. Tea/Coffee in bedrooms.

B&B PPS:	£15/£17	SNGL OCC. DBLE/TPL:	£21.50/£23.50	SNGL RM:	-
PART BRD:	-	% RED. CHILDREN:	25%	DINNER:	

Arklow 1km

Mrs Dina Hayes
TARA
Gorey Road, Arklow, Co Wicklow

OPEN:	March-October
No. ROOMS:	6
ENSUITE:	4

TEL: **0402 39333**   FAX: -

Charming Bungalow with conservatory, on N11. TV. Tea/Coffee, Hairdryer facilities in all bedrooms. Ireland guide highly acclaimed premises.

B&B PPS:	£15/£17.50	SNGL OCC. DBLE/TPL:	£21.50/£24	SNGL RM:	-
PART BRD:	-	% RED. CHILDREN:	50%	DINNER:	-

Arklow 1.5km

Mrs Kathleen Hendley
SWANLAKE
Sea Road, Arklow, Co Wicklow

OPEN:	1st February-30th November
No. ROOMS:	3
ENSUITE:	3

TEL: **0402 32377**   FAX: -

Country home overlooking Beach & Caravan park on outskirts of town.

B&B PPS:	£17	SNGL OCC. DBLE/TPL:	£23.50	SNGL RM:	-
PART BRD:	£180	% RED. CHILDREN:	50%	DINNER:	£12

Arklow 7km

Mrs Deirdre Kelleher
RATHMORE
Coolroe Great, Arklow, Co Wicklow

OPEN:	All Year except Christmas
No. ROOMS:	3
ENSUITE:	3

TEL: **0402 37438/087 2208488**   FAX: **0402 37438**

Peaceful surroundings. Spacious bedrooms. Sun-room. 2km off main Arklow - Wexford Road(N11), turning left at Scarnagh Cross. Visa/ Access accepted.

B&B PPS:	£17/£17.50	SNGL OCC. DBLE/TPL:	£23.50/£25	SNGL RM:	-
PART BRD:	-	% RED. CHILDREN:	25%	DINNER:	£12.50

Arklow 1 km

Mrs Rita Kelly
FAIRY LAWN
Wexford Road, Arklow, Co Wicklow

OPEN:	All Year except Christmas
No. ROOMS:	4
ENSUITE:	3

TEL: **0402 32790**   FAX: -

Fairy Lawn 1 km from Arklow on N11, Tea/Coffee facilities in bedrooms. Recommended 300 best B&B Guide. Credit Cards accepted.

B&B PPS:	£15/£17	SNGL OCC. DBLE/TPL:	£21.50/£23.50	SNGL RM:	-
PART BRD:	-	% RED. CHILDREN:	50%	DINNER:	-

In Arklow

Mrs Paula O'Neill
WILLOWCREST
Coolgreaney Rd, Arklow, Co Wicklow

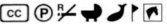
Arklow

OPEN:	**1st March-31st October**	
NO. ROOMS:	4	
ENSUITE:	4	(V)

TEL: **0402 39118**   FAX: **0402 39118**

Large split level house, in town, with Tea/Coffee facilities. Off main N11. All amenities closeby. Extensive Garden, Panoramic views.

B&B PPS:	**£17.50**	SNGL OCC. DBLE/TPL:	-	SNGL RM:	-
PART BRD:	-	% RED. CHILDREN:	**10%**	DINNER:	-

Arklow 1km

Mrs Rose Proctor
CEDAR LODGE
Wexford Road, Arklow, Co Wicklow

Arklow

OPEN:	**1st April-30th September**	
NO. ROOMS:	3	
ENSUITE:	2	(V)

TEL: **0402 32797**   FAX: -

Spacious Dormer Bungalow on N11. Ideal touring base. Dublin - Rosslare, one hour. Tea/Coffee in bedrooms. Credit cards accepted.

B&B PPS:	**£15/£17**	SNGL OCC. DBLE/TPL:	**£21.50**	SNGL RM:	-
PART BRD:	-	% RED. CHILDREN:	**25%**	DINNER:	-

In Arklow

Mrs Brenda Tyndall
ARKGLEN
Vale Road, Arklow, Co Wicklow

Arklow

OPEN:	**1st March-31st October**	
NO. ROOMS:	4	
ENSUITE:	3	(V)

TEL: **0402 32454**   FAX: **0402 39118**

Luxury bungalow, in beautiful grounds, off N11 Route. 5 mins walk to town. Tea/Coffee facilities in bedrooms. Credit Cards.

B&B PPS:	**£17.50**	SNGL OCC. DBLE/TPL:	-	SNGL RM:	-
PART BRD:	-	% RED. CHILDREN:	**10%**	DINNER:	-

Roundwood 3km

Mrs Anne Brady
GORSE HAVEN
Annagolan, Ashford, Co Wicklow

Ashford

OPEN:	**1st May-30th September**	
NO. ROOMS:	4	
ENSUITE:	3	(V)

TEL: **0404 40398**   FAX: -

Country residence on Ashford/Glendalough Road. Convenient to Glendalough, Roundwood, Devils Glen, Mount Usher, Dun Laoghaire 35mins, Dublin 55mins.

B&B PPS:	**£15/£17**	SNGL OCC. DBLE/TPL:	**£23/£27**	SNGL RM:	-
PART BRD:	-	% RED. CHILDREN:	**20%**	DINNER:	-

In Ashford

Mrs Phyl Long
BARTRAGH
Dublin Road, Ashford, Co Wicklow

Ashford

OPEN:	**All Year except Christmas**	
NO. ROOMS:	4	
ENSUITE:	4	(V)

TEL: **0404 40442**   FAX: -

300 metres from Ashford on Dublin Road, (N11). Walking distance to Pub/ Restaurants. 30 Minutes Dun Laoghaire Ferryport . Access/Visa/American Express.

B&B PPS:	**£17.50**	SNGL OCC. DBLE/TPL:	**£25**	SNGL RM:	-
PART BRD:	-	% RED. CHILDREN:	-	DINNER:	-

Ashford

Mrs Aine Shannon
CARRIGLEN
Ballinahinch, Ashford, Co Wicklow

TEL: **0404 40627**   FAX: -

Ashford 1km

		OPEN:	All Year		
		NO. ROOMS:	3		
		ENSUITE:	3		(V)

Modern bungalow 1 km Ashford, 45 min Dublin. Close to Devils Glen, Glendalough, Mount Usher, Horse Riding, Beach, Golf, Wicklow Mountains.

cc (P) 🔧 🐾 🏠

B&B PPS:	£17	SNGL OCC. DBLE/TPL:	£23.50	SNGL RM:	-
PART BRD:	-	% RED. CHILDREN:	10%	DINNER:	-

Avoca

Mrs Doreen Burns
GREENHILLS
Knockanree Lower, Avoca, Co Wicklow

TEL: **0402 35197**   FAX: **0402 35197**

Avoca 2km

		OPEN:	May-September		
		NO. ROOMS:	3		
		ENSUITE:	3		(V)

Bungalow in scenic peaceful surroundings near Avoca - The location of "Ballykissangel". Ideal touring area. Convenient to Handweavers, Glendalough, Dublin, Rosslare.

(P) 🔧 🐾 🏠

B&B PPS:	£17.50	SNGL OCC. DBLE/TPL:	£24	SNGL RM:	-
PART BRD:	-	% RED. CHILDREN:	-	DINNER:	-

Avoca

Mervyn & Jackie Burns
ASHDENE
Knockanree Lower, Avoca, Co Wicklow

TEL: **0402 35327**   FAX: **0402 35327**   EMAIL: **ashdene@tinet.ie**

		OPEN:	15th March-31st October		
		NO. ROOMS:	5		
		ENSUITE:	4		(V)

Many recommendations. Near Avoca. Handweavers "Ballykissangel!" Tennis Court. Tea/ Coffee facilities. Restaurants nearby. Convenient Dublin/Rosslare. Ideal touring/walking centre.

cc 🔧 (P) ✂ 🔧 🐾 🏠 (S)

B&B PPS:	£15/£17.50	SNGL OCC. DBLE/TPL:	£21.50/£24	SNGL RM:	£15
PART BRD:	-	% RED. CHILDREN:	25%	DINNER:	-

Avoca

Mrs Maisie Caswell
THE ARBOURS
Avoca, Co Wicklow

TEL: **0402 35294**   FAX: -

Arklow

		OPEN:	15th May-15th October		
		NO. ROOMS:	5		
		ENSUITE:	-		(V)

Set in forest with wildlife. Near handweavers, Avondale, Glendalough. Rosslare, Dublin 50 miles. Walking maps available. Frommer, Lonely Planet recommended.

🔧 (P) ➡ 🔧 🐾 🏠 (S)

B&B PPS:	£15	SNGL OCC. DBLE/TPL:	£21.50	SNGL RM:	£15
PART BRD:	£180	% RED. CHILDREN:	-	DINNER:	£13

Avoca

Aidan & Susan Dempsey
THE OLD COACH HOUSE
COUNTRY HOME & RESTAURANT
The Meetings of the Waters,
Vale of Avoca, Co Wicklow

TEL: **0402 35408**   FAX: **0402 35720**

Avoca

		OPEN:	All Year except Christmas		
		NO. ROOMS:	5		
		ENSUITE:	5		(V)

Restored Georgian Coach House. 500 yds Meetings of the Waters. Outside Village Avoca/Ballykissangel. Owner/Chef Restaurant AA QQQ. TV bedrooms.

cc 🍴 🔧 🕐 (P) ✂ 🔲 ✕ 🖥 ➡ 🌸 🔧 🐾 🏠

B&B PPS:	£20/£24	SNGL OCC. DBLE/TPL:	£26.50/£30.50	SNGL RM:	-
PART BRD:	-	% RED. CHILDREN:	50%	DINNER:	£19

Avoca 3km

Mrs Rose Gilroy
KOLIBA
Beech Road, Avoca, Co Wicklow

Avoca

TEL: **0402 32737**   FAX: **0402 32737**

OPEN:	All Year except Christmas
NO. ROOMS:	3
ENSUITE:	3

(V)

"Koliba" Country residence overlooking Arklow Bay/Vale of Avoca. Location of Ballykissangel. Dublin/Rosslare I hr. 3km Dublin side Arklow N11.

B&B PPS:	£17	SNGL OCC. DBLE/TPL:	£23.50	SNGL RM:	-
PART BRD:	-	% RED. CHILDREN:	25%	DINNER:	-

In Avoca

Mrs Bernie Ivers
CHERRYBROOK
COUNTRY HOME
Avoca, Co Wicklow

Avoca

TEL: **0402 35179**   FAX: **0402 35179**

OPEN:	1st January-22nd December
NO. ROOMS:	4
ENSUITE:	3

(V)

Bungalow in Vale of Avoca, home Ireland's oldest handweaving Mill. 5 Mins walk "Fitzgeralds Bar" Ballykissangel Fame. Derek McKenzie Hook recommended.

B&B PPS:	£17.50	SNGL OCC. DBLE/TPL:	£25	SNGL RM:	-
PART BRD:	£215	% RED. CHILDREN:	25%	DINNER:	£14

Redcross 4km

Phil & Pat Loughran
FOREST BAY
Lr. Ballinvalley, Barranisky, Avoca,
Co Wicklow

Avoca

TEL: **0402 39142**   FAX: -

OPEN:	13th March-30th September
NO. ROOMS:	3
ENSUITE:	3

(V)

Country residence 600ft above sea level overlooking Brittas Bay. Spectacular views/relaxing atmosphere. Home Cooking, Breakfast menu. Ideal touring base.

B&B PPS:	£18	SNGL OCC. DBLE/TPL:	£25	SNGL RM:	-
PART BRD:	-	% RED. CHILDREN:	25%	DINNER:	£14

Avoca 5 km

Mrs Aine McGovern
ROCKVIEW
Beech Rd, Avoca, Co Wicklow

Avoca

TEL: **0402 39011**   FAX: -

OPEN:	1st March-31st October
NO. ROOMS:	4
ENSUITE:	4

(V)

Quiet countryside overlooking Arklow Bay with panoramic view. Dublin/Rosslare I .5hrs. 3 km off Dublin side, Arklow N11, 5km from Avoca

B&B PPS:	£17	SNGL OCC. DBLE/TPL:	£25	SNGL RM:	-
PART BRD:	-	% RED. CHILDREN:	50%	DINNER:	-

Blessington 6km

Mrs Andrea Begg
AVELIN
Poulaphouca, Ballymore Eustace,
Blessington, Co Wicklow

Blessington

TEL: **045 864524**   FAX: **045 864524**   EMAIL: **begg@iol.ie**

OPEN:	All Year except Christmas
NO. ROOMS:	3
ENSUITE:	1

(V)

Quiet location near lakes. Within easy reach of Dublin, Powerscourt., Glendalough, Kildare. 4 miles south of Blessington near Maxol garage.

BUS NO. **65**

B&B PPS:	£15/£17.50	SNGL OCC. DBLE/TPL:	£21.50/£24	SNGL RM:	-
PART BRD:	£180	% RED. CHILDREN:	25%	DINNER:	£15

Mrs Maura Byrne
ESCOMBE
Lockstown, Valleymount, Glendalough Rd, Blessington, Co Wicklow

Blessington

TEL: **045 867157** FAX: **045 867450**

OPEN:	All Year except Christmas
NO. ROOMS:	6
ENSUITE:	5

(V)

By Lakes, Glendalough, Russborough 15 mins. Dublin, Ferries, Airport, Powerscourt, National Stud, Japanese Gardens, all 45 mins. Credit Cards accepted.

Blessington 11km

B&B PPS:	£17.50	SNGL OCC. DBLE/TPL:	£23.50	SNGL RM:	-
PART BRD:	-	% RED. CHILDREN:	25%	DINNER:	-

Angela Corley
SHALIMAR
Crosscool Harbour, Blessington, Co Wicklow

Blessington

TEL: **045 865259** FAX: -

OPEN:	All Year except Christmas
NO. ROOMS:	3
ENSUITE:	2

(V)

Luxurious home, scenic area on N81. 2 km North of Blessington. Dublin Airport, Ferries, Japanese Gardens, Glendalough 35 mins. Punchestown, Golf nearby.

BUS NO. **65**

Blessington 2km

B&B PPS:	£15/£19	SNGL OCC. DBLE/TPL:	£21.50/£25	SNGL RM:	-
PART BRD:	-	% RED. CHILDREN:	25%	DINNER:	-

Mrs Mary Curley
THE HEATHERS
Poulaphouca, Ballymore-Eustace, Blessington, Co Wicklow

Blessington

TEL: **045 864554/088 673112** FAX: -

OPEN:	All Year except Christmas
NO. ROOMS:	3
ENSUITE:	1

(V)

Bungalow beside Poulaphouca Lakes. 6 km Blessington, 3 km Russborough House. 25 mins Glendalough, near National Stud, Japanese Gardens, Golf, Angling.

BUS NO. **65**

Blessington 6km

B&B PPS:	£15/£17	SNGL OCC. DBLE/TPL:	£21.50/£23.50	SNGL RM:	-
PART BRD:	£185	% RED. CHILDREN:	20%	DINNER:	£15

Mrs Patricia Gyves
HAYLANDS HOUSE
Dublin Road, Blessington, Co Wicklow

Blessington

TEL: **045 865183** FAX: -

OPEN:	2nd January-21st December
NO. ROOMS:	6
ENSUITE:	5

(V)

Spacious bungalow on N81 in scenic area. Convenient to Dublin 30 mins Ferries, Airport. Bedrooms in quiet surroundings. Car park.

BUS NO. **65**

In Blessington

B&B PPS:	£15/£17	SNGL OCC. DBLE/TPL:	£21.50/£23.50	SNGL RM:	-
PART BRD:	-	% RED. CHILDREN:	25%	DINNER:	-

Mrs June Smith
THE CONIFERS
Poulaphouca, Ballymore-Eustace, Blessington, Co Wicklow

Blessington

TEL: **045 864298** FAX:

OPEN:	All Year except Christmas
NO. ROOMS:	4
ENSUITE:	2

(V)

Modern residence on the N81 in quiet rural setting adjacent to Horse Racing, Lakes, Mountains, Russborough, Dublin 40 mins.

BUS NO. **65**

Blessington 6km

B&B PPS:	£15/£17	SNGL OCC. DBLE/TPL:	£21.50/£23.50	SNGL RM:	-
PART BRD:	-	% RED. CHILDREN:	20%	DINNER:	-

Bray 1km

Tony & Ada Hopkins
GLENDALE B&B
2 Glendale Drive, Bray, Co Wicklow

Bray

OPEN:	April-September
NO. ROOMS:	4
ENSUITE:	4

(V)

TEL: **01 2863165**   FAX: **01 2863165**

Modern Residence with continental decor. Base for Touring. Golf, Fishing, Horse-riding nearby. Bus, Train service. Dunlaoghaire 20 min, Dublin 30 min

BUS NO. **45, 84**

B&B PPS:	**£17/£20**	SNGL OCC. DBLE/TPL:	**£25/£30**	SNGL RM:	-
PART BRD:	-	% RED. CHILDREN:	-	DINNER:	-

In Bray

Mrs Peggy Kelly
ROSSLYN HOUSE
Killarney Road, Bray, Co Wicklow

Bray

OPEN:	All Year except Christmas
NO. ROOMS:	4
ENSUITE:	4

(V)

TEL: **01 2860993**   FAX: **01 2862419**

Elegant Victorian residence beside Bray Town Hall. Close to Rapid Rail, Bus, Car Ferry, Mountains, Sea. 20km Dublin N11 route.

BUS NO. **45, 45A, 84**

B&B PPS:	**£17.50/£20**	SNGL OCC. DBLE/TPL:	**£25/£30**	SNGL RM:	-
PART BRD:	-	% RED. CHILDREN:	**25%**	DINNER:	-

Bray 1km

Mrs Alice Loughman
LOYOLA
Vevay Road, Bray, Co Wicklow

Bray

OPEN:	1st March-31st October
NO. ROOMS:	4
ENSUITE:	3

(V)

TEL: **01 2863757**   FAX: -

Highly recommended . Near Beach, Wicklow Mountains, Ferryports, DART.Golf, Horseriding, Tea/Coffee, TV , Breakfast Choice, DunLaoghaire 6 miles, Dublin 12 miles

BUS NO. **45, 84**

B&B PPS:	**£16/£20**	SNGL OCC. DBLE/TPL:	**£20/£30**	SNGL RM:	-
PART BRD:	-	% RED. CHILDREN:	-	DINNER:	-

In Bray

Mr William MacDonald
SANS SOUCI
Meath Road, Bray, Co Wicklow

Bray

OPEN:	10th March-20th November
NO. ROOMS:	6
ENSUITE:	3

(V)

TEL: **01 2828629**   FAX: -

Gracious Victorian House. Beside Sea. Comfortable bedrooms/Delicious Breakfasts/Elegant Dining Room/Spacious Lounge. Dublin 30 minutes. Available for conferences.

BUS NO. **45, 84, DART**

B&B PPS:	**£16/£21**	SNGL OCC. DBLE/TPL:	**£25/£40**	SNGL RM:	**£20/£25**
PART BRD:	-	% RED. CHILDREN:	**25%**	DINNER:	-

Bray 1km

Mrs Marie O'Dowd
ST GORETTI
Dublin Road, Bray, Co Wicklow

Bray

OPEN:	1st March-19th December
NO. ROOMS:	3
ENSUITE:	2

(V)

TEL: **01 2822976**   FAX: -

Modern residence on N11. Close to Bus, Rail and Car Ferry. Dublin 12 miles, Dun Laoghaire 6 miles. Tea/Coffee facilities.

BUS NO. **45, 45a, 84**

B&B PPS:	**£16/£20**	SNGL OCC. DBLE/TPL:	**£22.50/£26.50**	SNGL RM:	-
PART BRD:	-	% RED. CHILDREN:	-	DINNER:	-

In Bray

Mrs Kathleen Roseingrave
IVERAGH
44 Meath Road, Bray, Co Wicklow

OPEN:	17th March-30th October
NO. ROOMS:	6
ENSUITE:	4

Ⓥ

TEL: **01 2863877**   FAX: -

Detached period residence beside sea. Close to Rapid Rail, Bus, Car Ferry, Sporting Amenities. Dun Laoghaire 6 mls, Dublin 12 mls.

BUS NO. **84 / 45**

B&B PPS:	**£16/£20**	SNGL OCC. DBLE/TPL:	**£20/£30**	SNGL RM:	-
PART BRD:	-	% RED. CHILDREN:	**10%**	DINNER:	-

In Bray

Mrs Christina Smith
RATHLIN HOUSE
Killarney Road, Bray, Co Wicklow

OPEN:	1st March-1st November
NO. ROOMS:	4
ENSUITE:	3

Ⓥ

TEL: **01 2862655**   FAX: -

Victorian residence on 1 acre, beside Town Hall. Close to Sea, Rapid Rail, Bus, Car Ferry, Sporting Amenities. Dublin 20km (N11).

BUS NO. **45, 45A, 84, 85,**

B&B PPS:	**£17.50/£20**	SNGL OCC. DBLE/TPL:	**£25/£30**	SNGL RM:	-
PART BRD:	-	% RED. CHILDREN:	**10%**	DINNER:	-

Brittas Bay 2km

Mrs Peggy Tighe
PARKWOOD HOUSE
Jack White's Cross, Brittas Bay, Co Wicklow

OPEN:	April-September
NO. ROOMS:	4
ENSUITE:	4

Ⓥ

TEL: **0404 47221**   FAX: **0404 47221**

Dublin/Rosslare 1 hour. 0.5km off N11. Walking distance Expressway Bus, Pub/Restaurant & Beach. Golf European Club 2km. Visa/Access.

B&B PPS:	**£17.50**	SNGL OCC. DBLE/TPL:	**£25**	SNGL RM:	-
PART BRD:	-	% RED. CHILDREN:	**20%**	DINNER:	-

Enniskerry 3km

Mrs May Clarke
CREGG HOUSE
Glencree Road, Enniskerry, Co Wicklow

OPEN:	1st March-30th September
NO. ROOMS:	3
ENSUITE:	-

TEL: **01 2863557**   FAX: -

Quiet rural setting with panoramic view of Mountains. Croquet Lawn. Close to Powerscourt Gardens, Golf Course and Wicklow Way.

BUS NO. **185**

B&B PPS:	**£15**	SNGL OCC. DBLE/TPL:	**£21.50**	SNGL RM:	-
PART BRD:	-	% RED. CHILDREN:	**25%**	DINNER:	-

In Enniskerry

Mrs Eilish Cummins
CORNER HOUSE
Enniskerry, Co Wicklow

OPEN:	1st January-22nd December
NO. ROOMS:	3
ENSUITE:	1

TEL: **01 2860149**   FAX: -

Old world style house situated in Enniskerry Village. Close to Powerscourt Gardens and Waterfall. All bedrooms have showers.

BUS NO. **44**

B&B PPS:	**£16/£17**	SNGL OCC. DBLE/TPL:	**£22**	SNGL RM:	-
PART BRD:	-	% RED. CHILDREN:	-	DINNER:	-

Enniskerry 1km

Mrs Kay Lynch
CHERBURY MONASTERY
Enniskerry, Co Wicklow

Enniskerry

OPEN:	**All Year except Christmas**
No. ROOMS:	3
ENSUITE:	3

(V)

TEL: **01 2828679**   FAX: -

Large Bungalow, Landscaped gardens. Ideal base for touring Wicklow. Convenient Powerscourt, Glendalough, Golf, Car Ferry, Airport, Dublin 20km.

BUS No. **44**

B&B PPS:	**£17/£20**	SNGL OCC. DBLE/TPL:	-	SNGL RM:	-
PART BRD:	-	% RED. CHILDREN:	-	DINNER:	-

Enniskerry 4km

Kay O'Connor
OAKLAWN
Glaskenny, Enniskerry, Co Wicklow

Enniskerry

OPEN:	**1st March-31st October**
No. ROOMS:	3
ENSUITE:	-

(V)

TEL: **01 2860493**   FAX: -   EMAIL: **johnb@indigo.ie**

Delightful bungalow. Just off Glencree Road, idyllic country setting. Beside Powerscourt and Wicklow Way. Convenient Car Ferries, Airport, Dublin 25 km.

BUS No. **185**

B&B PPS:	**£16**	SNGL OCC. DBLE/TPL:	-	SNGL RM:	**£20**
PART BRD:	-	% RED. CHILDREN:	-	DINNER:	-

In Annamoe

Mrs Carmel Hawkins
CARMEL'S
Glendalough, Annamoe, Co Wicklow

Glendalough

OPEN:	**1st March-31st October**
No. ROOMS:	4
ENSUITE:	4

(V)

TEL: **0404 45297**   FAX: **0404 45297**

Select home set in the heart of Wicklow mountains. 5 mins drive from Glendalough. Near Airport & Ferries. AA, RAC Approved.

B&B PPS:	**£17/£18**	SNGL OCC. DBLE/TPL:	**£27/£36**	SNGL RM:	-
PART BRD:	-	% RED. CHILDREN:	**25%**	DINNER:	-

Laragh 0.5km

Ann Kenna
AVALON
Glendalough, Co Wicklow

Glendalough

OPEN:	**1st March-31st October**
No. ROOMS:	3
ENSUITE:	3

(V)

TEL: **0404 45331**   FAX: **0404 45331**   EMAIL: **annkenna@tinet.ie**

"Avalon" amidst the Scenic/Historic Glendalough & Wicklow Mountains. Walkers paradise .5 km Wicklow Way. Ideal touring base. Convenient Airport & Ferries

B&B PPS:	**£18**	SNGL OCC. DBLE/TPL:	**£26**	SNGL RM:	-
PART BRD:	-	% RED. CHILDREN:	-	DINNER:	-

In Greystones

Malcolm & Penny Hall
GLANDORE
St Vincent Rd, Burnaby Estate, Greystones, Co Wicklow

Greystones

OPEN:	**1st January-31st December**
No. ROOMS:	4
ENSUITE:	2

(V)

TEL: **01 2874364**   FAX: **01 2874364**

House of great charm, set in mature gardens in beautiful old world estate. Five minutes from all amenities.

BUS No. **84**

B&B PPS:	**£17/£19**	SNGL OCC. DBLE/TPL:	**£23.50/£25.50**	SNGL RM:	-
PART BRD:	-	% RED. CHILDREN:	**50%**	DINNER:	-

Greystones 5km

Mary & Michael Hogan
THORNVALE
Kilpedder, Greystones, Co Wicklow

Greystones

OPEN:	All Year
No. Rooms:	5
Ensuite:	4

(V)

TEL: **01 2810410 /086 8121269**   FAX: -

Bungalow in the heart of the Gardening, Golfing Capital of Ireland. 30 min from Dublin on N11 route. 1.5 acre gardens.

Bus No. **184**

B&B PPS:	£17	SNGL OCC. DBLE/TPL:	£23.50	SNGL RM:	£20
PART BRD:	-	% RED. CHILDREN:	-	DINNER:	-

In Greystones

Mrs Kathleen Nunan
SILLAN LODGE
Church Lane, Greystones, Co Wicklow

Greystones

OPEN:	March- October
No. Rooms:	3
Ensuite:	1

(V)

TEL: **01 2875535**   FAX:

Situated off quiet road. Extensive grounds. Mountain & Sea Views. Close to City, Car Ferry and Rapid Rail Services.

Bus No. **84, 84X, 184**

B&B PPS:	£16/£25	SNGL OCC. DBLE/TPL:	£22.50/£31.50	SNGL RM:	-
PART BRD:	-	% RED. CHILDREN:	-	DINNER:	-

Greystones 6km

Mrs Denise Toolan
PRIMROSE LODGE
Kilquade Hill, Kilquade (Near Greystones), Co Wicklow

Greystones

OPEN:	1st March-31st October
No. Rooms:	3
Ensuite:	2

(V)

TEL: **01 2877291**   FAX: -

Overlooking Druids Glen Golf, Spacious Bungalow, Homely Atmosphere, Snooker, Tennis. Adjacent Glenroe. Ferry 30 minutes. Exit N11 Kilpedder for Kilquade.

B&B PPS:	£15/£35	SNGL OCC. DBLE/TPL:	£22/£41.50	SNGL RM:	-
PART BRD:	-	% RED. CHILDREN:	20%	DINNER:	-

In Greystones

Mrs Patricia Treacy
CASTANEA
Rathdown Road, Greystones, Co Wicklow

Greystones

OPEN:	1st March-31st October
No. Rooms:	4
Ensuite:	4

(V)

TEL: **01 2876373**   FAX: **01 2876373**

Secluded bungalow on own grounds. Convenient to Rail and Bus, Sea and Mountains, Restaurants, Cinema, Golf, Sailing, Tennis, Walking.

Bus No. **84, 84X, 184**

B&B PPS:	£17.50/£20	SNGL OCC. DBLE/TPL:	£24/£26.50	SNGL RM:	-
PART BRD:	-	% RED. CHILDREN:	33%	DINNER:	-

Blessington 2km

Mrs Kathleen Healy
HOLLYWOOD LODGE
Hollywood, Glendalough Road, Co Wicklow

Hollywood

OPEN:	1st March-30th October
No. Rooms:	4
Ensuite:	4

(V)

TEL: **045 864230**   FAX: -

Amidst the Wild Beauty of the Wicklow Mountains, near Glendalough. Dublin Ferries, Airport, National Stud, Japanese Gardens, Powerscourt, all 45 mins.

Bus No. **65**

B&B PPS:	£17	SNGL OCC. DBLE/TPL:	£23.50	SNGL RM:	-
PART BRD:	-	% RED. CHILDREN:	25%	DINNER:	-

TP and Frances MacDermott
AN T'AOIBHNEAS
Sliabhcorragh, Hollywood, Co Wicklow

Hollywood

OPEN:	1st March-30th November
No. Rooms:	3
Ensuite:	3

TEL: **045 864577**   FAX: -

Tasteful pleasant home in a natural environment with exquisite mountain views. Located 2 miles off N81 on Hollywood/Glendalough Road.

| B&B PPS: | **£17** | SNGL Occ. DBLE/TPL: | **£23.50** | SNGL RM: | - |
| PART BRD: | - | % RED. CHILDREN: | **50%** | DINNER: | - |

Hollywood 3km

Margaret Berkery
CULLAUN
Sea Road, Kilcoole, Co Wicklow

Kilcoole/Greystones

OPEN:	May-October
No. Rooms:	3
Ensuite:	3

TEL: **01 2875998**   FAX: -

Dormer bungalow, private car parking, only 5 km from Greystones and 30 mins drive from Car Ferry (via N11). Adjacent Glenroe/Druids Glen.

BUS NO. **84, 84A**

| B&B PPS: | **£17** | SNGL Occ. DBLE/TPL: | **£23.50** | SNGL RM: | - |
| PART BRD: | - | % RED. CHILDREN: | **50%** | DINNER: | - |

Greystones 5km

Mrs Teresa Marry
ROS NA RI
Kilmacanogue, Co Wicklow

Kilmacnogue

OPEN:	1st March-31st October
No. Rooms:	3
Ensuite:	3

TEL: **01 2860034**   FAX: -

Country house scenic location one acre landscaped gardens between Great & Little Sugarloaf Mountains, with private car parking.

| B&B PPS: | **£17.50** | SNGL Occ. DBLE/TPL: | **£23.50** | SNGL RM: | - |
| PART BRD: | - | % RED. CHILDREN: | - | DINNER: | - |

In Bray

Catherine Tierney
DRUIDS HOUSE
Kilmacullagh, Newtownmountkennedy, Co Wicklow

Newtownmountkennedy

OPEN:	1st January-31st December
No. Rooms:	3
Ensuite:	3

TEL: **01 2819477**   FAX: -

Base Glendalough, Powerscourt, Mountusher Gardens, Glenroe. Walking distance Druids Glen Golf. Dublin 30 minutes. Breakfast menu. Tea/Coffee/TV all rooms.

| B&B PPS: | **£17** | SNGL Occ. DBLE/TPL: | **£23.50** | SNGL RM: | - |
| PART BRD: | - | % RED. CHILDREN: | **25%** | DINNER: | - |

In Newtownmountkennedy

Mrs Ann Griffin
LETTERMORE
Corballis, Rathdrum, Co Wicklow

Rathdrum

OPEN:	1st March-31st October
No. Rooms:	6
Ensuite:	3

TEL: **0404 46506**   FAX: -

Country home 2 km south of Rathdrum on Avoca Rd, adjacent Avondale, Meeting of the Water, Glendalough. Credit Cards accepted. Tea/Coffee facilities.

| B&B PPS: | **£15/£17** | SNGL Occ. DBLE/TPL: | **£21.50/£23.50** | SNGL RM: | - |
| PART BRD: | **£190** | % RED. CHILDREN: | **25%** | DINNER: | **£12** |

Rathdrum 2km

Rathdrum 1km

Mrs Carmel Jordan
BEECHLAWN
Corballis, Rathdrum, Co Wicklow

Rathdrum

OPEN:	**1st April-31st October**
NO. ROOMS:	4
ENSUITE:	3

(V)

TEL: **0404 46474**   FAX: -

Bungalow on 1.5 acres on Rathdrum/Avoca Rd. Close to Avondale, Glendalough, Bus, Train Station. Bike rental arranged. Tea/Coffee facilities.

B&B PPS:	**£15/£18**	SNGL OCC. DBLE/TPL:	**£21.50/£24.50**	SNGL RM:	-
PART BRD:	**£180**	% RED. CHILDREN:	**25%**	DINNER:	**£12**

Rathdrum 2km

Mrs Maeve Scott
ST. BRIDGET'S
Corballis, Rathdrum, Co Wicklow

Rathdrum

OPEN:	**All Year except Christmas**
NO. ROOMS:	3
ENSUITE:	-

(V)

TEL: **0404 46477**   FAX: -

Quiet, countryside location, 2 mins off main Rathdrum/Avoca Road. Adjacent Avondale, Meetings of the Water, Glendalough. Bedrooms ground floor.

B&B PPS:	**£15.50/£16.50**	SNGL OCC. DBLE/TPL:	**£22/£25**	SNGL RM:	-
PART BRD:	**£200**	% RED. CHILDREN:	**10%**	DINNER:	**£14**

Rathdrum 0.5km

Mrs Eileen Sheehan
THE HAWTHORNS
Corballis, Rathdrum, Co Wicklow

Rathdrum

OPEN:	**All Year except Christmas**
NO. ROOMS:	3
ENSUITE:	1

(V)

TEL: **0404 46683/46217**   FAX: **0404 46217**

Modern bungalow in large garden on Avoca Road. Close to Train and Bus services. Close to Avondale, Glendalough. Access, Visa.

B&B PPS:	**£15/£18**	SNGL OCC. DBLE/TPL:	**£21.50/£24.50**	SNGL RM:	-
PART BRD:	-	% RED. CHILDREN:	**50%**	DINNER:	-

Rathdrum 3km

Aedamar & Tony Walsh
MOUNT BRACKEN HOUSE
Cunniamstown Beg, Rathdrum, Co Wicklow

Rathdrum

OPEN:	**All Year except Christmas**
NO. ROOMS:	6
ENSUITE:	6

(V)

TEL: **0404 46311**   FAX: **0404 46922**

Country home with picturesque and peaceful surroundings. Main Rathdrum/Glenealy Road. Adjacent Avondale, Meeting of the Waters, Avoca, Glendalough, Wicklow Way.

B&B PPS:	**£19.50**	SNGL OCC. DBLE/TPL:	**£26**	SNGL RM:	-
PART BRD:	-	% RED. CHILDREN:	**50%**	DINNER:	-

Roundwood 2km

Mrs Nancy O'Brien
WOODSIDE
Roundwood, Co Wicklow

Roundwood

OPEN:	**1st March-30th September**
NO. ROOMS:	3
ENSUITE:	2

(V)

TEL: **01 2818195**   FAX: -

Family home on the R755. N11 - 10 km. Glendalough 12km. Ideal location for touring Wicklow Mountains. Dublin via DART From Bray 1 Hour.

B&B PPS:	**£15/£18**	SNGL OCC. DBLE/TPL:	**£21.50/£26**	SNGL RM:	-
PART BRD:	-	% RED. CHILDREN:	-	DINNER:	-

— Wicklow 2km

Mrs Fiona Byrne
GLEN NA SMOLE
Ashtown Lane Marlton Road, Wicklow, Co Wicklow

Wicklow

Open:	March-November
No. Rooms:	4
Ensuite:	2

(V)

Tel: **0404 67945**   Fax: **0404 68155**

Comfortable family home. Award winning breakfasts. 2 km Grand Hotel off Wicklow/Wexford Road. Golf, Fishing arranged. Credit Cards Accepted.

B&B PPS:	**£15/£17**	Sngl Occ. Dble/Tpl:	**£22/£30**	Sngl Rm:	
Part Brd:	**£180**	% Red. Children:	**50%**	Dinner:	**£12.50**

— In Wicklow

Mrs Rita Byrne
ROSITA
Dunbur Park, Wicklow Town, Co Wicklow

Wicklow

Open:	All Year except Christmas
No. Rooms:	4
Ensuite:	4

(V)

Tel: **0404 67059**   Fax: -

Luxurious spacious home overlooking Wicklow Bay. Take coast road turn into Dunbur Park at Pedestrian crossing, 5 minutes from Town.

B&B PPS:	**£17/£18**	Sngl Occ. Dble/Tpl:	**£25**	Sngl Rm:	-
Part Brd:	-	% Red. Children:	**20%**	Dinner:	-

— Wicklow 2km

Catherine Doyle
DROM ARD
Ballynerrin Lr, Wicklow Town, Co Wicklow

Wicklow

Open:	1st March-31st October
No. Rooms:	4
Ensuite:	3

(V)

Tel: **0404 66056**   Fax: -

Newly built spilt-level home with splendid views of Mountains, Sea, Countryside. Ideal base for Dublin, Rosslare or touring South East.

B&B PPS:	**£15/£17**	Sngl Occ. Dble/Tpl:	**£21.50/£23.50**	Sngl Rm:	**£20/£22**
Part Brd:	-	% Red. Children:	**50%**	Dinner:	-

— In Wicklow

Mrs Lyla Doyle
SILVER SANDS
Dunbur Road, Wicklow, Co Wicklow

Wicklow

Open:	All Year except Christmas
No. Rooms:	5
Ensuite:	3

(V)

Tel: **0404 68243**   Fax: -

Overlooking Wicklow Bay. Through Wicklow Town, take coast road, 1km town centre. Frommer recommended and Elsie Dillards "300 Best B&Bs".

B&B PPS:	**£16/£18**	Sngl Occ. Dble/Tpl:	**£22.50/£24.50**	Sngl Rm:	-
Part Brd:	-	% Red. Children:	**50%**	Dinner:	-

— Wicklow 12km

Henry & Sarah Fleming
SARAVILLE
Redcross, Wicklow, Co Wicklow

Wicklow

Open:	17th March-30th September
No. Rooms:	4
Ensuite:	2

(V)

Tel: **0404 41745**   Fax: -

Residence situated in Redcross Village. 5 km off N11. Central to all tourist amenities in Wicklow, convenient to Dublin and Rosslare.

B&B PPS:	**£15/£17**	Sngl Occ. Dble/Tpl:	**£21.50/£23.50**	Sngl Rm:	-
Part Brd:	**£190**	% Red. Children:	**25%**	Dinner:	**£13**

Wicklow 1km

Mrs Helen Gorman
THOMOND HOUSE
St Patricks Road Upr Wicklow, Co Wicklow

Wicklow

OPEN:	1st March-31st October
NO. ROOMS:	5
ENSUITE:	2

(V)

TEL: **0404 67940**   FAX: **0404 67940**

Balconied house. Panoramic view Sea, Mountains. Frommer, Let's Go recommended. 1 km past RC Church, St. Patrick's Rd. Golf, Cycling arranged.

| B&B PPS: | £15/£17.50 | SNGL OCC. DBLE/TPL: | £21.50/£24 | SNGL RM: | £18/£20 |
| PART BRD: | - | % RED. CHILDREN: | 20% | DINNER: | - |

Wicklow 1.5km

Mrs Hilary McGowan
ARCH HOUSE
Ballynerrin, Wicklow Town, Co Wicklow

Wicklow

OPEN:	All Year except Christmas
NO. ROOMS:	4
ENSUITE:	3

(V)

TEL: **0404 68176/087 2371053**   FAX: -

Dormer bungalow with panoramic views of Wicklow Bay and Mountains. Golf , Fishing , Horseriding nearby. A friendly welcome awaits you.

| B&B PPS: | £16/£17 | SNGL OCC. DBLE/TPL: | £22.50/£23.50 | SNGL RM: | - |
| PART BRD: | - | % RED. CHILDREN: | 50% | DINNER: | - |

In Wicklow

Mrs Ann Mitchell
OLANDA
Dunbur Park, Wicklow, Co Wicklow

Wicklow

OPEN:	All Year
NO. ROOMS:	4
ENSUITE:	2

(V)

TEL: **0404 67579**   FAX: -

Bungalow in quiet location, 5 minutes walk to town. Take coast road, turn right at pedestrian crossing.

| B&B PPS: | £15/£17 | SNGL OCC. DBLE/TPL: | £21.50/£23.50 | SNGL RM: | - |
| PART BRD: | - | % RED. CHILDREN: | 50% | DINNER: | - |

Mrs Carmen Nolan
CARDEN
3 Ballyguile More, Greenhills Road, Wicklow, Co Wicklow

Wicklow

OPEN:	March-November
NO. ROOMS:	3
ENSUITE:	-

(V)

TEL: **0404 66070**   FAX: -

New luxurious country home with spectacular views of Wicklow Bay and Countryside. TV's all rooms. Opposite scenic view car park.

| B&B PPS: | £18 | SNGL OCC. DBLE/TPL: | £24.50 | SNGL RM: | - |
| PART BRD: | - | % RED. CHILDREN: | - | DINNER: | - |

Wicklow 2 km

Frank & Martina O'Rourke
SEACREST HOUSE
Ashtown Lane, Wicklow, Co Wicklow

Wicklow

OPEN:	All Year
NO. ROOMS:	6
ENSUITE:	4

(V)

TEL: **0404 67772**   FAX: -

Large Country residence, 2 Km Wicklow town, 3 Km N11 Dublin/Rosslare Road, Family Rooms available, Golf Holidays a speciality.

| B&B PPS: | £16/£18 | SNGL OCC. DBLE/TPL: | £23/£25 | SNGL RM: | - |
| PART BRD: | - | % RED. CHILDREN: | 50% | DINNER: | - |

In Wicklow Town

Una Redmond
MAC REAMOINN TOWNHOUSE
Summerhill, Wicklow Town, Co Wicklow

Wicklow

OPEN:	1st February-21st December
NO. ROOMS:	4
ENSUITE:	4

(V)

TEL: **0404 61113**   FAX: -

A warm welcome awaits you at our tastefully decorated townhouse. A stroll from many Restaurants and Pubs. Ideal touring base.

| B&B PPS: | **£18/£20** | SNGL OCC. DBLE/TPL: | **£24.50/£26.50** | SNGL RM: | - |
| PART BRD: | - | % RED. CHILDREN: | **33.3%** | DINNER: | - |

Wicklow 4km

Mrs Ellen Sinnott
CRAMOND HOUSE
Ballinteskin, Wicklow, Co Wicklow

Wicklow

OPEN:	All Year except Christmas
NO. ROOMS:	3
ENSUITE:	3

(V)

TEL: **0404 69822/086 8174433**   FAX: -

Family home set on 2 acres mature gardens. Relaxing location just outside Wicklow town. Warm welcome assured golf & beaches nearby.

| B&B PPS: | **£17** | SNGL OCC. DBLE/TPL: | **£23.50** | SNGL RM: | - |
| PART BRD: | - | % RED. CHILDREN: | **50%** | DINNER: | - |

Dunluce Castle.

Take it all in.

Make sure Northern Ireland is part of your holiday plans this year. Go North and experience all the wonders for yourself.

A cruise on the Fermanagh Lakes. A hill walk in the Sperrins. Breathe in the beauty of the Giant's Causeway. The Mountains of Mourne. The green Glens of Antrim.

Touch the history of Derry. Of Armagh's Cathedral city. And the warmth of the people.

Golf. Fishing. Sailing. Horse-riding. Activities awaiting discovery in idyllic surroundings. Superb restaurants. Pubs and live entertainment. You're really spoilt for choice.

And don't forget to visit Belfast. A city steeped in history with a fine tradition of culture, crafts, sports and business.

Northern Ireland Tourist Board

16 Nassau Street, Dublin 2. CallSave 1850 230 230.
St. Annes Court, 59 North Street, Belfast BT1 1NB. Tel: 01232 231221.

© ERA-Maptec

Discover the North West and discover the best of Ireland! This is truly the greenest part of Europe's Green Island...unspoilt, uncrowded and undiscovered.

In the counties of Cavan, Donegal, Leitrim, Monaghan and Sligo there is a wealth of scenery, heritage and hospitality. With geography that ranges from wild Atlantic coast through gentle meandering rivers to sylvan lakeland, and a history that dates from Neolithic archaeology through to modern Irish writing, every interest can be met.

For the active there are classic links and parkland golf courses; superb equestrian centres; hill walking and mountain climbing; summer schools of every variety; wide open beaches, some with world class surfing; and at the end of every day Irish hospitality at its best in bars and restaurants.

Area Representatives

CAVAN
Mrs. Brid Myles, Halcyon, Drumalee, Cavan Town, Co. Cavan.
Tel: 049-31809. Fax: 049-62531.

DONEGAL
Mrs. Margaret Maguire, Hill Crest House, Lurgybrack, Sligo Road, Letterkenny, Co. Donegal. Tel: 074-22300 / 25137. Fax: 074-25137.

Mrs. Bernie Cahill, Lismolin Country House, Fintra Road, Killybegs, Co. Donegal. Tel: 073-31035. Fax: 073-32310.

Mrs. Mary Conlon, Teevogue, Bundoran Road, Ballyshannon, Co. Donegal. Tel: 072-51386.

LEITRIM
Mrs. Valerie Rowley, Corbally Lodge, Dublin Road, Carrick-on-Shannon, Co. Leitrim. Tel: 078-20228.

SLIGO
Mrs. Maeve Walsh, Cruckawn House, Ballymote/Boyle Road, Tubbercurry, Co. Sligo. Tel: 071-85188. Fax: 071-85188.

Tourist Information Offices

Sligo
Temple Street
Tel: (071) 61201

Carrick-on-Shannon
The Marina
Tel: (078) 20170

Cavan
Farnham Street
Tel: (049) 31942

Donegal Town
Tel: (073) 21148

Letterkenny
Derry Road
Tel: (074) 21160

Longford Town
Tel: (043) 46566

Monaghan
Market House
Tel: (047) 81122

In Bailieborough

Mrs Anna Mai Crosby
HILL TOP LODGE
Curkish Lane, Kingscourt Rd.,
Bailieborough, Co Cavan

TEL: **042 66320**　　FAX: -

Bailieborough

OPEN:	1st January-15th December
NO. ROOMS:	4
ENSUITE:	2

(V)

Modern dormer bungalow .5km from Bailieboro on Kingscourt Rd. In top class Angling, Hike Walking, Pony Riding available. Scenic area.

B&B PPS:	£16/£17	SNGL OCC. DBLE/TPL:	£22.50/£23.50	SNGL RM:	£15
PART BRD:	£180	% RED. CHILDREN:	10%	DINNER:	-

Cavan 4km

Mr Michael Cusack
GLEN VILLA
Stragelliffe, Cavan, Co Cavan

TEL: **049 62511**　　FAX: -

Cavan

OPEN:	All Year except Christmas
NO. ROOMS:	4
ENSUITE:	2

(V)

Family run modern home in quiet setting, convenient to Swimming Pool, Sports Complex, Equestrian Centre, Genealogical Research Centre, Golf, Fishing.

B&B PPS:	£15/£17	SNGL OCC. DBLE/TPL:	£21.50/£23.50	SNGL RM:	-
PART BRD:	-	% RED. CHILDREN:	25%	DINNER:	-

In Cavan

Ann & Paddy Gaffney
OAKDENE
29 Cathedral Rd., Cavan, Co Cavan

TEL: **049 31698**　　FAX: -

Cavan

OPEN:	All Year except Christmas
NO. ROOMS:	4
ENSUITE:	1

(V)

Warm hospitality, comfortable home, residential area, convenient to Town Centre. Bus route/Golf Club/ Equestrian Centre.

B&B PPS:	£15/£17	SNGL OCC. DBLE/TPL:	£21.50	SNGL RM:	-
PART BRD:	-	% RED. CHILDREN:	10%	DINNER:	-

Cavan 2km

Ben & Teresa Gaffney
ROCKVILLA
Moynehall, Cavan, Co Cavan

TEL: **049 61885**　　FAX: -

Cavan

OPEN:	All Year except Christmas
NO. ROOMS:	3
ENSUITE:	3

(V)

Modern home, 300m of the N55. Help with genealogical research in Cavan. Golf, fishing, equestrian centre, swimming, sports complex nearby.

B&B PPS:	£17	SNGL OCC. DBLE/TPL:	£23.50	SNGL RM:	-
PART BRD:	-	% RED. CHILDREN:	25%	DINNER:	-

Cavan 1km

Brid & Walter Myles
HALCYON
Drumalee, Cavan Town, Co Cavan

TEL: **049 31809**　　FAX: **049 62531**

Cavan

OPEN:	All Year except Christmas
NO. ROOMS:	5
ENSUITE:	4

(V)

Spacious family run home. Extensive library, help with Ancestral Tracing. Equestrian Centre, Swimming Pool Complex, Golf and Angling nearby.

B&B PPS:	£15/£17	SNGL OCC. DBLE/TPL:	£21.50/£23.50	SNGL RM:	-
PART BRD:	-	% RED. CHILDREN:	25%	DINNER:	£12

Killeshandra 2km

Mrs Maura O'Reilly
CLOONEEN HOUSE
Clooneen, Killeshandra, Co Cavan

Killeshandra

OPEN:	April-October
NO. ROOMS:	4
ENSUITE:	2

(V)

TEL: **049 34342**   FAX: **049 34342**

Dormer bungalow, Killeshandra/Belturbet Road (T52/R201) Ideal stopover between Dublin/Donegal. Help with Ancestral Tracing. Killykeen Park Walks, Fishing, Pony Trekking

B&B PPS:	£15/£17	SNGL OCC. DBLE/TPL:	£21.50/£23.50	SNGL RM:	-
PART BRD:	-	% RED. CHILDREN:	20%	DINNER:	£12

Virginia 3km

Mrs Julie Fox
LISDUFF HOUSE B & B
Lisduff, Virginia, Co Cavan

Virginia

OPEN:	All Year
NO. ROOMS:	5
ENSUITE:	5

(V)

TEL: **046 45054**   FAX: **046 45054**

Renovated 18th century Farmhouse ,N.3, overlooking Lough Crew, Hill of Four, Lough Ramor, Blackwater River, St Killian's Heritage Centre, Mullagh.

B&B PPS:	£18	SNGL OCC. DBLE/TPL:	£24.50	SNGL RM:	-
PART BRD:	-	% RED. CHILDREN:	10%	DINNER:	-

Virginia 1km

Mrs Emily McHugo
THE WHITE HOUSE
Oldcastle Road, Virginia, Co Cavan

Virginia

OPEN:	All Year except Christmas
NO. ROOMS:	4
ENSUITE:	3

(V)

TEL: **049 47515**   FAX: **049 47515**   EMAIL: **mchugo@iol.ie**

Warm welcome, complimenary tea & scones on arrival. Excellent cuisine. TV in bedrooms. Visit Newgrange, Loughcrew, St. Killian, Fore Abbey.

B&B PPS:	£18	SNGL OCC. DBLE/TPL:	£25	SNGL RM:	-
PART BRD:	-	% RED. CHILDREN:	-	DINNER:	-

Virginia 1km

Mrs. Bernie O'Reilly
ST. KYRAN'S
Dublin Road, Virginia, Co Cavan

Virginia

OPEN:	1st April-30th September
NO. ROOMS:	4
ENSUITE:	2

(V)

TEL: **049 47087**   FAX: -

Luxurious, ranch-type bungalow on Lough Ramor's shore. Panoramic view, mature gardens; excellent breakfast menu; electric blankets, tea making facilities.

B&B PPS:	£15/£18	SNGL OCC. DBLE/TPL:	£21.50/£24.50	SNGL RM:	-
PART BRD:	-	% RED. CHILDREN:	10%	DINNER:	-

TELEPHONE

- Operator assisted calls within Ireland   Dial 10
- International telephone operator   Dial 114
- Directory Enquiries   Dial 1190

FOR TROUBLE-FREE TELEPHONE CALLS FROM PUBLIC PAY PHONES IT IS ADVISABLE TO PURCHASE A TELEPHONE CALLCARD AVAILABLE IN POST OFFICES AND WHEREVER YOU SEE A CALLCARD SIGN.

TO DIAL IRELAND FROM ABROAD: Country Access Code + 353 + Area Code (omit first zero) + Local Number

Mrs Margaret Bonner
BAYVIEW HOUSE
Annagry
The Rosses, Co Donegal

Annagry / The Rosses

OPEN:	1st April-31st October	
NO. ROOMS:	5	
ENSUITE:	3	(V)

TEL: **075 48175**   FAX: -

Magnificent panoramic view Mount Errigal. Dunlewey Lakeside Centre 15 km, Glenveagh Park 25 km, Donegal Airport 3 km, Daniel O Donnells' Hotel 8 km.

B&B PPS:	**£15/£17**	SNGL OCC. DBLE/TPL:	**£21.50/£23.50**	SNGL RM:	-
PART BRD:	-	% RED. CHILDREN:	**20%**	DINNER:	-

— In Annagry

Charles & Marian Bennett
BAY VIEW COUNTRY HOUSE
Portnoo Road, Ardara, Co Donegal

Ardara

OPEN:	1st February-15th December	
NO. ROOMS:	6	
ENSUITE:	6	(V)

TEL: **075 41145**   FAX: **075 41858**

Spacious, overlooking sea. Large gardens. Breakfast award 1994. Recommended: Frommers, AA, Real Guide, Fodors. Tea/coffee facilities. Turf fire. Credit Cards.

B&B PPS:	**£17**	SNGL OCC. DBLE/TPL:	**£23.50**	SNGL RM:	-
PART BRD:	-	% RED. CHILDREN:	**25%**	DINNER:	-

— Ardara 1km

Colm & Therese Campbell
HOMEWARD BOUND
Hillhead (Glenties Road), Ardara, Co Donegal

Ardara

OPEN:	13th March - 31st October	
NO. ROOMS:	6	
ENSUITE:	6	(V)

TEL: **075 41246**   FAX: **075 41246**

Relax, enjoy grandstand view of this picturesque town, in peaceful surroundings. Wonderful family atmosphere, good home cooking with great coffee.

B&B PPS:	**£17**	SNGL OCC. DBLE/TPL:	**£24**	SNGL RM:	-
PART BRD:	**£190**	% RED. CHILDREN:	**50%**	DINNER:	**£13**

— In Ardara

Mrs Eva Friel
THALASSA COUNTRY HOME
Narin - Portnoo, Co Donegal

Ardara - Portnoo

OPEN:	February-November	
NO. ROOMS:	4	
ENSUITE:	4	(V)

TEL: **075 45151**   FAX: -

Magnificent Coastal region overlooking Ocean, Lakes, 18-hole Golf Course, Beaches, Scenic walks. Ancient Historic Monuments. Recommended Guide de Routard.

B&B PPS:	**£17**	SNGL OCC. DBLE/TPL:	-	SNGL RM:	-
PART BRD:	**£195**	% RED. CHILDREN:	**20%**	DINNER:	**£12.50**

— Ardara 5km

Vincent & Susan McConnell
ROSEWOOD COUNTRY HOUSE
Killybegs Road, Ardara, Co Donegal

Ardara

OPEN:	1st January-20th December	
NO. ROOMS:	6	
ENSUITE:	6	(V)

TEL: **075 41168**   FAX: **075 41168**

Recommended Le Guide de Routard, Interconnection, Rusejuber Ireland and 300 best B&B's. Fresh baked muffins for breakfast. Visa & Master Card.

B&B PPS:	**£17**	SNGL OCC. DBLE/TPL:	**£23.50**	SNGL RM:	-
PART BRD:	-	% RED. CHILDREN:	**25%**	DINNER:	-

— Ardara 1km

In Ardara

Ray & Eileen Molloy
GREENHAVEN
Sea & Mountain View Hse, Portnoo Road, Ardara, Co Donegal
TEL: **075 41129**   FAX: **075 41129**   -

Ardara

OPEN:	**All Year except Christmas**
No. ROOMS:	6
ENSUITE:	6

(V)

Frommer/Foder recommended. Relax and enjoy excellent view of Sea & Mountain from dining room. Lounge, Patio & garden. Brewed Coffee.

B&B PPS:	**£17**	SNGL OCC. DBLE/TPL:	-	SNGL RM:	-
PART BRD:	-	% RED. CHILDREN:	**20%**	DINNER:	

Ballybofey/Stranorlar 1km

Mrs Gertrude Patton
FINN VIEW HOUSE
Lifford Road, Ballybofey/Stranorlar, Co Donegal
TEL: **074 31351**   FAX: -

Ballybofey / Stranorlar

OPEN:	**1st April-30th September**
No. ROOMS:	3
ENSUITE:	-

(V)

Modern dormer bungalow. Ideal touring centre for Glenveagh National Park and Giants Causeway. Salmon Fishing, 18 hole Golf Course.

B&B PPS:	**£15**	SNGL OCC. DBLE/TPL:	**£21.50**	SNGL RM:	-
PART BRD:	-	% RED. CHILDREN:	**20%**	DINNER:	-

Ballyshannon 1km

Mrs Mary Conlon
TEEVOGUE
Bundoran Road, Ballyshannon, Co Donegal
TEL: **072 51386**   FAX: -

Ballyshannon

OPEN:	**May-October**
No. ROOMS:	4
ENSUITE:	3

(V)

Bungalow overlooking Bay on N 15, convenient to Donegal China, Belleek China, Celtic Weave, Beaches, Horse Riding, Golf. Rooms ensuite with TV.

B&B PPS:	**£15/£17**	SNGL OCC. DBLE/TPL:	**£21.50/£23.50**	SNGL RM:	-
PART BRD:	-	% RED. CHILDREN:	**33.3%**	DINNER:	**£13**

Donegal Town 22 km

Mary & Eddie Farrell
CARRICKBOY HOUSE
East Port, Ballyshannon, Co Donegal
TEL: **072 51278**   FAX: -

Ballyshannon

OPEN:	**All Year except Christmas**
No. ROOMS:	4
ENSUITE:	4

(V)

Always a warm welcome. Ideal base for touring local beauty spots, Donegal, Rossnowlagh, Bundoran & Belleek. All amenities within walking distance.

B&B PPS:	**£17**	SNGL OCC. DBLE/TPL:	**£23.50**	SNGL RM:	**£18**
PART BRD:	**£180**	% RED. CHILDREN:	**20%**	DINNER:	**£12**

Ballyshannon 1km

John & Clare Hughes
RANDWICK
Bundoran Road, Ballyshannon, Co Donegal
TEL: **072 52545**   FAX: -

Ballyshannon

OPEN:	**March-December**
No. ROOMS:	5
ENSUITE:	4

(V)

House situated on N15 overlooking the "Erne Estuary". Convenient all local amenities. Groups catered for. 1KM Ballyshannon. On Parle Francaise.

B&B PPS:	**£15/£18**	SNGL OCC. DBLE/TPL:	**£21.50/£24.50**	SNGL RM:	-
PART BRD:	**£180**	% RED. CHILDREN:	**33%**	DINNER:	**£12**

Ballyshannon 2km

Siobain & George Luke
ASPEN
Parkhill, Ballyshannon, Co Donegal

Ballyshannon

OPEN:	**All Year**
NO. ROOMS:	3
ENSUITE:	3

(V)

TEL: **072 52065**   FAX: -   EMAIL: **gluke@tinet.ie**

New purpose-built Bungalow. Friendly family atmosphere. Quiet location off N15. Enroute to Donegal Town (20kms). Convenient to all amenities.

B&B PPS:	**£17**	SNGL OCC. DBLE/TPL:	**£23.50**	SNGL RM:	-
PART BRD:	-	% RED. CHILDREN:	-	DINNER:	**£12**

Ballyshannon 3km

Mrs Agnes McCaffrey
CAVANGARDEN HOUSE
Donegal Road, Ballyshannon, Co Donegal

Ballyshannon

OPEN:	**All Year except Christmas**
NO. ROOMS:	6
ENSUITE:	6

(V)

TEL: **072 51365**   FAX: -

Georgian house 1750, Donegal Road (route N15) on 380-acres, 0.5km Driveway, Antique furniture, Beach, Golf Course, Fishing, Belleek. Frommer recommended.

B&B PPS:	**£17/£18**	SNGL OCC. DBLE/TPL:	**£23.50/£24.50**	SNGL RM:	-
PART BRD:	**£195**	% RED. CHILDREN:	**50%**	DINNER:	**£12**

In Ballyshannon

Mrs B McCaffrey
ROCKVILLE HOUSE
Belleek Road, Ballyshannon, Co Donegal

Ballyshannon

OPEN:	**1st April-30th October**
NO. ROOMS:	6
ENSUITE:	4

(V)

TEL: **072 51106**   FAX: -

Late 17th century, overlooking River Erne. Convenient to Bundoran, Rossnowlagh Beaches & Belleek Pottery. Experience peace & beauty of old refurbished building.

B&B PPS:	**£15/£17**	SNGL OCC. DBLE/TPL:	**£21.50/£23.50**	SNGL RM:	-
PART BRD:	-	% RED. CHILDREN:	-	DINNER:	-

Ballyshannon 5km

Mrs Rose McCaffrey
ARDPATTON HOUSE
Cavangarden
Ballyshannon, Co Donegal

Ballyshannon

OPEN:	**All Year except Christmas**
NO. ROOMS:	6
ENSUITE:	6

(V)

TEL: **072 51546**   FAX: -

Period house (route N15) on 380 acres. Log fires, Canoeing, Water Sking, Golf, Beaches. Frommer recommended also 300 Best B & Bs

B&B PPS:	**£17**	SNGL OCC. DBLE/TPL:	**£23.50**	SNGL RM:	-
PART BRD:	**£180**	% RED. CHILDREN:	**50%**	DINNER:	**£14**

Ballyshannon 2km

Kate Melly
"KALMIA"
Finner, Ballyshannon, Co Donegal

Ballyshannon

OPEN:	**June-August**
NO. ROOMS:	5
ENSUITE:	5

(V)

TEL: **072 51549**   FAX: -

Modern bungalow mid-way between Bundoran - Ballyshannon. Convenient to Beaches, Horse Riding, Golf, Water-skiing, Donegal China, Belleek Pottery.

B&B PPS:	**£17**	SNGL OCC. DBLE/TPL:	**£23.50**	SNGL RM:	-
PART BRD:	-	% RED. CHILDREN:	-	DINNER:	-

In Ballyshannon

Mrs Bridget Nolan-Coyle
MULLAC NA SI
Bishop Street, Ballyshannon, Co Donegal

TEL: **072 52702**   FAX: **072 52702**

Ballyshannon

OPEN:	1st March-31st October
NO. ROOMS:	3
ENSUITE:	2

(V)

Modern house in scenic location. Convenient to Beach and all amenities. Ideal touring base for Donegal/North West. Within town boundary.

| B&B PPS: | £15/£17 | SNGL OCC. DBLE/TPL: | £21.50/£23.50 | SNGL RM: | - |
| PART BRD: | - | % RED. CHILDREN: | 20% | DINNER: | |

In Bundoran

Mrs Mary Delaney & Family
STRAND VIEW HOUSE
East End Bundoran, Co Donegal

TEL: **072 41519**   FAX: -

Bundoran

OPEN:	All Year except Christmas
NO. ROOMS:	6
ENSUITE:	6

(V)

Mature modern townhouse, on main route (N15). Beside Beach, Golf Course, Waterworld. All rooms have TV. Beside Restaurants.

| B&B PPS: | £17 | SNGL OCC. DBLE/TPL: | - | SNGL RM: | - |
| PART BRD: | - | % RED. CHILDREN: | 20% | DINNER: | £12 |

In Bundoran

Bernie Dillon
GILLAROO LODGE
West End, Bundoran, Co Donegal

TEL: **072 42357**   FAX: **072 42172**   EMAIL: **gillaroo@iol.ie**

Bundoran

OPEN:	All Year except Christmas
NO. ROOMS:	4
ENSUITE:	3

(V)

Superbly located spacious B&B on Main Road, close to Beaches, Waterworld, Golf, Hillwalking, Angling Centre, Permits, Boats. Drying room available.

| B&B PPS: | £15/£17 | SNGL OCC. DBLE/TPL: | £22.50/£23.50 | SNGL RM: | - |
| PART BRD: | - | % RED. CHILDREN: | 25% | DINNER: | - |

Bundoran 1km

Mrs Marlene Fergus
CEOL-NA-MARA
Tullan Strand, Bundoran, Co Donegal

TEL: **072 41287**   FAX: -

Bundoran

OPEN:	1st March-31st October
NO. ROOMS:	4
ENSUITE:	4

(V)

Superb scenic location by the Beach, overlooking Atlantic Ocean. Golf, Fishing & Horse Riding nearby.

| B&B PPS: | £17/£17.50 | SNGL OCC. DBLE/TPL: | - | SNGL RM: | - |
| PART BRD: | - | % RED. CHILDREN: | - | DINNER: | - |

In Bundoran

Bridie Flannery
CANGORT HOUSE
Finnerville, Bundoran, Co Donegal

TEL: **072 41705**   FAX: -

Bundoran

OPEN:	March-October
NO. ROOMS:	3
ENSUITE:	3

(V)

New luxury home in peaceful location. Golf, Fishing, Beaches and Horseriding nearby. Tea/Coffee, hairdryers, TV in rooms. Home cooking.

| B&B PPS: | £17 | SNGL OCC. DBLE/TPL: | £23.50/£25 | SNGL RM: | £22 |
| PART BRD: | - | % RED. CHILDREN: | 50% | DINNER: | - |

Mrs Mary Hamrogue
CASA MIA
West End, Bundoran, Co Donegal

Bundoran

OPEN:	All Year except Christmas
NO. ROOMS:	4
ENSUITE:	4

TEL: **072 41684**   FAX: -

Spacious comfortable home on mature gardens. Convenient for touring, N 15. Golfing, Horse Riding & Trekking, Fishing & Waterworld. All with TV & hairdryers.

B&B PPS:	**£17**	SNGL OCC. DBLE/TPL:	**£23.50**	SNGL RM:	-
PART BRD:	-	% RED. CHILDREN:	**50%**	DINNER:	-

— Bundoran 1km —

Mrs J Martin
MOUNT ROYD COUNTRY HOME
Carrigans, Co Donegal

Carrigans Near Derry

OPEN:	All Year except Christmas
NO. ROOMS:	4
ENSUITE:	3

TEL: **074 40163**   FAX: -

Giants Causeway 1 hr. Grianan Aileach nearby. Groundfloor bedroom. Old style home. Galtee breakfast winner. Frommer, Guide de Routard, AA . Q.Q.Q.Q.

B&B PPS:	**£15/£17**	SNGL OCC. DBLE/TPL:	**£21.50/£23.50**	SNGL RM:	-
PART BRD:	-	% RED. CHILDREN:	**50%**	DINNER:	**£12**

— Derry City 8km —

Mrs Bernadette Doherty
HILL HOUSE
Dunmore, Carrigart, Co Donegal

Carrigart

OPEN:	January-November
NO. ROOMS:	4
ENSUITE:	1

TEL: **074 55221**   FAX: -

Large 2 storey house, overlooking Downings & Mulroy Bay. 1.5 km from Sandy Beaches & Two 18 hole Golf Courses. 15 km from Glenveagh National Park.

B&B PPS:	**£15/£17**	SNGL OCC. DBLE/TPL:	**£21.50/£23.50**	SNGL RM:	**£15**
PART BRD:	-	% RED. CHILDREN:	**25%**	DINNER:	-

— Carrigart 1.5km —

Ann & Myles Gallagher
SONAS
Upper Carrick, Carrigart, Letterkenny, Co Donegal

Carrigart

OPEN:	All Year except Christmas
NO. ROOMS:	4
ENSUITE:	4

TEL: **074 55401**   FAX: **074 55195**   EMAIL: **sonas1@indigo.ie**

"Sonas" Modern Dormer Bungalow overlooking Bay combining modern facilities with old style hospitality. Ideal touring base. Home baking, Power showers.

B&B PPS:	**£17**	SNGL OCC. DBLE/TPL:	**£23.50**	SNGL RM:	-
PART BRD:	**£180**	% RED. CHILDREN:	**33.3%**	DINNER:	**£12**

— Carrigart 5km —

Fidelma McLaughlin
FOUR ARCHES
Urris, Clonmany, Inishowen, Co Donegal

Clonmany - Inishowen

OPEN:	All Year except Christmas
NO. ROOMS:	5
ENSUITE:	5

TEL: **077 76561/76109**   FAX: -

Spanish styled bungalow, surrounded by Sea and Mountain. Ideal for Climbing, Swimming, Golfing and touring the Inishowen Peninsula.

B&B PPS:	**£17**	SNGL OCC. DBLE/TPL:	**£23.50**	SNGL RM:	-
PART BRD:	-	% RED. CHILDREN:	**50%**	DINNER:	-

— Clonmany 5km —

Creeslough 4km

Marjorie McFadden
LOCH NA TOOHEY
Ballyboes, Creeslough, Letterkenny, Co Donegal

Creeslough

TEL: **074 38061**   FAX: -

OPEN: **Easter-30th September**
No. ROOMS: 4
ENSUITE: 4
(V)

House extending to Fishing Lake, Boat Hire, Tennis Court. Central to Blue Flag Beaches, Golf, Glenveigh National Park, Ards Forest Park.

| B&B PPS: | £17/£20 | SNGL OCC. DBLE/TPL: | £23.50/£26.50 | SNGL RM: | - |
| PART BRD: | - | % RED. CHILDREN: | 20% | DINNER: | |

Malin 6km

Mrs Anne Lynch
CEECLIFF HOUSE
Culdaff, Inishowen, Co Donegal

Culdaff

TEL: **077 79159**   FAX: **077 79159**

OPEN: **All Year except Christmas**
No. ROOMS: 4
ENSUITE: 3
(V)

Family run home. Excellent views of Beach, River & Mountains. Close to all amenities. Home cooking, a la carte & Special diets.

| B&B PPS: | £15/£17 | SNGL OCC. DBLE/TPL: | £21.50/£23.50 | SNGL RM: | - |
| PART BRD: | £190 | % RED. CHILDREN: | 20% | DINNER: | £12 |

Donegal 8km

Mrs Sile Callaghan
THE GAP LODGE
Barnesmore Gap, Donegal Town, Co Donegal

Donegal Town

TEL: **073 21956**   FAX: -

OPEN: **All Year**
No. ROOMS: 5
ENSUITE: 4
(V)

Our spacious home is 10 mins drive from Donegal Town on N 15. Dinner available 6 pm to 8pm. Credit Cards accepted.

| B&B PPS: | £15/£17 | SNGL OCC. DBLE/TPL: | £21.50/£23.50 | SNGL RM: | - |
| PART BRD: | £180 | % RED. CHILDREN: | 50% | DINNER: | £12 |

Donegal Town 1km

Mrs Marie Campbell
LYNDALE
Doonan, Donegal Town, Co Donegal

Donegal Town

TEL: **073 21873**   FAX: -

OPEN: **1st April-31st October**
No. ROOMS: 4
ENSUITE: 3
(V)

Spilt-level bungalow, 200 metres off Coast Road (N56). Home baking, Breakfast menu. TV, Electric blankets, Hairdryers, Tea/Coffee facilities in rooms.

| B&B PPS: | £15/£17 | SNGL OCC. DBLE/TPL: | £21.50 | SNGL RM: | - |
| PART BRD: | - | % RED. CHILDREN: | 20% | DINNER: | - |

Donegal 1km

Mrs Kathleen Durcan
CRANAFORD
Ardeskin, Donegal Town, Co Donegal

Donegal Town

TEL: **073 21455**   FAX: -

OPEN: **1st April-30th September**
No. ROOMS: 3
ENSUITE: 2
(V)

Modern bungalow in peaceful location, yet convenient to all amenities. Ideal touring base.

| B&B PPS: | £15/£17 | SNGL OCC. DBLE/TPL: | £21.50/£23.50 | SNGL RM: | - |
| PART BRD: | - | % RED. CHILDREN: | 25% | DINNER: | - |

Mrs Sheila Gatins
HILLCREST COUNTRY HOME
Ballyshannon Road, Laghey, Donegal, Co Donegal

Donegal Town

OPEN:	**April-October**
NO. ROOMS:	4
ENSUITE:	2

TEL: **073 21837**   FAX: **073 21674**

Quiet location off N 15. Golf course, Beach nearby. Recommended 300 Best B&B's. Five mins drive Donegal Town. Tea/coffee facilities.

B&B PPS:	**£15/£17**	SNGL OCC. DBLE/TPL:	-	SNGL RM:	-
PART BRD:	-	% RED. CHILDREN:	25%	DINNER:	-

— Donegal Town 4km —

Mrs. Margaret Geary
"KNOCKNAGOW"
Ballydevitt, Donegal, Co Donegal

Donegal Town

OPEN:	**Easter-30 September**
NO. ROOMS:	3
ENSUITE:	1

TEL: **073 21052**   FAX: -

Modern bungalow situated in quiet countryside, close to all amenities. Ideal touring base, excellent shops, Crafts, Restaurants nearby.

B&B PPS:	**£15/£17**	SNGL OCC. DBLE/TPL:	**£21.50**	SNGL RM:	-
PART BRD:	-	% RED. CHILDREN:	20%	DINNER:	-

— Donegal 1km —

Mrs Mary J Harvey
CLYBAWN
Station Road, Mountcharles, Co Donegal

Donegal / Mountcharles

OPEN:	**April-September**
NO. ROOMS:	4
ENSUITE:	3

TEL: **073 35076**   FAX: -

Modern bungalow in scenic location overlooking Donegal Bay. Lake, River and Sea Fishing nearby. Donegal Town 6 km, Murvagh Golf Course 15 km.

B&B PPS:	**£15/£17**	SNGL OCC. DBLE/TPL:	**£21.50/£23.50**	SNGL RM:	-
PART BRD:	**£180**	% RED. CHILDREN:	33.3%	DINNER:	£12

— Donegal 6km —

Bried McGinty
MEADOW LANE B & B
Birchill
Donegal Town, Co Donegal

Donegal Town

OPEN:	**1st January-15th December**
NO. ROOMS:	4
ENSUITE:	4

TEL: **073 23300**   FAX: -

Luxurious Country Home on N15. Magnificient views of Bluestack Mountain. Ideal touring base.

B&B PPS:	**£17/£18**	SNGL OCC. DBLE/TPL:	**£23.50/£24.50**	SNGL RM:	**£18/£20**
PART BRD:	**£185**	% RED. CHILDREN:	25%	DINNER:	£12

— Donegal Town 4km —

Mrs Mary McGinty
ARDEEVIN
Lough Eske, Barnesmore, Donegal, Co Donegal

Donegal Town / Lough Eske

OPEN:	**1st March-20th November**
NO. ROOMS:	6
ENSUITE:	6

TEL: **073 21790**   FAX: **073 21790**

Country residence, magnificant view Lough Eske, Bluestack Mountains. Le Guide de Routard , Frommer recommended. RAC acclaimed. AA listed. Award winning B&B.

B&B PPS:	**£18/£20**	SNGL OCC. DBLE/TPL:	**£24.50/£26.50**	SNGL RM:	-
PART BRD:	-	% RED. CHILDREN:	25%	DINNER:	-

— Donegal 8km —

Mrs Noreen McGinty
THE ARCHES COUNTRY HOUSE
Lough Eske
Barnesmore, Co Donegal

Donegal Town / Lough Eske

OPEN:	**All Year**
NO. ROOMS:	**6**
ENSUITE:	**6**

 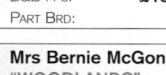

TEL: **073 22029**   FAX: **073 22029 (man)**

Luxurious residence, all rooms having panoramic views of Lough Eske/Bluestacks. Guide de Routard, Lonely Planet, Birrbauns recommended. Boating available.

B&B PPS:	**£18/£20**	SNGL OCC. DBLE/TPL:	**£25**	SNGL RM:	-
PART BRD:	-	% RED. CHILDREN:	**20%**	DINNER:	**£12.50**

Donegal Town 8km

Mrs Bernie McGonigle
"WOODLANDS"
Coast Road, Doonan, Donegal Town, Co Donegal

Donegal Town

OPEN:	**Easter-30th September**
NO. ROOMS:	**5**
ENSUITE:	**5**

TEL: **073 21453**   FAX: -

Modern bungalow on N56, 1km west Donegal town. Ideal touring base, Fishing Golf , Horse Riding close by. Tea/Coffee facilities.

B&B PPS:	**£17**	SNGL OCC. DBLE/TPL:	**£23.50**	SNGL RM:	-
PART BRD:	-	% RED. CHILDREN:	**20%**	DINNER:	-

Donegal Town 1km

Marie McGowan
THE WATERS EDGE
Glebe, Donegal Town, Co Donegal

Donegal Town

OPEN:	**All Year except Christmas**
NO. ROOMS:	**4**
ENSUITE:	**4**

TEL: **073 21523**   FAX: -

Sligo road, opposite School. Turn into cul-de-sac at Ballinderg House. 5th House down. Overlooking Bay/ 15th Century Abbey Ruins.

B&B PPS:	**£17/£22**	SNGL OCC. DBLE/TPL:	**£23.50/£28.50**	SNGL RM:	-
PART BRD:	-	% RED. CHILDREN:	-	DINNER:	-

In Donegal

Mrs Mary McHugh
LAKELAND
Birchill, Ballybofey Road, Donegal, Co Donegal

Donegal Town

OPEN:	**Easter-30th September**
NO. ROOMS:	**4**
ENSUITE:	**3**

TEL: **073 22481**   FAX: -

5 mins drive from Donegal Town on N15. Modern home with panoramic views of Lough Eske/Mountains. Ideal touring base.

B&B PPS:	**£15/£17**	SNGL OCC. DBLE/TPL:	-	SNGL RM:	-
PART BRD:	-	% RED. CHILDREN:	**20%**	DINNER:	-

Donegal 4km

Mrs Mary T Martin
"BAYSIDE"
Mullinasole, Laghey, Co Donegal

Donegal Town

OPEN:	**March-October**
NO. ROOMS:	**4**
ENSUITE:	**4**

TEL: **073 22768**   FAX: -

Coastal residence off N 15 overlooking inlet of Donegal Bay. Golf Course and Beach 1 km. Central touring location. Tea/coffee facilities.

B&B PPS:	**£17**	SNGL OCC. DBLE/TPL:	**£23.50**	SNGL RM:	-
PART BRD:	-	% RED. CHILDREN:	**33%**	DINNER:	-

Donegal Town 6km

Mrs Georgina Morrow
HIGHFIELD
The Haugh, Lough Eske Road, Donegal Town, Co Donegal

Donegal Town

OPEN:	February-November
NO. ROOMS:	3
ENSUITE:	2

(V)

TEL: **073 22393**   FAX: -

Peaceful country home on elevated site with beautiful view. Tea/coffee making facilities, Hairdryers all rooms. Ideal touring base.

B&B PPS:	**£15/£17**	SNGL OCC. DBLE/TPL:	**£25**	SNGL RM:	-
PART BRD:	-	% RED. CHILDREN:	**20%**	DINNER:	-

Donegal 2km

Mrs Bernie Mulhern
MILLTOWN HOUSE
Ardlenagh, Sligo Road, Donegal Town, Co Donegal

Donegal Town

OPEN:	All Year except Christmas
NO. ROOMS:	4
ENSUITE:	3

(V)

TEL: **073 21985**   FAX: **073 21985**

Spacious country home on N 15. Ideal touring base. Convenient to Beaches, Golf, Fishing, Craft village. Opposite Park Golf Driving Range.

B&B PPS:	**£15/£17.50**	SNGL OCC. DBLE/TPL:	**£21.50/£24**	SNGL RM:	-
PART BRD:	-	% RED. CHILDREN:	**33%**	DINNER:	-

Donegal 2km

Mrs Breege Mulhern
ROSEARL
The Glebe
Donegal Town, Co Donegal

Donegal Town

OPEN:	All Year except Christmas
NO. ROOMS:	4
ENSUITE:	3

(V)

TEL: **073 21462**   FAX: -

Modern spacious home in quiet residential area. 5 mins walk town-centre. Golf, Beaches, Crafts nearby. Ideal touring base.

B&B PPS:	**£15/£17.50**	SNGL OCC. DBLE/TPL:	-	SNGL RM:	-
PART BRD:	-	% RED. CHILDREN:	**33.3%**	DINNER:	-

In Donegal

Mrs Eileen Mulhern
ARDLENAGH VIEW
Ardlenagh, Sligo Road (N15), Donegal P.O., Co Donegal

Donegal Town

OPEN:	January-November
NO. ROOMS:	5
ENSUITE:	4

(V)

TEL: **073 21646**   FAX: -

Spacious home on N 15. Beautiful view of Donegal Bay and Hills. Donegal craft village 1 km. Golf course and Beach nearby.

B&B PPS:	**£15/£17.50**	SNGL OCC. DBLE/TPL:	**£21.50/£24**	SNGL RM:	-
PART BRD:	-	% RED. CHILDREN:	**33.3%**	DINNER:	-

Donegal 2km

Ms Caroline Needham
INCHBURGH B & B
Doonan, Donegal Town, Co Donegal

Donegal Town

OPEN:	1st April-1st November
NO. ROOMS:	3
ENSUITE:	2

(V)

TEL: **073 21273**   FAX: -

Modern Bungalow situated 3/4 km from Donegal Town. Peaceful location just off main road. TV's, Tea/Coffee facilities in all rooms.

B&B PPS:	**£16.50/£18.50**	SNGL OCC. DBLE/TPL:	-	SNGL RM:	-
PART BRD:	-	% RED. CHILDREN:	-	DINNER:	-

In Donegal

Mrs Anne-Marie Sheerin
ST CRONE'S
Main Street, Mountcharles, Co Donegal

Donegal / Mountcharles

OPEN:	1st April-31st October
NO. ROOMS:	4
ENSUITE:	3

TEL: **073 35132**   FAX: -

Modern family run home in centre of village. Ideal base for Touring south Donegal. Private parking. Tea/coffee facilities. Home baking.

B&B PPS:	£15/£17	SNGL OCC. DBLE/TPL:	-	SNGL RM:	£15/£17
PART BRD:	-	% RED. CHILDREN:	50%	DINNER:	

— Donegal 6km —

Mrs P Timoney
DRUMCLIFFE HOUSE
Coast Road, Donegal Town, Co Donegal

Donegal Town

OPEN:	All Year except Christmas
NO. ROOMS:	5
ENSUITE:	2

TEL: **073 21200**   FAX: **073 22667**   -

Lovely period home, with interesting furniture and antiques. Le Guide du Routard, Frommer, Franz Rappel, Von Birgit/Manfred, Wobcke recommended.

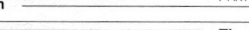

B&B PPS:	£15/£17	SNGL OCC. DBLE/TPL:	£22/£24	SNGL RM:	-
PART BRD:	£180	% RED. CHILDREN:	20%	DINNER:	£12

— In Donegal —

Mrs Marietta Herraghty
AN CROSSOG
Downings, Letterkenny, Co Donegal

Downings

OPEN:	May-October
NO. ROOMS:	4
ENSUITE:	3

TEL: **074 55498**   FAX: -

To a backdrop of Sea and Mountains, enjoy excellent food commended by International travel guides. 30KM from Letterkenny (R245).

B&B PPS:	£15/£17	SNGL OCC. DBLE/TPL:	£21.50/£23.50	SNGL RM:	-
PART BRD:	£180	% RED. CHILDREN:	25%	DINNER:	£13

— Carrigart 5km —

Fiona Kennedy
SEA VIEW
Ramonagham Lane, Dunfanaghy, Letterkenny, Co Donegal

Dunfanaghy

OPEN:	3rd January-21st December
NO. ROOMS:	4
ENSUITE:	3

TEL: **074 36505**   FAX: **074 36505**

Modern house, panoramic views of Beach/Pier. Golf Course and Hillsides, large gardens, Bar "B" Q and patio for visitors use.

B&B PPS:	£17/£18	SNGL OCC. DBLE/TPL:	£23.50/£24.50	SNGL RM:	£19/£22
PART BRD:	-	% RED. CHILDREN:	20%	DINNER:	-

— Dunfanaghy 3km —

Mrs Roisin McHugh
ROSMAN HOUSE
Dunfanaghy, Co Donegal

Dunfanaghy

OPEN:	All Year
NO. ROOMS:	6
ENSUITE:	6

TEL: **074 36273/36393**   FAX: **074 36273**

Luxurious modern bungalow with spectacular views. 300 Best B&B's recommended. Rooms alarm/radio, TV, Electric blankets, Hairdryers, tea/coffee. Breakfast menu.

B&B PPS:	£17/£18	SNGL OCC. DBLE/TPL:	£23.50/£25	SNGL RM:	-
PART BRD:	-	% RED. CHILDREN:	20%	DINNER:	£15

— Dunfanaghy 0.3km —

371

In Dunfanaghy

Mrs Anne Marie Moore
THE WHINS
Dunfanaghy, Co Donegal

Dunfanaghy

OPEN:	1st January-31st December
NO. ROOMS:	4
ENSUITE:	4

Ⓥ

TEL: **074 36481**   FAX: **074 36171**

Elegant home opposite beach, golf course. Recommended, for comfort, hospitality, and "fine breakfasts" - New York Times. Tea/Coffee, in residents lounge.

B&B PPS:	**£17/£18**	SNGL OCC. DBLE/TPL:	**£23.50/£25**	SNGL RM:	-
PART BRD:	-	% RED. CHILDREN:	**20%**	DINNER:	-

Dunfanaghy 0.2km

Bridget Moore
CARRIGAN HOUSE
Kill, Dunfanaghy, Co Donegal

Dunfanaghy

OPEN:	7th January-20th December
NO. ROOMS:	4
ENSUITE:	4

Ⓥ

TEL: **074 36276**   FAX: **074 36171**

Carrigan House is ideally located over the natural splendor of Horn Head and Atlantic Ocean. Tea/Coffee in residents lounge.

B&B PPS:	**£17/£18**	SNGL OCC. DBLE/TPL:	**£23.50/£25**	SNGL RM:	-
PART BRD:	-	% RED. CHILDREN:	**20%**	DINNER:	-

In Dungloe

Mrs Noreen Greene
SEA VIEW
Mill Road, Dungloe, Co Donegal

Dungloe

OPEN:	1st March-1st November
NO. ROOMS:	4
ENSUITE:	4

Ⓥ

TEL: **075 21353**   FAX: -

Spacious house overlooking Dungloe Bay and mountains. Convenient to Beaches and Golf Course. Ideal for fishing entusiasts. 5 min walk town centre.

B&B PPS:	**£17**	SNGL OCC. DBLE/TPL:	-	SNGL RM:	**£23.50**
PART BRD:	-	% RED. CHILDREN:	**50%**	DINNER:	-

In Dungloe

Mary Mc Cole
RONINNIS
Mill Road, Dungloe, Co Donegal

Dungloe

OPEN:	1st April-30th September
NO. ROOMS:	4
ENSUITE:	2

Ⓥ

TEL: **075 21094**   FAX: -

Modern spacious bungalow. Ideal Touring Centre, Glenveigh, Aranmore Island, NW Donegal. Golf, Fishing, Pitch and Putt and Sandy Beaches nearby.

B&B PPS:	**£15/£17**	SNGL OCC. DBLE/TPL:	**£21.50/£23.50**	SNGL RM:	-
PART BRD:	-	% RED. CHILDREN:	-	DINNER:	-

Dungloe 2km

Mrs B McLaughlin
MARTELLO HOUSE
Meenmore, Dungloe, Co Donegal

Dungloe

OPEN:	1st March-31st October
NO. ROOMS:	4
ENSUITE:	4

Ⓥ

TEL: **075 21669**   FAX: -

Family run Bungalow, peaceful setting. Breathtaking sea view. Ideal for Fishing, Golf, Beaches, Touring Arranmore Island, Glenveagh. Clock, Radios, Hairdryers.

B&B PPS:	**£17**	SNGL OCC. DBLE/TPL:	**£23.50**	SNGL RM:	-
PART BRD:	-	% RED. CHILDREN:	**50%**	DINNER:	-

Dungloe 1.5km

Mrs Patricia Sweeney
LAKE LODGE
Tubberkeen, Dungloe, Co Donegal

Dungloe

OPEN:	1st April-31st October
NO. ROOMS:	4
ENSUITE:	2

(V)

TEL: **075 21784**   FAX: -

Country Home in peaceful, scenic location. 1.5 km from Dungloe on Maghery scenic route. Beaches and all amenities convenient. Anglers paradise.

B&B PPS:	£17	SNGL OCC. DBLE/TPL:	£23.50	SNGL RM:	£17.50
PART BRD:	£190	% RED. CHILDREN:	50%	DINNER:	£12.50

Falcarragh 1km

Christina Cannon
CUAN-NA-MARA
Ballyness, Falcarragh, Co Donegal

Falcarragh

OPEN:	May-September
NO. ROOMS:	4
ENSUITE:	2

(V)

TEL: **074 35327**   FAX: -

Dormer bungalow overlooking Ballyness Bay & Tory Island. Glenveagh National Park 16 km. Golf, Hill walking, Electric blankets, Tea/coffee facilities.

B&B PPS:	£15/£17	SNGL OCC. DBLE/TPL:	£21.50	SNGL RM:	-
PART BRD:	-	% RED. CHILDREN:	50%	DINNER:	-

In Falcarragh

Ms Margaret Murphy
FERNDALE
Falcarragh, Letterkenny, Co Donegal

Falcarragh

OPEN:	Easter-15th September
NO. ROOMS:	4
ENSUITE:	1

(V)

TEL: **074 65506**   FAX: -

Bungalow on scenic route N.W. 200 m from Falcarragh. Beaches, Mountains, Fishing, Golfing nearby. Within easy reach of Glenveagh National Park.

B&B PPS:	£15/£17	SNGL OCC. DBLE/TPL:	£21.50/£23.50	SNGL RM:	£15
PART BRD:	-	% RED. CHILDREN:	50%	DINNER:	-

Killybegs 28km

Mrs J P Byrne
CORNER HOUSE
Cashel, Glencolumbkille, Co Donegal

Glencolumkille

OPEN:	April-September
NO. ROOMS:	4
ENSUITE:	3

(V)

TEL: **073 30021**   FAX: -

Situated in peaceful valley of Glencolumbkille, Ardara road, five minutes from Folk Museum, Sandy Beaches, Hill climbing & Good fishing.

B&B PPS:	£15/£17	SNGL OCC. DBLE/TPL:	£21.50/£23.50	SNGL RM:	-
PART BRD:	-	% RED. CHILDREN:	20%	DINNER:	-

In Glenties

Mary Ita Boyle
AVALON
Glen Road, Glenties, Co Donegal

Glenties

OPEN:	All Year except Christmas
NO. ROOMS:	4
ENSUITE:	3

(V)

TEL: **075 51292**   FAX: **075 51292**   EMAIL: **miboyle@tinet.ie**

Family run home, scenic location. Ideal touring base. Glenties, setting for Brian Friels play "Dancing at Lughnasa". Local museum, R253.

B&B PPS:	£15/£17	SNGL OCC. DBLE/TPL:	£21.50/£23.50	SNGL RM:	-
PART BRD:	£180	% RED. CHILDREN:	33%	DINNER:	£12.50

— Glenties 1km —

Mrs Margaret McCafferty — **Glenties**
CLARADON COUNTRY HOUSE
Glen Road, Glenties, Co Donegal

OPEN:	1st January-20th December
NO. ROOMS:	4
ENSUITE:	3

(V)

TEL: **075 51113**   FAX: -   EMAIL: **mccafferty@tinet.ie**

Scenic views, central for Co Donegal. Beach/Golf 8 miles, Scenic Walks, Fishing, Local Heritage/Museum. Tidy Town Winner. On R253.

B&B PPS:	**£15/£17**	SNGL OCC. DBLE/TPL:	**£21.50/£23.50**	SNGL RM:	-
PART BRD:	**£188**	% RED. CHILDREN:	**33%**	DINNER:	**£12.50**

— In Glenties —

Mrs Marguerite Mc Loone — **Glenties**
MARGUERITE'S
Lr Main Street, Glenties, Co Donegal

OPEN:	All Year
NO. ROOMS:	4
ENSUITE:	4

(V)

TEL: **075 51699**   FAX: -

Modern new house located in Town. Ideal base for touring. Beach/Golf 8 miles , local Museum, Scenic Walks, Fishing.

B&B PPS:	**£17**	SNGL OCC. DBLE/TPL:	**£23.50**	SNGL RM:	-
PART BRD:	-	% RED. CHILDREN:	**33%**	DINNER:	-

— Glenties 2km —

Jean Porter — **Glenties**
LYNDALE
Mullantyboyle, Glenties, Co Donegal

OPEN:	Easter-30th September
NO. ROOMS:	4
ENSUITE:	2

(V)

TEL: **075 51483**   FAX: -

Modern home. Central heating, Electric blankets, Turf fire, Home cooking. Ideal base for touring Glenveagh, Glencolumbcille. Country walks, Angling locally.

B&B PPS:	**£15/£17**	SNGL OCC. DBLE/TPL:	**£21.50/£23.50**	SNGL RM:	-
PART BRD:	**£180**	% RED. CHILDREN:	**33%**	DINNER:	**£12**

— Kilcar 1km —

Mrs Mairead Byrne — **Kilcar**
HILLCREST
Cashel,
Kilcar, Co Donegal

OPEN:	All Year
NO. ROOMS:	3
ENSUITE:	3

(V)

TEL: **073 38243**   FAX: -

Situated 1km on Carrick/Glencolmcille Coast Road. Homebaking, T.V. in bedrooms, Scenic walks, Fishing, Beach, Slieve League 9km.

B&B PPS:	**£17**	SNGL OCC. DBLE/TPL:	**£23.50**	SNGL RM:	-
PART BRD:	**£180**	% RED. CHILDREN:	**33.3%**	DINNER:	**£12**

— Killybegs 1km —

Mrs Bernie Cahill — **Killybegs**
LISMOLIN COUNTRY HOME
Fintra Road, Killybegs, Co Donegal

OPEN:	All Year except Christmas
NO. ROOMS:	5
ENSUITE:	5

(V)

TEL: **073 31035/32310**   FAX: **073 32310**

Frommer, Guide de Routard recommended. Quiet location, west of Killybegs. Mountain view, Scenic walks. Bedrooms have TV, Hairdryer, Electric blankets.

B&B PPS:	**£17**	SNGL OCC. DBLE/TPL:	**£23.50**	SNGL RM:	-
PART BRD:	**£195**	% RED. CHILDREN:	**30%**	DINNER:	**£13.50**

Killybegs 5km

Mrs Helena Cunningham
OCEAN VIEW
Largy, Killybegs, Co Donegal

OPEN:	**May-September**
NO. ROOMS:	**5**
ENSUITE:	**5**

 (V)

TEL: **073 31576**   FAX: -

Luxurious dormer bungalow on elevated site with spectacular view of Donegal Bay and Sligo mountains. Beach and Restaurants nearby.

B&B PPS:	**£17**	SNGL OCC. DBLE/TPL:	**£23.50**	SNGL RM:	-
PART BRD:	-	% RED. CHILDREN:	**25%**	DINNER:	

Killybegs 1km

Mrs Ann Keeney
HOLLYCREST LODGE
Donegal Road, Killybegs, Co Donegal

OPEN:	**March-October**
NO. ROOMS:	**4**
ENSUITE:	**3**

(V)

TEL: **073 31470**   FAX: -

Recommended 300 Best B&B's. Ideal touring base, 1 km East of Killybegs. Guest's TV lounge. Bedrooms Tea/coffee facilities, Hairdryers.

B&B PPS:	**£15/£17**	SNGL OCC. DBLE/TPL:	**£21.50/£23.50**	SNGL RM:	-
PART BRD:	-	% RED. CHILDREN:	**25%**	DINNER:	-

Killybegs 3km

Frankie & Ann McClean
CREDO HOUSE
Benroe, Killybegs, Co Donegal

OPEN:	**April-October**
NO. ROOMS:	**3**
ENSUITE:	**3**

(V)

TEL: **073 31364/087 413784**   FAX: **073 31364**

Quiet location by the Sea, Panoramic view of Killybegs Harbour. Fine food, fabulous scenery, friendly atmosphere, Fishing, Horseriding, Walking nearby.

B&B PPS:	**£17**	SNGL OCC. DBLE/TPL:	**£23.50**	SNGL RM:	-
PART BRD:	-	% RED. CHILDREN:	**25%**	DINNER:	**£12.50**

Killybegs 1km

Mrs Sadie McKeever
LOUGH HEAD HOUSE
Donegal Road, Killybegs, Co Donegal

OPEN:	**May-31st October**
NO. ROOMS:	**3**
ENSUITE:	**2**

(V)

TEL: **073 31088**   FAX: -

Inside Ireland recommended. View of Killybegs Harbour & Light House. Scenic walks nearby. Fishing trips arranged. Electric blankets. Smoke free home.

B&B PPS:	**£15/£17**	SNGL OCC. DBLE/TPL:	**£22/£25**	SNGL RM:	-
PART BRD:	-	% RED. CHILDREN:	-	DINNER:	-

In Killybegs

Phyllis Melly
BANNAGH HOUSE
Fintra Road, Killybegs, Co Donegal

OPEN:	**Easter-31st October**
NO. ROOMS:	**4**
ENSUITE:	**4**

(V̶)

TEL: **073 31108**   FAX: -

Modern bungalow on elevated site overlooking Killybegs Harbour and Fishing Fleet. Rooms ensuite. Private car park. Frommer recommended, 300 best B&B's.

B&B PPS:	**£17**	SNGL OCC. DBLE/TPL:	**£20/£25**	SNGL RM:	-
PART BRD:	-	% RED. CHILDREN:	**20%**	DINNER:	-

Mrs Ellen O'Keeney
GLENLEE HOUSE
Fintra Road, Killybegs, Co Donegal

Killybegs

OPEN:	All Year except Christmas
NO. ROOMS:	5
ENSUITE:	5

(V)

TEL: **073 31026** FAX: **073 31026**

Modern bungalow on main Killybegs - Glencolmcille Road, situated on right - hand side with fountain in garden. Beautiful Fintra Beach 1km.

B&B PPS:	£17	SNGL OCC. DBLE/TPL:	£23.50	SNGL RM:	-
PART BRD:	-	% RED. CHILDREN:	33.3%	DINNER:	-

— Killybegs 1km

Tully Family
TULLYCULLION HOUSE
**Tullaghacullion
Killybegs, Co Donegal**

Killybegs

OPEN:	1st March-30th November
NO. ROOMS:	4
ENSUITE:	4

(V)

TEL: **073 31842** FAX: **073 31842**

New luxurious country home. Conservatory. Secluded, elevated 2 acre site. Panoramic view overlooking Killybegs Port/Farmland/ Mountains. Boat shaped signs (N56).

B&B PPS:	£17	SNGL OCC. DBLE/TPL:	£23.50	SNGL RM:	-
PART BRD:	-	% RED. CHILDREN:	25%	DINNER:	-

— Killybegs 2km

Catherine A Walsh
OILEAN ROE HOUSE
Fintra Road, Killybegs, Co Donegal

Killybegs

OPEN:	1st March-30th September
NO. ROOMS:	4
ENSUITE:	3

(V)

TEL: **073 31192** FAX: -

Spacious 2 storey home, near Beach & Restaurants. Convenient to Slieve League, Glencolumbkille & Killybegs Harbour.

B&B PPS:	£15/£17	SNGL OCC. DBLE/TPL:	£21.50/£23.50	SNGL RM:	-
PART BRD:	-	% RED. CHILDREN:	50%	DINNER:	-

— Killybegs 1km

Daniel & Genevieve McElwee
FERN HOUSE
**Lower Main Street, Kilmacrenan,
Letterkenny, Co Donegal**

Kilmacrennan

OPEN:	April-October
NO. ROOMS:	4
ENSUITE:	4

TEL: **074 39218** FAX: -

Bright spacious two storey town house in centre of village on N56. Convenient to all amenities. Glenveigh National Park 16km.

B&B PPS:	£17	SNGL OCC. DBLE/TPL:	£23.50	SNGL RM:	-
PART BRD:	-	% RED. CHILDREN:	33.3%	DINNER:	-

— Letterkenny

Mrs Sophia Boyle
BRIDGEBURN HOUSE
Trentagh, Letterkenny, Co Donegal

Letterkenny

OPEN:	All Year
NO. ROOMS:	4
ENSUITE:	2

TEL: **074 37167** FAX: -

15 mins drive from Letterkenny N56 to village Kilmacrenan, turn left at signpost for Churchill - 5km. Ideal for Glenveigh, Glebe Gallery.

B&B PPS:	£15/£17	SNGL OCC. DBLE/TPL:	£21.50/£23.50	SNGL RM:	£15/£17
PART BRD:	£180	% RED. CHILDREN:	50%	DINNER:	£12

— Letterkenny 9km

Letterkenny 1km

Mrs Jennie Bradley
RADHARC NA GIUISE
Kilmacrennan Road, Letterkenny, Co Donegal
TEL: **074 22090/25139**   FAX: -

Letterkenny	
OPEN:	**15th January-1st December**
NO. ROOMS:	**6**
ENSUITE:	**6**

Frommer recommended spacious home overlooking town on N 56 to Dunfanaghy, 0.5 km above hospital. TV, Tea/coffee and Hairdryer in bedrooms.

B&B PPS:	**£17**	SNGL OCC. DBLE/TPL:	**£23.50/£25**	SNGL RM:	-
PART BRD:	-	% RED. CHILDREN:	**33%**	DINNER:	-

Letterkenny 1km

Mrs Elizabeth Cullen
ARDLEE
Gortlee, Letterkenny, Co Donegal
TEL: **074 21943**   FAX: -

Letterkenny	
OPEN:	**All Year except Christmas**
NO. ROOMS:	**6**
ENSUITE:	**5**

Modern house in quiet location, yet convenient to town, Bus Station. Tea making facilities + TV all rooms. Ideal touring base.

B&B PPS:	**£15/£17**	SNGL OCC. DBLE/TPL:	**£21.50/£23.50**	SNGL RM:	-
PART BRD:	-	% RED. CHILDREN:	**33%**	DINNER:	-

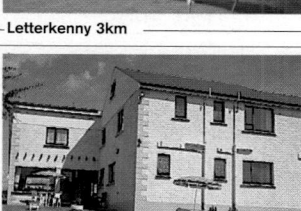

Letterkenny 3km

Mrs Mary Duggan
BELVEDERE HOUSE
Ballaghderg, Kilmacrenan Road, Letterkenny, Co Donegal
TEL: **074 23031**   FAX: -

Letterkenny	
OPEN:	**1st March-31st October**
NO. ROOMS:	**3**
ENSUITE:	**3**

Bungalow situated in quiet countryside overlooking Errigal, Muckish Mts. En route to Glenveigh National Park on N56. 400m off main road.

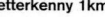

B&B PPS:	**£17**	SNGL OCC. DBLE/TPL:	**£23.50**	SNGL RM:	**£21**
PART BRD:	-	% RED. CHILDREN:	**33.3%**	DINNER:	-

Letterkenny 1km

Danny & May Herrity
TOWN VIEW
Leck Road, Letterkenny, Co Donegal
TEL: **074 21570/25138**   FAX: -

Letterkenny	
OPEN:	**All Year**
NO. ROOMS:	**6**
ENSUITE:	**6**

Frommer recommended regional breakfast winner. Cross bridge at Dunnes Stores, keep left for 1 km. TV, Tea/coffee, Hairdryers all rooms.

B&B PPS:	**£17**	SNGL OCC. DBLE/TPL:	**£23.50**	SNGL RM:	-
PART BRD:	**£200**	% RED. CHILDREN:	-	DINNER:	**£13**

Letterkenny 3km

Breid & Paddy Kelly
ARDGLAS
Lurgybrack
Sligo Road, Letterkenny, Co Donegal
TEL: **074 22516/25140**   FAX: **074 25140**

Letterkenny	
OPEN:	**1st April-31st October**
NO. ROOMS:	**6**
ENSUITE:	**5**

Spacious home admist magnificient scenery. 1KM from Dryarch roundabout on N13 to Sligo. Frommer recommended. TV, Hairdryer, Tea facilities.

B&B PPS:	**£15/£17**	SNGL OCC. DBLE/TPL:	**£21.50/£25.50**	SNGL RM:	-
PART BRD:	-	% RED. CHILDREN:	**30%**	DINNER:	-

Letterkenny 2km

Mrs Mary T Lee
BELLA VISTA
Dromore/Derry Road, Letterkenny, Co Donegal
TEL: **074 22529**   FAX: -

OPEN:	April-October
NO. ROOMS:	3
ENSUITE:	3

Quiet seculeded location overlooking Lough Swilly off Derry/Letterkenny dual carriageway (N13). Ideal for touring Donegal, Giants Causeway. Frommer recommended.

| B&B PPS: | £17 | SNGL OCC. DBLE/TPL: | £23.50 | SNGL RM: | - |
| PART BRD: | - | % RED. CHILDREN: | 50% | DINNER: | - |

Letterkenny 6km

Mrs Mary McBride
RINNEEN
Woodland, Ramelton Road, Letterkenny, Co Donegal
TEL: **074 24591**   FAX: -

OPEN:	1st March-31st October
NO. ROOMS:	3
ENSUITE:	1

Smoke-free home situated in peaceful countryside. Warm welcome. Convenient to local facilities. Ideal base for touring beautiful Donegal.

| B&B PPS: | £15/£18 | SNGL OCC. DBLE/TPL: | £21.50/£24.50 | SNGL RM: | £15/£18 |
| PART BRD: | - | % RED. CHILDREN: | 33% | DINNER: | - |

Letterkenny 2km

Mrs Maureen McCleary
GLENCAIRN HOUSE
Ramelton Road, Letterkenny, Co Donegal
TEL: **074 24393/25242**   FAX: -

OPEN:	All Year except Christmas
NO. ROOMS:	6
ENSUITE:	5

Panoramic view from patio, on R245 Convenient for Mount Errigal Hotel/Restaurants Golfing & touring. TV, hairdryers, Tea/coffee facilities all Bedrooms.

| B&B PPS: | £15/£17 | SNGL OCC. DBLE/TPL: | £21.50/£23.50 | SNGL RM: | - |
| PART BRD: | - | % RED. CHILDREN: | 33.3% | DINNER: | - |

Letterkenny 3km

Larry & Margaret Maguire
HILL CREST HOUSE
Lurgybrack, Sligo Road N13, Letterkenny, Co Donegal
TEL: **074 22300/25137**   FAX: **074 25137**

OPEN:	All Year except Christmas
NO. ROOMS:	6
ENSUITE:	5

Frommer, AA, RAC recommended home on Ballybofey/Sligo road. 1 km Clanree Hotel. TV, Hairdryer, Tea facilities, Orthopaedic beds all rooms.

| B&B PPS: | £15/£17 | SNGL OCC. DBLE/TPL: | £21.50/£28 | SNGL RM: | - |
| PART BRD: | - | % RED. CHILDREN: | 33% | DINNER: | - |

Letterkenny 3km

Mrs Sara Maguire
PARK HOUSE
Doobalagh, Sligo Road, Letterkenny, Co Donegal
TEL: **074 24492**   FAX: -

OPEN:	All Year except Christmas
NO. ROOMS:	3
ENSUITE:	3

Panoramic view, 2 miles from Dry / Arch roundabout, on N13 to Sligo. Ideal base for touring north-west. T.V, hairdryers tea/coffee facilities.

| B&B PPS: | £17 | SNGL OCC. DBLE/TPL: | £23.50/£25 | SNGL RM: | - |
| PART BRD: | - | % RED. CHILDREN: | 33% | DINNER: | - |

Eugene & Ann O'Donnell
WHITE PARK B&B
Ballyraine
Letterkenny, Co Donegal

Letterkenny

OPEN:	All Year except Christmas
NO. ROOMS:	6
ENSUITE:	6

TEL: **074 24067**   FAX: -

 (V)

Modern spacious home. Convenient to Golf, Fishing, Pitch & Putt, Horseriding. Excellent location for touring. Near the Mount Errigal Hotel.

B&B PPS:	£17	SNGL OCC. DBLE/TPL:	£23.50	SNGL RM:	£23.50
PART BRD:	-	% RED. CHILDREN:	50%	DINNER:	-

— Letterkenny 1km —

Mrs Madeline Wilkinson
WILLOW HOUSE
Kilmacrennan Road, Letterkenny, Co Donegal

Letterkenny

OPEN:	1st April-31st October
NO. ROOMS:	4
ENSUITE:	4

TEL: **074 21871**   FAX: -

(V)

1 km from hospital roundabout. N56 road to Glenveagh National Park and Dunfanaghy. Outstanding scenery. TV, Tea/Coffee facilities. Visa .

B&B PPS:	£17	SNGL OCC. DBLE/TPL:	£23.50	SNGL RM:	-
PART BRD:	-	% RED. CHILDREN:	50%	DINNER:	-

— Letterkenny 2km —

Mrs Angela Quigley
ROSSBOROUGH HOUSE
Coneyburrow Road, Lifford, Co Donegal

Lifford

OPEN:	All Year except Christmas
NO. ROOMS:	6
ENSUITE:	6

TEL: **074 41132**   FAX: -

(V)

On Main Sligo Road, set in mature gardens. Conference facilities, games room. touring base - Glenveagh National Park, Giants Causeway, Visa.

B&B PPS:	£17	SNGL OCC. DBLE/TPL:	£23.50/£26.50	SNGL RM:	£17
PART BRD:	£180	% RED. CHILDREN:	50%	DINNER:	£12

— Lifford —

Mrs Theresa McHugh
HAZELWOOD
Narin-Portnoo, Co Donegal

Narin / Portnoo

OPEN:	1st April-30th September
NO. ROOMS:	3
ENSUITE:	1

TEL: **075 45182**   FAX: -

(V)

Country home ideally situated for Scenic Walks. Turf fire in TV lounge, Orthopaedic beds. Beach, Golf course, Fishing nearby.

B&B PPS:	£15/£17	SNGL OCC. DBLE/TPL:	-	SNGL RM:	-
PART BRD:	-	% RED. CHILDREN:	33.3%	DINNER:	-

— Ardara 6km —

Mrs Anne Campbell
ARDEEN
Ramelton, Co Donegal

Ramelton

OPEN:	Easter-October
NO. ROOMS:	5
ENSUITE:	3

TEL: **074 51243**   FAX: -

(V)

Old country home overlooking Lough Swilly. Warm welcome, Antique furnishings. Convenient to Glenveagh National Park.

B&B PPS:	£17/£18.50	SNGL OCC. DBLE/TPL:	£22/£23.50	SNGL RM:	£18.50
PART BRD:	-	% RED. CHILDREN:	25%	DINNER:	-

 — In Ramelton —

In Ramelton

Mrs Ena Corry
CRAMMOND HOUSE
Market Square, Ramelton, Co Donegal

Ramelton

OPEN:	April-October
No. ROOMS:	3
ENSUITE:	1

TEL: **074 51055**   FAX: -

Warm hospitality offered in 18th century home. Convenient to Restaurants etc. Family & triple rooms available. Le Guide du Routard recommended.

B&B PPS:	**£15/£17**	SNGL OCC. DBLE/TPL:	**£21.50/£23.50**	SNGL RM:	-
PART BRD:	-	% RED. CHILDREN:	50%	DINNER:	-

In Ramelton

Teresa & Jim McCahill
MEADOWELL HOUSE
Burnside Road, Ramelton, Co Donegal

Ramelton

OPEN:	Easter-31st October
No. ROOMS:	4
ENSUITE:	2

TEL: **074 51290**   FAX: -

Ideal base for touring Fanad Head/National Park. Home from home. Visa accepted.

B&B PPS:	**£15/£17**	SNGL OCC. DBLE/TPL:	**£21.50/£23.50**	SNGL RM:	**£19**
PART BRD:	-	% RED. CHILDREN:	50%	DINNER:	-

In Raphoe

Mrs Shirley Chambers
STRABANE ROAD
Raphoe, Co Donegal

Raphoe

OPEN:	April-November
No. ROOMS:	4
ENSUITE:	2

TEL: **074 45410**   FAX: -

3 min walk from Raphoe, Beltony Stone Circle, 4km Ruins Bishops Castle 500m. Home baking, Tea making facilities. TV all rooms.

B&B PPS:	**£17**	SNGL OCC. DBLE/TPL:	-	SNGL RM:	-
PART BRD:	-	% RED. CHILDREN:	-	DINNER:	-

Dunkineely 6km

Mary & Martin Shovlin
HARBOUR LIGHTS
Saint John's Point, Dunkineely, Co Donegal

Saint John's Point

OPEN:	1st March-31st October
No. ROOMS:	4
ENSUITE:	4

TEL: **073 37291**   FAX: -

Modern bungalow situated on St John's Point Peninsula. Breathtaking view of Sea and Mountains. The perfect place to relax and unwind.

B&B PPS:	**£17**	SNGL OCC. DBLE/TPL:	**£23.50**	SNGL RM:	-
PART BRD:	-	% RED. CHILDREN:	25%	DINNER:	-

RESERVATIONS

- Confirm phone bookings in writing without delay with agreed deposit.
- To avoid misunderstandings later, check rate on booking and clarify any additional changes which may apply to your booking.
- Give details of any special requirements.
- State clearly day, date of arrival and departure date.

Ballinamore 2km

Mrs Eileen Breen
SUI MHUIRE
Cleendargan, Ballinamore, Co Leitrim

Ballinamore

OPEN:	April-October
NO. ROOMS:	6
ENSUITE:	6

TEL: **078 44189**   FAX: -

Situated 2.5 acres, scenic surroundings. Excellent fishing, golf, own boats. Entry, exit drives. Situated route N202 Swanlinbar/Enniskillen Road. Highly Recommended.

B&B PPS:	**£17**	SNGL OCC. DBLE/TPL:	**£23.50**	SNGL RM:	-
PART BRD:	**£180**	% RED. CHILDREN:	25%	DINNER:	£12

Carrick-on-Shannon 2.5km

Mrs Patricia Butler
WEIR VIEW
Jamestown, Carrick-on-Shannon N4, Co Leitrim

Carrick on Shannon

OPEN:	1st March-31st October
NO. ROOMS:	4
ENSUITE:	2

TEL: **078 24726**   FAX: -

East just off the main Dublin Carrick-on-Shannon N4 in quiet surroundings. Warm comfortable home. Laundry, fishing. Breakfast choice.

B&B PPS:	**£15/£17**	SNGL OCC. DBLE/TPL:	**£21.50/£23.50**	SNGL RM:	-
PART BRD:	-	% RED. CHILDREN:	-	DINNER:	£12

Carrick-on-Shannon 1km

Mrs Valerie Cahill
ATTYRORY LODGE
Dublin Road, Carrick-on-Shannon, Co Leitrim

Carrick-on-Shannon

OPEN:	All Year except Christmas
NO. ROOMS:	5
ENSUITE:	5

TEL: **078 20955**   FAX: -

Roots dating 100 years in Leitrim. Complementary interior capturing warmth and history in style. Rough guide recommended. Midway Dublin-Donegal, N4

B&B PPS:	**£17**	SNGL OCC. DBLE/TPL:	**£23.50**	SNGL RM:	-
PART BRD:	-	% RED. CHILDREN:	25%	DINNER:	£12

Carrick-on-Shannon 1km

Mrs Margaret Clarke
SUNNYBANK
Station Road, Carrick-on-Shannon, Co Leitrim

Carrick-on-Shannon

OPEN:	May-September
NO. ROOMS:	4
ENSUITE:	-

TEL: **078 20988**   FAX: -

Recommended, Ireland - The Rough Guide; Lets go. Modern house, set in mature lawns, beside Rail and Bus facilities.

B&B PPS:	**£15**	SNGL OCC. DBLE/TPL:	-	SNGL RM:	£15
PART BRD:	**£180**	% RED. CHILDREN:	25%	DINNER:	£12

In Keshcarrigan

Gerard & Jeanette Conefrey
CANAL VIEW HOUSE
Keshcarrigan, Carrick-on-Shannon, Co Leitrim

Carrick-on-Shannon

OPEN:	All Year
NO. ROOMS:	6
ENSUITE:	6

TEL: **078 42056**   FAX: -

Friendly country home and delightful Restaurant overlooking Shannon-Erne Waterway. Bicycle Hire and Boat Trips locally. Coarse Fishing on doorstep.

B&B PPS:	**£20**	SNGL OCC. DBLE/TPL:	**£26.50**	SNGL RM:	-
PART BRD:	**£190**	% RED. CHILDREN:	25%	DINNER:	£15

In Carrick-on-Shannon

Mrs Breedge Nolan
VILLA FLORA
Station Road, Carrick-on-Shannon,
Co Leitrim

Carrick-on-Shannon

OPEN:	1st April-30th September
NO. ROOMS:	4
ENSUITE:	3

(V)

TEL: **078 20338** FAX: -

Modernized Georgian House, walking distance to Town Centre and Railway Station. Adjacent N4. Fishing and Boating Facilities, Pub Entertainment.

| B&B PPS: | **£15/£17** | SNGL OCC. DBLE/TPL: | **£21.50/£23.50** | SNGL RM: | - |
| PART BRD: | - | % RED. CHILDREN: | 25% | DINNER: | - |

Carrick-on-Shannon 2.5km

PJ & Valerie Rowley
CORBALLY LODGE
Dublin Road, Carrick-on-Shannon N4,
Co Leitrim

Carrick-on-Shannon

OPEN:	1st March-31st October
NO. ROOMS:	4
ENSUITE:	3

(V)

TEL: **078 20228** FAX: -

Country peacefulness. Antique furnishings. Laundry, Fishing. Breakfast choice. Dublin/Sligo/Donegal route. Recommended Best 300 B & Bs. Frommer Guide. Credit Cards.

| B&B PPS: | **£15/£17** | SNGL OCC. DBLE/TPL: | **£21.50/£23.50** | SNGL RM: | - |
| PART BRD: | - | % RED. CHILDREN: | - | DINNER: | - |

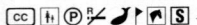

Carrick-on-Shannon 1km

Eleanor & Seamus Shortt
MOYRANE HOUSE
Dublin Road, Carrick-on-Shannon,
Co Leitrim

Carrick-On-Shannon

OPEN:	April-October
NO. ROOMS:	4
ENSUITE:	3

(V)

TEL: **078 20325** FAX: -

Truly Irish home, peacefully set back from N4 Dublin/Sligo/Donegal route. Highly recommended. Breakfast choice. French spoken. Credit cards.

| B&B PPS: | **£15/£17** | SNGL OCC. DBLE/TPL: | **£21.50/£23.50** | SNGL RM: | £17 |
| PART BRD: | - | % RED. CHILDREN: | 25% | DINNER: | £12 |

Drumshanbo 2km

Mrs Mairin Heron
FRAOCH BAN
Corlough, Drumshanbo, Co Leitrim

Drumshanbo

OPEN:	April-October
NO. ROOMS:	5
ENSUITE:	5

(V)

TEL: **078 41260** FAX: -

Warm comfortable home overlooking Lough Allen. All rooms having spectacular views of Lake and Mountains. Walking, Equestrian, Canoeing Centre nearby.

| B&B PPS: | **£17** | SNGL OCC. DBLE/TPL: | **£23.50** | SNGL RM: | - |
| PART BRD: | **£180** | % RED. CHILDREN: | 25% | DINNER: | £12 |

TELEPHONE

- Operator assisted calls within Ireland — Dial 10
- International telephone operator — Dial 114
- Directory Enquiries — Dial 1190

FOR TROUBLE-FREE TELEPHONE CALLS FROM PUBLIC PAY PHONES IT IS ADVISABLE TO PURCHASE A TELEPHONE CALLCARD AVAILABLE IN POST OFFICES AND WHEREVER YOU SEE A CALLCARD SIGN.

TO DIAL IRELAND FROM ABROAD: Country Access Code + 353 + Area Code (omit first zero) + Local Number

Carrickmacross 2km

Mrs Eileen Duffy
DUFF-FINN HOUSE
**Tullynaskeagh, Ardee Road,
Carrickmacross, Co Monaghan**
TEL: **042 61480**   FAX: -

Carrickmacross

OPEN:	All Year
NO. ROOMS:	6
ENSUITE:	4

(V)

Modern Bungalow within walking distance from Nuremore Hotel. Fishing, Golf, Pitch & Putt, Equestrian Centre all 5 minutes walk.

B&B PPS:	£15/£17	SNGL OCC. DBLE/TPL:	£21.50/£23.50	SNGL RM:	£17/£18
PART BRD:	-	% RED. CHILDREN:	25%	DINNER:	-

Carrickmacross 3km

Margaret Flanagan
SHANMULLAGH HOUSE
**Killanny Rd (off Dundalk Rd)
Carrickmacross, Co Monaghan**
TEL: **042 63038**   FAX: **042 61915**

Carrickmacross

OPEN:	All Year
NO. ROOMS:	6
ENSUITE:	5

(V)

Modern artistically decorated house in rural surroundings. Convenient to Nuremore Hotel & Country Club. Golf, Fishing, Horse Riding locally.

B&B PPS:	£17	SNGL OCC. DBLE/TPL:	£23.50	SNGL RM:	-
PART BRD:	-	% RED. CHILDREN:	20%	DINNER:	-

Carrickmacross 3km

Mrs Nuala Russell
NUREBEG HOUSE
**Ardee Road, Carrickmacross,
Co Monaghan**
TEL: **042 61044**   FAX: -

Carrickmacross

OPEN:	All Year except Christmas
NO. ROOMS:	4
ENSUITE:	2

(V)

Situated N2 Dublin/Derry Road. Beside Nuremore Hotel, 2 miles Carrickmacross. Fishing, Horse Riding, Golf locally. Central touring, Newgrange, Carlingford.

B&B PPS:	£17	SNGL OCC. DBLE/TPL:	£23.50	SNGL RM:	-
PART BRD:	£180	% RED. CHILDREN:	33.3%	DINNER:	£12

Monaghan 1km

Mrs Mary McArdle
THE CEDARS
**Clones Road, Monaghan,
Co Monaghan**
TEL: **047 82783**   FAX: -

Monaghan

OPEN:	8th January-18th December
NO. ROOMS:	3
ENSUITE:	2

(V)

Split-level bungalow, quiet location, safe parking. Forest Park, Walking, Fishing, Horseriding, Golf, Swimming. Convenient for touring Northern Ireland.

B&B PPS:	£15/£17	SNGL OCC. DBLE/TPL:	£22	SNGL RM:	-
PART BRD:	-	% RED. CHILDREN:	25%	DINNER:	-

SYMBOLS

LOOK OUT FOR THESE SYMBOLS WHICH SHOULD BE DISPLAYED BY ALL MEMBERS OF TOWN & COUNTRY HOMES .

Ballisodare Village 1.5km

Mrs Mary Savage
MOUNTAIN VIEW
Corhownagh
Ballina Road, Ballisodare, Co Sligo

Ballisodare

OPEN:	April-September
No. ROOMS:	3
ENSUITE:	2

Ⓥ

TEL: **071 67398**   FAX: -

Modern Bungalow in scenic surroundings, ideal Touring Centre, Fishing, Golf, Horse Riding and Beaches nearby.

B&B PPS:	**£15/£17**	SNGL OCC. DBLE/TPL:	**£21.50/£23.50**	SNGL RM:	-
PART BRD:	-	% RED. CHILDREN:	25%	DINNER:	-

In Ballymote

Mrs Kay Hogge
CORRAN HOUSE
Sligo Road, Ballymote, Co Sligo

Ballymote

OPEN:	All Year except Christmas
No. ROOMS:	4
ENSUITE:	4

Ⓥ

TEL: **071 83074**   FAX: -

Select hospitable home; bedrooms with T.V, radio, tea facilities, hairdryer, electric blankets. Close to Golf, Fishing, Heritage sites. AA QQQ.

B&B PPS:	**£17**	SNGL OCC. DBLE/TPL:	**£23.50**	SNGL RM:	-
PART BRD:	-	% RED. CHILDREN:	33.3%	DINNER:	-

In Ballymote

Mrs. Noreen Mullin
"MILLHOUSE"
Keenaghan, Ballymote, Co Sligo

Ballymote

OPEN:	6th January-20th December
No. ROOMS:	5
ENSUITE:	4

Ⓥ

TEL: **071 83449**   FAX: -

"Galtee Breakfast Award. Friendly home in peaceful setting, Private Tennis Court. Touring base for Northwest. Fishing, Golf, Megalithic Tombs, Castle."

B&B PPS:	**£17**	SNGL OCC. DBLE/TPL:	**£23.50**	SNGL RM:	**£15**
PART BRD:	-	% RED. CHILDREN:	50%	DINNER:	-

Cliffoney 2km

Mrs. Beatrice McLoughlin
VILLA ROSA
Donegal Road, Bunduff,
Cliffoney P.O., Co Sligo

Bunduff/Cliffoney

OPEN:	1st March-31st October
No. ROOMS:	6
ENSUITE:	4

Ⓥ

TEL: **071 66173**   FAX: -

N15, Chef proprietor, group cookery demonstrations, group lace classes, walks on Hills, Seashore, Lakeshore, Creevykeel Megalithic tomb, Bird Sanctuary. AA, QQQ.

B&B PPS:	**£15/£17**	SNGL OCC. DBLE/TPL:	**£21.50/£23.50**	SNGL RM:	**£15**
PART BRD:	**£180**	% RED. CHILDREN:	-	DINNER:	**£20**

Sligo 9km

Mrs Masie Rooney
CASTLETOWN HOUSE
Drumcliffe, Co Sligo

Drumcliffe

OPEN:	March-October
No. ROOMS:	3
ENSUITE:	-

Ⓥ

TEL: **071 63204**   FAX: -

Situated beneath the bliss of Benbulbin Mountains. Peaceful location. Hospitality, nearby W. B. Yeats grave. Glencar Waterfalls. Restaurant.

B&B PPS:	**£15**	SNGL OCC. DBLE/TPL:	**£21.50**	SNGL RM:	-
PART BRD:	**£180**	% RED. CHILDREN:	20%	DINNER:	**£12**

Mrs Maura Ashe
EMARA LODGE
Tormore, Glencar, Co Sligo

Glencar

OPEN:	1st April-30th September
NO. ROOMS:	3
ENSUITE:	2

(V)

TEL: **071 41074**   FAX: -

Solar heated bungalow with large conservatory in beautiful countryside. Delicious home cooking. Ideal Fishing, Hill-walking, Landscape painting, Wildlife.

B&B PPS:	£15/£17	SNGL OCC. DBLE/TPL:	£21.50/£23.50	SNGL RM:	-
PART BRD:	£181	% RED. CHILDREN:	50%	DINNER:	£12

Sligo 10km

Mrs Una Brennan
ARMADA LODGE
Donegal Road N15, Grange North, Co Sligo

Grange

OPEN:	1st May-30th September
NO. ROOMS:	6
ENSUITE:	6

(V)

TEL: **071 63250**   FAX: **071 63250**   EMAIL: **armadalodge@tinet.ie**

Overlooking Sea/Mountains off Donegal Rd. Tennis, Horseriding on Sandy Beach, Scenic Walks, Boat Pier/ trips. Rooms- TV, Tea/Coffee/Hairdryer, C.C.

B&B PPS:	£17	SNGL OCC. DBLE/TPL:	£23.50	SNGL RM:	£19
PART BRD:	-	% RED. CHILDREN:	20%	DINNER:	-

Grange 2km

Mrs Maureen McGowan
MOUNT EDWARD LODGE
Off N15, Ballinfull, Grange, Co Sligo

Grange

OPEN:	15th January-November
NO. ROOMS:	5
ENSUITE:	3

(V)

TEL: **071 63263**   FAX: -

Overlooking Sea/Mountains, Location off N15 Mid-way Sligo/.Donegal. Lissadell House, Yeats grave nearby. Electric blankets, Golf, Fishing, Mountain Climbing.

B&B PPS:	£15/£17	SNGL OCC. DBLE/TPL:	-	SNGL RM:	£20/£22
PART BRD:	-	% RED. CHILDREN:	20%	DINNER:	-

Grange 2km

Mrs Kathleen Neary
ROSSWICK
Grange, Co Sligo

Grange

OPEN:	April-October
NO. ROOMS:	4
ENSUITE:	1

(V)

TEL: **071 63516**   FAX: -

Village setting on N15. Panoramic views of Ben Bulben. Restaurants, Golf, Fishing, Horseriding, Hill walking, Beaches, Expressway bus service.

B&B PPS:	£15/£17	SNGL OCC. DBLE/TPL:	£23.50	SNGL RM:	-
PART BRD:	-	% RED. CHILDREN:	20%	DINNER:	-

In Grange

Mrs Teresa Waters
SHADDAN LODGE
Streedagh, Grange, Co Sligo

Grange

OPEN:	April-October
NO. ROOMS:	4
ENSUITE:	3

(V)

TEL: **071 63350**   FAX: -   EMAIL: **shaddan@iol.ie**

Overlooking Donegal Bay in heart William Butler Yeats country under Benbulben. Healing massage therapy, Chelation, Reiki, Reflexology, Stress management available.

B&B PPS:	£15/£17	SNGL OCC. DBLE/TPL:	£21.50/£23.50	SNGL RM:	-
PART BRD:	£200	% RED. CHILDREN:	20%	DINNER:	£12

Grange 2km

Rosses Point 5km

Mrs Mary Conefrey
BAYVIEW
Doonierin, Cregg, Rosses Point, Co Sligo

TEL: **071 62148**   FAX: -

Rosses Point

OPEN:	1st March-31st October
NO. ROOMS:	4
ENSUITE:	2

Quiet location down cul-de-sac leading to sea. Beautiful views of Drumcliffe Bay, Benbulben Mountains. Near Beaches, Golf, Restaurants, Hill Walking.

| B&B PPS: | **£15/£!7** | SNGL OCC. DBLE/TPL: | **£21.50/£23.50** | SNGL RM: | - |
| PART BRD: | - | % RED. CHILDREN: | **50%** | DINNER: | - |

Sligo 4km

Mrs Ita Connolly
IORRAS
Ballincar
Rosses Point Road, Sligo, Co Sligo

TEL: **071 44911**   FAX: -

Rosses Point

OPEN:	1st April-31st October
NO. ROOMS:	3
ENSUITE:	3

Modern spacious home situated 2kms on Sligo to Rosses Point Road. TV, Tea/coffee in bedrooms. Golf, Sailing, Beach nearby.

| B&B PPS: | **£17** | SNGL OCC. DBLE/TPL: | **£23.50** | SNGL RM: | - |
| PART BRD: | - | % RED. CHILDREN: | **50%** | DINNER: | - |

Sligo 4km

Mrs. Eithne Curran
CHANNEL BREEZE
Ballincar, Rosses Point Road, Co Sligo

TEL: **071 45542**   FAX: -

Rosses Point

OPEN:	1st April-30th September
NO. ROOMS:	4
ENSUITE:	2

Bungalow with panoramic views of Sligo Bay and Mountains, ideal base in Yeats Country, many recommendations, Beaches, Golf, Fishing.

| B&B PPS: | **£15/£17** | SNGL OCC. DBLE/TPL: | **£21.50/£23.50** | SNGL RM: | - |
| PART BRD: | - | % RED. CHILDREN: | - | DINNER: | - |

Sligo 3.5km

Mrs I Fullerton
SEA PARK HOUSE
Rosses Point Road, Co Sligo

TEL: **071 45556**   FAX: -

Rosses Point

OPEN:	1st January-21st December
NO. ROOMS:	6
ENSUITE:	4

Situated 3.5 km from Sligo on Rosses Point Road. 5 Min from Beach, Golf, Sailing. Choice menu, TV, Tea/Coffee, Hairdryers.

| B&B PPS: | **£15/£17** | SNGL OCC. DBLE/TPL: | **£21.50/£23.50** | SNGL RM: | - |
| PART BRD: | - | % RED. CHILDREN: | **33.3%** | DINNER: | - |

Sligo Town 8km

Mrs Cait Gill
KILVARNET HOUSE
Rosses Point, Co Sligo

TEL: **071 77202**   FAX: -

Rosses Point

OPEN:	1st March-30th November
NO. ROOMS:	4
ENSUITE:	4

Modern comforts, traditional hospitality. In heart of Yeats Country, within walking distance of championship Golf Course, Yacht Club, Beaches, Restaurants.

| B&B PPS: | **£17.50** | SNGL OCC. DBLE/TPL: | **£24** | SNGL RM: | - |
| PART BRD: | - | % RED. CHILDREN: | - | DINNER: | - |

Rosses Point 5km

Kelly Family
SERENITY
Doonierin, Kintogher, Rosses Point, Co Sligo

Rosses Point

TEL: **071 43351**   FAX: -

OPEN:	1st May-30th September
NO. ROOMS:	4
ENSUITE:	3

(V)

A touch of class, cul-de-sac location. Spectacular panoramic Mountain views. Overlooking Drumcliffe Bay. Beautiful gardens. Ideal base whatever your interests.

| B&B PPS: | £15/£17 | SNGL OCC. DBLE/TPL: | £21.50/£23.50 | SNGL RM: | - |
| PART BRD: | - | % RED. CHILDREN: | - | DINNER: | - |

Sligo 4km

Mrs Marian Nealon
SANIUD
Ballincar, Rosses Point, Co Sligo

Rosses Point

TEL: **071 42773**   FAX: -

OPEN:	1st April-30th September
NO. ROOMS:	4
ENSUITE:	2

(V)

Warm comfortable home. Quiet location beside Ballincar House Hotel. Convenient to Beaches, Golf, Sailing, Tennis in heart of Yeats country.

| B&B PPS: | £15/£17 | SNGL OCC. DBLE/TPL: | £21.50/£23.50 | SNGL RM: | - |
| PART BRD: | - | % RED. CHILDREN: | 25% | DINNER: | - |

Sligo 4km

Mrs. Teresa Noone
SILVER SEAS
Cregg, Rosses Point, Sligo, Co Sligo

Rosses Point

TEL: **071 45997**   FAX: -

OPEN:	March-November
NO. ROOMS:	4
ENSUITE:	3

(V)

Spacious home on elevated site, Panoramic Views of Sea and Mountains. Ideal base for Touring, Golf, Sailing, Beaches nearby.

| B&B PPS: | £15/£17 | SNGL OCC. DBLE/TPL: | £21.50/£23.50 | SNGL RM: | - |
| PART BRD: | - | % RED. CHILDREN: | 25% | DINNER: | - |

Sligo 4km

Mrs Mary Scanlon
PHILMAR HOUSE
Ballincar, Rosses Point Road, Co Sligo

Rosses Point

TEL: **071 45014**   FAX: -

OPEN:	1st April-31st October
NO. ROOMS:	4
ENSUITE:	2

(V)

Old style with modern comfort. Large gardens for guests. Enjoyment close to Yeats country. Championship Golf course, Beaches, Yachting, Tennis.

| B&B PPS: | £15/£18 | SNGL OCC. DBLE/TPL: | £21.50/£25 | SNGL RM: | - |
| PART BRD: | - | % RED. CHILDREN: | - | DINNER: | - |

Sligo 4km

Mrs Renagh Burns
OCHILLMORE HOUSE
Scarden-Beg, Strandhill Road, Co Sligo

Sligo

TEL: **071 68032**   FAX: -

OPEN:	All Year
NO. ROOMS:	4
ENSUITE:	4

(V)

Modern spacious dormer bungalow situated 4km from Sligo on main Strandhill (Airport Rd). Close Beach, Golf, Megalithic Tombs, Horseriding.

| B&B PPS: | £15 | SNGL OCC. DBLE/TPL: | £20 | SNGL RM: | - |
| PART BRD: | - | % RED. CHILDREN: | 50% | DINNER: | - |

Mrs Carmel Carr		Sligo	
ST MARTINS			
Cummeen, Strandhill Road, Sligo, Co Sligo		OPEN: **1st March-31st October**	
		No. ROOMS: 4	
		ENSUITE: 4	
TEL: **071 60614**	FAX: -		

Spacious home 4km past Southern Hotel main Strandhill/Airport Road. Colour TV's, hairdryers, orthopaedic beds, electric blankets. Frommer Guide Recommended.

B&B PPS:	£17	SNGL OCC. DBLE/TPL:	£23.50	SNGL RM:	-
PART BRD:	-	% RED. CHILDREN:	25%	DINNER:	-

— Sligo 4km

Mary & Tommy Carroll		Sligo	
ARD CUILINN LODGE			
Drumiskabole Sligo, Co Sligo		OPEN: **1st April-20th October**	
		No. ROOMS: 4	
		ENSUITE: 2	
TEL: **071 62925**	FAX: -		

Country home in tranquil scenic surroundings. Guide du Routard/Petit Fute listed. Ikm off N4. On Road leading to Lough Gill.

B&B PPS:	£15/£18	SNGL OCC. DBLE/TPL:	-	SNGL RM:	-
PART BRD:	-	% RED. CHILDREN:	20%	DINNER:	-

— Sligo 5km

Mrs Phil Clancy		Sligo	
SEISNAUN			
Kintogher (off Donegal Road), Sligo, Co Sligo		OPEN: . **May-October**	
		No. ROOMS: 4	
		ENSUITE: 2	
TEL: **071 43948**	FAX: -		

Panoramic views, Yeats Country, Benbulben, Drumcliffe Bay. Three miles North of Sligo. Signposted off Donegal Road. Frommer recommended. Credit cards.

B&B PPS:	£15/£17	SNGL OCC. DBLE/TPL:	£21.50/£23.50	SNGL RM:	£15
PART BRD:	-	% RED. CHILDREN:	25%	DINNER:	-

— Sligo 4.5km

Mrs Mary Conway		Sligo	
STONECROFT			
off Donegal Road, Kintogher, Co Sligo		OPEN: **1st March-8th December**	
		No. ROOMS: 4	
		ENSUITE: 3	
TEL: **071 45667**	FAX: -		

Cosy home in Yeats country 300m off N15 Donegal Road. Near Drumcliffe Church. Superb views. Credit Cards, TV, Tea facilities.

B&B PPS:	£17	SNGL OCC. DBLE/TPL:	£23..50	SNGL RM:	-
PART BRD:	-	% RED. CHILDREN:	20%	DINNER:	-

— Sligo 4km

SYMBOLS

LOOK OUT FOR THESE SYMBOLS WHICH SHOULD BE DISPLAYED BY ALL MEMBERS OF TOWN & COUNTRY HOMES .

Sligo 4km

Mrs. Elleen Cullinan
THE ROWANS
Kilmacowen, Ballisodare, Co Sligo

		Sligo	
	OPEN:	1st March-31st October	
	NO. ROOMS:	4	
	ENSUITE:	2	

TEL: **071 67337**   FAX: **071 67337**

Scenic setting 300 metre off N4, Signposted 1km from Ballisodare, near Beaches, Golf, Horse Riding, Carramore Tombs. Electric blankets. "Inside Ireland".

B&B PPS:	£15/£17	SNGL OCC. DBLE/TPL:	£21.50/£23.50	SNGL RM:	-
PART BRD:	£180	% RED. CHILDREN:	50%	DINNER:	£12

Sligo 3km

Peter & Martha Davey
CARBURY HOUSE
Teesan, Sligo, Co Sligo

		Sligo	
	OPEN:	All Year	
	NO. ROOMS:	6	
	ENSUITE:	6	

TEL: **071 43378**   FAX: **071 47433**

Luxurious spacious home on N15. Warm welcome. All rooms ensuite, TVs, Orthopaedic beds. Teas/coffee making facilities. 3 kms from Sligo.

B&B PPS:	£17/£19	SNGL OCC. DBLE/TPL:	£22/£24	SNGL RM:	-
PART BRD:	-	% RED. CHILDREN:	50%	DINNER:	-

Sligo

Des and Nan Faul
"AISLING"
Cairns Hill, Sligo, Co Sligo

		Sligo	
	OPEN:	All Year except Christmas	
	NO. ROOMS:	5	
	ENSUITE:	3	

TEL: **071 60704**   FAX: -

Frommer, AA listed. T.V's, hairdryers, electric blankets, overlooking Sligo Bay off N4, signposted 300 metres Sligo Park Hotel. Non smoking.

B&B PPS:	£15/£17	SNGL OCC. DBLE/TPL:	£21.50	SNGL RM:	-
PART BRD:	-	% RED. CHILDREN:	-	DINNER:	-

Sligo 4km

Mrs Josephine Feeney
THURMORE
Tully, Donegal Road, Sligo, Co Sligo

		Sligo	
	OPEN:	1st April-30th September	
	NO. ROOMS:	3	
	ENSUITE:	2	

TEL: **071 43890**   FAX: -

Situated in the Yeats Country on N15, overlooking Benbulben, Lissadel and Drumcliffe Bay. Restaurants, Beaches, Golf, Tennis nearby. Ideal touring base.

B&B PPS:	£15/£17	SNGL OCC. DBLE/TPL:	£21.50/£23.50	SNGL RM:	-
PART BRD:	-	% RED. CHILDREN:	-	DINNER:	-

Sligo 4km

Mrs Sheila Galbraith
KESWICK
Kintogher
Donegal Road, Sligo, Co Sligo

		Sligo	
	OPEN:	1st June-15th September	
	NO. ROOMS:	3	
	ENSUITE:	2	

TEL: **071 43723**   FAX: -

Bungalow in scenic surroundings on N15 to Donegal. Overlooking Benbulben Mountain. Ideal base for touring Yeats country.

B&B PPS:	£15/£17	SNGL OCC. DBLE/TPL:	£21.50/£23.50	SNGL RM:	-
PART BRD:	-	% RED. CHILDREN:	-	DINNER:	-

Mrs Mary Geraghty-Sweeney
CLANBRACKEN HOUSE
Kevinsfort, Strandhill Road, Sligo, Co Sligo

Sligo

OPEN:	All Year except Christmas
NO. ROOMS:	3
ENSUITE:	3

Ⓥ

TEL: **071 43675 / 087 2215147**   FAX: -

Modern six bedroomed house Woodland Setting. 15 mins walk Bus/Train Station (in Strandhill direction). First left immediately past Larkhill Road.

| B&B PPS: | **£17/£20** | SNGL OCC. DBLE/TPL: | **£23.50/£26.50** | SNGL RM: | - |
| PART BRD: | - | % RED. CHILDREN: | **50%** | DINNER: | - |

— Sligo 1km

Mrs Mary Gilmartin
GLENLURG HOUSE
Lisnalurg, off Donegal Road N15, Sligo, Co Sligo

Sligo

OPEN:	All Year except Christmas
NO. ROOMS:	3
ENSUITE:	3

Ⓥ

TEL: **071 45387**   FAX: **071 45387**

Excellent accomodation in quiet scenic location. 200 metres off N15. Home baking, Restaurants, Golf, Tennis, Beaches nearby. Ideal touring base.

| B&B PPS: | **£17/£20** | SNGL OCC. DBLE/TPL: | **£25** | SNGL RM: | - |
| PART BRD: | - | % RED. CHILDREN: | **20%** | DINNER: | - |

— Sligo 3km

Mrs A Ginty
BENVIEW
Tully, Donegal Road, Rathcormac, Co Sligo

Sligo

OPEN:	1st June-30th September
NO. ROOMS:	3
ENSUITE:	2

Ⓥ

TEL: **071 43951**   FAX: -

Situated in scenic surroundings, views of Benbulben, Glencar, Drumcliffe Bay, Yeats Grave nearby. Within walking distance of Pub & Shop. N15.

| B&B PPS: | **£15/£17** | SNGL OCC. DBLE/TPL: | **£21.50/£23.50** | SNGL RM: | - |
| PART BRD: | - | % RED. CHILDREN: | **50%** | DINNER: | - |

— Sligo 4km

Mrs T Haughey
RATHNASHEE
Teesan, Donegal Road N15, Sligo, Co Sligo

Sligo

OPEN:	1st March-31st October
NO. ROOMS:	3
ENSUITE:	2

Ⓥ

TEL: **071 43376/087 2204423**   FAX: **071 42283**

Welcoming traditional Irish home. Books. Good food, conversation. Midway Sligo-Drumcliff, en route Donegal. Recommended Frommers. Guide du Routard. John Watney.

| B&B PPS: | **£15/£17** | SNGL OCC. DBLE/TPL: | **£21.50/£23.50** | SNGL RM: | - |
| PART BRD: | - | % RED. CHILDREN: | - | DINNER: | **£12** |

— Sligo 3km

Mary Hennessy
DAINGEAN
Hazelwood Road, Ballinode, Co Sligo

Sligo

OPEN:	All Year except Christmas
NO. ROOMS:	3
ENSUITE:	3

Ⓥ

TEL: **071 45706**   FAX: -

Friendly family home, situated 1.5 km from Town Centre. Close to all amenities. Spacious garden. Hazelwood Park, Lough Gill, Parkes Castle nearby.

| B&B PPS: | **£17** | SNGL OCC. DBLE/TPL: | - | SNGL RM: | **£22** |
| PART BRD: | - | % RED. CHILDREN: | **50%** | DINNER: | - |

— Sligo 1.5km

Sligo 3km

Mrs Christina Jones
CHESNUT LAWN
Cummeen, Strandhill Road, Sligo, Co Sligo

Sligo

OPEN:	All Year except Christmas
NO. ROOMS:	3
ENSUITE:	3

Ⓥ

TEL: **071 62781**   FAX: -

Modern spacious dormer bungalow situated 3 km from Sligo on main Strandhill Airport Road. Close to Megalithic Tombs. T.V, hairdryers.

B&B PPS:	£17	SNGL OCC. DBLE/TPL:	£23.50	SNGL RM:	-
PART BRD:	-	% RED. CHILDREN:	50%	DINNER:	-

Sligo 2km

Mrs. Veronica Kane
GLENVIEW
Cummeen,Strandhill Road, Co Sligo

Sligo

OPEN:	All Year
NO. ROOMS:	4
ENSUITE:	4

Ⓥ

TEL: **071 70401/62457**   FAX: **071 62457**

Modern bungalow Strandhill Road, Megalithic Tombs. Golf, Beaches, Airport, Colour TV, Hairdryers, Electric Blankets, Tea making facilities, Lets Go recommended.

B&B PPS:	£17	SNGL OCC. DBLE/TPL:	£23.50	SNGL RM:	-
PART BRD:	-	% RED. CHILDREN:	50%	DINNER:	-

Sligo 3km

Mrs Marie Kelly
ST. JUDE'S
Rathonoragh
Strandhill Road, Sligo, Co Sligo

Sligo

OPEN:	1st April-31st October
NO. ROOMS:	3
ENSUITE:	2

Ⓥ

TEL: **071 60858**   FAX: -

Modern dormer bungalow on Strandhill/Airport Road, close to Megalithic Tombs, Golf, Beaches, Horse Riding nearby, T.V and hairdryers.

B&B PPS:	£15/£17	SNGL OCC. DBLE/TPL:	£21.50/£23.50	SNGL RM:	-
PART BRD:	-	% RED. CHILDREN:	25%	DINNER:	-

Sligo 1km

Mrs Shirley Kilfeather
LAR-EASA
12 Kestrel Drive, Kevinsfort, Strandhill Road, Co Sligo

Sligo

OPEN:	All Year except Christmas
NO. ROOMS:	3
ENSUITE:	3

Ⓥ

TEL: **071 69313**   FAX: **071 68593**

Country setting 1 km from Sligo, T.V, tea making, and hairdryers. Close to Golf, Beaches and lakes. Limited Salmon fishery rights Ballisodare River.

B&B PPS:	£17	SNGL OCC. DBLE/TPL:	£23.50	SNGL RM:	-
PART BRD:	-	% RED. CHILDREN:	20%	DINNER:	-

In Sligo

Mrs Ursula Leyden
RENATE HOUSE
Upper John Street, Sligo, Co Sligo

Sligo

OPEN:	3rd January-23rd December
NO. ROOMS:	6
ENSUITE:	4

Ⓥ

TEL: **071 62014**   FAX: **071 67655**

Frommer listed. Beside Bus, Train station, all amenities, Restaurants, Pubs, Tourist Office, Theatre, Hospitals, Churches.

B&B PPS:	£15/£17	SNGL OCC. DBLE/TPL:	£21.50/£23.50	SNGL RM:	-
PART BRD:	-	% RED. CHILDREN:	20%	DINNER:	-

Mary Lynch
REALT NA MARA
Sea Road, (off Strandhill Road), Sligo, Co Sligo

Sligo

OPEN:	1st April-31st October
NO. ROOMS:	3
ENSUITE:	2

TEL: **071 70838**   FAX: **071 50900**

Luxury accommodation 1.5km Sligo Town. AA QQQQ selected 1996. Complimentary Tea/Coffee on arrival, home baking. Warm welcome

B&B PPS:	£15.50/£17	SNGL OCC. DBLE/TPL:	£22/£23.50	SNGL RM:	£22
PART BRD:	-	% RED. CHILDREN:	33.3%	DINNER:	

— Sligo 1.5km

Ronan and Doreen MacEvilly
TREE TOPS
Cleveragh Road, (off Pearse Rd) N4 Sligo Town, Co Sligo

Sligo Town

OPEN:	All Year except Christmas
NO. ROOMS:	5
ENSUITE:	4

TEL: **071 60160**   FAX: **071 62301**   EMAIL: **treetops@iol.ie**

5 minutes walk town centre. T.V, Hairdryers, Direct Dial Telephones, tea facilities all rooms. Non smoking. Frommer, Guide du Routard recommended.

B&B PPS:	£15/£17	SNGL OCC. DBLE/TPL:	£21.50/£23.50	SNGL RM:	-
PART BRD:	-	% RED. CHILDREN:	20%	DINNER:	-

— In Sligo

Mary McGoldrick
ST MARTIN DE PORRES
Drumshanbo Road, Carraroe, Sligo, Co Sligo

Sligo

OPEN:	6th January-22nd December
NO. ROOMS:	4
ENSUITE:	4

TEL: **071 62793**   FAX: -

Peaceful rural setting, 1km off N4 at Carraroe Junction. Secure parking, convenient to Lough Gill, Megalithic Tombs, Forest Walks.

B&B PPS:	£17	SNGL OCC. DBLE/TPL:	£23.50	SNGL RM:	£17
PART BRD:	-	% RED. CHILDREN:	50%	DINNER:	-

— Sligo 4Km

Mrs Kathleen McGuinness
PINEHAVEN
Green Road, Sligo, Co Sligo

Sligo

OPEN:	1st March- 31st October
NO. ROOMS:	3
ENSUITE:	3

TEL: **071 61900**   FAX: -

Overlooking Lough Gill and Lake Isle of Innisfree. Beside Swimming Pool, Woodlands, Golf, Fishing. TV, rooms ensuite. 1.5KM off N4.

B&B PPS:	£17	SNGL OCC. DBLE/TPL:	£23.50	SNGL RM:	-
PART BRD:	-	% RED. CHILDREN:	50%	DINNER:	-

— Sligo 2km

Evelyn and Declan McPartland
TEACH EAMAINN
off N16 Hazelwood, Clogherevagh, Co Sligo

Sligo

OPEN:	1st April-30th November
NO. ROOMS:	6
ENSUITE:	6

TEL: **071 43393**   FAX: **071 43393**

Situated on two acres off N16. Tea room, over looking Knocknarae, Benbulben, Ox Mountains, Sligo Bay. T.V and Hairdryers. Parties special rate.

B&B PPS:	£17	SNGL OCC. DBLE/TPL:	£23.50	SNGL RM:	£22
PART BRD:	£180	% RED. CHILDREN:	25%	DINNER:	£12

— Sligo 2km

Mrs Norah Mugan
MOIN NA TAOIBH
Lisnalurg off Donegal Rd N15, Sligo, Co Sligo

Sligo

OPEN:	All Year except Christmas
NO. ROOMS:	4
ENSUITE:	4

TEL: **071 43584**   FAX: -

Recommended "Best Guide". Non Smoking large rooms. Quality beds, Electric Blankets, Hairdryers,Tea/Coffee. New architect designed peaceful, panoramic views. Parking

B&B PPS:	**£17/£19**	SNGL OCC. DBLE/TPL:	**£25/£30**	SNGL RM:	-
PART BRD:	-	% RED. CHILDREN:	-	DINNER:	-

Sligo 2km

Mary Murphy
OLNEGMACHT
Tonafortes, Sligo, Co Sligo

Sligo

OPEN:	1st May-30th September
NO. ROOMS:	3
ENSUITE:	3

TEL: **071 60134**   FAX: -

Traditional style luxury home off N4 near Sligo Park Hotel. Golf, Fishing, Swimming, Bowling and Hill Walking nearby. Highly recommended.

B&B PPS:	**£17**	SNGL OCC. DBLE/TPL:	**£25**	SNGL RM:	-
PART BRD:	-	% RED. CHILDREN:	-	DINNER:	-

Sligo 2km

Mel & Kathleen Noonan
STRADBROOK
Cornageeha, Pearse Road, Sligo, Co Sligo

Sligo Town

OPEN:	All Year
NO. ROOMS:	4
ENSUITE:	4

TEL: **071 69674/50663**   FAX: **071 69674**

"Welcoming family home on N4. Sligo Park Hotel 100 metres. All facilities. French/Irish spoken. Guide de Routard/Stillwells listed."

B&B PPS:	**£17**	SNGL OCC. DBLE/TPL:	**£23.50**	SNGL RM:	-
PART BRD:	-	% RED. CHILDREN:	**25%**	DINNER:	-

Sligo 1.5km

Mrs Bernie O'Connor
ALVERNO
Cairns Hill Rd, off N4, Sligo, Co Sligo

Sligo

OPEN:	1st January-20th December
NO. ROOMS:	3
ENSUITE:	2

TEL: **071 62893**   FAX: -

Modern family home, 200m from Park Hotel. Signposted. Off Pearse Road (N4). Scenic area. Overlooks Sligo Bay.

B&B PPS:	**£15/£17**	SNGL OCC. DBLE/TPL:	**£21.50/£23.50**	SNGL RM:	-
PART BRD:	-	% RED. CHILDREN:	**33.3%**	DINNER:	-

Sligo 1.5km

Elma O'Halloran
ROSSCAHILL
19 Marymount, Pearse Road, Sligo, Co Sligo

Sligo Town

OPEN:	1st April-1st November
NO. ROOMS:	3
ENSUITE:	3

TEL: **071 61744**   FAX: -

Entering Sligo, N4, Turn left into Marymount opposite ESSO station before second set of traffic lights. Located in quiet Cul-de- Sac.

B&B PPS:	**£17**	SNGL OCC. DBLE/TPL:	**£23.50**	SNGL RM:	**£21**
PART BRD:	-	% RED. CHILDREN:	**25%**	DINNER:	-

In Sligo

Mrs. Olivia Quigley
BENWISKIN LODGE
Shannon Eighter, Off Donegal Road
N15, Sligo, Co Sligo

Sligo

Open:	1st January-31st December
No. Rooms:	5
Ensuite:	5

(V)

Tel: **071 41088**   Fax: -

Warm welcoming home. 50 m off N15. Interesting homemade country furniture.
Rooms ensuite, orthopaedic beds, TV,s, hairdryers, teamaking facilities, home baking.

B&B PPS:	£17/£19	Sngl Occ. Dble/Tpl:	£23.50/£25.50	Sngl Rm:	£17/£22
Part Brd:	-	% Red. Children:	-	Dinner:	-

— Sligo 2km

Marie Scanlon
DAWNHURST
Pearse Road, Sligo, Co Sligo

Sligo Town

Open:	All Year except Christmas
No. Rooms:	4
Ensuite:	3

(V)

Tel: **071 60595**   Fax: -

Large detached houe in own grounds on N4. 5 mins walk town, 5 mins Sligo Park
Hotel, Race Course.

B&B PPS:	£15/£17	Sngl Occ. Dble/Tpl:	£21.50/£23.50	Sngl Rm:	-
Part Brd:	-	% Red. Children:	-	Dinner:	-

— In Sligo Town

Mrs Carmel Connolly
KNOCKNAREA HOUSE
Shore Road, Strandhill, Co Sligo

Strandhill

Open:	March-October
No. Rooms:	4
Ensuite:	4

(V)

Tel: **071 68313**   Fax: -

Detatched house near Beach, Golf,(18 hole) Scenic Walks, Fishing, Surfing, Horse
Riding, Bus Terminal, Airport, very scenic area.

B&B PPS:	£15	Sngl Occ. Dble/Tpl:	£18	Sngl Rm:	£15
Part Brd:	-	% Red. Children:	50%	Dinner:	-

— Sligo 8km

Florrie Gilmartin
BURMA LODGE
Burma Road, Strandhill, Co Sligo

Strandhill

Open:	All Year except Christmas
No. Rooms:	4
Ensuite:	4

(V)

Tel: **071 68233/68579**   Fax: -

Spacious home, centre Strandhill Village. TV's, Hairdryers, Electric Blankets, Tea
facilities. Ideal touring base, Beach, Golf, Horseriding, Fishing, Flying Club.

B&B PPS:	£17	Sngl Occ. Dble/Tpl:	£23.50	Sngl Rm:	-
Part Brd:	-	% Red. Children:	33.3%	Dinner:	-

— Sligo 8km

Mrs Monica Brennan
ROCKVILLE
Charlestown Road, Tubbercurry,
Co Sligo

Tubbercurry

Open:	!st January-20th December
No. Rooms:	4
Ensuite:	3

(V)

Tel: **071 85270**   Fax: -

"Cead Mile Failte" Quiet, friendly Irish home on N17. Home baking, Hairdryers,
Electric blankets, Laundry facilities, Gardens, Irish music, Golf.

B&B PPS:	£15/£17	Sngl Occ. Dble/Tpl:	£21.50/£23.50	Sngl Rm:	-
Part Brd:	-	% Red. Children:	33.3%	Dinner:	£14

— In Tubbercurry

Tubbercurry 2km

Mrs. Nancy Brennan
CULLEEN

Sligo Road, Tubbercurry, Co Sligo

Tubbercurry

OPEN:	1st March-31 October
NO. ROOMS:	6
ENSUITE:	4

TEL: **071 85083**   FAX: -

Ⓥ

Situated on farm. Landscaped gardens, home cooking. Tourist attractions, Golf, Fishing, Horseriding etc. Rooms ensuite with T.V. On N17.

B&B PPS:	£15/£17	SNGL OCC. DBLE/TPL:	£21.50/£24	SNGL RM:	£18
PART BRD:	-	% RED. CHILDREN:	33%	DINNER:	-

Tubbercurry

Joan Brett
ST ENDA'S

Charlestown Road, Tubbercurry, Co Sligo

Tubbercurry

OPEN:	1st May-1st October
NO. ROOMS:	4
ENSUITE:	2

TEL: **071 85100**   FAX: -

Ⓥ

Comfortable bungalow situated on N17. Electric blankets, Scenic area, nice gardens. Golf and Fishing nearby. Knock Shrine 22 miles.

B&B PPS:	£17	SNGL OCC. DBLE/TPL:	£23.50	SNGL RM:	-
PART BRD:	-	% RED. CHILDREN:	33.3%	DINNER:	-

Tubbercurry 6km

Mrs Noreen Donoghue
ROSSLI HOUSE

Doocastle, Tubbercurry, Co Sligo

Tubbercurry

OPEN:	All Year
NO. ROOMS:	4
ENSUITE:	3

TEL: **071 85099**   FAX: **071 85099**

Ⓥ

Luxury home. Tea/Coffee, Hairdryers,Electric Blankets, Laundry Facilities, Landscaped Gardens, Conservatory. Frommer Guide, Le Guide du Routard, Interconnections recommended.

B&B PPS:	£15/£17	SNGL OCC. DBLE/TPL:	£21.50/£23.50	SNGL RM:	£17/£19
PART BRD:	£180	% RED. CHILDREN:	33.3%	DINNER:	£12

Tubbercurry

Mrs Teresa Kelly
PINEGROVE

Ballina Road, Tubbercurry, Co Sligo

Tubbercurry

OPEN:	All Year
NO. ROOMS:	5
ENSUITE:	5

TEL: **071 85235**   FAX: -

Ⓥ

Friendly atmophere, home-baking, evening meals, electric blankets. Gardens, Fishing, Shooting & Golf. Knock Shrine. 300 metres off N17.

B&B PPS:	£17	SNGL OCC. DBLE/TPL:	£23.50	SNGL RM:	-
PART BRD:	-	% RED. CHILDREN:	33%	DINNER:	£14

In Tubbercurry

Mrs Mary Kennedy
CINRAOI

Ballymote/Boyle Road, Tubbercurry, Co Sligo

Tubbercurry

OPEN:	All Year except Christmas
NO. ROOMS:	3
ENSUITE:	2

TEL: **071 85268**   FAX: **071 85268**

Ⓥ

Modern bungalow on own grounds. Golf, Fishing nearby. Knock Airport 17 miles. Very quiet and peaceful. Le Guide du Routard listed.

B&B PPS:	£15/£17	SNGL OCC. DBLE/TPL:	£21.50/£23.50	SNGL RM:	-
PART BRD:	-	% RED. CHILDREN:	-	DINNER:	£13

In Tubbercurry

Mrs. Teresa O'Gorman
ANNALEA HOUSE
Tubbercurry, Co Sligo

Tubbercurry

OPEN:	All Year except Christmas
NO. ROOMS:	3
ENSUITE:	3

TEL: **071 85141**   FAX: -

Bungalow located on N17 with colourful landscaped garden, viewed from conservatory. Fishing, Golf available locally. TV, tea maker in rooms.

| B&B PPS: | **£17** | SNGL OCC. DBLE/TPL: | **£23.50** | SNGL RM: | - |
| PART BRD: | - | % RED. CHILDREN: | **50%** | DINNER: | **£13** |

In Tubbercurry

Mrs Maeve Walsh
CRUCKAWN HOUSE
Ballymote/Boyle Rd(off N17)
Tubbercurry, Co Sligo

Tubbercurry

OPEN:	1st March-1st November
NO. ROOMS:	5
ENSUITE:	5

TEL: **071 85188**   FAX: **071 85188**

Country peacefulness, overlooking Golf Course, sun lounge, gardens, evening meals, laundry facilities, fishing. Frommer, Le Guide du Routard, AA QQQ award.

| B&B PPS: | **£17/£17.50** | SNGL OCC. DBLE/TPL: | **£23.50/£25** | SNGL RM: | - |
| PART BRD: | - | % RED. CHILDREN: | **33%** | DINNER: | **£14** |

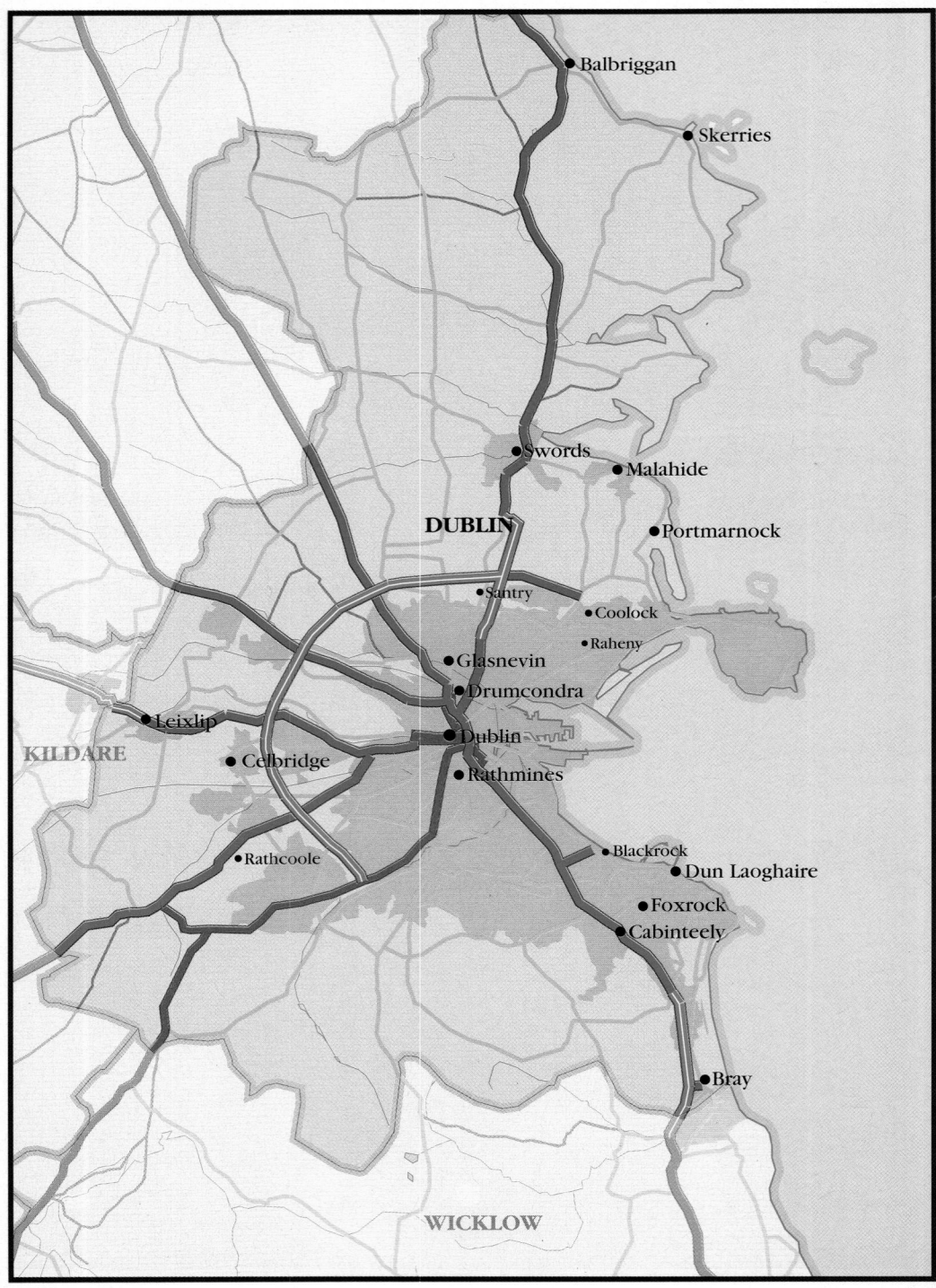

Balbriggan

Skerries

Swords

Malahide

DUBLIN

Portmarnock

Santry

Coolock

Glasnevin

Raheny

Drumcondra

Leixlip

Dublin

KILDARE

Celbridge

Rathmines

Blackrock

Dun Laoghaire

Rathcoole

Foxrock

Cabinteely

Bray

WICKLOW

Dublin, Ireland's capital, steeped in history and buzzing with youthful energy. From its gracious Georgian Squares and terraces, mountain walks and sandy beaches to the intimacy of its pub and cafe life, Dublin is a thriving centre for culture. It is home to a

great literary tradition where the cosmopolitan and charming converge in an atmosphere of delightful diversity.

Fine museums and art galleries chronicle its long and colourful past while the pubs and cafes buzz with traditional entertainment. Dublin's attractions are many from castles, museums and art galleries to the lively spirit of Temple Bar within a half hour of the city centre there are mountain walks, stately homes and gardens, sandy beaches and quaint fishing villages.

During your stay with us you will sample some of the charm of Dublin and particularly the warmth and wit of its people that has never ceased to win the heart of the visitor.

Area Representatives

DUBLIN
Mrs. Rita Kenny, Seaview, 166 Bettyglen, Raheny, Dublin 5.
Tel: 01- 831 5335.

Mrs. Margaret McLoughlin-O'Connell, Loyola,
18 Charleville Road, Phibsboro, Dublin 7.
Tel: 01-838 9973. Fax: 868 6569.

 ## *Tourist Information Offices*

Dublin Tourism Centre
Suffolk Street
Dublin 2.

Callers within the Republic
of Ireland
Tel: 1550 11 22 33*
(*=recorded)
(Calls cost 58p per minute
incl VAT from domestic
phones)
Internet:
http:///www.visit.ie/dublin
email:
information@dublintourism.ie

Arrivals Hall
Dublin Airport

Dun Laoghaire Ferry
Terminal
Dun Laoghire
Co. Dublin

Baggot Street Bridge
Dublin 2

The Square Towncentre
Tallaght
Dublin 24.

City Centre 2km

Carmel Chambers
25 Anglesea Road, Ballsbridge, Dublin 4

Ballsbridge

OPEN:	All Year except Christmas
NO. ROOMS:	4
ENSUITE:	1

TEL: **01 6687346**   FAX: **01 6687346**

Edwardian home. Located in popular Ballsbridge, close to Bus, Rail (DART), Embassies, Art Galleries, Trinity College, Point Theatre & RDS.

BUS NO: **7A, 7, 8, 45, 84, 63**

| B&B PPS: | £20/£25 | SNGL OCC. DBLE/TPL: | £22.50/£30 | SNGL RM: | £20/£22.50 |
| PART BRD: | - | % RED. CHILDREN: | - | DINNER: | |

City Centre 2km

Mrs Cathy Cotter
LANSA TOWN HOUSE
68 Merrion Rd, Ballsbridge, Dublin 4

Ballsbridge

OPEN:	All Year
NO. ROOMS:	4
ENSUITE:	4

TEL: **01 6680416**   FAX: **01 6600803**   EMAIL: **incr0200@indigo.ie**

Residence built 1900. Combining old world charm with modern luxury facilities. Opp. RDS & near Point Theatre, US Embassy, DART.

BUS NO: **5, 6, 7, 7A, 8, 45, DART**

| B&B PPS: | £25/£40 | SNGL OCC. DBLE/TPL: | £35/£50 | SNGL RM: | - |
| PART BRD: | - | % RED. CHILDREN: | 50% | DINNER: | - |

In Ballsbridge

Mrs Phil Dowling
"MERRION LODGE"
148 Merrion Rd, Ballsbridge, Dublin 4

Ballsbridge

OPEN:	1st January-31st December
NO. ROOMS:	6
ENSUITE:	6

TEL: **01 2691565**   FAX: **01 2839998**

Superb residence in Dublin's most elegant suburb. Convenient to Embassies, RDS, Elm Park, UCD, The Point and Ferries.

BUS NO: **7, 8 , 45**

| B&B PPS: | £25/£45 | SNGL OCC. DBLE/TPL: | £35/£60 | SNGL RM: | - |
| PART BRD: | - | % RED. CHILDREN: | 25% | DINNER: | - |

In Ballsbridge

Colm Dunne
AARON HOUSE
152 Merrion Road, Ballsbridge, Dublin 4

Ballsbridge

OPEN:	1st January-27th December
NO. ROOMS:	6
ENSUITE:	6

TEL: **01 2601644**   FAX: **01 2601651**   -

Luxurious accommodation. All rooms en-suite. Convenient to Point Theatre, RDS, Golf Clubs, all Embassies, Restaurants, direct-dial telephones.

BUS NO: **5, 7, 8, 45,**

| B&B PPS: | £25/£39 | SNGL OCC. DBLE/TPL: | £35/£50 | SNGL RM: | £30/£40 |
| PART BRD: | - | % RED. CHILDREN: | 25% | DINNER: | - |

Dublin City Centre 1.5km

Mrs Mary Egan
HADDINGTON LODGE
49 Haddington Rd, Ballsbridge, Dublin 4

Ballsbridge

OPEN:	12th February-12th December
NO. ROOMS:	5
ENSUITE:	5

TEL: **01 6600974**   FAX: -

Georgian House, adjacent City Centre, Top Hotel, Restaurants, Embassies. All rooms with private bathrooms, colour TV & electric blankets.

BUS NO: **10, 6, 7, 8**

| B&B PPS: | £23/£25 | SNGL OCC. DBLE/TPL: | £40/£45 | SNGL RM: | - |
| PART BRD: | - | % RED. CHILDREN: | - | DINNER: | - |

In Ballsbridge

Leslie Griffin
AARON COURT

144 Merrion Road, Ballsbridge, Dublin 4

Ballsbridge

OPEN:	**All Year**
NO. ROOMS:	**4**
ENSUITE:	**4**

TEL: **01 2602631** FAX: **01 2691383**

Elegant family residence in the heart of Ballsbridge. All rooms en-suite, direct dial phones, TV. RDS, Point, Restaurant, Embassies.

BUS NO: **5,7,8,45, DART**

B&B PPS:	**£25/£39**	SNGL. OCC. DBLE/TPL:	**£39/£45**	SNGL RM:	-
PART BRD:	-	% RED. CHILDREN:	**50%**	DINNER:	

Dublin City 2km

Mrs Peggie Massey
49 Merrion Road, Ballsbridge, Dublin 4

Ballsbridge

OPEN:	**10th January-16th December**
NO. ROOMS:	**3**
ENSUITE:	**3**

TEL: **01 2600692** FAX: **01 2837744**

Large detached house. Close to all amenities. Tea/coffee making facilities and colour TV in all bedrooms. Ample parking.

BUS NO: **5, 7, 7A, 8 , 45**

B&B PPS:	**£24/£30**	SNGL. OCC. DBLE/TPL:	**£25/£36**	SNGL RM:	-
PART BRD:	-	% RED. CHILDREN:	**20%**	DINNER:	

Dublin City 1.5km

Mrs Sheila Matthews
ELVA

5 Pembroke Park, Ballsbridge, Dublin 4

Ballsbridge

OPEN:	**1st January-30th November**
NO. ROOMS:	**3**
ENSUITE:	**3**

TEL: **01 6602931** FAX: **01 6605417**

Period house, convenient to Trinity College and Major Conference Centres. All rooms have private facilities, TV, hairdryer, direct-dial telephone.

BUS NO: **10**

B&B PPS:	**£25/£35**	SNGL. OCC. DBLE/TPL:	**£35**	SNGL RM:	**£35**
PART BRD:	-	% RED. CHILDREN:	-	DINNER:	-

BOOKINGS

We recommend your first and last night is pre-booked. Your hosts will make a booking for you at your next selected home for the cost of the phone call. When travelling in high season (June, July, August), it is essential to pre-book your accommodation – preferably the evening before, or the following morning to avoid disappointment.

SOME HOMES ARE CLOSED DURING THE WINTER. WHEN TRAVELLING OFF-SEASON IT IS ADVISABLE TO CALL AHEAD AND GIVE A TIME OF ARRIVAL TO ENSURE YOUR HOSTS ARE AT HOME TO GREET YOU.

Teresa Muldoon
OAK LODGE
4 Pembroke Park, Off Clyde Road, Ballsbridge, Dublin 4

Ballsbridge

OPEN:	All Year
NO. ROOMS:	4
ENSUITE:	2

TEL: **01 6606096/6681721**   FAX: **01 6681721**

Victorian residence. Close RDS, universities, US Embassy, DART. Breakfast menu, tea/coffee making available, TV in all rooms, cot available.

BUS NO: **10, 46A**

B&B PPS:	**£22.50/£25**	SNGL OCC. DBLE/TPL:	-	SNGL RM:	**£20/£25**
PART BRD:	-	% RED. CHILDREN:	**50%**	DINNER:	-

City Centre 1.5km

Mrs Therese Clifford Sanderson
CAMELOT
37 Pembroke Park, Ballsbridge, Dublin 4

Ballsbridge

OPEN:	All Year
NO. ROOMS:	3
ENSUITE:	3

TEL: **01 6680331**   FAX: **01 6671916**

Victorian home, friendly atmmosphere. Close to City Centre, RDS, American Embassy, Museums, Art Galleries, Universities. Fine Restaurants within walking distance.

BUS NO: **10, 46A**

B&B PPS:	**£25/£27**	SNGL OCC. DBLE/TPL:	**£35**	SNGL RM:	-
PART BRD:	-	% RED. CHILDREN:	-	DINNER:	-

Dublin 2km

Olive Walsh
LUCCA HOUSE
2 Ailesbury Way, Ailesbury Rd, Ballsbridge, Dublin 4

Ballsbridge

OPEN:	All Year except Christmas
NO. ROOMS:	3
ENSUITE:	2

TEL: **01 2696448**   FAX: **01 2696448**

Spacious townhouse located Dublin's premier road, convenient RDS, St Vincents Hospital and many good restaurants. Adjacent light-rail - city centre 6 minutes.

BUS NO: **5, 7, 8, 45,3,52**

B&B PPS:	**£25/£35**	SNGL OCC. DBLE/TPL:	-	SNGL RM:	-
PART BRD:	-	% RED. CHILDREN:	-	DINNER:	-

Dublin City 3km

Joan Donnellan
HAZELHURST
166 Stillorgan Rd, Donnybrook, Dublin 4

Donnybrook

OPEN:	All Year except Christmas
NO. ROOMS:	6
ENSUITE:	6

TEL: **01 2838509**   FAX: **01 2600346**

Luxurious spacious residence situated on N11. Adjacent Embassies, UCD, Montrose Hotel, RTE, RDS, main route to Ferry. Private car park.

BUS NO: **10, 46A**

B&B PPS:	**£25/£27.50**	SNGL OCC. DBLE/TPL:	**£35/£45**	SNGL RM:	-
PART BRD:	-	% RED. CHILDREN:	**25%**	DINNER:	-

Dublin 3km

Ms Rita Hurson
WOODBINE LODGE
45 Woodbine Road, Donnybrook, Dublin 4

Donnybrook

OPEN:	All Year except Christmas
NO. ROOMS:	4
ENSUITE:	4

TEL: **01 2830303**   FAX: **01 2837958**

Elegant home, quiet Road off N11. TV, phones/ rooms. Parking. Convenient City Centre, Ferryports, Lansdowne Road near, UCD, RTE, Embassies.

BUS NO: **7, 8, 10, 46A, DART**

B&B PPS:	**£25**	SNGL OCC. DBLE/TPL:	**£35/£45**	SNGL RM:	-
PART BRD:	-	% RED. CHILDREN:	**40%**	DINNER:	-

Dublin 3km

Owen & Louise Curley
LIFFEY VALE
Palmerstown, Dublin 20

Palmerstown

OPEN:	15th January-30th November
NO. ROOMS:	4
ENSUITE:	4

 (V)

TEL: **01 6263853**   FAX: **01 6263853**

Dormer bungalow just off Western Bypass (N4). 400 metres from M50, 8km from Dublin. Extensive landscaped gardens.

BUS NO: **25, 66, 67**

B&B PPS:	**£20/£25**	SNGL OCC. DBLE/TPL:	**£27/£31.50**	SNGL RM:	-
PART BRD:	-	% RED. CHILDREN:	**25%**	DINNER:	-

— Dublin 8km

Mrs Mai Bird
ST DUNSTANS
25A Oakley Road, Ranelagh, Dublin 6

Ranelagh

OPEN:	All Year except Christmas
NO. ROOMS:	3
ENSUITE:	-

(V)

TEL: **01 4972286**   FAX: -

Edwardian townhouse. Frommer recommended. Convenient City Centre, RDS, Ferry, Jurys, Universities. Launderette, Restaurants, Banks and Post Office in immediate vicinity.

BUS NO: **11, 11A, 13,11b**

B&B PPS:	**£16.50/£20**	SNGL OCC. DBLE/TPL:	**£23**	SNGL RM:	-
PART BRD:	-	% RED. CHILDREN:	-	DINNER:	-

— Dublin 2.2km

Mrs Mary Loftus
28 Charleston Ave, Ranelagh, Dublin 6

Ranelagh

OPEN:	1st February-4th November
NO. ROOMS:	3
ENSUITE:	3

(V)

TEL: **01 4978150**   FAX: **01 4978150/4967651**   EMAIL: **antoin@eire.com**

Comfortable Victorian home in a quiet cul-de-sac convenient to City Centre, Universities, Ferry. RDS, DART and excellent Restaurants.

BUS NO: **11,13, 15A,18, 44 48A 83, 62**

B&B PPS:	**£24/£30**	SNGL OCC. DBLE/TPL:	**£35/£45**	SNGL RM:	-
PART BRD:	-	% RED. CHILDREN:	-	DINNER:	-

— Dublin 1.5km

Mrs Mary Byrne
LITTLE SILVER
2 Fonthill Park, Rathfarnham, Dublin 14

Rathfarnham

OPEN:	March-October
NO. ROOMS:	3
ENSUITE:	-

(V)

TEL: **01 4931677**   FAX:

Modern house near, 16, 47, 47A, 47B bus stops. Leisure Centre, Restaurants and Shops.

BUS NO: **16,47, 7A,47B**

B&B PPS:	**£18/£25**	SNGL OCC. DBLE/TPL:	**£24.50/£31.50**	SNGL RM:	**£20**
PART BRD:	-	% RED. CHILDREN:	**10%**	DINNER:	-

— Dublin 6km

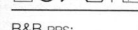

Mrs Monica Byrne
RICHMON HOUSE
59 Marian Crescent, Rathfarnham, Dublin 14

Rathfarnham

OPEN:	March-October
NO. ROOMS:	3
ENSUITE:	-

(V)

TEL: **01 4947582**   FAX: **01 4947582**

Modern home in quiet cul-de-sac close to 15B Bus Terminus, Restaurants, Shops, Sports Facilities. Beside routes from Car Ferry to South, West.

BUS NO: **15B**

B&B PPS:	**£18/£23**	SNGL OCC. DBLE/TPL:	**£24.50/£29.50**	SNGL RM:	-
PART BRD:	-	% RED. CHILDREN:	-	DINNER:	-

 — Dublin 6km

Mrs Beatrice O'Connor
15 Butterfield Avenue,
Rathfarnham, Dublin 14

Rathfarnham

OPEN:	1st February-31st October
NO. ROOMS:	3
ENSUITE:	2

TEL: **01 4943660**   FAX: -

Family home, 15B bus stop outside house to City Centre. Near N81 and M50 to Airport. Restaurants, Tea making facilties.

BUS NO: **15B, 75**

B&B PPS:	**£16/£20**	SNGL OCC. DBLE/TPL:	**£20/£25**	SNGL RM:	-
PART BRD:	-	% RED. CHILDREN:	-	DINNER:	-

Dublin 6km

Mrs Nuala Wells
35 Anne Devlin Avenue,
Rathfarnham, Dublin 14

Rathfarnham

OPEN:	All Year except Christmas
NO. ROOMS:	3
ENSUITE:	-

TEL: **01 4947403**   FAX: -

Centrally heated. House adjacent 15B Bus Terminus behind church, shops, golf course, leisure centres, swimming pools. Near Wicklow Way commencement.

BUS NO: **15B**

B&B PPS:	**£16/£18**	SNGL OCC. DBLE/TPL:	**£22.50/£24.50**	SNGL RM:	**£18**
PART BRD:	-	% RED. CHILDREN:	-	DINNER:	

Dublin 6km

Mrs Beda Wolfe
NEWCOURT
31 Silverwood Road, Rathfarnham,
Dublin 14

Rathfarnham

OPEN:	1st March-1st December
NO. ROOMS:	3
ENSUITE:	1

TEL: **01 4944103**   FAX: -

Modern house, beside terminus 15B Bus. Near Badminton, Hockey, Tennis, Swimming, Golf . On route South, West, Car Ferry, M50 Airport.

BUS NO: **15B**

B&B PPS:	**£18/£23**	SNGL OCC. DBLE/TPL:	**£25/£29.50**	SNGL RM:	-
PART BRD:	-	% RED. CHILDREN:	**10%**	DINNER:	-

Dublin City 5km

Mrs Margaret Crofton
GARVILLE MANOR
1 Garville Avenue, Rathgar, Dublin 6

Rathgar

OPEN:	15th January-20th December
NO. ROOMS:	6
ENSUITE:	2

TEL: **01 4964444/087 2206659**   FAX: **01 4964444**

Period residence 2km city. 15 bus-stop at door. Excellent cuisine, guest telephone, TV, hairdryer, tea/coffee maker, radio alarms in rooms.

BUS NO: **14,15,15A/B/C,18,47,83,**

B&B PPS:	**£23.50/£26**	SNGL OCC. DBLE/TPL:	**£30/£35**	SNGL RM:	-
PART BRD:	-	% RED. CHILDREN:	-	DINNER:	-

Dublin City 2km

Mr & Mrs R J Doyle
HILTON HOUSE
23 Highfield Road, Rathgar, Dublin 6

Rathgar

OPEN:	All Year
NO. ROOMS:	7
ENSUITE:	-

TEL: **01 4976837**   FAX: -

Beautiful large Victorian residence near Dublin City Centre. Convenient Restaurants, Bank, Lounge Bars, Point Theatre, RDS and RTE. Car park.

BUS NO: **15, 15A, 15B**

B&B PPS:	**£20/£25**	SNGL OCC. DBLE/TPL:	**£20/£25**	SNGL RM:	**£20/£25**
PART BRD:	-	% RED. CHILDREN:	**25%**	DINNER:	-

Dublin 3km

Rathmines

Mrs Aida Boyle
ST JUDES
6 Fortfield Tce, Upper Rathmines, Dublin 6

OPEN:	6th January-18th December	
NO. ROOMS:	4	
ENSUITE:		(V)

TEL: 01 4972517　　　FAX: -

Very well maintained Georgian residence. Quiet locality. 7 minutes walk to good Restaurants, Shops, Banks, Churches. Convenient RDS and Point Theatre.

BUS NO: 14A, 13

Dublin 3km

B&B PPS:	£17/£22	SNGL OCC. DBLE/TPL:	£23.50/£28.50	SNGL RM:	-
PART BRD:	-	% RED. CHILDREN:	10%	DINNER:	-

Naas Road

Mrs Bridget Healy
ASHFIELD HOUSE
110 Naas Road, Dublin 12

OPEN:	All Year except Christmas	
NO. ROOMS:	3	
ENSUITE:	2	(V)

TEL: 01 4600003　　　FAX: -

Friendly comfortable "Home from Home" B & B. Frequent bus service to City & all amenities. Near M50. City end N7 route.

BUS NO: 51,51B,68,68A,69

Dublin City 4km

B&B PPS:	£18/£20	SNGL OCC. DBLE/TPL:	£24.50/£26.50	SNGL RM:	-
PART BRD:	-	% RED. CHILDREN:	25%	DINNER:	-

Sandymount

Mrs Dolores Abbott Murphy
14 Sandymount Castle Park, Sandymount off Gilford Road, Dublin 4

OPEN:	1st May-30th September	
NO. ROOMS:	4	
ENSUITE:	1	(V)

TEL: 01 2698413　　　FAX: -

Quiet , safe location beside Village, Sea, Bus, Rail (DART), Embassies, Museums, Art Galleries, Point Theatre, RDS, UCD, Trinity, St Vincents Hospital.

BUS NO: 3

Dublin 2km

B&B PPS:	£16/£20	SNGL OCC. DBLE/TPL:	£25	SNGL RM:	£25
PART BRD:	-	% RED. CHILDREN:	-	DINNER:	-

South Circular Road

Mrs Kathleen Lee
ARDAGH HOUSE
6 St Annes Road Sth, South Circular Road, Dublin 8

OPEN:	6th January-20th December	
NO. ROOMS:	4	
ENSUITE:	2	(V)

TEL: 01 4536615　　　FAX: -

Home overlooking Grand Canal. Convenient to all points of interest. Frommer recommended, 2.5km to City. Road opposite John Player & Sons.

BUS NO: 19,22,22A

Dublin City 2.5km

B&B PPS:	£18/£20	SNGL OCC. DBLE/TPL:	£22/£25	SNGL RM:	£18
PART BRD:	-	% RED. CHILDREN:	-	DINNER:	-

Templeogue

Mrs Noreen Devine
293 Orwell Park Grove Templeogue, Dublin 6W

OPEN:	All Year except Christmas	
NO. ROOMS:	4	
ENSUITE:	4	(V)

TEL: 01 4500007　　　FAX: 01 4565725

Located off N81, 5 mins from Templeogue Village, Car Ferry Route, M50, (Airport 20 mins). All rooms have TV, Hairdryers, Tea/Coffee facilities.

BUS NO: 150, 54A, 15A

Dublin 6km

B&B PPS:	£19/£24	SNGL OCC. DBLE/TPL:	£25.50/£30.50	SNGL RM:	£25/£30
PART BRD:	-	% RED. CHILDREN:	50%	DINNER:	-

Mrs Maureen Durkan
4 Glendown Court,
Off Templeville Road,
Templeogue, Dublin 6W

Templeogue

Open:	31st January-30th November
No. Rooms:	4
Ensuite:	-

Ⓥ

Tel: 01 4562157   Fax: -

Smoke-free luxury home, near N4, N7, Car Ferry route, Golf, Hockey, Swimming, Mountains, Forest Walks, Sports Centre.

Bus No: 15A, 54A, 150

B&B PPS:	£18/£20	Sngl Occ. Dble/Tpl:	£25/£26.50	Sngl Rm:	-
Part Brd:	-	% Red. Children:	-	Dinner:	-

Dublin 6km

Mrs Noreen McBride
3 Rossmore Grove,
Off Wellington Lane, Templeogue,
Dublin 6W

Templeogue

Open:	All Year except Christmas
No. Rooms:	4
Ensuite:	2

Ⓥ

Tel: 01 4902939   Fax: 01 4929416   Email: denismb@iol.ie

Frommer, AA recommended. 20 mins City & Airport. Bus every 10 mins to City. Off N81. Near M50 Motorway, restaurant nearby.

Bus No: 150, 54A

B&B PPS:	£18/£20	Sngl Occ. Dble/Tpl:	£24.50/£26.50	Sngl Rm:	-
Part Brd:	-	% Red. Children:	-	Dinner:	-

Dublin 6km

Mrs Mary McGreal
SEEFIN
28 Rossmore Grove, Templeogue,
Dublin 6W

Templeogue

Open:	15th January-15th December
No. Rooms:	3
Ensuite:	2

Ⓥ

Tel: 01 4907286   Fax: -

Smoke-free luxury home off N81, on Ferry and City Bus Routes. 5 mins M50 Motorway. Restaurants, Pubs, Sporting Facilities locally.

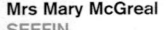

Bus No: 150, 54A

B&B PPS:	£18/£20	Sngl Occ. Dble/Tpl:	£25/£30	Sngl Rm:	-
Part Brd:	-	% Red. Children:	-	Dinner:	-

Dublin City 6km

E & M Coman
MARELLE
92 Rathfarnham Road, Terenure,
Dublin 6W

Terenure

Open:	All Year
No. Rooms:	5
Ensuite:	5

Ⓥ̸

Tel: 01 4904690   Fax: -

Old style residence, beautifully appointed. 15 mins City ample car parking. AA listed. Historical area, Golf Courses & Hockey ground nearby.

Bus No: 15, 16, 47

B&B PPS:	£26/£30	Sngl Occ. Dble/Tpl:	£46	Sngl Rm:	£35/£40
Part Brd:	-	% Red. Children:	-	Dinner:	-

Dublin 5km

Mrs Ellie Kiernan
LOUGHKIERN
65 Rockfield Ave, Off Kimmage Rd West
Terenure, Dublin 12

Terenure

Open:	All Year except Christmas
No. Rooms:	3
Ensuite:	1

Ⓥ

Tel: 01 4551509   Fax: -

Comfortable modern family home. 15 mins to City. Convenient to Restaurants, Sports Centre, Bus, Park, Links Road and Ferry Terminal.

Bus No: 15A, 150

B&B PPS:	£16/£20	Sngl Occ. Dble/Tpl:	£22.50/£26.50	Sngl Rm:	-
Part Brd:	-	% Red. Children:	25%	Dinner:	-

Dublin City 4km

Mrs Thelma Hayes
124 Clonkeen Road, Blackrock, Co Dublin

Blackrock

Open:	**1st January-1st December**
No. Rooms:	**4**
Ensuite:	**2**

Tel: **01 2895552**   Fax: -

Modern house on City Bus route. Convenient to Restaurants and N11. Parking. Dunlaoghaire Ferry 8 mins. TV lounge.

Bus No: **45, 46A**

B&B PPS:	**£18/£20**	Sngl Occ. Dble/Tpl:	**£20/£24**	Sngl Rm:	**£20/£24**
Part Brd:	-	% Red. Children:	-	Dinner:	-

Blackrock 2km

Monica & Michael Leydon
AARONA
150 Clonkeen Road, Deansgrange, Blackrock, Co Dublin

Blackrock

Open:	**All Year**
No. Rooms:	**3**
Ensuite:	**3**

Tel: **01 2893972**   Fax: **01 2898622**

Exquisitely situated beside all amenities. Bus to City Centre. Dunlaoghaire, Ferry Port 5 mins. Highest standards maintained in friendly family atmosphere.

Bus No: **45**

B&B PPS:	**£20/£22.50**	Sngl Occ. Dble/Tpl:	**£27.50**	Sngl Rm:	**£27.50**
Part Brd:	-	% Red. Children:	-	Dinner:	-

Dun Laoghaire 2km

Kitty McEvoy
87 Monkstown Avenue, Blackrock, Co Dublin

Blackrock

Open:	**All Year except Christmas**
No. Rooms:	**3**
Ensuite:	-

Tel: **01 2804004**   Fax: -

Modern relaxed home, ample parking off main road. Convenient to all transport and Ferry.

Bus No: **46A,7,8**

B&B PPS:	**£16/£18**	Sngl Occ. Dble/Tpl:	**£22/£25**	Sngl Rm:	**£20/£22**
Part Brd:	-	% Red. Children:	-	Dinner:	-

Dun Laoghaire 1km

Mrs Mary Corbett Monaghan
46 Windsor Park
Off Stradbrook Road, Blackrock, Co Dublin

Blackrock

Open:	**1st April-31st October**
No. Rooms:	**3**
Ensuite:	-

Tel: **01 2843711**   Fax: -

Bright comfortable family home, convenient to Ferry, Restaurants, Bus and Salthill DART Station. Secure car parking. Ideal touring base.

Bus No: **46A, 7, 8**

B&B PPS:	**£16**	Sngl Occ. Dble/Tpl:	**£22.50**	Sngl Rm:	**£20.50**
Part Brd:	-	% Red. Children:	-	Dinner:	-

Dun Laoghaire 2km

Mrs Margaret Walsh
ACHILL
Shandon Park, Off Monkstown Road, Blackrock, Co Dublin

Blackrock

Open:	**April-November**
No. Rooms:	**3**
Ensuite:	**3**

Tel: **01 2801118**   Fax: -

Secluded split-level house in quiet cul-de-sac, near Seapoint DART, Buses, Restaurants and Car Ferry; hairdryers, electric blankets; Home cooking.

 Bus No: **7, 7A,8**

B&B PPS:	**£26**	Sngl Occ. Dble/Tpl:	**£35**	Sngl Rm:	-
Part Brd:	-	% Red. Children:	**50%**	Dinner:	-

Blackrock 1km

In Dun Laoghaire

Mrs Helen Callanan
PARKVIEW HOUSE
**1 Rosmeen Gardens, Dun Laoghaire,
Co Dublin**

TEL: 01 2806083   FAX: -

Dun Laoghaire

OPEN:	**All Year except Christmas**
NO. ROOMS:	4
ENSUITE:	2

Victorian residence overlooking Park & Harbour. Parking. Beside DART, Buses & Ferry. Frommer Europe, Irish Bed & Breakfast recommended.

BUS NO: **7,7A,8,DART**

B&B PPS:	**£18/£22**	SNGL OCC. DBLE/TPL:	**£25/£35**	SNGL RM:	-
PART BRD:	-	% RED. CHILDREN:	**25%**	DINNER:	-

In Dun Laoghaire

Mrs. Anne D'Alton
ANNESGROVE
**28 Rosmeen Gardens, Dun Laoghaire,
Co Dublin**

TEL: 01 2809801   FAX: -

Dun Laoghaire

OPEN:	**All Year except Christmas**
NO. ROOMS:	4
ENSUITE:	2

Quiet Cul-de-Sac beside DART, Buses & Ferry. Breakfast from 7 a.m, room rates. Frommer, Europe Ireland, Cadogan and Irish Bed and Breakfast.

BUS NO: **7,7A,8,46A & DART**

B&B PPS:	**£18/£22**	SNGL OCC. DBLE/TPL:	**£30/£40**	SNGL RM:	-
PART BRD:	-	% RED. CHILDREN:	**25%**	DINNER:	-

In Dun Laoghaire

Alan & Colette Di Felice
BELMONT
**3 Mulgrave Tce, Dun Laoghaire,
Co Dublin**

TEL: **01 2801422**   FAX: **01 2801422**

Dun Laoghaire

OPEN:	**All Year except Christmas**
NO. ROOMS:	3
ENSUITE:	1

Quiet location, adjacent Bus, Trains, Shops. Car Ferry 5 min. walk. Tea making in rooms. Breakfast menu. 300-yds from TSB.

BUS NO: **7,7A, 8, & 46A.**

B&B PPS:	**£17/£19.50**	SNGL OCC. DBLE/TPL:	**£22/£28**	SNGL RM:	-
PART BRD:	-	% RED. CHILDREN:	-	DINNER:	-

In Dun Laoghaire

Mrs Marie Dunne
**30 Rosmeen Gardens
Dun Laoghaire, Co Dublin**

TEL: 01 2803360   FAX: -

Dun Laoghaire

OPEN:	**May-September**
NO. ROOMS:	3
ENSUITE:	-

Cul-de-Sac beside DART Train, Buses, Ferry and Restaurants. Frommer Europe recommended. Breakfast from 7 a.m. Parking.

BUS NO: **7,7A,8,& DART**

B&B PPS:	**£18/£20**	SNGL OCC. DBLE/TPL:	**£20/£25**	SNGL RM:	-
PART BRD:	-	% RED. CHILDREN:	-	DINNER:	-

RESERVATIONS

- Confirm phone bookings in writing without delay with agreed deposit.
- To avoid misunderstandings later, check rate on booking and clarify any additional changes which may apply to your booking.
- Give details of any special requirements.
- State clearly day, date of arrival and departure date.

In Dun Laoghaire

Mrs. Valerie Fitzgibbon
RATHOE
12 Rosmeen Gardens
Dun Laoghaire, Co Dublin

Dun Laoghaire

OPEN:	1st March-30th November
NO. ROOMS:	3
ENSUITE:	

TEL: **01 2808070**   FAX: -

Mature home, cul-de-sac. Walking distance, DART, Bus, Ferry, early breakfast. Recommendation Frommers Europe.

Ⓟ ✕   BUS NO: **Dart 7,7A,& 8**

B&B PPS:	£18/£20	SNGL OCC. DBLE/TPL:	£25/£30	SNGL RM:	£20/£25
PART BRD:	-	% RED. CHILDREN:	10%	DINNER:	-

In Dun Laoghaire

Steve & Maria Gavin
LYNDEN
2 Mulgrave Tce., Dun Laoghaire, Co Dublin

Dun Laoghaire

OPEN:	All Year
NO. ROOMS:	4
ENSUITE:	2

TEL: **01 2806404**   FAX: **01 2806404**

Georgian house. Quiet location. Adjacent Buses, Train, Shops. Car Ferry 5 mins walk. Early breakfasts. parking, TV & tea making facilities.

[cc]   BUS NO: **7,7A,8,45A,46A, 59,111, DART**

B&B PPS:	£16.50/£19	SNGL OCC. DBLE/TPL:	£23/£25.50	SNGL RM:	-
PART BRD:	-	% RED. CHILDREN:	50%	DINNER:	-

In Dun Laoghaire

Mrs Patricia Gorby
AVONDALE HOUSE
3 Northumberland Ave, Dun Laoghaire, Co Dublin

Dun Laoghaire

OPEN:	January-December
NO. ROOMS:	6
ENSUITE:	-

TEL: **01 2809628/2805764**   FAX: -

Georgian residence in Dun Laoghaire, 5 mins walk from Ferryport and DART Station. Guest sitting room with TV. Early breakfasts.

✕ ♣ ⬛[S]   BUS NO: **7, 7A, 8, 46A**

B&B PPS:	£17.50	SNGL OCC. DBLE/TPL:	£25	SNGL RM:	£25
PART BRD:	-	% RED. CHILDREN:	25%	DINNER:	-

Dun Laoghaire 1km

Mrs Ann Harkin
7 Claremont Villas
(Off Adelaide Road), Glenageary,
Dun Laoghaire, Co Dublin

Dun Laoghaire

OPEN:	All Year except Christmas
NO. ROOMS:	5
ENSUITE:	4

TEL: **01 2805346**   FAX: -

122-year old Victorian home, near Ferry, Bus, Train. Quiet cul-de-sac. Early breakfast, tea-making facilities, laundry service. Tourist information.

[cc]   BUS NO: **8, 59, DART**

B&B PPS:	£18/£20	SNGL OCC. DBLE/TPL:	£24.50/£26.50	SNGL RM:	-
PART BRD:	-	% RED. CHILDREN:	50%	DINNER:	-

Dun Laoghaire

Mrs Mary Kane
2 Granite Hall,
Rosmeen Gardens
Dun Laoghaire, Co Dublin

Dun Laoghaire

OPEN:	All Year except Christmas
NO. ROOMS:	3
ENSUITE:	2

TEL: **01 2809105**   FAX: -

Comfortable detached family home in quiet cul-de-sac within walking distance DART, Sea Front and all amenities. Parking.

Ⓟ ✕   BUS NO: **7, 7A, 8**

B&B PPS:	£22.50/£25	SNGL OCC. DBLE/TPL:	£30	SNGL RM:	£20
PART BRD:	-	% RED. CHILDREN:	-	DINNER:	-

Dun Laoghaire

Mrs Mary Lehane
CILL DARA
5 Tivoli Road, Dun Laoghaire, Co Dublin

Dun Laoghaire

OPEN:	1st January-30th November
NO. ROOMS:	3
ENSUITE:	2

TEL: **01 2807355**   FAX: -

Modern friendly home. Opposite Dun Laoghaire Golf Club. Early breakfast served. Convenient Ferries, Buses, DART, Trains, Restaurants, Shops & Seafront.

B&B PPS:	£18/£20	SNGL OCC. DBLE/TPL:	£27/£33	SNGL RM:	-
PART BRD:	-	% RED. CHILDREN:	-	DINNER:	

Dun Laoghaire 3km

Rosemary Masterson
GLENVIEW HOUSE
5 Glenview, Rochestown Ave, Dun Laoghaire, Co Dublin

Dun Laoghaire

OPEN:	1st January-20th December
NO. ROOMS:	4
ENSUITE:	4

TEL: **01 2855043**   FAX: **01 2855043**   EMAIL: **glenview@goireland.ie**

Modern comfortable home. Convenient - DART, Buses, Ferries, Restaurants & Pubs. TV, Tea/Coffee bedrooms. Private Parking. Touring base, Dublin, Wicklow.

B&B PPS:	£20/£25	SNGL OCC. DBLE/TPL:	£26.50/£31.50	SNGL RM:	-
PART BRD:	-	% RED. CHILDREN:	10%	DINNER:	-

In Dun Laoghaire

Mrs Joan M Murphy
ROSMEEN HOUSE
Rosmeen Gardens, Dun Laoghaire, Co Dublin

Dun Laoghaire

OPEN:	1st February-1st December
NO. ROOMS:	4
ENSUITE:	2

TEL: **01 2807613**   FAX: -

Attractive Spanish type villa. Frommer Europe and Ireland recommended. Early breakfast, walking distance Train, Bus and Ferry.

BUS NO: **7, 8, DART**

B&B PPS:	£18/£22.50	SNGL OCC. DBLE/TPL:	£25/£30	SNGL RM:	-
PART BRD:	-	% RED. CHILDREN:	20%	DINNER:	-

Dun Laoghaire 1km

Mary O'Farrell
WINDSOR LODGE
3 Islington Ave, Sandycove, Dun Laoghaire, Co Dublin

Dun Laoghaire

OPEN:	All Year
NO. ROOMS:	4
ENSUITE:	4

TEL: **01 2846952**   FAX: **01 2846952**

Period residence overlooking Scotsmans Bay. 1min Bus and Train, 15 mins Dublin City Centre, 7 mins Ferry.

BUS NO: **7, 8**

B&B PPS:	£18/£22	SNGL OCC. DBLE/TPL:	-	SNGL RM:	-
PART BRD:	-	% RED. CHILDREN:	50%	DINNER:	-

Dalky 2km

Mrs Bridie O'Leary
ROSEMONT
51 Bellevue Road, Glenageary, Dun Laoghaire

Dun Laoghaire

OPEN:	1st January-30th November
NO. ROOMS:	4
ENSUITE:	3

TEL: **Co Dublin**   FAX: **01 2851021**

Bright comfortable home. Quiet location, convenient to Bus, Train and Ferry. Close to Fitzpatrick Castle, Killiney. Early breakfast. Private parking.

BUS NO: **59, 7, 7A**

B&B PPS:	£18	SNGL OCC. DBLE/TPL:	£24.50	SNGL RM:	£20
PART BRD:	-	% RED. CHILDREN:	25%	DINNER:	-

Dun Laoghaire

Mrs Connie O'Sullivan
DUNCREE
16 Northumberland Avenue, Dun Laoghaire, Co Dublin

Dun Laoghaire

OPEN:	All Year
NO. ROOMS:	4
ENSUITE:	2

TEL: **01 2806118** FAX: -

Spacious Georgian house in Dun Laoghaire. 5 mins walk from DART, Bus and Ferry, Dublin 20 mins by train. Early breakfast.

BUS NO: **7, 7A, 8**

B&B PPS:	**£17/£19**	SNGL OCC. DBLE/TPL:	**£20**	SNGL RM:	-
PART BRD:	-	% RED. CHILDREN:	**25%**	DINNER:	

In Dun Laoghaire

Mrs Marie Power
ARIEMOND
47 Mulgrave Street, Dun Laoghaire, Co Dublin

Dun Laoghaire

OPEN:	All Year except Christmas
NO. ROOMS:	4
ENSUITE:	2

TEL: **01 2801664** FAX: **01 2801664**

Georgian house town centre. Ferry 5 minutes walk. Beside Buses and Train. Early breakfast.

BUS NO: **8, 7, 46A, 45A, DART**

B&B PPS:	**£16.50/£19**	SNGL OCC. DBLE/TPL:	**£25/£30**	SNGL RM:	-
PART BRD:	-	% RED. CHILDREN:	-	DINNER:	-

In Dun Laoghaire

Brendan Smyth
INNISFREE
31 Northumberland Avenue, Dun Laoghaire, Co Dublin

Dun Laoghaire

OPEN:	All Year except Christmas
NO. ROOMS:	6
ENSUITE:	4

TEL: **01 2803093/01 2805598** FAX: - EMAIL: **djsmyth@clubi.ie**

Spacious Georgian house quietly located in Dun Laoghaire. Ferry and DART 5 minutes walk. Dublin 20 minutes by train. Early beakfast. Parking.

BUS NO: **46 ,46A, 75, 7, 8,**

B&B PPS:	**£15/£18.50**	SNGL OCC. DBLE/TPL:	**£21.50/£26**	SNGL RM:	-
PART BRD:	-	% RED. CHILDREN:	**25%**	DINNER:	-

Dun Laoghaire 3km

Mrs Mary T Barry
GOLDIWIL
Church Road, Killiney, Co Dublin

Killiney

OPEN:	1st January-23rd December
NO. ROOMS:	3
ENSUITE:	1

TEL: **01 2852809** FAX: - -

Mature residence on 1 acre landscaped gardens. Private parking. One triple & double room. 4 minutes drive Ferry. 1 ensuite on ground floor.

BUS NO: **7, 7A, 111**

B&B PPS:	**£19/£28**	SNGL OCC. DBLE/TPL:	**£23/£31**	SNGL RM:	-
PART BRD:	-	% RED. CHILDREN:	**20%**	DINNER:	**£25**

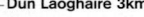

Betty MacAnaney
70 Avondale Road, Killiney, Co Dublin

Killiney

OPEN:	1st February-30th November
NO. ROOMS:	4
ENSUITE:	3

TEL: **01 2859952** FAX: **01 2859952** -

Quiet area, 4- minute drive Ferry. Close Fitzpatrick Castle, Killiney Hill. All rooms tea/coffee maker, hairdryer. 12-minute walk DART Station.

BUS NO: **59**

B&B PPS:	**£16.50/£19**	SNGL OCC. DBLE/TPL:	**£23/£25.50**	SNGL RM:	-
PART BRD:	-	% RED. CHILDREN:	**20%**	DINNER:	-

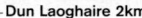
Dun Laoghaire 2km

Bray 3km

Mrs Lorraine Cullen
ARAS
25 Rathmichael Manor,
Loughlinstown/Shankill, Co Dublin

Loughlinstown Shankill

OPEN:	1st January-1st December
NO. ROOMS:	4
ENSUITE:	2

(V)

TEL: **01 2827060**   FAX: **01 2827060**

Modern comfortable home, Dublin/Wicklow Border. Beside Sea, Golf, Bray 3 km, Dun Laoghaire Car Ferry 6 km. City 12 km. At Loughlinstown Roundabout .

Ⓟ ✂ 🐾   BUS NO: **45, 84**

B&B PPS:	£16/£20	SNGL OCC. DBLE/TPL:	£23	SNGL RM:	-
PART BRD:	-	% RED. CHILDREN:	-	DINNER:	-

In Lucan

Colette Egan
MOAT LODGE
Newcastle Road, Lucan, Co Dublin

Lucan

OPEN:	All Year
NO. ROOMS:	4
ENSUITE:	4

(V)

TEL: **01 6241584**   FAX: -

Exclusive 17th Century House convenient to shops, bus, City Centre. Ideal base for Golf & Fishing. Off N4. Near N7, N3, M50.

Ⓟ ⊗ ☕   BUS NO: **66A,67,67A,25,25A,66,.**

B&B PPS:	£18	SNGL OCC. DBLE/TPL:	£24.50	SNGL RM:	-
PART BRD:	-	% RED. CHILDREN:	50%	DINNER:	-

Lucan 1km

Seamus & Patricia McCormack
BEAUMONT
Newcastle Road, Lucan, Co Dublin

Lucan

OPEN:	All Year
NO. ROOMS:	4
ENSUITE:	4

(V)

TEL: **01 6281956**   FAX: -

Modern bungalow just off N4, convenient to City, Airport and Car Ferry. Private car park. Bedrooms non-smoking.

Ⓟ ⊗ ✂ 🎵 🐾   BUS NO: **25, 25A, 66, 67**

B&B PPS:	£18/£20	SNGL OCC. DBLE/TPL:	£25/£30	SNGL RM:	-
PART BRD:	-	% RED. CHILDREN:	20%	DINNER:	-

In Lucan

Mrs Ethna McDonald
KEW LODGE
57 Kew Park, Lucan, Co Dublin

Lucan

OPEN:	All Year except Christmas
NO. ROOMS:	3
ENSUITE:	2

(V)

TEL: **01 6280057**   FAX: -

Modern home, 15 mins City, 30 mins Airport, Ferries. Beside Bus Eireann stop, Spa Hotel, N4, N7, Golf, Fishing, Entertainment.

[CC] Ⓟ ⊗ ✂ ☕ 🚗 🎵 🐾   BUS NO: **66, 66A,67**

B&B PPS:	£15/£17	SNGL OCC. DBLE/TPL:	£21.50/23.50	SNGL RM:	-
PART BRD:	-	% RED. CHILDREN:	50%	DINNER:	-

Rathcoole 2km

Brenda & Gerry Beirne
BEECHBROOK LODGE
Kilteel Road, Rathcoole, Co Dublin

Rathcoole

OPEN:	All Year except Christmas
NO. ROOMS:	3
ENSUITE:	3

(V)

TEL: **01 4580827 / 086 2491542**   FAX: -

Spacious country lodge on 2 acres. Tennis/Basketball Court. Adjoining Golf/Equestrian Centre. Ideal base touring Wicklow/Kildare. City Airport - 25 mins.

[CC] 📶 Ⓟ ⊗ 🚗 🎵 🐾   BUS NO: **69**

B&B PPS:	£18/£18.50	SNGL OCC. DBLE/TPL:	£25	SNGL RM:	-
PART BRD:	-	% RED. CHILDREN:	-	DINNER:	-

In Rathcoole

Mrs Ann Eagers
BANNER HOUSE
Main St, Rathcoole, Co Dublin

Rathcoole

OPEN:	**All Year except Christmas**
NO. ROOMS:	3
ENSUITE:	2

(V)

TEL: **01 4589337**   FAX: -

Spacious modern residence, 100 yds off N7. Beside Pub/ Restaurant. Golf annd Horseriding nearby. Airport, City Centre, 25 Minutes. In Rathcoole village.

BUS NO: **69**

B&B PPS:	£16/£20	SNGL OCC. DBLE/TPL:	£22.50/£26.50	SNGL RM:	-
PART BRD:	-	% RED. CHILDREN:	50%	DINNER:	

Rathcoole 2km

Elizabeth Freeland
HILLBROOK
Redgap, Rathcoole, Co Dublin

Rathcoole

OPEN:	**All Year except Christmas**
NO. ROOMS:	4
ENSUITE:	2

(V)

TEL: **01 4580060/087 2391203**   FAX: -

Welcoming home in scenic countryside, adjacent to Golf, Horseriding, Forest Walks. Dublin City 30 minutes. Convenient to all main routes.

B&B PPS:	£18/£20	SNGL OCC. DBLE/TPL:	£24.50/£26.50	SNGL RM:	£18/£20
PART BRD:	-	% RED. CHILDREN:	50%	DINNER:	-

Rathcoole 1.5km

Elizabeth Keogh
BEARNA RUA LODGE
Redgap, Rathcoole, Co Dublin

Rathcoole

OPEN:	**All Year except Christmas**
NO. ROOMS:	3
ENSUITE:	3

(V)

TEL: **01 4589920**   FAX: -

Tastefully furnished. Country location. Panoramic views. Convenient to Horseriding, Golf Clubs. City Centre 16km, Airport 25 minutes (M50)

BUS NO: **69**

B&B PPS:	£18/£20	SNGL OCC. DBLE/TPL:	£24.50/£26.50	SNGL RM:	-
PART BRD:	-	% RED. CHILDREN:	20%	DINNER:	-

Rathcoole 2km

Irene O'Brien
WINDMILL HILL
Rathcoole, Co Dublin

Rathcoole

OPEN:	**All Year except Christmas**
NO. ROOMS:	4
ENSUITE:	3

(V)

TEL: **01 4589559**   FAX: -

Luxury bungalow in scenic setting. Close to Horse Riding, Golf Courses, Horse Racing and Goffs. Off Dublin/Limerick/Cork road.

BUS NO: **69**

B&B PPS:	£16/£22	SNGL OCC. DBLE/TPL:	£22.50/£28.50	SNGL RM:	-
PART BRD:	—	% RED. CHILDREN:	20%	DINNER:	-

Rathcoole 3km

Mrs Mary Spillane
GREENACRES
Kilteel Road, Rathcoole, Co Dublin

Rathcoole

OPEN:	**All Year except Christmas**
NO. ROOMS:	5
ENSUITE:	4

(V)

TEL: **01 4580732**   FAX: -

Bungalow 2 miles from Rathcoole on Kilteel Rd, opposite Beech Park Golf Club. Riding stables locally.

BUS NO: **69**

B&B PPS:	£16/£20	SNGL OCC. DBLE/TPL:	£22.50/£26.50	SNGL RM:	£25
PART BRD:	-	% RED. CHILDREN:	20%	DINNER:	-

Dublin City 8km

Nola Martini
PINEHILL
Sandyford Village, Dublin 18

Sandyford Village

OPEN:	**All Year except Christmas**
NO. ROOMS:	**4**
ENSUITE:	**2**

(V)

TEL: **01 2952061** FAX: **01 2958291**

Charming Cottage style home with modern amenities. Close to Leopardstown Race Course (Stillorgan), Dun Laoghaire Ferry Port.

[cc] [P] [icons] [S] BUS NO: **44, 114, DART**

B&B PPS:	**£22.50/£25**	SNGL OCC. DBLE/TPL:	**£29/£31.50**	SNGL RM:	**£25**
PART BRD:	-	% RED. CHILDREN:	**50%**	DINNER:	-

Bray 3km

Mrs Eileen McNamee
CORGLASS
15 Shanganagh Grove, Quinns Road, Shankill, Co Dublin

Shankill

OPEN:	**1st February-30th November**
NO. ROOMS:	**3**
ENSUITE:	**2**

(V)

TEL: **01 2820370** FAX: -

Comfortable house, Frommer recommended, South Dublin, quiet cul-de-sac, beside Sea, Golf, Dunlaoghaire Ferry and scenic Wicklow. Off N11

[P] [icons] [S] BUS NO: **45, 45A,84, DART**

B&B PPS:	**£18/£20**	SNGL OCC. DBLE/TPL:	-	SNGL RM:	**£18/£20**
PART BRD:	-	% RED. CHILDREN:	-	DINNER:	-

Bray 5km

Mrs Anne Murphy
3 Seaview Lawn
Shankill, Co Dublin

Shankill

OPEN:	**1st March-30th November**
NO. ROOMS:	**3**
ENSUITE:	**2**

(V)

TEL: **01 2823447** FAX: -

Modern comfortable home, off N11, quiet cul-de-sac. Convenient to Train, Bus, Dun Laoghaire Car Ferry.

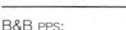
[icons] [P] [icons] [S] BUS NO: **45, 84**

B&B PPS:	**£16/£18**	SNGL OCC. DBLE/TPL:	**£22.50/£25**	SNGL RM:	**£18/£20**
PART BRD:	-	% RED. CHILDREN:	**20%**	DINNER:	-

— Dublin 4km

Mrs Mary O'Reilly
RATHLEEK
13 Brookwood Road, Artane, Dublin 5

Artane

OPEN:	March-31st October	
NO. ROOMS:	3	
ENSUITE:	-	

TEL: **01 8310555**　　FAX: -

Modern house, 10 mins airport, Beaumont Hospital, City Centre, Irish Ferries, Car Ferry, Connolly Station, Central Bus Station. DART. Sea Front.

BUS NO: **42,42B,42C**

B&B PPS:	**£17**	SNGL OCC. DBLE/TPL:	**£23.50**	SNGL RM:	**£23.50**
PART BRD:	-	% RED. CHILDREN:	-	DINNER:	-

— Dublin 5km

Ciaran & Marie Foley
BEAUMONT LODGE
36 Coolatree Road, Beaumont, Dublin 9

Beaumont

OPEN:	1st May-31st October	
NO. ROOMS:	4	
ENSUITE:	-	

TEL: **01 8373949**　　FAX: -

Modern comfortable house, 100 yards gates Beaumont Hospital, 5 mins from Airport. Convenient to City many amenities.

BUS NO: **16,16A,20B,51A**

B&B PPS:	**£16**	SNGL OCC. DBLE/TPL:	**£22.50**	SNGL RM:	**£20**
PART BRD:	-	% RED. CHILDREN:	**20%**	DINNER:	-

Mrs Eve Mitchell
ASHBROOK HOUSE
River Road, Ashtown, Castleknock, Dublin 15

Castleknock

OPEN:	2nd January-20th December	
NO. ROOMS:	4	
ENSUITE:	4	

TEL: **01 8385660**　　FAX: **01 8386867**

A beautiful old Georgian house, close to Phoenix Park, large Gardens & Tennis court. 10 mins City Centre, 15 mins Airport.

BUS NO: **37,39,39A**

B&B PPS:	**£25/£30**	SNGL OCC. DBLE/TPL:	**£35/£40**	SNGL RM:	-
PART BRD:	-	% RED. CHILDREN:	**50%**	DINNER:	-

— In Castleknock

Mrs Marie O'Reilly
67 The Pines, Auburn Ave, Castleknock, Dublin 15

Castleknock

OPEN:	1st March-31st October	
NO. ROOMS:	3	
ENSUITE:	1	

TEL: **01 8215560**　　FAX: -

Select area, close Phoenix Park. Adjacent M50 Motorway linking with routes North, South, West. City 15 mins. Airport 15 mins.

BUS NO: **37,39**

B&B PPS:	**£16/£18**	SNGL OCC. DBLE/TPL:	**£22.50/£24.50**	SNGL RM:	-
PART BRD:	-	% RED. CHILDREN:	-	DINNER:	-

— Dublin 6km

Mrs Bernadette Barker
AIRPORT B&B
Derryolam, Dardistown, Airport Road, Cloghran, Dublin

Cloghran

OPEN:	All Year except Christmas	
NO. ROOMS:	3	
ENSUITE:	2	

TEL: **01 8428341**　　FAX: -

Bungalow beside Dublin Airport, 1km. Private Parking. 5km City Centre. On main bus route.

BUS NO: **41A, B, C,33**

B&B PPS:	**£18/£20**	SNGL OCC. DBLE/TPL:	**£20/£25**	SNGL RM:	**£19**
PART BRD:	-	% RED. CHILDREN:	**20%**	DINNER:	-

— Dublin City 5km

Dublin City Centre 3km

Miss Nuala Betson
THE VILLA
150 Howth Road, Clontarf, Dublin 3

Clontarf

OPEN:	**All Year except Christmas**
NO. ROOMS:	5
ENSUITE:	4

TEL: 01 8332377   FAX: **01 8332377 (Man)**

Comfortable detached house, quiet surroundings, en-suite rooms with TV, radio, tea making facilities. Private Parking. Near City Centre, Airport, Car Ferry.

BUS NO: **42A, 29A,31,32, DART**

B&B PPS:	**£20/£22.50**	SNGL OCC. DBLE/TPL:	**£28/£30**	SNGL RM:	**£22.50**
PART BRD:	-	% RED. CHILDREN:	**20%**	DINNER:	-

Dublin City 4km

Una Brennan
KERRIA
98 Castle Avenue, Clontarf, Dublin 3

Clontarf

OPEN:	**All Year except Christmas**
NO. ROOMS:	3
ENSUITE:	1

TEL: 01 8334571   FAX: -

Family run home overlooking Cricket/ Rugby grounds. Convenient to City, Rail, Bus, Ferry, Airports, Beaches, Point Theatre, Clontarf Castle Hotel.

BUS NO: **130, 29A,31,32, DART**

B&B PPS:	**£18/£22.50**	SNGL OCC. DBLE/TPL:	**£25/£30**	SNGL RM:	**£20**
PART BRD:	-	% RED. CHILDREN:	-	DINNER:	-

Dublin City 3km

Mrs Susan Delahunty
GLENBROOK
34 Howth Road, Clontarf, Dublin 3

Clontarf

OPEN:	**All Year except Christmas**
NO. ROOMS:	3
ENSUITE:	2

TEL: **01 8331117**   FAX: -

Victorian town house, close to Ferryport and Airport. Howth Harbour, Golf Clubs and St Anne's Park nearby.

BUS NO: **29A,31,32,42A/B**

B&B PPS:	**£20/£25**	SNGL OCC. DBLE/TPL:	**£30**	SNGL RM:	**£20/£25**
PART BRD:	-	% RED. CHILDREN:	**20%**	DINNER:	-

Dublin 5km

Miss M Dereymont
18 Seacourt
St Gabriel's Road, Clontarf, Dublin 3

Clontarf

OPEN:	**February-October**
NO. ROOMS:	3
ENSUITE:	1

TEL: **01 8333313**   FAX: -

Georgian residence, convenient to City, Airport, B&I Ferry, Restaurants, Pubs, Point Theatre, non smoking. Highly recommended. Adults only.

BUS NO: **130**

B&B PPS:	**£18.50/£21**	SNGL OCC. DBLE/TPL:	**£30/£37**	SNGL RM:	-
PART BRD:	-	% RED. CHILDREN:	-	DINNER:	-

Dublin 5km

Mrs Carmel Drain
BAYVIEW
265 Clontarf Road, Dublin 3

Clontarf

OPEN:	**All Year except Christmas**
NO. ROOMS:	3
ENSUITE:	2

TEL: **01 8339870**   FAX: **01 8339870**

Overlooking Dublin Bay, convenient Beach, Park, Golf, Ferry, Airport, City, Point Theatre. Main Bus route. Tea, Coffee, Hairdryers, TV, Menu.

          BUS NO: **130**

B&B PPS:	**£20/£22**	SNGL OCC. DBLE/TPL:	**£25/£27**	SNGL RM:	-
PART BRD:	-	% RED. CHILDREN:	**30%**	DINNER:	-

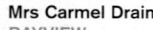

Dublin 3km

Gladys Duggan
124 Howth Road, Clontarf,
Dublin 3

Clontarf	
Open:	All Year except Christmas
No. Rooms:	4
Ensuite:	-

Tel: **01 8339522**   Fax: -

Magnificent unique Victorian house 1820's. Own grounds, private parking. City Centre 10 minutes by Bus. Airport and Car Ferry 15mins.

ⓟ⊗🚲♣   Bus No: **28A,29A,31A,32A**

B&B PPS:	£20	Sngl Occ. Dble/Tpl:	£26.50	Sngl Rm:	-
Part Brd:	-	% Red. Children:	50%	Dinner:	-

Dublin City 3km

Mary Dunwoody
ELDAR
19, Copeland Avenue, Clontarf,
Dublin 3

Clontarf	
Open:	1st March-30th November
No. Rooms:	4
Ensuite:	2

Tel: **01 8339091**   Fax: -

Situated between Malahide/Howth Road. Griffith Avenue End. Convenient all services. Tea/Coffee, Hairdryer, Ironing facilities all rooms.

ⓟ⊗✂🖵📺   Bus No: **20,28,29,31,32,42**

B&B PPS:	£17/£20	Sngl Occ. Dble/Tpl:	£22/£25	Sngl Rm:	-
Part Brd:	-	% Red. Children:	-	Dinner:	-

Dublin City 4km

Jackie Egan
VALENTIA HOUSE
37 Kincora Court, Clontarf, Dublin 3

Clontarf	
Open:	All Year except Christmas
No. Rooms:	3
Ensuite:	3

Tel: **01 8338060/088 632706**   Fax: -

Family run town house, convenient to City, Airport, Ferry, Point Depot, Beaches, Golf Clubs, Restaurants. Quiet location. Private parking.

ⓟ✂🖵🚲📺   Bus No: **130**

B&B PPS:	£19/£22	Sngl Occ. Dble/Tpl:	£25.50/£28.50	Sngl Rm:	-
Part Brd:	-	% Red. Children:	50%	Dinner:	-

Dublin 5km

Mrs Oonagh Egan
144 Kincora Road,
Clontarf, Dublin 3

Clontarf	
Open:	6th January-20th December
No. Rooms:	5
Ensuite:	4

Tel: **01 8339990**   Fax: **01 8339990**

Convenient to City, Rail, Bus, Ferry, Airport, Beaches, Golf Clubs, Point Theatre. Private parking. (TV, telephone, tea/coffee facilities in rooms).

cc ☎ⓟ⊗✂🖵🚲♣♣🖊📺   Bus No: **130**

B&B PPS:	£20/£25	Sngl Occ. Dble/Tpl:	£25/£30	Sngl Rm:	-
Part Brd:	-	% Red. Children:	25%	Dinner:	-

Dublin City 5km

Bridget Geary
69 Hampton Court, Vernon Ave,
Clontarf, Dublin 3

Clontarf	
Open:	1st April-30th September
No. Rooms:	3
Ensuite:	1

Tel: **01 8331199**   Fax: -

Modern house in quiet area, parking, 15mins Airport, City Centre, Ferry, Point Theatre. Convenient Clontarf Castle Hotel. Frommer recommended.

ⓟ🖵 S   Bus No: **130**

B&B PPS:	£17/£20	Sngl Occ. Dble/Tpl:	£23.50/£26.50	Sngl Rm:	-
Part Brd:	-	% Red. Children:	-	Dinner:	-

— Dublin 5km

Mrs Margo Harahan
JAYMARA
67 Hampton Court, Off Vernon Avenue, Clontarf, Dublin 3

Clontarf

OPEN: 1st April-31st October
No. Rooms: 3
Ensuite: 2

V

TEL: 01 8336992 FAX: -

Semi detached between Vernon Ave & Castle Ave. Parking, 15 mins Airport, Ferry, Point Theatre, city. 5 mins Clontarf Castle. Cash Accepted.

Bus No: **130,28,29,31, DART**

| B&B PPS: | £17/£20 | SNGL OCC. DBLE/TPL: | £23.50/£26.50 | SNGL RM: | - |
| PART BRD: | - | % RED. CHILDREN: | - | DINNER: | - |

— Dublin 4km

Mrs Moira Kavanagh
SPRINGVALE
69 Kincora Drive, Off Kincora Grove, Clontarf, Dublin 3

Clontarf

OPEN: All Year except Christmas
No. Rooms: 4
Ensuite:

V

TEL: 01 8333413 FAX: -

Modern house, quiet residential area. 15 mins Airport, Car Ferry, City, Point Theatre. Frommer Recommended. Tea/coffee facilities. 4 rooms with shower only.

Bus No: **29A,31,32,130, DART**

| B&B PPS: | £17 | SNGL OCC. DBLE/TPL: | £23.50 | SNGL RM: | - |
| PART BRD: | - | % RED. CHILDREN: | 20% | DINNER: | - |

— Dublin 3km

Mrs Eileen Cummiskey Kelly
GARRYBAWN
18 Copeland Avenue, Clontarf, Dublin 3

Clontarf

OPEN: All Year except Christmas
No. Rooms: 3
Ensuite: 2

V

TEL: 01 8333760 FAX: 01 8333760

Semi detached house situated between Malahide Road and Howth Road, colour TV in all bedrooms.

Bus No: **20, 20B, 42, 31**

| B&B PPS: | £20/£25 | SNGL OCC. DBLE/TPL: | £30 | SNGL RM: | - |
| PART BRD: | - | % RED. CHILDREN: | - | DINNER: | - |

— Dublin City 5km

Mrs Eileen P Kelly
TORC HOUSE
17 Seacourt, (off Seafield Road), Clontarf, Dublin 3

Clontarf

OPEN: 1st March-31st October
No. Rooms: 3
Ensuite: 2

TEL: 01 8332547 FAX: -

Detached Georgian house, residential area. Convenient City, Airport, Ferry Port, Beach, Golf, St. Annes Garden, Point . Frommer/RAC/Sullivan Guide recommended.

Bus No: **130**

| B&B PPS: | £20/£22 | SNGL OCC. DBLE/TPL: | £28/£30 | SNGL RM: | - |
| PART BRD: | - | % RED. CHILDREN: | - | DINNER: | - |

— Dublin 5km

Mrs Mary A Murphy
ST JUDE
19 Seacourt, off Seafield Rd, Clontarf, Dublin 3

Clontarf

OPEN: 1st April-30th September
No. Rooms: 3
Ensuite: 2

TEL: 01 8332555 FAX: -

Detached Georgian house residential area. Convenient City Centre, Airport, Ferry (B&I), Beach, Golf, Point Theatre, parking.

Bus No: **130**

| B&B PPS: | £18/£22 | SNGL OCC. DBLE/TPL: | £18 | SNGL RM: | - |
| PART BRD: | - | % RED. CHILDREN: | - | DINNER: | - |

Mrs Myra O'Flaherty
SEA BREEZE
312 Clontarf Road, Dublin 3

Clontarf

OPEN:	**All Year except Christmas**
NO. ROOMS:	3
ENSUITE:	3

TEL: **01 8332787**   FAX: -

On seafront close to Ferry, Airport, Golf Links. Frequent bus service to and from City. All rooms with private facilities.

BUS NO: **130**

Dublin 5km

B&B PPS:	£20	SNGL OCC. DBLE/TPL:	£25	SNGL RM:	-
PART BRD:	-	% RED. CHILDREN:	10%	DINNER:	-

Helen Stafford
FERRYVIEW HOUSE
96 Clontarf Road, Clontarf, Dublin 3

Clontarf

OPEN:	**All Year**
NO. ROOMS:	6
ENSUITE:	4

TEL: **01 8335893**   FAX: **01 8532141**

Comfortable spacious home facing South on Dublin Bay. Close to City, Car Ferry, Airport and Point Theatre. Bus 130 to door.

   BUS NO: **130**

Dublin 3km

B&B PPS:	£17/£20	SNGL OCC. DBLE/TPL:	£20/£25	SNGL RM:	£20/£25
PART BRD:	-	% RED. CHILDREN:	20%	DINNER:	-

Mrs Mary C Yalloway
MIZPAH
196 Kincora Road, Clontarf, Dublin 3

Clontarf

OPEN:	**1st March-31st October**
NO. ROOMS:	3
ENSUITE:	-

TEL: **01 8333270**   FAX: **01 8333270**

Quiet residential area, convenient City, Airport, Ferry, Point Theatre, Golf, Beach. Private parking. Electric Blankets, Tea/Coffee facilities in rooms.

   BUS NO: **130**

Dublin City 4km

B&B PPS:	£18	SNGL OCC. DBLE/TPL:	£24.50	SNGL RM:	-
PART BRD:	-	% RED. CHILDREN:	-	DINNER:	-

Mrs Mary Connor
KILSHANE HOUSE
48 Crawford Avenue, Drumcondra, Dublin 9

Drumcondra

OPEN:	**1st January-23rd December**
NO. ROOMS:	3
ENSUITE:	1

TEL: **01 8308506**   FAX: -

Centrally located close to Botanic Gardens, Shopping, Theatres, Restaurants, Car Ferry, Airport.

BUS NO: **3,11,16,11A,16A,41A**

Dublin 2km

B&B PPS:	£16/£18	SNGL OCC. DBLE/TPL:	£20/£25	SNGL RM:	£20
PART BRD:	-	% RED. CHILDREN:	-	DINNER:	-

Mrs Roma Gibbons
JOYVILLE
24 St Alphonsus Road, Drumcondra, Dublin 9

Drumcondra

OPEN:	**All Year except Christmas**
NO. ROOMS:	4
ENSUITE:	-

TEL: **01 8303221**   FAX:

Victorian town house off main airport road. Convenient to Car Ferry, Botanic Gardens, City Centre.

BUS NO: **3,11,11A,16,16A ,41**

Dublin City 1km

B&B PPS:	£15	SNGL OCC. DBLE/TPL:	£20	SNGL RM:	-
PART BRD:	-	% RED. CHILDREN:	-	DINNER:	-

Mrs Hilda Gibson
THE GABLES
50 Iona Crescent, off Holybank Road, Drumcondra, Dublin 9

Drumcondra

TEL: **01 8300538**   FAX: -

OPEN:	All Year except Christmas	
No. ROOMS:	4	
ENSUITE:	3	

Comfortable family home off main Airport Road,(N1), 10 minutes Airport, Car Ferry, City Centre, Point Theatre, Private Car Park.

Ⓟ Ⓢ   Bus No: **3,11,16,33,36,41 ,51A**

B&B PPS:	**£20**	SNGL OCC. DBLE/TPL:	**£27**	SNGL RM:	**£20/£22**
PART BRD:	-	% RED. CHILDREN:	**20%**	DINNER:	-

Dublin 2km

Mrs Ann Griffin
MUCKROSS HOUSE
Claude Road, off Whitworth Rd, Drumcondra, Dublin 9

Drumcondra

TEL: **01 8304888**   FAX: **01 8304888**

OPEN:	2nd January-20th December	
No. ROOMS:	5	
ENSUITE:	5	

(V)

Situated off main airport road (N1). Convenient to City Centre, Airport, Car Ferry & Point Depot. Private enclosed car parking.

Ⓟ   Bus No: **13,40,40A,40B**

B&B PPS:	**£20**	SNGL OCC. DBLE/TPL:	**£26.50**	SNGL RM:	-
PART BRD:	-	% RED. CHILDREN:	**25%**	DINNER:	-

Dublin 1km

Mrs Frances Hughes
326 Collins Avenue
Drumcondra, Whitehall, Dublin 9

Drumcondra

TEL: **01 8370754**   FAX: -

OPEN:	1st March-30th November	
No. ROOMS:	3	
ENSUITE:	2	

Woodlands, attractive detached modern house. Very large car parking space in front, convenient to City Centre, Airport, Buses and DART travel.

Bus No: **20B, 16A, 16**

B&B PPS:	**£17.50/£20**	SNGL OCC. DBLE/TPL:	**£25/£30**	SNGL RM:	-
PART BRD:	-	% RED. CHILDREN:	**25%**	DINNER:	-

Dublin City 3km

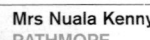

Mrs Nuala Kenny
RATHMORE
22 Walnut Rise, Courtlands, off Griffith Ave, Drumcondra, Dublin 9

Drumcondra

TEL: **01 8370986**   FAX: -

OPEN:	All Year except Christmas	
No. ROOMS:	3	
ENSUITE:	-	

Modern home situated off main airport road. City centre, Airport, Car Ferry - 10/15 mins. TV, Tea making facilities in all rooms.

Ⓢ   Bus No: **3,16,16A,41**

B&B PPS:	**£16**	SNGL OCC. DBLE/TPL:	**£22**	SNGL RM:	**£20**
PART BRD:	-	% RED. CHILDREN:	**10%**	DINNER:	-

Dublin City Centre 3km

SYMBOLS

LOOK OUT FOR THESE SYMBOLS WHICH SHOULD BE DISPLAYED BY ALL MEMBERS OF TOWN & COUNTRY HOMES.

Mrs Cait Cunningham Murray
30 Walnut Ave
Courtlands Estate, off Griffith Ave
Drumcondra, Dublin 9

Drumcondra

OPEN:	March-October
NO. ROOMS:	3
ENSUITE:	2

TEL: **01 8379327**   FAX: -

Modern home, off Griffith Ave overlooking park. off N1 convenient to Airport, City Centre and B & I ferry. Smoke free home.

BUS No: **3,16,16A,36,41,41A**

— Dublin City 4km

B&B PPS:	**£15/£17.50**	SNGL OCC. DBLE/TPL:	-	SNGL RM:	-
PART BRD:	-	% RED. CHILDREN:	-	DINNER:	-

Mrs Gemma Rafferty
GREEN-VIEW
36 Walnut Avenue, Courtlands,
Off Griffith Ave, Drumcondra, Dublin 9

Drumcondra

OPEN:	All Year except Christmas
NO. ROOMS:	3
ENSUITE:	2

TEL: **01 8376217**   FAX: -

Peaceful location opposite Park off N1 10 mins City Centre, Airport, Car Ferry, Golf Courses.

BUS No: **3,16,16A,36,41A, 41B**

— Dublin City 4km

B&B PPS:	**£16/£18.50**	SNGL OCC. DBLE/TPL:	-	SNGL RM:	-
PART BRD:	-	% RED. CHILDREN:	-	DINNER:	-

Irene Coyle Ryan
BLANFORD HOUSE
37 Lambay Road, off Griffith Ave
Drumcondra, Dublin 9

Drumcondra

OPEN:	All Year except Christmas
NO. ROOMS:	4
ENSUITE:	1

TEL: **01 8378036**   FAX: **01 8378036**

Town house near Dublin City Airport, Ferry Port, Botanic Gardens. Forbairt, Point Theatre. Dublin City University.

BUS No: **11, 11A**

— Dublin City 3km

B&B PPS:	**£16/£20**	SNGL OCC. DBLE/TPL:	**£25/£30**	SNGL RM:	**£20**
PART BRD:	-	% RED. CHILDREN:	-	DINNER:	-

Mrs Teresa Ryan
PARKNASILLA
15 Iona Drive
Drumcondra, Dublin 9

Drumcondra

OPEN:	1st January-21st December
NO. ROOMS:	4
ENSUITE:	2

TEL: **01 8305724**   FAX: -

Edwardian detached residence, off main Airport Road N1, 10 minutes to City Centre, Airport, Boat Ferry, Bus & Rail Terminals.

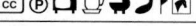 BUS No: **11,16,16A,41,13,19,19A,134**

— Dublin 1.5km

B&B PPS:	**£18/£20**	SNGL OCC. DBLE/TPL:	**£20/£22.50**	SNGL RM:	-
PART BRD:	-	% RED. CHILDREN:	**20%**	DINNER:	-

Larry & Mary Weatherman
CLONLIFFE B&B
94 Clonliffe Road, Dublin 3

Drumcondra

OPEN:	All Year
NO. ROOMS:	3
ENSUITE:	2

TEL: **01 8379656/088 2782879**   FAX: **01 8379656**

Townhouse residential area. Off street parking. 15 mins Airport, 10 mins Ferryport. Convenient Golf, Beach, Horseriding, Point. From Airport, left Independant Bridge.

BUS No: **51A**

— Dublin 2km

B&B PPS:	**£16/£18**	SNGL OCC. DBLE/TPL:	**£22.50/£24.50**	SNGL RM:	-
PART BRD:	-	% RED. CHILDREN:	**45%**	DINNER:	-

Glasnevin

Paddy & Liz Kenny
CRUAGH
9 Glasnevin Avenue, Dublin 11

TEL: **01 8422086**   FAX: -

1.5 km from MI & M50, 2 km from N2, Airport 10 mins, City Centre & Ferryport 15 - 20 mins. Adjacent D.C.U.

Ⓟ

OPEN:	All Year except Christmas
NO. ROOMS:	3
ENSUITE:	-

Ⓥ

BUS NO: **13,13A,19A,36,36A,11,11A,11B**

Dublin City 5km

| B&B PPS: | £15/£17 | SNGL OCC. DBLE/TPL: | £21.50/£23.50 | SNGL RM: | - |
| PART BRD: | - | % RED. CHILDREN: | 25% | DINNER: | - |

Navan Road

Mrs Geraldine Higgins O'Malley
GUDINUF
**175 Navan Rd,
Dublin 7**

TEL: **01 8380360**   FAX: -

Period style house with sun balcony. Bedrooms ensuite. TV's, hairdryers, tea/coffee facilities in all rooms.

OPEN:	All Year except Christmas
NO. ROOMS:	5
ENSUITE:	3

Ⓥ

BUS NO: **37, 38, 39, 70**

Dublin City Centre 5km

| B&B PPS: | £20/£22 | SNGL OCC. DBLE/TPL: | £28/£30 | SNGL RM: | £23 |
| PART BRD: | - | % RED. CHILDREN: | 25% | DINNER: | - |

Phibsboro

Mrs Margaret McLoughlin-O'Connell
LOYOLA
18 Charleville Road, Phibsboro, Dublin 7

TEL: **01 8389973**   FAX: **01 8686569**

Victorian house convenient to Rail, Bus, Airport, Car Ferry Terminals. Zoo, Public Parks, Mater Hospital, link roads.

OPEN:	All Year except Christmas
NO. ROOMS:	3
ENSUITE:	2

Ⓥ

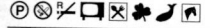

BUS NO: **10, 22, 120**

Dublin City 1km

| B&B PPS: | £17/£20 | SNGL OCC. DBLE/TPL: | £23.50/£26.50 | SNGL RM: | - |
| PART BRD: | - | % RED. CHILDREN: | 20% | DINNER: | - |

Raheny

Mrs Maureen Flynn
FOUR SEASONS
15 Grange Park Green, Raheny, Dublin 5

TEL: **01 8486612**   FAX: -

Modern luxury home. M1/M50, 7 minutes. Public transport services nearby. Airport/City 20 minutes. Private Parking. Restaurants in Village.

OPEN:	2nd January-20th December
NO. ROOMS:	3
ENSUITE:	3

Ⓥ

BUS NO: **29A, 31, 32**

Dublin City 7km

| B&B PPS: | £18.50 | SNGL OCC. DBLE/TPL: | - | SNGL RM: | - |
| PART BRD: | - | % RED. CHILDREN: | - | DINNER: | - |

Raheny

Mrs Eileen Keane
BREIFNE
23 Bettyglen, Raheny, Dublin 5

TEL: **01 8313976**   FAX: -

Large detached house overlooking sea. Private parking. 10 km Dublin Airport, 6 km B&I Car Ferry, 4 km City Centre, guest lounge.

OPEN:	All Year except Christmas
NO. ROOMS:	3
ENSUITE:	2

Ⓥ

BUS NO: **31, 31A, 32**

In Raheny

| B&B PPS: | £16/£18.50 | SNGL OCC. DBLE/TPL: | £22.50/£25 | SNGL RM: | £19/£20 |
| PART BRD: | - | % RED. CHILDREN: | 25% | DINNER: | - |

Dublin City 5km

Mrs Rita Kenny
SEAVIEW
166 Bettyglen
Raheny, Dublin 5

Raheny

OPEN:	All Year except Christmas
NO. ROOMS:	3
ENSUITE:	2

(V)

TEL: **01 8315335**   FAX: -

Convenient to Airport, Car Ferry, DART Rail, Buses, Beaches, Golf Courses, Parks. Orthopaedic beds. Tea facilities in rooms. Room Rates.

BUS NO: **31,31A,32,32B**

B&B PPS:	£16.50/£19	SNGL OCC. DBLE/TPL:	£23/£26	SNGL RM:	-
PART BRD:	-	% RED. CHILDREN:	20%	DINNER:	-

In Raheny Village

Mrs Marlene Moran
90 Foxfield Road
Raheny, Dublin 5

Raheny

OPEN:	May-September
NO. ROOMS:	3
ENSUITE:	2

(V)

TEL: **01 8313119**   FAX: -

Modern family home off Howth road. Convenient to Airport, Seaport, Golf Course, Buses & DART Station. No Smoking, Private Parking.

BUS NO: **31, 31A, 32, DART**

B&B PPS:	£18.50	SNGL OCC. DBLE/TPL:	-	SNGL RM:	£16
PART BRD:	-	% RED. CHILDREN:	20%	DINNER:	-

Dublin 5km

Mrs Nancy Patton
RATHMULLAN HOUSE
110 Bettyglen Est, off Howth Road,
Raheny, Dublin 5

Raheny

OPEN:	All Year except Christmas
NO. ROOMS:	3
ENSUITE:	-

(V)

TEL: **01 8318463**   FAX: -

Modern family 5km from Howth, convenient to Buses, DART Train, Car Ferry, Bird Santuary and Golf links. Raheny 10 mins. Airport 30 mins.

BUS NO: **31,31B,32,32A,32B**

B&B PPS:	£17	SNGL OCC. DBLE/TPL:	£23	SNGL RM:	-
PART BRD:	-	% RED. CHILDREN:	20%	DINNER:	-

Dublin 4km

Mrs Anne Brannigan
HAZELWOOD
34 Lorcan Drive, Santry, Dublin 9

Santry

OPEN:	All Year except Christmas
NO. ROOMS:	3
ENSUITE:	1

(V)

TEL: **01 8426065/088 666803**   FAX: -

Comfortable family home off main Airport road (N1). 2 km Airport. Beside Omni-Park shopping, Leisure complex, convenient to City Centre.

BUS NO: **16,16A,33,33B,41,41A,41B,41C**

B&B PPS:	£17/£20	SNGL OCC. DBLE/TPL:	£23.50/£26.50	SNGL RM:	-
PART BRD:	-	% RED. CHILDREN:	-	DINNER:	-

Dublin City 5km

Mrs A Levins
132 Santry Close
Santry, Dublin 9

Santry

OPEN:	February-December
NO. ROOMS:	3
ENSUITE:	1

(V)

TEL: **01 8424515**   FAX: -

Located in cul-de-sac off Airport Road (N1), opposite Santry Stadium, 2 km from Airport, 5 km from City. Knowledge of Italian & French.

BUS NO: **41,41A,41B,41C, 33,33B**

B&B PPS:	£16/£18.50	SNGL OCC. DBLE/TPL:	£23/£25	SNGL RM:	-
PART BRD:	-	% RED. CHILDREN:	-	DINNER:	-

Balbriggan 4km

Jacqueline Clarke
KNIGHTSWOOD B&B
6 Knightswood, Balrothery, Balbriggan, Co Dublin

Balbriggan

OPEN:	15th May-30th September	
No. ROOMS:	3	
ENSUITE:	1	V

TEL: **01 8411621**   FAX: -

Comfortable detached residence in quiet rural setting. Convenient to Airport, Golf Courses, Seaside and Hostelry. Situated 0.5km off the N1.

[cc] P 💬 👜 📺

B&B PPS:	£17/£20	SNGL OCC. DBLE/TPL:	£23.50/£35	SNGL RM:	-
PART BRD:	-	% RED. CHILDREN:	25%	DINNER:	-

Swords 11km

Thomas & Mary Hoey
STELLAS REST
Burrow Road, Portrane, Donabate, Co Dublin

Donabate

OPEN:	1st March-30th November	
No. ROOMS:	4	
ENSUITE:	3	V

TEL: **01 8436302**   FAX: -

Turn right 3km north of Swords. Spacious heated bungalow. Parking, Beaches, Golfers Paradise, 15 mins Airport.

P 👜📺 👜   BUS No: **33B**

B&B PPS:	£16/£18	SNGL OCC. DBLE/TPL:	£22.50/£24.50	SNGL RM:	-
PART BRD:	-	% RED. CHILDREN:	50%	DINNER:	-

Howth 1.5km

Mrs Rosaleen Hobbs
HAZELWOOD
2 Thormanby Woods, Thormanby Road, Howth, Dublin 13

Howth

OPEN:	All Year except Christmas	
No. ROOMS:	4	
ENSUITE:	2	

TEL: **01 8391391**   FAX: **01 8391391**   EMAIL: **101706.3526@ compu serve.com.ie**

Modern dormer bungalow situated in own grounds. Ample car parking. Convenient Golf, Beach, Restaurants, Scenic Cliff Walks and Fishing Village.

P ⊗ 👜 🎵 👜   BUS No: **31B, DART**

B&B PPS:	£17/£21	SNGL OCC. DBLE/TPL:	£25/£27	SNGL RM:	-
PART BRD:	-	% RED. CHILDREN:	50%	DINNER:	-

Swords 9km

Freda Rigney
IVY BUNGALOW
Ballough, Lusk, Co Dublin

Lusk

OPEN:	All Year	
No. ROOMS:	4	
ENSUITE:	2	V

TEL: **01 8437031/ 088 565914**   FAX: -

Quaint country home off Belfast Dublin Road. 10 min Airport. 30 mins City Centre. Peaceful surroundings. Ground floor accommodation. Ideal touring base.

P ⊗ 👜📺 👜

B&B PPS:	£16/£20	SNGL OCC. DBLE/TPL:	£25/£30	SNGL RM:	-
PART BRD:	-	% RED. CHILDREN:	50%	DINNER:	-

Malahide 1.25km

Mrs Helen Dennis
CARLIM LODGE
Streamstown, Malahide, Co Dublin

Malahide

OPEN:	January-November	
No. ROOMS:	4	
ENSUITE:	3	V

TEL: **01 8452839**   FAX: -

Secluded wooded setting beside Malahide Castle. Adjacent to Golf, Horseriding, Yachting, Beach. Airport 10 mins, Ferry 20 mins. TV, coffee makers.

P 👜📺 ☕ 🎵 👜 [S]   BUS No: **42,102,230,**

B&B PPS:	£17/£20	SNGL OCC. DBLE/TPL:	£23.50/£26.50	SNGL RM:	£19/£20
PART BRD:	-	% RED. CHILDREN:	50%	DINNER:	-

Malahide 3km

Christopher & Nora Duff
MEADOW VIEW
Posey Lane, Kinsealy, Malahide, Co Dublin

Malahide

OPEN:	1st March-31st October
No. Rooms:	3
Ensuite:	3

TEL: **01 8460359**   FAX: **01 8460359** -

Quiet country setting, Castle/Golf/Cinemas/Airport 10 minutes. Ferry/City 20 minutes. Behind "Top" garage on Malahide Road (R107). 3 minutes M50.

Bus No: **42,43**

B&B PPS:	£17/£18	SNGL OCC. DBLE/TPL:	£28	SNGL RM:	-
PART BRD:	-	% RED. CHILDREN:	50%	DINNER:	-

Malahide 2km

Mrs Margaret Farrelly
LYNFAR
Kinsealy Lane, Malahide, Co Dublin

Malahide

OPEN:	1st February-30th November
No. Rooms:	3
Ensuite:	3

TEL: **01 8463897**   FAX: -

Home set in private grounds, off street parking, near Malahide Castle. Convenient to B&I Ferry. Airport 15 mins.

Bus No: **42**

B&B PPS:	£18/£20	SNGL OCC. DBLE/TPL:	£26/£30	SNGL RM:	-
PART BRD:	-	% RED. CHILDREN:	10%	DINNER:	-

Malahide 3km

Mrs Monica Fitzsimons
PEBBLE MILL
Kinsealy, Malahide, Co Dublin

Malahide

OPEN:	March-October
No. Rooms:	3
Ensuite:	3

TEL: **01 8461792**   FAX: **01 8461792**

Country home, Airport 6 mins, B&I 15mins. Adjacent to Golf, Horseriding, Yachting, Castle. Room rates. TV, hairdryers, tea/coffee all rooms.

Bus No: **42, 43**

B&B PPS:	£18/£20	SNGL OCC. DBLE/TPL:	£25	SNGL RM:	-
PART BRD:	-	% RED. CHILDREN:	50%	DINNER:	-

Malahide 1km

Emma Gaule S.R.N.
CARA
104 Biscayne(Off Coast Rd), Malahide, Co Dublin

Malahide

OPEN:	6th January-30th November
No. Rooms:	3
Ensuite:	2

TEL: **01 8452041**   FAX: **01 8454207**

Pass Grand Hotel 2nd turn right after Stuart Hotel. Beach, Restaurants nearby. TV, Tea/Coffee. Triple bedroom. Airport 15 min, City 30 min.

Bus No: **42,102, DART, 230 Airport**

B&B PPS:	£16/£18	SNGL OCC. DBLE/TPL:	£26/£30	SNGL RM:	-
PART BRD:	-	% RED. CHILDREN:	20%	DINNER:	-

Malahide 3km

Mrs Maura Halpin
HEATHER VIEW
Malahide Road, Kinsealy, Co Dublin

Malahide

OPEN:	All Year except Christmas
.No. Rooms:	5
Ensuite:	4

TEL: **01 8453483**   FAX: **01 8453818**

Luxury home, Airport 10mins. Castle 1km. Ferry/City 20 mins. Rooms with TV. Tea/coffee maker, hairdryer, clockradio. Room rates, breakfast menu.

Bus No: **42,43, Airport 230**

B&B PPS:	£16/£20	SNGL OCC. DBLE/TPL:	£30/£32	SNGL RM:	-
PART BRD:	-	% RED. CHILDREN:	20%	DINNER:	-

Malahide 1.5km

Mrs Noreen Handley
AISHLING
59 Biscayne (off Coast Rd), Malahide, Co Dublin
TEL: **01 8452292**   FAX: -

Malahide

OPEN:	April-September
NO. ROOMS:	3
ENSUITE:	2

(V)

Pass Grand Hotel, 2nd turn right after Stuart Hotel. Excellent accommodation, overlooking Beach. Adjacent Golf, Yachting, Castle, Restaurants,15 mins Airport.

BUS NO: **32A,42,102,230 Airport**

B&B PPS:	**£15/£17**	SNGL OCC. DBLE/TPL:	-	SNGL RM:	-
PART BRD:	-	% RED. CHILDREN:	-	DINNER:	-

In Malahide

Liz Dagg-Hanley
MAYWOOD HOUSE
13 St Andrews Grove
Off Church Road, Malahide, Co Dublin
TEL: **01 8451712**   FAX: **01 8451712**

Malahide

OPEN:	All Year except Christmas
NO. ROOMS:	4
ENSUITE:	3

(V)

Home in quiet cul-de-sac (off Church Road) in Malahide. Beside Restaurants, Public Transport, Golf, Beach. TV, tea/coffee facilities. 15 mins Airport.

BUS NO: **42, 32A, 230**

B&B PPS:	**£16/£20**	SNGL OCC. DBLE/TPL:	-	SNGL RM:	-
PART BRD:	-	% RED. CHILDREN:	**50%**	DINNER:	-

Malahide 2km

Olive Hopkins
EVERGREEN
Kinsaley Lane, Malahide, Co Dublin
TEL: **01 8460185**   FAX: -   -

Malahide

OPEN:	1st February-30th November
NO. ROOMS:	3
ENSUITE:	2

(V)

Country area, Private Parking, TV, Tea/Coffee, Airport 10 mins. Adjacent Golf, Beach, Yachting. First right before main entrance Malahide Castle.

BUS NO: **42**

B&B PPS:	**£15/£18**	SNGL OCC. DBLE/TPL:	**£21.50/£25**	SNGL RM:	-
PART BRD:	-	% RED. CHILDREN:	**50%**	DINNER:	-

Malahide 3km

Mrs Ann Kearney
WESTBROOK HOUSE
Malahide Road, Kinsealy, Malahide, Co Dublin
TEL: **01 8450796**   FAX: **01 8450905**

Malahide

OPEN:	All Year except Christmas
NO. ROOMS:	6
ENSUITE:	6

(V)

Country house. Airport 6km, Castle 1km. Tea/coffee, hairdryer, breakfast menu, room rates, car parking. Proprietress graduate Dublin College Catering.

BUS NO: **42**

B&B PPS:	**£18/£20**	SNGL OCC. DBLE/TPL:	**£30**	SNGL RM:	-
PART BRD:	-	% RED. CHILDREN:	-	DINNER:	-

Malahide 4.5km

Mrs Jane F Kiernan
LISCARA
Malahide Road, Kinsealy, Dublin 17
TEL: **01 8483751**   FAX: **01 8483751**   -

Malahide

OPEN:	1st March-30th November
NO. ROOMS:	6
ENSUITE:	6

(V)

Private parking. Airport 10 mins, City/Ferry 20 mins. Convenient Golf, Indoor Bowling, Cinemas, Malahide Castle & Town, Swimming Pools. M50 1 Mile

BUS NO: **42, 43**

B&B PPS:	**£17/£20**	SNGL OCC. DBLE/TPL:	**£30**	SNGL RM:	-
PART BRD:	-	% RED. CHILDREN:	**25%**	DINNER:	-

Malahide 2km

Mrs Cathy McConnell
SAN JUAN
Baskin Lane, Kinsealy, Dublin 17

Malahide	
OPEN:	1st March-30th November
NO. ROOMS:	3
ENSUITE:	2

TEL: **01 8460424**   FAX: -   (V)

Country style residence on one acre. 5 mins to Airport, close to Malahide Castle/Village, 20 mins to City Centre.

Ⓟ⊗⅄♣✈🏠   BUS NO: **42, 43**

B&B PPS:	**£15/£18**	SNGL OCC. DBLE/TPL:	**£25/£28**	SNGL RM:	**£20/£22**
PART BRD:	-	% RED. CHILDREN:	25%	DINNER:	-

Malahide 1km

Mrs Brigid Mangan
CILL MUIRE HOUSE
18 Yellow Wall's Rd, Malahide, Co Dublin

Malahide	
OPEN:	All Year except Christmas
NO. ROOMS:	4
ENSUITE:	4

TEL: **01 8452178**   FAX: **01 8452178**   (V)

Old house with modern facilities, tea/coffee, hairdryer, TV. Airport 6km. Restaurants, Yachting, Golf, Beach within walking distance.

Ⓟ🖵🖵✈🏠   BUS NO: **42**

B&B PPS:	**£18.50**	SNGL OCC. DBLE/TPL:	**£30**	SNGL RM:	-
PART BRD:	-	% RED. CHILDREN:	10%	DINNER:	-

Malahide 1km

Mrs Jo Morris
CLADDAGH
170 Biscayne, Coast Road, Malahide, Co Dublin

Malahide	
OPEN:	All Year except Christmas
NO. ROOMS:	3
ENSUITE:	-

TEL: **01 8452668**   FAX: -   (V)

Modern home, convenient to Airport, Ferry, Golf, Malahide Castle, within walking distance of Beach, Village, Restaurants, 25 mins to City.

♿ⓅⓈ   BUS NO: **42,102,230**

B&B PPS:	**£16**	SNGL OCC. DBLE/TPL:	**£22.50**	SNGL RM:	**£20**
PART BRD:	-	% RED. CHILDREN:	10%	DINNER:	-

Malahide 1.5km

Mrs Elizabeth O'Brien
PEGASUS
56 Biscayne, Coast Rd Malahide, Co Dublin

Malahide	
OPEN:	1st March-31st October
NO. ROOMS:	3
ENSUITE:	1

TEL: **01 8451506**   FAX: -   (V)

Continue through Village along Coast Rd, second turn right after Stuart Hotel, first left, left again, second house on right.

Ⓟ⊗⅄   BUS NO: **42,32A,102,230**

B&B PPS:	**£16/£17.50**	SNGL OCC. DBLE/TPL:	**£25/£30**	SNGL RM:	-
PART BRD:	-	% RED. CHILDREN:	-	DINNER:	-

In Malahide

Mrs Sile O'Donovan
CASTLELAKE GUEST ACC.
15 St Andrew's Grove Malahide, Co Dublin

Malahide	
OPEN:	All Year except Christmas
NO. ROOMS:	4
ENSUITE:	4

TEL: **01 8455042**   FAX: **01 8455042**   (V)

Quiet cul-de-sac (off Church Rd). Ensuite accommodation, including large family room. Close to all amenities and public transport. Airport 4 miles.

ccⓅ🖵🖵🏠   BUS NO: **42**

B&B PPS:	**£18/£20**	SNGL OCC. DBLE/TPL:	**£26/£28**	SNGL RM:	-
PART BRD:	-	% RED. CHILDREN:	25%	DINNER:	-

Malahide 2km

Mrs Jean O'Leary
HAZELGROVE
Blackwood Lane, Malahide, Co Dublin

Malahide

OPEN:	1st March-15th October
No. ROOMS:	3
ENSUITE:	3

TEL: **01 8462629**   FAX: **01 8462629**

Gracious Home, Landscaped Private Grounds, Airport 8km, Castle 2km, City 10km. M50 4km, Adjacent 9 Golf Clubs. Breakfast menu, Tea/Coffee facilities.

BUS No: **42, 102, 230**

B&B PPS:	£18/£20	SNGL OCC. DBLE/TPL:	£30	SNGL RM:	-
PART BRD:	-	% RED. CHILDREN:	25%	DINNER:	

In Malahide Village

Mrs Mary Sweeney
SOMERTON
The Mall, Malahide Village, Co Dublin

Malahide

OPEN:	All Year except Christmas
No. ROOMS:	4
ENSUITE:	4

TEL: **01 8454090**   FAX: -

In the heart of Malahide Village. Well proportioned ensuite accommodation. Malahide's many amenities and Marina within walking distance. Airport 4 miles.

BUS No: **32A,42,102,230**

B&B PPS:	£22.50	SNGL OCC. DBLE/TPL:	£30/£35	SNGL RM:	-
PART BRD:	-	% RED. CHILDREN:	25%	DINNER:	-

Malahide 3km

Mrs Anne Askew
HOWTH VIEW
9 Beach Park, on Blackberry Lane Portmarnock, Co Dublin

Portmarnock

OPEN:	All Year except Christmas
No. ROOMS:	4
ENSUITE:	4

TEL: **01 8460665**   FAX: -

Situated off Coast Road near Beach. Malahide Castle 3 miles. On Airport & City Bus Route. Airport and Ferryport 20 mins.

BUS No: **32,32A,102,230**

B&B PPS:	£16/£18	SNGL OCC. DBLE/TPL:	£22/£25	SNGL RM:	-
PART BRD:	-	% RED. CHILDREN:	20%	DINNER:	-

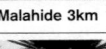

Malahide 3km

Mrs Margaret Creane
ROBINIA
452 Strand Rd, Portmarnock, Co Dublin

Portmarnock

OPEN:	All Year except Christmas
No. ROOMS:	3
ENSUITE:	2

TEL: **01 8462987**   FAX: -

Modern home overlooking Beach. Convenient to Golf, City, Malahide Castle. On Airport and City Bus route.

BUS No: **32, 32A, 102, 230**

B&B PPS:	£17/£20	SNGL OCC. DBLE/TPL:	£30/£32	SNGL RM:	-
PART BRD:	-	% RED. CHILDREN:	-	DINNER:	-

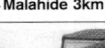

Malahide 2km

Mrs Mary Lee
TARA
Upper Carrickhill, 14 Portmarnock Crescent, Portmarnock, Co Dublin

Portmarnock

OPEN:	1st May-31st October
No. ROOMS:	3
ENSUITE:	1

TEL: **01 8462996**   FAX: -

First turn right after Sands Hotel then sharp left. Near Beach, City Bus Route, convenient to Golf Club, Airport, Ferryport.

BUS No: **32,32A, DART,102,230**

B&B PPS:	£16/£18	SNGL OCC. DBLE/TPL:	£24/£26	SNGL RM:	-
PART BRD:	-	% RED. CHILDREN:	25%	DINNER:	-

— Malahide 3km

Pat & Aileen Lynch
OAKLEIGH
30 Dewberry Park, Portmarnock, Co Dublin

Portmarnock

TEL: **01 8461628**   FAX: -

OPEN:	All Year
No. ROOMS:	3
ENSUITE:	2

(V)

Four bedroomes semi-detached overlooking green area with sea-view. Gardens front and rear of house

BUS No: **32, 32A,102, DART**

B&B PPS:	**£17.50**	SNGL OCC. DBLE/TPL:	**£25**	SNGL RM:	**£22.50**
PART BRD:	-	% RED. CHILDREN:	-	DINNER:	-

— Malahide 3km

Mrs Kathleen O'Brien
CLARA
22 Beach Park, Portmarnock, Co Dublin

Portmarnock

TEL: **01 8461936**   FAX: -

OPEN:	1st March-31st October
No. ROOMS:	3
ENSUITE:	2

(V)

Second right after Portmarnock Hotel, Golf Links (Blackberry Lane), right into Beach Park, right again. Convenient Airport, Golf, Ferry, Beach.

BUS No: **32,32A,102,230**

B&B PPS:	**£15/£17**	SNGL OCC. DBLE/TPL:	-	SNGL RM:	-
PART BRD:	-	% RED. CHILDREN:	-	DINNER:	-

— Malahide 2km

Mrs Margaret Treanor
SEAGLADE HOUSE
off Coast Road, At Round Tower, Portmarnock, Co Dublin

Portmarnock

TEL: **01 8462458/8460179**   FAX: -

OPEN:	All Year except Christmas
No. ROOMS:	6
ENSUITE:	5

(V)

Spacious home in secluded grounds of 3 acres, directly overlooking Irish Sea. Dublin Airport 15 mins, City Centre 25 mins.

BUS No: **32,32a,102,230**

B&B PPS:	**£18/£20**	SNGL OCC. DBLE/TPL:	**£32/£36**	SNGL RM:	-
PART BRD:	-	% RED. CHILDREN:	-	DINNER:	-

— Skerries 1km

Mrs Violet Clinton
THE REEFS
Balbriggan Coast Road Skerries, Co Dublin

Skerries

TEL: **01 8491574**   FAX: -

OPEN:	April-October
No. ROOMS:	5
ENSUITE:	3

(V)

Spacious bungalow overlooking Sea/Mourne Mountains. 'Ireland Guide recommended. Convenient to Golf/Sailing/Horseriding/Archaeological Area. Airport 20 mins. Dublin 30 mins.

BUS No: **33**

B&B PPS:	**£15.50/£17.50**	SNGL OCC. DBLE/TPL:	**£22**	SNGL RM:	-
PART BRD:	-	% RED. CHILDREN:	**25%**	DINNER:	-

Mrs Zita Devine
BENEDA
South Strand, Skerries, Co Dublin

Skerries

TEL: **01 8491042**   FAX: -

OPEN:	All Year except Christmas
No. ROOMS:	4
ENSUITE:	3

(V)

House built 1902. Facing sea, Islands, lighthouse. Beside Town Centre, Golf Course, Sailing, etc. Airport 15 mins. Dublin 36 mins.

BUS No: **33**

B&B PPS:	**£17.50/£20**	SNGL OCC. DBLE/TPL:	**£25/£26.50**	SNGL RM:	-
PART BRD:	-	% RED. CHILDREN:	**50%**	DINNER:	-

— Skerries

In Skerries

Mary Halpin
GREENVALE
Holmpatrick, Skerries, Co Dublin

Skerries

OPEN:	**All Year except Christmas**
NO. ROOMS:	3
ENSUITE:	3

(V)

TEL: **01 8490413**   FAX: -   EMAIL: **halpinm@indigo.ie**

Large Victorian House overlooking Sea and Islands in quiet location close to Town Centre. Dublin 30 kms, Airport 20 kms.

[cc] 🏠   BUS NO: **33**

B&B PPS:	**£18**	SNGL OCC. DBLE/TPL:	**£25**	SNGL RM:	-
PART BRD:	-	% RED. CHILDREN:	**50%**	DINNER:	-

In Skerries

Margaret Swan
HILL HOUSE
Milverton, Skerries, Co Dublin

Skerries

OPEN:	**1st March-30th September**
NO. ROOMS:	3
ENSUITE:	1

(V)

TEL: **01 8491873**   FAX: -

Luxury bungalow in quiet scenic area. Beaches, Golf, Sailing, Horse Riding, archaeological and historic interests nearby. Dublin 25 mins. Airport 15 mins.

BUS NO: **33**

B&B PPS:	**£16/£18**	SNGL OCC. DBLE/TPL:	**£22.50/£25**	SNGL RM:	-
PART BRD:	-	% RED. CHILDREN:	-	DINNER:	-

Howth 2km

Mrs Geraldine Conlan
THE MEADOWS
257 Sutton Park, Sutton, Dublin 13

Sutton

OPEN:	**All Year**
NO. ROOMS:	3
ENSUITE:	-

(V)

TEL: **01 8390257/087 462640**   FAX: -

Highly rated Bed & Breakfast. 15 mins from Dublin City by DART Train. 15 mins from Airport.

BUS NO: **31,32, DART**

B&B PPS:	**£18**	SNGL OCC. DBLE/TPL:	**£24.50**	SNGL RM:	-
PART BRD:	-	% RED. CHILDREN:	**50%**	DINNER:	-

Dublin City 10km

Eileen Hobbs
HILLVIEW
39 Sutton Park, Dublin Road, Sutton, Dublin 13

Sutton

OPEN:	**January-December**
NO. ROOMS:	3
ENSUITE:	1

(V)

TEL: **01 8324584**   FAX: -

Friendly comfortable home, peaceful surroundings. Close to Bayside DART Station, Howth 2 km, 15 min - to Airport, Ferry, City Centre. Amenities nearby.

BUS NO: **31, 32**

B&B PPS:	**£16/£17**	SNGL OCC. DBLE/TPL:	**£22.50/£23.50**	SNGL RM:	**£20/£22**
PART BRD:	-	% RED. CHILDREN:	**50%**	DINNER:	-

Dublin 10km

Mrs Mary McDonnell
DUN AOIBHINN
30 Sutton Park, Sutton, Dublin 13

Sutton

OPEN:	**All Year except Christmas**
NO. ROOMS:	3
ENSUITE:	3

TEL: **01 8325456**   FAX: **01 8325456**

Luxurious residence on DART route, adjacent coast road. City Centre/Airport 10km, Howth 3km. Turn left 1km after Texaco garage.

BUS NO: **31,31A,32,32A,32B, DART**

B&B PPS:	**£18/£20**	SNGL OCC. DBLE/TPL:	**£23/£25**	SNGL RM:	-
PART BRD:	-	% RED. CHILDREN:	**10%**	DINNER:	-

Dublin 7km

Sutton

Mrs Eileen Sutton
154 Sutton Park, Sutton,
Dublin 13

TEL: **01 8325167**   FAX: **01 8395516**

OPEN:	All Year except Christmas	
NO. ROOMS:	3	
ENSUITE:	2	

Excellent accommodation close to Seafront & DART Station. 15 mins Airport, Point Theatre, City Centre, Ferry, Golfing, Fishing, Restaurants, Amenities nearby

BUS NO: **DART**

B&B PPS:	£18.50/£20	SNGL OCC. DBLE/TPL:	£25/£26.50	SNGL RM:	£22.50
PART BRD:	-	% RED. CHILDREN:	-	DINNER:	

Swords 1km

Swords

Mrs Rosemarie Barrett O'Neill
BLACKBRIDGE LODGE
Lissenhall, Swords, Co Dublin

TEL: **01 8407276**   FAX: -

OPEN:	1st February-20th December	
NO. ROOMS:	3	
ENSUITE:	3	

Modern country home off Belfast/Dublin Road. 5 mins Airport, 15 mins City Centre. convenient to many tourist amenities.

BUS NO: **41,41b,41c,33**

B&B PPS:	£16/£20	SNGL OCC. DBLE/TPL:	£25/£35	SNGL RM:	-
PART BRD:	-	% RED. CHILDREN:	50%	DINNER:	-

Swords 1km

Swords/Airport

Mrs Catherine Cavanagh
RIVERSDALE
Balheary Road, Swords, Co Dublin

TEL: **01 8404802**   FAX: **01 8404802**   EMAIL: **michaelc@indigo.ie**

OPEN:	All Year except Christmas	
NO. ROOMS:	3	
ENSUITE:	3	

Modern bungalow off Belfast/ Dublin Road. Airport 6 minutes, City 15 minutes. N1 through Swords. Left at 'Big Tree Pub'. Follow signs.

BUS NO: **41,41b,33**

B&B PPS:	£18/£21	SNGL OCC. DBLE/TPL:	£25/£30	SNGL RM:	-
PART BRD:	-	% RED. CHILDREN:	33.3%	DINNER:	-

Swords 1km

Swords/Airport

Mrs Sara Daniels
DAWN HOUSE
Balheary, Swords, Co Dublin

TEL: **01 8403111**   FAX: **01 8403111**

OPEN:	All Year	
NO. ROOMS:	3	
ENSUITE:	3	

Quiet location, Country Home, off Belfast/Dublin Road, N1, 6 minutes Airport, 15 minutes City Centre, TV, extensive parking, ground floor accommodation.

 BUS NO: **41,41B,33,33B,41C**

B&B PPS:	£18/£20	SNGL OCC. DBLE/TPL:	£25/£26.50	SNGL RM:	-
PART BRD:	-	% RED. CHILDREN:	33%	DINNER:	-

Ballyboughal 3km

Swords/Ballyboughal

Margaret Farrell
HOLLYWOOD B&B
Hollywood, Ballyboughal, Co Dublin

TEL: **01 8433359**   FAX: -

OPEN:	All Year except Christmas	
NO. ROOMS:	3	
ENSUITE:	2	

Modern country home in peaceful setting adjoining farmlands, Golf Course, 15 minutes Dublin Airport, 25 minutes City Centre and Ferry.

B&B PPS:	£16/£19	SNGL OCC. DBLE/TPL:	£22.50/£25.50	SNGL RM:	-
PART BRD:	-	% RED. CHILDREN:	50%	DINNER:	-

Mrs Marie Jackson	Swords	
OAKVIEW COUNTRY HOME	Open:	All Year except Christmas
Leas Cross, Naul Road, Swords,	No. Rooms:	3
Co Dublin	Ensuite:	3

Tel: 01 8405256   Fax: 01 8405256   Email: **oakview@indigo.ie**

Modern Country Home. Peaceful surroundings. Large Car Park, adjacent Dublin Airport, Malahide Castle, Golf, Horse Riding. Tea/Coffee facilities.

Bus No: **60, 41B**

B&B PPS:	**£17.50/£20**	Sngl Occ. Dble/Tpl:	**£25/£35**	Sngl Rm:	-
Part Brd:	-	% Red. Children:	**50%**	Dinner:	

— Swords 3km —

Betty Keane	Swords	
HALF ACRE	Open:	All Year except Christmas
Hynestown, Naul, Co Dublin	No. Rooms:	3
	Ensuite:	3

Tel: **01 8413306**   Fax: -

Country home in historic Fingal at Naul, 8km off N1 at Balbriggan. Drogheda 18km, Airport 19km, Dublin 32km, Newgrange 24km.

B&B PPS:	**£17**	Sngl Occ. Dble/Tpl:	**£23.50**	Sngl Rm:	-
Part Brd:	-	% Red. Children:	**25%**	Dinner:	-

— Ballbriggan 8km —

Mrs Sheila White	Swords	
ARD-CILL	Open:	1st April-1st October
The Rath, Rolestown, Swords,	No. Rooms:	3
Co Dublin	Ensuite:	1

Tel: **01 8405172**   Fax: -

Spacious dormer bungalow in quiet country surroundings. Large Car Park, 15 mins Airport, 15 mins Malahide Castle. 5 mins Golf.

Bus No: **41B**

B&B PPS:	**£15/£18**	Sngl Occ. Dble/Tpl:	**£20/£30**	Sngl Rm:	-
Part Brd:	-	% Red. Children:	-	Dinner:	-

— Swords 6km —

APPROVED ACCOMMODATION SIGNS

This sign will be displayed at most premises which are approved by Quality Approved Bed & Breakfast Association Ltd., to Irish Tourist Board Standards.

Panneaux d'homologation des établissements
Ces panneaux sont affichés dans la plupart des établissements homologués par Quality Approved Bed & Breakfast Association Ltd., selon les normes de l'Office du tourisme irlandais.

Plakette für Geprüfte Unterkunft
Diese Plaketten werden an den meisten Häusern angezeigt, die von der Quality Approved Bed & Breakfast Association Ltd. auf die Einhaltung der Normen der irischen Fremdenverkehrsbehörde überprüft und zugelassen wurden.

Borden voor goedgekeurde accommodatie
Deze borden vindt u bij de meeste huizen die zijn goedgekeurd door de Quality Approved Bed & Breakfast Association Ltd voor de normen van de Ierse Toeristenbond.

Simbolo di sistemazione approvata
Questi simboli saranno esposti nella maggior parte delle case approvate dalla Quality Approved Bed & Breakfast Association Ltd (associazione dei Bed & Breakfast approvati per qualità), rispondenti agli standard dell'Ente del Turismo Irlandese.

Símbolo de alojamiento aprobado
Estos símbolos se muestran en los establecimientos que han sido aprobados por la Quality Approved Bed and Breakfast Association Ltd, bajos los estandars de la Oficina de Turismo Irlandesa.

Skyltar för Godkänd logi
Dessa skyltar finns vid de flesta gästhus som har godkänts av Quality Approved Bed & Breakfast Association Ltd. (Föreningen för kvalitetsgodkända gästhus AB), enligt irländska turisföreningens normer.